Where to Stay in England 2001
Contents

KEY TO SYMBOLS
A key to symbols can be found on the inside back cover.
Keep it open for easy reference.

A Warm Welcome

Welcome to our 26th edition – it's so easy to use, and packed with information.

For short breaks, family holidays, touring holidays or business stop-overs *Where to Stay* is all you need. This guide contains over 2000 places to stay in a wide choice of locations at prices to suit all budgets.

You'll also find

- ideas about what to do while you're away
- advice and information on booking your accommodation
- colour location maps
- local Tourist Information Centre telephone numbers
- information on events throughout the country

How to use The Guide

The guide is divided into the 10 English Regional Tourist Board regions (these are shown on page 13). Within these sections you will find a brief introduction to the area, contact details for the Regional Tourist Board, information about places to visit during your stay, and clear information entries on accommodation within the region. Accommodation is listed alphabetically in order of place name. If you would like to know more about the city, town or village in which you wish to stay, you will find brief descriptions at the end of each regional section. Or you can contact the local Tourist Information Centre - the telephone number can be found next to the town name on the accommodation entry pages.

Finding your
Accommodation

Whether you know exactly where you
want to stay or only have an idea
of the area you wish to visit, it
couldn't be easier to find
accommodation to suit you in
Where to Stay. You can find your
accommodation in several ways:

BY PLACE

if you know the town or village look in the comprehensive town index at the back.

BY AREA

if you know the area look at the full colour maps starting on page 16. All the places in black offer
accommodation featured in this guide.

BY REGION

if you know which part of England look in the relevant regional section. These are colour coded at
the top of each page. A map showing the regions can be found on page 13.

BY COUNTY

if you know which English county look at the county listing on page 14 to find the region it is in.

Exclusive hotel listings

Where to Stay is the only guide to contain details of ALL hotels which have been quality assessed by
the English Tourism Council, giving you the widest choice of accommodation.

Types of Accommodation

Hotel accommodation is featured in this guide and each entry includes a brief description of the
property and facilities.

There are two special types of hotel accommodation mentioned: **Townhouses** are small personally
run town centre hotels which concentrate on privacy, luxuriously furnished bedrooms and suites and
high quality service. May not have public rooms or formal dining arrangements but offer additional
high quality room service and are usually located in areas well served by restaurants.
Travel Accommodation includes purpose built bedroom accommodation which you will find along
major roads and motorways.

(We publish a separate guide for Bed and Breakfast guest accommodation).

Accommodation
Ratings & Awards

Ratings and awards are an indication of quality which help you find the most suitable accommodation to meet your needs and expectations. You'll find several in this guide:

STAR RATINGS FOR QUALITY

The English Tourism Council's quality assurance scheme awards **One to Five Stars** giving you reliable information about the quality of the accommodation you can expect. (See opposite). You'll find something to suit all budgets and tastes.

SPECIAL AWARDS FOR EXCELLENCE

Gold and Silver Awards - Part of the English Tourism Council scheme, Gold and Silver Awards are given to establishments achieving the highest levels of quality within their Star rating. So if you're looking for somewhere special, turn to page 9 for a list of Gold Award holders which have an entry in the regional sections of this guide. Silver award holders are too numerous to list, but they are clearly indicated in the accommodation entries.

The annual **England for Excellence awards** are the Oscar's of the tourism industry. Details of nominees and winners for 2000 can be found on page 12.

NATIONAL ACCESSIBLE SCHEME FOR SPECIAL NEEDS

Establishments which have a **National Accessible rating** provide access and facilities for wheelchair users and people who have difficulty walking. Turn to page 10 and 11 for further details.

How do we arrive at a Star rating?

The English Tourism Council has more than 50 trained assessors throughout England who visit properties annually, generally staying overnight as an anonymous guest.

They award ratings based on the overall experience of their stay, and there are strict guidelines to ensure every property is assessed to the same criteria. High standards of housekeeping are a major requirement; heating, lighting, comfort and convenience are also part of the assessment.

THE ASSESSOR'S ROLE - GUEST, ASSESSOR AND ADVISOR

An assessor books their accommodation as a 'normal' guest. He or she will take into account all aspects of the visiting experience, from how the telephone enquiry is dealt with to the quality of the service and facilities on offer.

During their stay the assessor will try to experience as many things as possible including the quality of food, the knowledge of staff and services, such as room service and dry cleaning if available. They will even check under the bed!

After paying the bill the assessor reveals who they are and asks to look round the rest of the establishment. The assessor will then advise the proprietor of the Star rating they have awarded, discussing the reasons why, as well as suggesting areas for improvement.

So you can see it's a very thorough process to ensure that when you book accommodation with a particular Star rating you can be confident it will meet your expectations. **After all, meeting customer expectations is what makes happy guests.**

Ratings you can trust

When you're looking for a place to stay, you need a rating system you can trust. The English Tourism Council's ratings give a clear guide to what to expect, in an easy-to-understand form. Properties are visited annually by trained, impartial assessors, so you can have the confidence that your accommodation has been thoroughly checked and rated for quality before you make your booking.

STAR RATINGS

Ratings are awarded from One to Five Stars. The more Stars, the higher the quality and the greater the range of facilities and level of service provided. The brief explanations of the Star ratings outlined here show what is included at each rating level (note that each rating also includes what is provided at a lower Star rating).

★ Practical accommodation with a limited range of facilities and services, and a high standard of cleanliness throughout (75% of rooms will have en-suite or private facilities). Friendly and courteous staff. A restaurant/eating area offering breakfast and dinner to you and your guests. Alcoholic drinks served in a bar or lounge.

★★ Good accommodation offering a personal style of service with additional facilities, normally including a lift. More comfortable bedrooms (all with en-suite or private facilities and colour TV). Food and drink is of a slightly higher standard.

★★★ Often a larger establishment with more spacious public areas and bedrooms, all offering a significantly greater quality and higher standard of facilities and services. A more formal style of service with a receptionist. A wide selection of drinks, light lunch and snacks served in a bar or lounge with greater attention to quality. Room service for continental breakfast and laundry service.

★★★★ Superior comfort and quality. All rooms with en-suite facilities. Strong emphasis on food and drink. Experienced staff responding to your needs and requests. Room service for all meals and 24 hour drinks, refreshments and snacks available.

★★★★★ Spacious and luxurious offering accommodation, extensive facilities, services and cuisine of the highest international quality. Professional, attentive staff, exceptional comfort and a sophisticated ambience.

Gold and Silver Awards

Look out, too, for the English Tourism Council's Gold and Silver Awards, which are awarded to properties achieving the highest levels of quality within their Star rating. While the overall rating is based on a combination of facilities and quality, the Gold and Silver Awards are based solely on quality.

Accommodation
Entries explained

Each accommodation entry contains detailed information to help you decide if it is right for you. This information has been provided by the proprietors themselves, and our aim has been to ensure that it is as objective and factual as possible. To the left of the establishment name you will find the Star rating and quality award, if appropriate.

At-a-glance symbols at the end of each entry give you additional information on services and facilities - a key can be found on the back cover flap. Keep this open to refer to as you read.

A sample entry is shown below.

Look out for Welcome Host, a nationally recognised customer care initiative, sponsored in England by the English Tourism Council. Establishments with the Welcome Host symbol [ ] have shown their commitment to courtesy and service and aim to provide high standards of service and a warm welcome for all visitors.

Sample Entry

① ③ ④ ⑤

KNUTSFORD Map ref 4A2 *Tourist Information Centre Tel: (01274) 753678*

★★★★

Silver
Award

Ad p44

PICKLINGS LODGE
Longtown Road, Pickmere,
Nr Knutsford WA16 0YZ
T: (01565) 989 F: (01565) 777333
E: picklings@knutsford.co.uk

Bedrooms: 2 single,
1 double
Bathrooms: 5 private

Lunch available
EM 1800 (LO 2130)
Parking for 18
CC: Access, Visa

B&B per night
S £27.00–£35.00
D £54.00–£70.00

HB per person:
DY £37.00–£45.00

17th C former lodge with extensive landscaped gardens, woodland and lake. Deep in the Cheshire countryside yet only minutes from the M6 motorway. Home-grown produce.

② ⑥ ⑧ ⑦

1 Town or village with map reference

2 Star rating and quality award (where applicable)

3 Establishment name, address and contact details

4 Accommodation details, including credit cards accepted

5 Prices per night for bed & breakfast (B&B) staying in a single (S) or double (D) room. The double room price is for two people. Half board (HB) prices are shown as a daily rate (DY) per person and include room, breakfast and dinner

6 National Accessible Scheme rating (where applicable)

7 Accommodation description

8 At-a-glance symbols (key on back cover flap)

Gold
Award Establishments

Hotels featured in the regional sections of this Where to Stay guide, which have achieved a Gold Award for an exceptionally high standard of quality, are listed on this page. Please use the Town Index at the back of the guide to find the page numbers for their full entry.

Silver Awards also represent high standards of quality and there are many establishments within this guide which have achieved this. Gold and Silver Awards are clearly indicated in the accommodation entries.

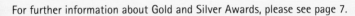

For further information about Gold and Silver Awards, please see page 7.

Brockencote Hall, Chaddesley Corbett, Worcestershire

Channel House Hotel, Minehead, Somerset

The Chester Grosvenor, Chester, Cheshire

Colwall Park Hotel, Malvern, Worcestershire

Dale Hill Hotel & Golf Club, Ticehurst, East Sussex

The Dorchester, London

Eastwell Manor Hotel, Ashford, Kent

Gilpin Lodge Country House Hotel & Restaurant, Windermere, Cumbria

The Landmark London, London

Linthwaite House Hotel, Windermere, Cumbria

Lucknam Park, Bath, Bath & North East Somerset

The Lygon Arms, Broadway, Worcestershire

Morston Hall, Blakeney, Norfolk

Northcote Manor Hotel, Blackburn, Lancashire

Nuthurst Grange Country House Hotel & Restaurant, Hockley Heath, West Midlands

Old Bank Hotel, Oxford, Oxfordshire

Old Vicarage Hotel, Bridgnorth, Shropshire

Hotel Riviera, Sidmouth, Devon

Sir Christopher Wren's House Hotel & Business Centre, Windsor, Berkshire

The Pictures:
1 The Landmark Hotel, London;
2 Colwall Park Hotel, Malvern, Worcestershire;
3 Linthwaite House Hotel, Windermere, Cumbria.

Swinside Lodge Hotel, Keswick, Cumbria

Thurlestone Hotel, Salcombe, Devon

Westover Hall Hotel, Milford-on-Sea, Hampshire

Wood Norton Hall & Conference Centre, Evesham, Worcestershire

National
Accessible Scheme

The English Tourism Council and National and Regional Tourist Boards throughout Britain assess all types of places to stay, on holiday or business, that provide accessible accommodation for wheelchair users and others who may have difficulty walking.

Accommodation establishments taking part in the National Accessible Scheme, and which appear in the regional sections of this guide are listed opposite. Use the Town Index at the back to find the page numbers for their full entries.

The Tourist Boards recognise three categories of accessibility:

 CATEGORY 1   Accessible to all wheelchair users including those travelling independently.

 CATEGORY 2   Accessible to a wheelchair user with assistance.

 CATEGORY 3   Accessible to a wheelchair user able to walk short distances and up at least three steps.

If you have additional needs or special requirements of any kind, we strongly recommend that you make sure these can be met by your chosen establishment before you confirm your booking.

The criteria the English Tourism Council and National and Regional Tourist Boards have adopted do not necessarily conform to British Standards or to Building Regulations. They reflect what the Boards understand to be acceptable to meet the practical needs of wheelchair users.

The National Accessible Scheme forms part of the Tourism for All Campaign that is being promoted by the English Tourism Council and National and Regional Tourist Boards. Additional help and guidance on finding suitable holiday accommodation for those with special needs can be obtained from:

Holiday Care,
2nd Floor, Imperial Buildings,
Victoria Road,
Horley, Surrey RH6 7PZ

Tel: (01293) 774535
Fax: (01293) 784647
Minicom: (01293) 776943

CATEGORY 1

- Aylmerton, Norfolk - Roman Camp Inn
- Bournemouth, Dorset
  - Durlston Court Hotel
  - Elstead Hotel
- Windermere, Cumbria
  - Burnside Hotel
  - Lindeth Howe Country House Hotel

CATEGORY 2

- Blakeney, Norfolk - The Pheasant Hotel
- Bridgnorth, Shropshire - Old Vicarage Hotel
- Bridgwater, Somerset - Friarn Court Hotel
- Great Yarmouth, Norfolk - Horse & Groom Motel
- Leeds, West Yorkshire - Weetwood Hall
- Norwich, Norfolk - Beeches Hotel
- Shap, Cumbria - Shap Wells Hotel
- St Ives, Cornwall - Chy-an-Dour Hotel

CATEGORY 3

- Bournemouth, Dorset
  - Belvedere Hotel
  - Norfolk Royale Hotel
- Cheltenham, Gloucestershire
  - The Prestbury House Hotel & Restaurant
- Chester, Cheshire
  - The Chester Grosvenor
  - Dene Hotel
  - Green Bough Hotel & Restaurant
- Colchester, Essex - Rose & Crown
- Eastbourne, East Sussex - Congress Hotel
- Finedon, Northamptonshire - Tudor Gate Hotel
- Grange-over-Sands, Cumbria - Netherwood Hotel
- Grimsby, North East Lincolnshire - Millfields
- Hull, East Riding of Yorkshire
  - Jarvis International Hotel
- Keswick, Cumbria - Derwentwater Hotel
- Kidderminster, Worcestershire
  - The Granary Hotel & Restaurant

- Langho, Lancashire
  - Mytton Fold Hotel & Golf Complex
- Leyburn, North Yorkshire
  - Golden Lion Hotel & Licensed Restaurant
- Luton, Bedfordshire - Thistle Luton
- Lytham St Annes, Lancashire - Chadwick Hotel
- Manchester, Greater Manchester
  - The Waterside Hotel & Galleon Leisure Club
- Middlesbrough, Tees Valley - TAD Centre
- Mildenhall, Suffolk - The Smoke House
- Newmarket, Suffolk - Heath Court Hotel
- Norwich, Norfolk - Old Rectory
- Nottingham, Nottinghamshire
  - The Nottingham Gateway Hotel
- Rotherham, South Yorkshire
  - Best Western Elton Hotel
- Southport, Merseyside
  - Scarisbrick Hotel
- Stamford, Lincolnshire - Garden House Hotel
- Stonor, Oxfordshire - The Stonor Arms Hotel
- Stratford-upon-Avon, Warwickshire
  - Welcombe Hotel & Golf Course
- Swanage, Dorset - The Pines Hotel
- Tenterden, Kent - Little Silver Country Hotel
- Torquay, Devon - Frognel Hall
- Wareham, Dorset - Kemps Country House Hotel
- Warrington, Cheshire
  - The Park Royal International Hotel, Health & Leisure Spa
- Winchester, Hampshire - Harestock Lodge Hotel
- Windermere, Cumbria - Linthwaite House Hotel
- Woodhall Spa, Lincolnshire - Petwood Hotel
- Wymondham, Norfolk
  - Wymondham Consort Hotel
- York, North Yorkshire
  - The Grange Hotel
  - Savages Hotel

(The information contained on these pages was correct at the time of going to press.)

The England for Excellence
Awards 2000

LA CREME DE LA CREME

If you are looking for somewhere truly outstanding, then why
not try one of the following hotels listed below. Having proved their
mettle at a regional level, each one has made it through to the semi-
finals of the 2000 England for Excellence Awards. Run by the English
Tourism Council in association with the Regional Tourist Boards, these
highly competitive annual awards reward only the very best in English
tourism. So if somewhere has made it through to the short-list, you can
be sure that they really are the bees knees. The hotels are divided into
two categories, those with over 50 bedrooms and smaller hotels with
under 50 bedrooms.

Sponsored by:

ENGLAND FOR
EXCELLENCE
AWARDS 2000

OVER 50 BEDROOMS

De Vere Oulton Hall Hotel, Leeds, West Yorkshire SILVER	Tel: 0113 282 1000
De Vere Slaley Hall Hotel, Hexham, Northumberland	Tel: 01434 673350
Four Seasons Hotel, Park Lane, London	Tel: 020 7499 0888
Lygon Arms, Broadway, Worcestershire	Tel: 01386 852255
Marriott Hanbury Manor Golf & Country Club, Ware, Hertfordshire WINNER	Tel: 01920 487722
Swallow Hotel, Liverpool, Merseyside	Tel: 0151 476 8000
The Grand Hotel, Eastbourne, East Sussex SILVER	Tel: 01323 412345
Tylney Hall Hotel, Hook, Hampshire	Tel: 01256 764881

UNDER 50 BEDROOMS

Holbeck Ghyll, Windermere, Cumbria SILVER	Tel: 015394 32375
Horton Grange, Newcastle upon Tyne, Tyne & Wear	Tel: 01661 860686
Morston Hall Hotel, Holt, Norfolk	Tel: 01263 741041
The Colonade, Little Venice, London SILVER	Tel: 020 7432 8430
The Hurtwood Inn Hotel, Peaslake, Surrey	Tel: 01306 730851
The Vineyard at Stockcross, Newbury, Berkshire WINNER	Tel: 01653 528770
The White Swan, Pickering, North Yorkshire	Tel: 01751 472288
Wood Norton Hall, Evesham, Worcestershire	Tel: 01386 420007

Regional
Tourist Board areas

This *Where to Stay* guide is divided into 10 regional sections as shown on the map below. To identify each regional section and its page number, please refer to the key below. The county index overleaf indicates in which regional section you will find a particular county.

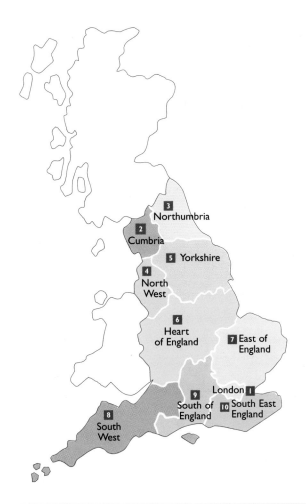

Key to Map	page
1 London	29
2 Cumbria	45
3 Northumbria	71
4 North West	85
5 Yorkshire	103
6 Heart of England	137
7 East of England	179
8 South West	209
9 South of England	253
10 South East England	281

Each of the ten English regions shown here has a Regional Tourist Board which can give you information about things to see or do locally. Contact details are given both at the beginning and end of each regional section.

LOCATION MAPS

Colour location maps showing all the cities, towns and villages with accommodation in the regional sections of this guide can be found on pages 16-28. Turn to the Town Index at the back of this guide for the page number on which you can find the relevant accommodation.

In which region is
the county I wish to visit?

COUNTY/UNITARY AUTHORITY	REGION
Bath & North East Somerset	South West
Bedfordshire	East of England
Berkshire	South of England
Bristol	South West
Buckinghamshire	South of England
Cambridgeshire	East of England
Cheshire	North West
Cornwall	South West
Cumbria	Cumbria
Derbyshire	Heart of England
Devon	South West
Dorset (Eastern)	South of England
Dorset (Western)	South West
Durham	Northumbria
East Riding of Yorkshire	Yorkshire
East Sussex	South East England
Essex	East of England
Gloucestershire	Heart of England
Greater London	London
Greater Manchester	North West
Hampshire	South of England
Herefordshire	Heart of England
Hertfordshire	East of England
Isle of Wight	South of England
Isles of Scilly	South West
Kent	South East England
Lancashire	North West
Leicestershire	Heart of England
Lincolnshire	Heart of England
Merseyside	North West
Norfolk	East of England
North East Lincolnshire	Yorkshire
North Lincolnshire	Yorkshire
North Somerset	South West
North Yorkshire	Yorkshire
Northamptonshire	Heart of England
Northumberland	Northumbria
Nottinghamshire	Heart of England
Oxfordshire	South of England
Rutland	Heart of England
Shropshire	Heart of England
Somerset	South West
South Gloucestershire	South West
South Yorkshire	Yorkshire
Staffordshire	Heart of England
Suffolk	East of England
Surrey	South East England
Tees Valley	Northumbria
Tyne & Wear	Northumbria
Warwickshire	Heart of England
West Midlands	Heart of England
West Sussex	South East England
West Yorkshire	Yorkshire
Wiltshire	South West
Worcestershire	Heart of England
York	Yorkshire

UNITARY AUTHORITIES

Please note that many new unitary authorities have been formed - for example Brighton & Hove and Bristol - and are officially separate from the county in which they were previously located. To aid the reader we have only included the major unitary authorities in the list above and on the colour maps.

Making a Booking

Please remember that changes may occur after the guide is printed. When you have found a suitable place to stay we advise you to contact the establishment to check availability, and also to confirm prices and any specific facilities which may be important to you. Further advice on how to make a booking can be found at the back of this guide, together with information about deposits and cancellations. When you have made your booking, if you have time, it is advisable to confirm it in writing.

Some of the hotels in this guide are members of groups or consortia which operate a central reservations booking service. These hotels include the ⓒⓡ symbol within their entry. A complete list of central reservations offices can be found on page 370-371.

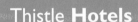

Thistle **Hotels**

Open for business

56 hotels in key locations throughout Britain – including 23 in London

Meeting Plan– making meeting successful

In-room hi-speed web access in partnership with **w⚫rldroom**connect
Internet Wariessness

Exciting dining options – Gengis, Faya, Co.Motion

For Reservations
Call **0800 18 17 16**

Visit **www.thistlehotels.com**

Or book through our WAP site
http://wap.thistlehotels.com

THISTLE HOTELS

MAP 1

A
B

Location
Maps

1

Every place name featured in the regional accommodation sections of this Where to Stay guide has a map reference to help you locate it on the maps which follow. For example, to find Colchester, Essex, which has 'Map ref 3B2', turn to Map 3 and refer to grid square B2.

All place names appearing in the regional sections are shown in black type on the maps. This enables you to find other places in your chosen area which may have suitable accommodation - the Town Index (at the back of this guide) gives page numbers.

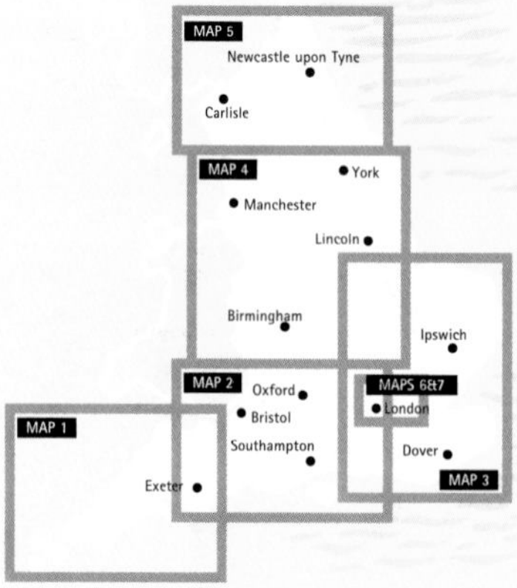

2

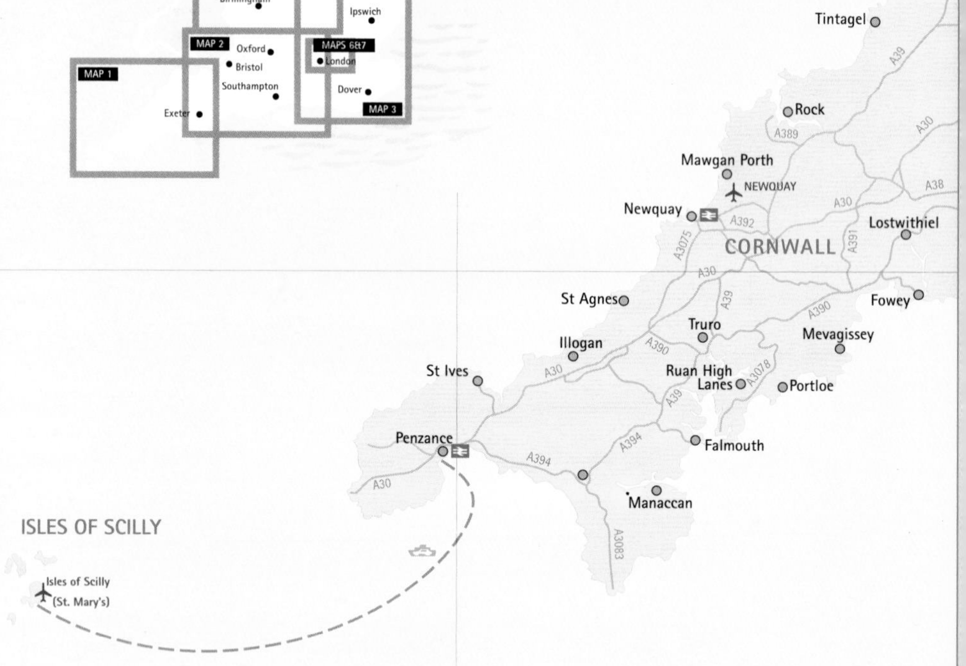

MAP 5
Newcastle upon Tyne
Carlisle
MAP 4 • York
• Manchester
Lincoln •
Birmingham
Ipswich
MAP 2 Oxford
MAPS 6&7
• Bristol • London
MAP 1
Southampton
Dover
Exeter MAP 3

Tintagel

Rock
A389

Mawgan Porth
NEWQUAY
Newquay A392
A30
Lostwithiel
CORNWALL

St Agnes
Truro
Fowey
Illogan
Mevagissey
Ruan High
Lanes
Portloe
St Ives
Penzance
Falmouth
A394
A30
Manaccan

3 ISLES OF SCILLY

Isles of Scilly
(St. Mary's)

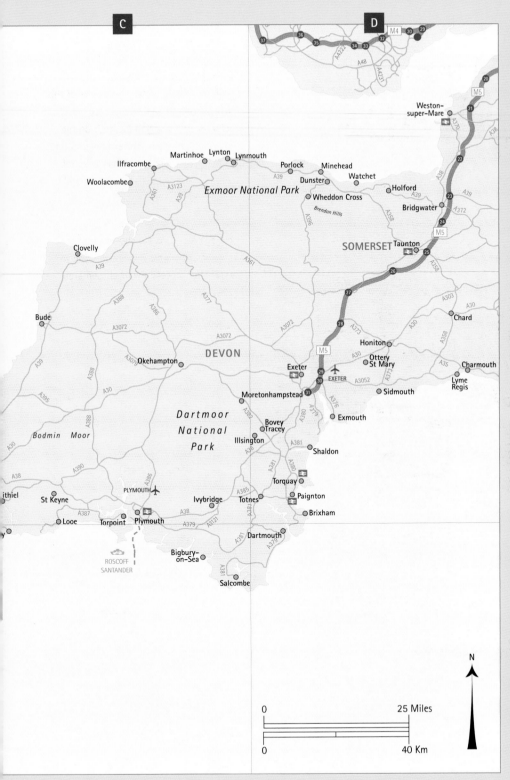

MAP 1

All place names in black offer accommodation in this guide.

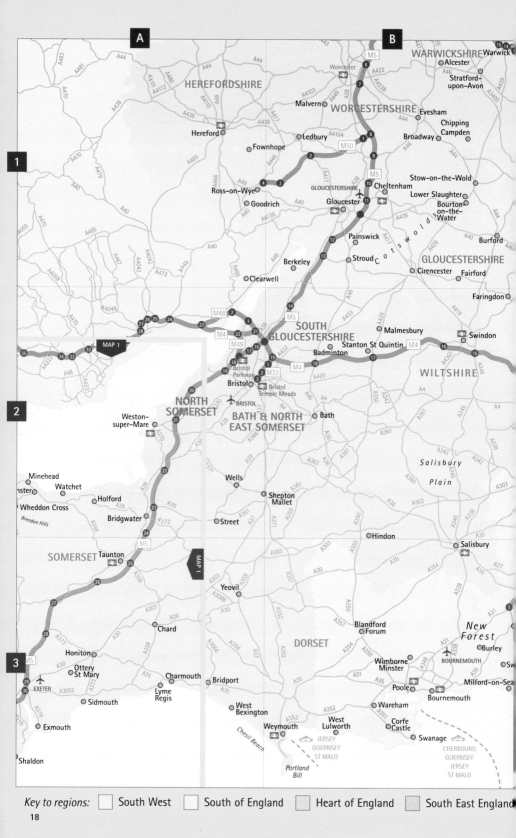

MAP 2

Key to regions: ☐ South West ☐ South of England ☐ Heart of England ☐ South East England

MAP 2

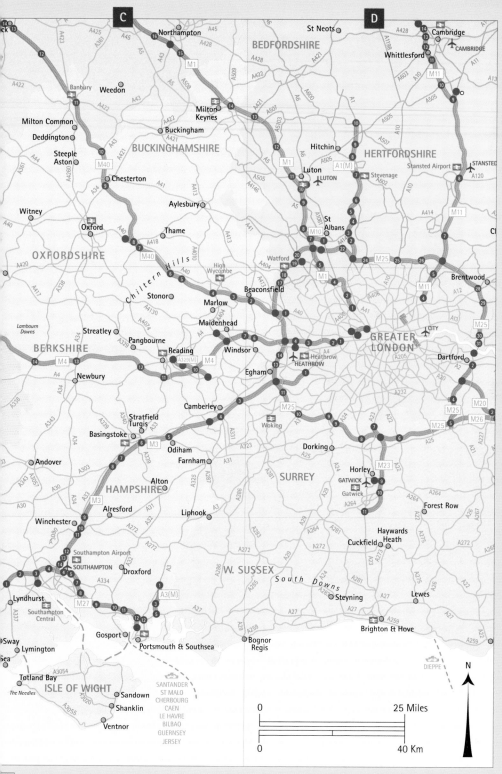

East of England

All place names in black offer accommodation in this guide.

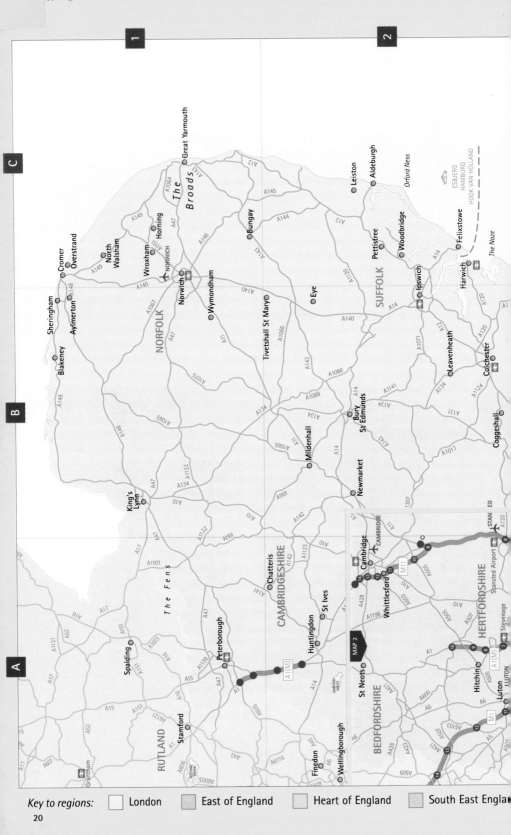

MAP 3

Key to regions: London | East of England | Heart of England | South East England

MAP 3

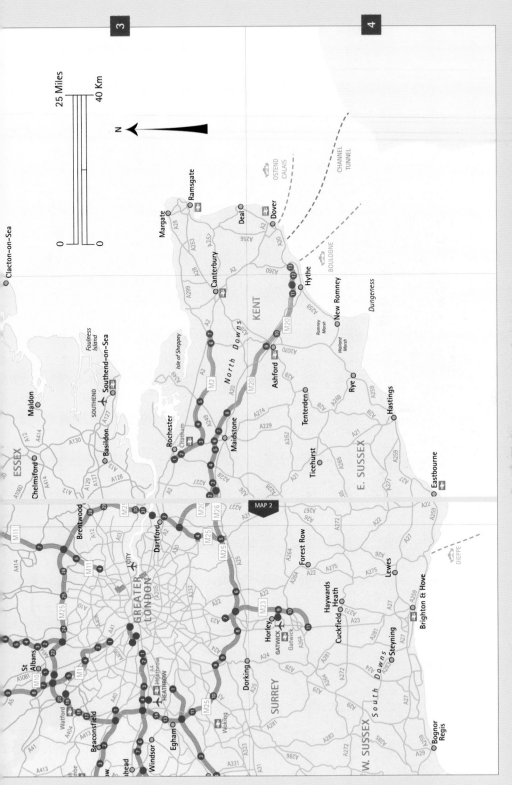

All place names in black offer accommodation in this guide.

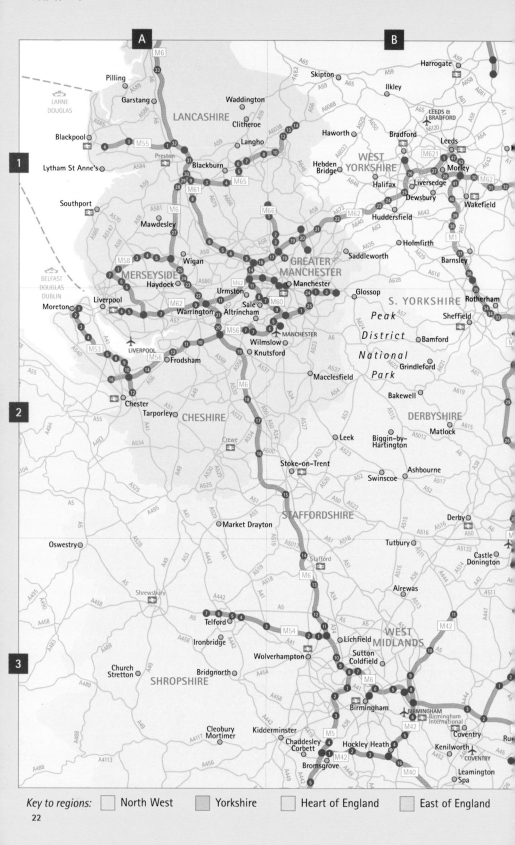

MAP 4

Key to regions: North West   Yorkshire   Heart of England   East of England

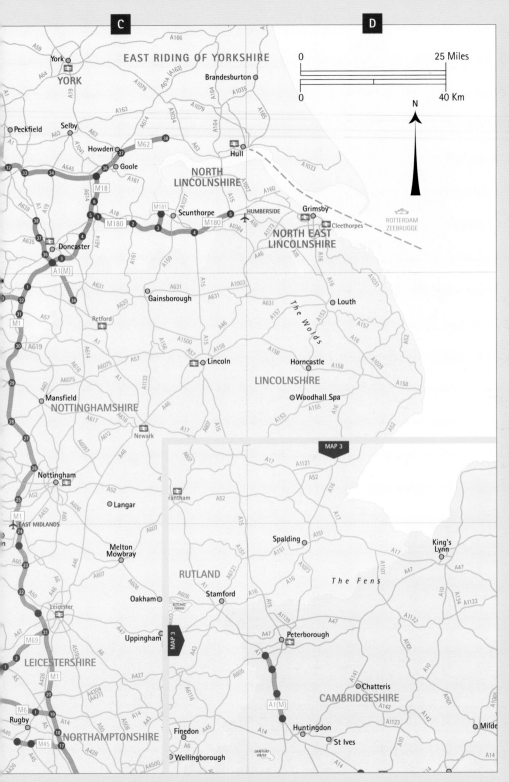

MAP 4

All place names in black offer accommodation in this guide.

MAP 5

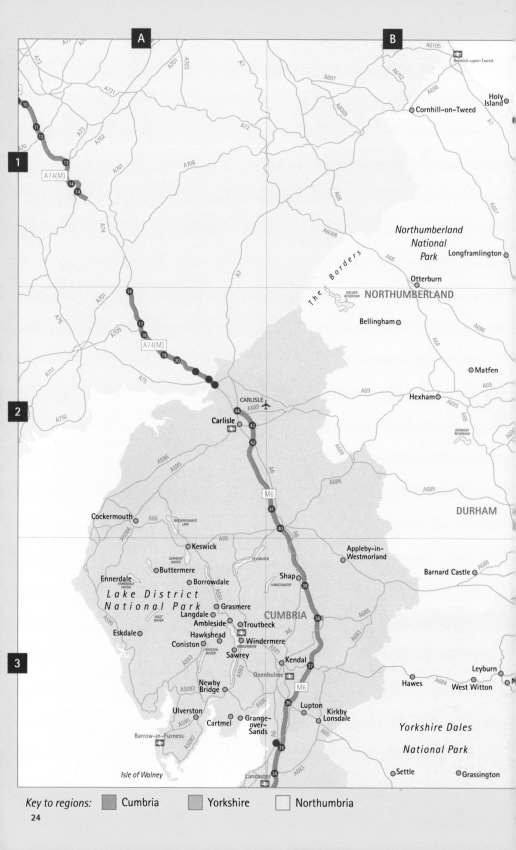

Key to regions: Cumbria Yorkshire Northumbria

MAP 5

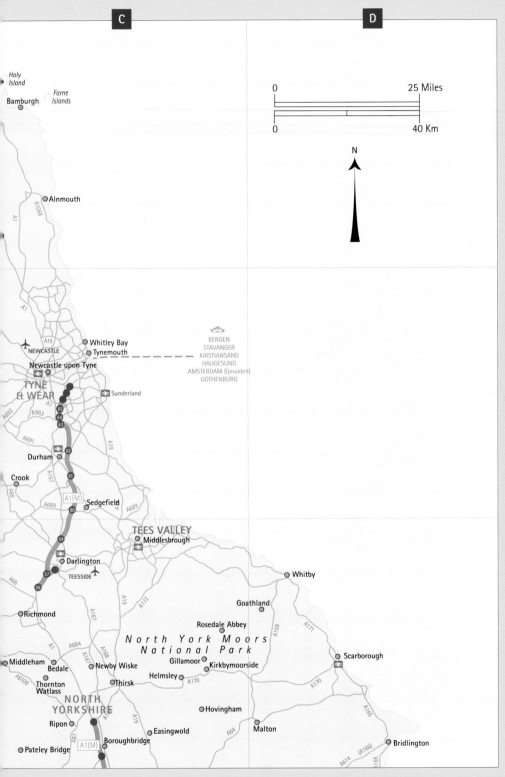

C | D

Holy Island

Farne Islands

Bamburgh

0 _____ 25 Miles

0 _____ 40 Km

N

Alnmouth

A1

A1068

A1

A19

BERGEN
STAVANGER
KIRSTIANSAND
HAUGESUND
AMSTERDAM (Ijmuiden)
GOTHENBURG

Whitley Bay
NEWCASTLE
Tynemouth
Newcastle upon Tyne

TYNE & WEAR

Sunderland

A692
A963
A691

65
64
63
62

A19

Durham

Crook

A167
A68

61

A1(M)
Sedgefield

A689
A689

60

TEES VALLEY
Middlesbrough

59

Darlington
TEESSIDE

Whitby

A66

57

56

Goathland

Richmond

A167
A19
A172

Rosedale Abbey

A169
A171

North York Moors
National Park

Scarborough

Middleham

A684
A168
A6108

Bedale
Newby Wiske

Gillamoor
Kirkbymoorside

Helmsley

A170

A170

Thornton Watlass

Thirsk

A165

NORTH YORKSHIRE

Hovingham

A64

Ripon

Pateley Bridge

A19

A1(M)

Boroughbridge

Easingwold

Malton

A614 (A166)

A59

Bridlington

All place names in black offer accommodation in this guide.

MAP 6

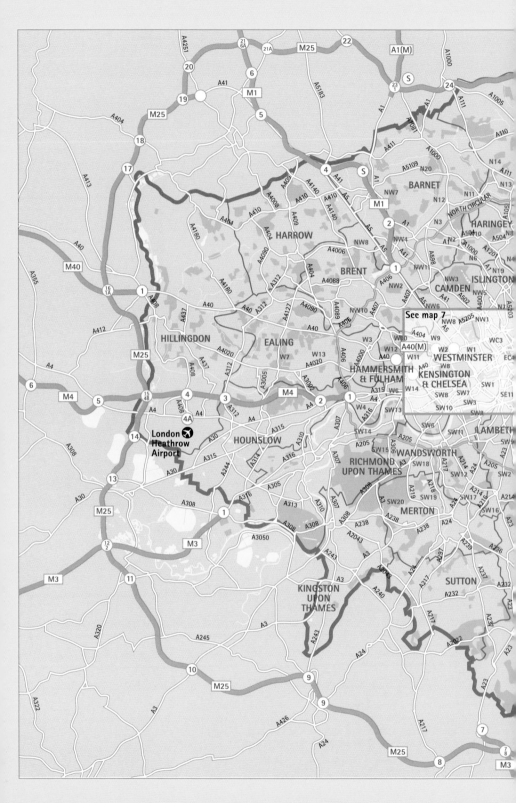

MAP 6

© Arka Cartographics Ltd. 1999

MAP 7

Central London

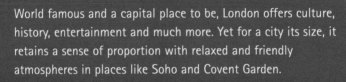

London LONDON

World famous and a capital place to be, London offers culture, history, entertainment and much more. Yet for a city its size, it retains a sense of proportion with relaxed and friendly atmospheres in places like Soho and Covent Garden.

Shoppers can spend, spend, spend in swanky Knightsbridge, or save, save, save at the Petticoat Lane, Brick Lane and Portobello markets. And for eating out, London is an explosion of tastes – traditional, international, and exotic. The outskirts of the city have their attractions, too, such as the Royal Observatory in Greenwich, and the botanical gardens at Kew.

For the perfect overview, book a flight on the world's highest observation wheel, 'The London Eye', open daily.

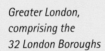

Greater London,
comprising the
32 London Boroughs

FOR MORE INFORMATION CONTACT:
London Tourist Board
6th floor, Glen House, Stag Place,
London SW1E 5LT
Telephone enquiries – see Visitorcall on page 34
Internet: www.LondonTown.com

The Pictures:
1 Piccadilly Circus;
2 Tower Bridge;
3 The maze at Hampton Court;
4 Canary Wharf.

Where to Go in London - see pages 30-32
Where to Stay in London - see pages 35-44

Whilst in
LONDON ...

You will find hundreds of interesting places to visit during your stay, just some of which are listed in these pages.

Contact any Tourist Information Centre in and around London for more ideas on days out.

Chessington World of Adventures

Leatherhead Road, Chessington KT9 2NE
Tel: (01372) 729560
Dr Chessington, creator of the World of Adventures, has invented thrilling rides and attractions for all the family, with crazy entertainers and rare animals in themed lands.

Design Museum

Shad Thames, London SE1 2YD
Tel: (020) 7403 6933
One of London's most inspiring attractions, concerned solely with the products, technologies and buildings of the 20th and 21st centuries.

Hampton Court Palace

Hampton Court, East Molesey KT8 9AU
Tel: (020) 8781 9500
The oldest Tudor palace in England with many attractions including the Tudor kitchens, tennis courts, maze, State Apartments and King's Apartments.

HMS Belfast

Morgan's Lane, Tooley Street, London SE1 2JH
Tel: (020) 7940 6300
World War II cruiser weighing 11,500 tonnes, now a floating naval museum with nine decks to explore. Many naval exhibitions also on show.

Kensington Palace State Apartments

Kensington Gardens, London W8 4PX
Tel: (020) 7937 7079
Furniture and ceiling paintings from the Stuart-Hanoverian periods, rooms from the Victorian era and works of art from the Royal Collection. Also Royal Ceremonial Dress Collection.

Kew Gardens (Royal Botanic Gardens)

Kew, Richmond TW9 3AB
Tel: (020) 8940 1171
Three hundred acres containing living collections of over 40,000 varieties of plants. Seven spectacular glasshouses, two art galleries, Japanese and rock garden.

London Aquarium

Riverside Building, London SE1 7PB
Tel: (020) 7967 8000
Dive down deep beneath the Thames and submerge yourself in one of Europe's largest displays of aquatic life.

London Dungeon

Tooley Street, London SE1 2SZ
Tel: 0891 600 0666
The world's first medieval horror museum. Now featuring two major shows, 'The Jack the Ripper Experience' and 'The Judgement Day Ride'.

London Eye

Jubilee Gardens, South Bank, London SE1
Tel: 0870 5000 600

At 135 metres (443ft) high, this is the world's highest observation wheel. It provides a 30-minute slow-moving flight over London.

London Planetarium

Marylebone Road, London NW1 5LR
Tel: (020) 7935 6861

Visitors can experience a virtual reality trip through space and wander through the interactive Space Zones before the show.

London Transport Museum

Covent Garden Piazza, London WC2E 7BB
Tel: (020) 7379 6344

The history of transport for everyone, from spectacular vehicles, special exhibitions, actors and guided tours to film shows, gallery talks and children's craft workshops.

London Zoo

Regent's Park, London NW1 4RY
Tel: (020) 7722 3333

One of the world's most famous zoos and home to over 600 species. Including the new 'Web of Life' exhibition, and a full daily events programme.

Madame Tussaud's

Marylebone Road, London NW1 5LR
Tel: (020) 7935 6861

World-famous collection of wax figures in themed settings which include The Garden Party, 200 Years, Superstars, The Grand Hall, The Chamber of Horrors and The Spirit of London.

Museum of London

London Wall, London EC2Y 5HN
Tel: (020) 7600 3699

Discover over 2,000 years of the capital's history, from prehistoric to modern times. Regular temporary exhibitions and lunchtime lecture programmes.

National Gallery

Trafalgar Square, London WC2N 5DN
Tel: (020) 7747 2885

Gallery displaying Western European paintings from about 1260-1900. Includes work by Botticelli, Leonardo da Vinci, Rembrandt, Gainsborough, Turner, Renoir, Cezanne.

National Maritime Museum

Romney Road, London SE10 9NF
Tel: (020) 8858 4422

This national museum explains Britain's worldwide influence through its explorers, traders, migrants and naval power. Features on ship models, costume and ecology of the sea.

National Portrait Gallery

St Martin's Place, London WC2H 0HE
Tel: (020) 7306 0055

Permanent collection of portraits of famous men and women from the Middle Ages to the present day. Usually free, but a charge may be made for some exhibitions.

Natural History Museum

Cromwell Road, London SW7 5BD
Tel: (020) 7942 5000

One of the most popular museums in the world and one of London's finest landmarks, it houses the natural wonders of the world.

Rock Circus

Piccadilly Circus, London W1V 9LA
Tel: (020) 7734 7203

Madame Tussaud's new Rock Circus features special audio, visual and animatronic effects, plus wax figures of the pop world's biggest names of past and present.

Royal Air Force Museum

Grahame Park Way, Hendon, London NW9 5LL
Tel: (020) 8205 2266

Britain's National Museum of Aviation features over 70 full-sized aircraft, Flight Simulator, 'Touch and Try' Jet Provost Trainer and Eurofighter 2000 Theatre.

The Pictures:
1 Harrods;
2 Big Ben;
3 The Whitechapel at the Tower of London;
4 Trafalgar Square;
5 Battersea Park Pagoda;
6 Hays Galleria;
7 China Town;
8 Richmond Lock.

31

Royal Observatory Greenwich

Greenwich Park, London SE10 9NF
Tel: (020) 8858 4422
Museum of time and space, and site of the Greenwich Meridian. Working telescopes and planetarium, timeball, Wren's Octagon Room and intricate clocks and computer simulations.

St Paul's Cathedral

St Paul's Churchyard, London EC4M 8AD
Tel: (020) 7236 4128
Wren's famous cathedral church of the diocese of London incorporating the Crypt, Ambulatory and Whispering Gallery.

Science Museum

Exhibition Road, London SW7 2DD
Tel: (020) 7942 4454
See, touch and experience the major scientific advances of the past 300 years. The world's finest collections in the history of science, technology and medicine.

Shakespeare's Globe Theatre Tours and Exhibition

New Globe Walk, Bankside, London SE1 9DT
Tel: (020) 7902 1500
Against the historical background of Elizabethan Bankside – the City of London's playground in Shakespeare's time – the exhibition focuses on actors, architecture and audiences.

Tate Modern

Bankside Power Station, Sumner Street, London SE1
Tel: (020) 7401 5081
Home of the Tate Gallery of Modern Art with displays of 20thC art ranging from Andy Warhol to Rachel Whiteread and Henri Matisse to Henry Moore.

Tower Bridge Experience

Tower Bridge, London SE1 2UP
Tel: (020) 7403 3761
Exhibition explaining the history of the bridge and how it operates. Original steam-powered engines on view. Panoramic views from fully-glazed walkways. Gift shop.

Tower of London

Tower Hill, London EC3N 4AB
Tel: (020) 7709 0765
Home of the 'Beefeaters' and ravens, the building spans 900 years of British history. On display are the nation's Crown Jewels, regalia and armoury robes.

Victoria and Albert Museum

Cromwell Road, London SW7 2RL
Tel: (020) 7942 2000
The V&A holds one of the world's largest and most diverse collections of the decorative arts, dating from 3000BC to the present day.

Vinopolis, City of Wine

Bank End, London SE1 9BU
Tel: (020) 7645 3700
Vinopolis offers all the pleasures of wine under one roof. The Wine Odyssey tour includes free tastings from over 200 wines. Four restaurants on site.

Westminster Abbey

Parliament Square, London SW1P 3PA
Tel: (020) 7222 5152
One of Britain's finest Gothic buildings. Scene of the coronation, marriage and burial of British monarchs. Includes nave and cloisters, Royal Chapels and Undercroft Museum.

The Pictures:
1 Guards at Buckingham Palace;
2 St Paul's Cathedral;
3 Tower Bridge at night;
4 Eros in Piccadilly Circus;
5 River Thames at night.

Find out more about
LONDON ...

A free information pack about holidays and attractions in London is available on written request from:

LONDON TOURIST BOARD AND CONVENTION BUREAU
6th Floor, Glen House, Stag Place, London SW1E 5LT.

TOURIST INFORMATION CENTRES

POINT OF ARRIVAL
● **Heathrow Terminals 1, 2, 3 Underground Station Concourse,** Heathrow Airport, TW6 2JA.
Open: Daily 0800-1800; 1 Jun-30 Sep, Mon-Sat 0800-1900, Sun 0800-1800.
● **Liverpool Street Underground Station,** EC2M 7PN.
Open: Daily 0800-1800; 1 Jun-30 Sep, Mon-Sat 0800-1900, Sun 0800-1800.
● **Victoria Station Forecourt,** SW1V 1JU.
Open: 1 Jun-30 Sep, Mon-Sat 0800-2100, Sun 0800-1800; 1 Oct-Easter, daily 0800-1800; Easter-31 May, Mon-Sat 0800-2000, Sun 0800-1800.
● **Waterloo International Terminal**
Arrivals Hall, London SE1 7LT. *Open: Daily 0830-2230.*

INNER LONDON
● **Britain Visitor Centre**
1 Regent Street, Piccadilly Circus, SW1Y 4XT.
Open: Mon 0930-1830, Tue-Fri 0900-1830, Sat & Sun 1000-1600; Jun-Oct, Sat 0900-1700.
● **Greenwich Tourist Information Centre**
Pepys House, 2 Cutty Sark Gardens SE10 9LW.
Tel: 0870 608 2000; Fax: (020) 8853 4607.
Open: Daily 1000-1700; 1 Jul-31 Aug, daily 1000-2000.
● **Lewisham Tourist Information Centre**
Lewisham Library,
199-201 Lewisham High Street, SE13 6LG.
Tel: (020) 8297 8317.
Open: Mon 1000-1700, Tue-Fri 0900-1700, Sat 1000-1600.
● **Southwark Information Centre**
London Bridge, 6 Tooley Street, SE1 2SY.
Tel: (020) 7403 8299.
Open: Easter-31 Oct, Mon-Sat 1000-1800, Sun 1030-1730; 1 Nov-Easter, Mon-Sat 1000-1600, Sun 1100-1600.

● **Tower Hamlets Tourist Information Centre**
18 Lamb Street, E1 6EA.
Fax: (020) 7375 2539.
Open: Mon, Tues, Thur & Fri 0930-1330,1430-1630, 0930-1300; Sun 1130-1430.

OUTER LONDON
● **Bexley Hall Place Visitor Centre**
Bourne Road, Bexley, Kent DA5 1PQ.
Tel: (01322) 558676; Fax: (01322) 522921.
Open: Mon-Sat 1000-1630, Sun 1400-1730.
● **Croydon Tourist Information Centre**
Katharine Street, Croydon CR9 1ET.
Tel: (020) 8253 1009;   Fax: (020) 8253 1008.
Open: Mon-Wed 0900-1800, Thu 0930-1800, Fri 0900-1800, Sat 0900-1700, Sun 1400-1700.
● **Harrow Tourist Information Centre**
Civic Centre, Station Road, Harrow HA1 2XF.
Tel: (020) 8424 1103; Fax: (020) 8424 1134.
Open: Mon-Fri 0900-1700.
● **Hillingdon Tourist Information Centre**
Central Library, 14 High Street, Uxbridge UB8 1HD.
Tel: (01895) 250706; Fax: (01895) 239794.
Open: Mon, Tue & Thu 0930-2000, Wed 0930-1730, Fri 1000-1730, Sat 0930-1600.
● **Hounslow Tourist Information Centre**
24 The Treaty Centre,
Hounslow High Street, Hounslow TW3 1ES.
Tel: (020) 8583 2929; Fax: (020) 8583 4714.
Open: Mon, Wed, Fri & Sat 0930-1730, Tue & Thu 0930-2000.
● **Kingston Tourist Information Centre**
Market House, Market Place,
Kingston upon Thames KT1 1JS.
Tel: (020) 8547 5592; Fax: (020) 8547 5594.
Open: Mon-Fri 1000-1700, Sat 0900-1600.
● **Richmond Tourist Information Centre**
Old Town Hall, Whittaker Avenue, Richmond TW9 1TP.
Tel: (020) 8940 9125; Fax: (020) 8940 6899.
Open: Mon-Sat 1000-1700; Easter Sunday-end Sep, Sun 1030-1330.

- **Swanley Tourist Information Centre**
London Road, BR8 7AE.
Tel: (01322) 614660.
Open: Mon-Thu 0930-1730, Fri 0930-1800, Sat 0900-1600.

- **Twickenham Tourist Information Centre**
The Atrium, Civic Centre, York Street, Twickenham, Middlesex TW1 3BZ.
Tel: (020) 8891 7272.
Open: Mon-Thu 0900-1715; Fri 0900-1700.

VISITORCALL

The London Tourist Board and Convention Bureau's 'Phone Guide to London' operates 24 hours a day. To access a full range of information call 09064 123456. To access specific lines dial 09064 123 followed by:

What's on this week	- 400
What's on next 3 months	- 401
Rock and pop concerts	- 422
Visitor attractions	- 480
Where to take children	- 424
Museums and galleries	- 429
Palaces (including Buckingham Palace)	- 481
Current exhibitions	- 403
Changing the Guard	- 411
West End shows	- 416
Eating out	- 485
London line 2000:	09064 663344

Calls cost 60p per minute at all times (as at June 2000). To order a Visitorcall card please call (020) 7971 0026.

ARTSLINE

London's information and advice service for disabled people on arts and entertainment. Call (020) 7388 2227.

HOTEL ACCOMMODATION SERVICE

Accommodation reservations can be made throughout London. Call the London Tourist Board's Telephone Accommodation Service on (020) 7932 2020 with your requirements and Mastercard/Visa/Switch details.

Reservations on arrival are handled at the Tourist Information Centres at Victoria Station, Heathrow Underground, Liverpool Street Station, Waterloo International and Heathrow Terminal 3. Go to any of them on the day when you need accommodation. A communication charge and a refundable deposit are payable when making a reservation.

WHICH PART OF LONDON?

The majority of tourist accommodation is situated in the central parts of London and is therefore very convenient for most of the city's attractions and night life.

However, there are many hotels in outer London which provide other advantages, such as easier parking. In the 'Where to Stay' pages which follow, you will find accommodation listed under INNER LONDON (covering the E1 to W14 London Postal Area) and OUTER LONDON (covering the remainder of Greater London). Colour maps 6 and 7 at the front of the guide show place names and London Postal Area codes and will help you to locate accommodation in your chosen area of London.

The Pictures:
1 Buckingham Palace;
2 Big Ben and the Houses of Parliament;
3 Westminster Abbey.

Getting to
LONDON ...

BY ROAD: Major trunk roads into London include: A1, M1, A5, A10, A11, M11, A13, A2, M2, A23, A3, M3, A4, M4, A40, M40, A41, M25 (London orbital).
London Transport is responsible for running London's bus services and the underground rail network. (020) 7222 1234 (24 hour telephone service; calls answered in rotation).

BY RAIL: Main rail termini:
Victoria/Waterloo/Charing Cross – serving the South/South East;
King's Cross – serving the North East; Euston – serving the North West/Midlands;
Liverpool Street – serving the East; Paddington – serving the Thames Valley/West.

Where to stay in LONDON

Accommodation entries in this region are listed under Inner London (covering the postcode areas E1 to W14) and Outer London (covering the remainder of Greater London) - please refer to the colour location maps 6 and 7 at the front of this guide.

At-a-glance symbols at the end of each accommodation entry give useful information about services and facilities. A key to symbols can be found inside the back cover flap. Keep this open for easy reference.

A complete listing of all English Tourism Council assessed hotels appears at the back of this guide.

INNER LONDON
LONDON E1

★★★★
Ad p15

THISTLE TOWER
St Katharine's Way, London,
E1W 1LD
T: (020) 7481 2575
F: (020) 7488 4106
E: tower.businesscentre@thistle.co.uk
I: www.thistlehotels.com

Bedrooms: 89 single,
330 double, 360 twin,
22 triple; suites available
Bathrooms: 801 en suite

Lunch available
EM 1730 (LO 2230)
Parking for 116
CC: Amex, Barclaycard,
Delta, Diners, Eurocard,
JCB, Mastercard, Solo,
Switch, Visa, Visa Electron

B&B per night:
S £190.00–£223.00
D £211.00–£261.00

OPEN All year round

®
Thistle Hotels/Utell
International

Beside Tower Bridge and the Tower of London and overlooking St Katharine's Docks. Close to the City and the West End. Ideally located for both business and pleasure.

🅰 💺 📞 🖥 🖵 🌸 🗝 🛈 Ⓢ 🔾 🕭 🌙 ▣ 🎞 ✉ 📖 🍴 255 ✴ 🐾 SP T

LONDON EC1

Rating
Applied For
Ad p15

THISTLE CITY BARBICAN
Central Street, Clerkenwell, London,
EC1V 8DS
T: (020) 7956 6000
F: (020) 7253 1005
E: barbican@thistle.co.uk
I: www.thistlehotels.com

Bedrooms: 65 single,
133 double, 247 twin,
18 triple, 2 family
rooms; suites available
Bathrooms: 465 en suite

Lunch available
EM 1800 (LO 2230)
Parking for 12
CC: Amex, Barclaycard,
Diners, Eurocard, JCB,
Mastercard, Switch, Visa

B&B per night:
S £132.00–£136.00
D £147.00–£172.00

OPEN All year round

®
Thistle Hotels

On the edge of London's square mile, this hotel is within easy walking distance of the Barbican Centre and the historic City of London.

🅰 💺 📞 🖥 🖵 🌸 🗝 🛈 Ⓢ 🔾 ▣ 🎞 📖 🍴 140 ✄ ✴ 🐾 SP T

CONFIRM YOUR BOOKING
You are advised to confirm your booking in writing.

★★★

JURYS LONDON INN

60 Pentonville Road, Islington, London, N1 9LA
T: (020) 7282 5500
F: (020) 7282 5511
E: padhraic_flavin@jurys.com
I: www.jurys.com

B&B per night:
S Max £89.00
D Max £89.00

OPEN All year round

Utell International

Each of our rooms is equipped to an excellent standard, including air conditioning, direct-dial telephone, tea/coffee facilities, modem points and satellite TV. Situated in Islington, a cultural quarter of London which offers many sights and experiences for the business or leisure traveller.

Bedrooms: 116 double, 113 twin
Bathrooms: 229 en suite

Lunch available
EM 1800 (LO 2130)
CC: Amex, Barclaycard, Delta, Diners, Eurocard, Mastercard, Switch, Visa, Visa Electron

🅰️🏇☎️🖥️📠♿🍷⑤📺🌓🚻🏧🖐️🚭🍴30🛩️Ⓣ🌐

★★★★★
Gold
Award

THE LANDMARK LONDON

222 Marylebone Road, London, NW1 6JQ
T: (020) 7631 8000
F: (020) 7631 8080
E: reservations@thelandmark.co.uk
I: www.landmarklondon.co.uk

B&B per night:
D Min £302.27

OPEN All year round

Conveniently located within easy reach of the West End and City. With some of the largest bedrooms in London, the hotel seamlessly integrates the elegance and grandeur of British Victorian style with the luxury and facilities of one of the world's leading hotels. Price shown excludes breakfast.

Bedrooms: 185 double, 114 twin; suites available
Bathrooms: 299 en suite

Lunch available
EM 1900 (LO 2230)
Parking for 80
CC: Amex, Barclaycard, Delta, Diners, Eurocard, JCB, Maestro, Mastercard, Solo, Switch, Visa, Visa Electron

🅰️🏇🛏️☎️🖥️📠🍷📱⑤🚭🚻🌓🚻🏧🖐️🍴380🎿🏌️🎣🏇🚭🆂🅿️♿Ⓣ

Rating Applied For	THISTLE EUSTON			
Ad p15	43 Cardington Street, Euston, London, NW1 2LP T: (020) 7387 4400 F: (020) 7387 5122 E: euston@thistle.co.uk	Bedrooms: 60 single, 67 double, 172 twin, 44 triple, 17 family rooms Bathrooms: 360 en suite	Lunch available EM 1730 (LO 2230) Parking for 20 CC: Amex, Barclaycard, Delta, Diners, Eurocard, Mastercard, Solo, Switch, Visa	B&B per night: S £132.00–£156.00 D £151.00–£175.00 OPEN All year round Ⓒ Thistle Hotels

Situated between Regents Park and the British Library, close to Euston station. This hotel is in easy reach of the City and the West End.

🅰️🏇🛏️☎️🖥️📠♿🍷📱⑤🚭🚻📺🌓🚻🏧🖐️🍴100🚭🆂🅿️Ⓣ

★★★★
Ad p15

HENDON HALL (A THISTLE COUNTRY HOUSE HOTEL)

Ashley Lane, off Parson Street, Hendon, London, NW4 1HF
T: (020) 8203 3341
F: (020) 8203 9709
E: hendon.hall@thistle.co.uk

Bedrooms: 1 single, 36 double, 21 twin; suites available
Bathrooms: 58 en suite

Lunch available
EM 1900 (LO 2200)
Parking for 70
CC: Amex, Barclaycard, Delta, Diners, Eurocard, JCB, Mastercard, Switch, Visa

B&B per night:
S £184.00–£219.00
D £184.00–£219.00

OPEN All year round

Ⓒ
Thistle Hotels/Utell International

Elegant refurbished 18thC Georgian mansion. Convenient for Wembley and the A1/M1 going north. Attractive gardens, first-class restaurant.

🅰️🏇🛏️☎️🖥️📠🍷⑤🚭🚻🌓🚻🏧🖐️🍴330✳️🚭🆂🔲🅿️♿Ⓣ

RATING All accommodation in this guide has been rated, or is awaiting a rating, by a trained English Tourism Council assessor.

LONDON SE1

NOVOTEL LONDON WATERLOO

113 Lambeth Road, London,
SE1 7LS
T: (020) 7793 1010
F: (020) 7793 0202
E: h1785@accor-hotels.com
I: www.novotel.com

Bedrooms: 187 double;
suites available
Bathrooms: 187 en suite

Lunch available
EM 1900 (LO 2345)
Parking for 40
CC: Amex, Barclaycard,
Delta, Diners, Eurocard,
Maestro, Mastercard,
Switch, Visa

B&B per night:
S £104.00–£142.00
D £114.00–£166.00

HB per person:
DY £124.00–£162.00

OPEN All year round

Three minutes from Waterloo station by car. Conveniently located opposite Houses of Parliament and Big Ben. Good transport links. Comfort cooled rooms with mini-bar, hairdryers.

LONDON SE3

★★

CLARENDON HOTEL

8-16 Montpelier Row, Blackheath, London,
SE3 0RW
T: (020) 8318 4321
F: (020) 8318 4378

B&B per night:
S £70.00–£90.00
D £79.00–£150.00

HB per person:
DY £85.00–£105.00

OPEN All year round

This Georgian-fronted hotel commands superb views over historic Blackheath and Greenwich. An ideal tourist base for visiting London, Greenwich and the Garden of England, Kent. Make your stay a memorable one: enjoy dinner in the Meridian restaurant, brandy by the log fire or visit our nautical chart bar.

Bedrooms: 40 single,
53 double, 54 twin,
32 triple, 7 family
rooms; suites available
Bathrooms: 186 en suite

Lunch available
EM 1830 (LO 2145)
Parking for 80
CC: Amex, Barclaycard,
Delta, Eurocard, JCB,
Maestro, Mastercard,
Solo, Switch, Visa, Visa
Electron

LONDON SW1

★★★★

DOLPHIN SQUARE HOTEL

Dolphin Square, Chichester Street,
London, SW1V 3LX
T: (020) 7834 3800 &
0800 616607 (Reservations)
F: (020) 7798 8735
E: reservations@
dolphinsquarehotel.co.uk
I: www.dolphinsquarehotel.co.uk

Bedrooms: 55 double,
54 twin, 10 triple,
29 family rooms; suites
available
Bathrooms: 148 en suite

Lunch available
EM 1800 (LO 2230)
Parking for 17
CC: Amex, Barclaycard,
Delta, Diners, Eurocard,
Mastercard, Solo, Switch,
Visa, Visa Electron

B&B per night:
S £140.00–£195.00
D £165.00–£175.00

HB per person:
DY £168.00–£178.00

OPEN All year round

CR
Utell International

Dolphin Square Hotel, a 4 Star all suite property, combines the luxury and convenience of a hotel with the flexibility and independence of an apartment.

★★★★
Silver
Award
Ad p15

ROYAL HORSEGUARDS THISTLE HOTEL

2 Whitehall Court, London,
SW1A 2EJ
T: (020) 7839 3400
F: (020) 7930 3269
E: royal.horseguards@thistle.co.uk
I: www.thistlehotels.com

Bedrooms: 9 single,
175 double, 96 twin;
suites available
Bathrooms: 280 en suite

Lunch available
EM
CC: Amex, Barclaycard,
Delta, Diners, Eurocard,
JCB, Maestro, Mastercard,
Switch, Visa

B&B per night:
S £277.00–£286.00
D £309.00–£339.00

OPEN All year round

CR
Thistle Hotels

Luxury hotel overlooking the Thames and the London Eye. Just minutes from Trafalgar Square, Covent Garden and Piccadilly. Close to Westminster Abbey and the Houses of Parliament.

IMPORTANT NOTE Information on accommodation listed in this guide has been supplied by the proprietors. As changes may occur you are advised to check details at the time of booking.

LONDON SW1 continued

★★★★ THISTLE VICTORIA
Silver Award
Ad p15

101 Buckingham Palace Road, London, SW1W 0SJ	Bedrooms: 96 single, 53 double, 206 twin,	Lunch available EM 1730 (LO 2200)	B&B per night: S £168.00–£173.00
T: (020) 7834 9494	5 triple, 6 family rooms;	CC: Amex, Barclaycard,	D £217.00–£243.00
F: (020) 7630 1978	suites available	Delta, Diners, Eurocard,	
E: grosvenor@thistle.co.uk	Bathrooms: 366 en suite	JCB, Mastercard, Switch, Visa	OPEN All year round

Elegant and spacious in the great Victorian tradition, offering modern facilities. Ideal for London sightseeing, being within walking distance of Buckingham Palace and the Houses of Parliament.

Thistle Hotels

Ⓜ 🐎 🏠 ☎ 🖥 ⌨ ♿ ❄ Ⓢ ✂ 🅿 ✚ 🛗 ⛁ ⚓ ⌅200 ♨ ✗ ⚓ SP 🏧 T

★★★★ THISTLE WESTMINSTER
Ad p15

49 Buckingham Palace Road, Victoria, London, SW1W 0QT	Bedrooms: 7 single, 43 double, 14 twin,	Lunch available EM 1200 (LO 2300)	B&B per night: S £209.00–£215.00
T: (020) 7834 1821	54 triple, 15 family rooms	CC: Amex, Barclaycard,	D £235.00–£272.00
F: (020) 7931 7542	Bathrooms: 133 en suite	Delta, Diners, Eurocard,	
E: royalwestminster@cix.co.uk		Mastercard, Switch, Visa	OPEN All year round
I: www.cix.co.uk/			

An elegant hotel close to Buckingham Palace, St James's Park, the River Thames, Victoria station and the Houses of Parliament.

Thistle Hotels/Utell International

Ⓜ 🐎 ☎ 🏠 ⌨ ♿ ❄ Ⓢ ✂ 🅿 TV ● ♿ ⌨ ⛁ ⚓ ⌅180 ♨ SP T

LONDON SW5

★★★ THE BURNS HOTEL

18-26 Barkston Gardens, Kensington, London, SW5 0EN	Bedrooms: 38 single, 14 double, 43 twin,	EM 1830 (LO 2130) CC: Amex, Barclaycard,	B&B per night: S £112.00–£115.00
T: (020) 7373 3151	10 triple	Delta, Diners, JCB,	D £138.00–£141.00
F: (020) 7370 4090	Bathrooms: 105 en suite	Mastercard, Switch, Visa,	
E: burnshotel@vienna-group.co.uk		Visa Electron	HB per person:
I: www.vienna-group.co.uk			DY £128.00–£132.00

Elegant hotel offering the attention to detail and service that a discerning traveller would expect. Close to the West End, Knightsbridge, Earl's Court and Olympia.

OPEN All year round

Utell International

Ⓜ 🐎 ♿ ☎ 🏠 ⌨ ♿ ❄ Ⓢ ✂ 🅿 TV ● ♿ ⌨ ⛁ ✿ SP 🏧 T

★★★ HOGARTH HOTEL

33 Hogarth Road, Kensington, London, SW5 0QQ	Bedrooms: 7 single, 27 double, 50 twin,	Lunch available EM (LO 2200)	B&B per night: S £100.00–£118.00
T: (020) 7370 6831	1 triple	Parking for 18	D £137.00–£157.00
F: (020) 7373 6179	Bathrooms: 85 en suite	CC: Amex, Barclaycard,	
E: hogarth@marstonhotels.co.uk		Delta, Diners, Eurocard,	HB per person:
I: www.marstonhotels.co.uk		Mastercard, Switch, Visa	DY £68.50–£78.50

Modern hotel near Earl's Court within walking distance of Olympia and Earl's Court Exhibition Centres. Designer bedrooms are well-equipped and have benefited from recent refurbishment.

OPEN All year round

🐎 ☎ 🏠 ⌨ ♿ ❄ Ⓢ ✂ 🅿 ● ♿ ⌨ ⛁ ⌅50 ♨ SP T

LONDON SW19

★★★★ CANNIZARO HOUSE (A THISTLE COUNTRY HOUSE HOTEL)
Silver Award
Ad p15

Westside, Wimbledon Common, London, SW19 4UE	Bedrooms: 30 double, 15 twin; suites available	Lunch available EM 1900 (LO 2230)	B&B per night: S £211.00–£237.00
T: (020) 8879 1464	Bathrooms: 45 en suite	Parking for 90	D £211.00–£237.00
F: (020) 8879 7338		CC: Amex, Barclaycard,	
E: cannizaro.house@thistle.co.uk		Delta, Diners, Eurocard,	OPEN All year round
		JCB, Mastercard, Switch, Visa	

A historic Georgian mansion set in the gardens of Cannizaro Park on the edge of Wimbledon Common. Meeting and conference facilities for up to 100. Award-winning restaurant.

Thistle Hotels/Utell International

Ⓜ 🐎 ♿ 🏠 ☎ 🖥 ⌨ ♿ ❄ Ⓢ ✂ ● ♿ ⌨ ⛁ ⚓ ⌅ ♨ ⛳ ✿ ✗ 🚲 SC ♨ SP 🏧 T

CENTRAL RESERVATIONS OFFICES

The symbol Ⓒ and a group name in an entry indicate that bookings can be made through a central reservations office. These are listed in a separate section towards the back of this guide.

LONDON W1

★★★★★ Gold Award

THE DORCHESTER

Park Lane, London, W1A 2HJ
T: (020) 7629 8888 (24 hours)
F: (020) 7409 0114
E: reservations@dorchesterhotel.com
I: www.dorchesterhotel.com

Bedrooms: 32 single, 125 double, 40 twin; suites available
Bathrooms: 197 en suite

Lunch available
EM 1800 (LO 2330)
Parking for 24
CC: Amex, Barclaycard, Delta, Diners, Eurocard, JCB, Mastercard, Solo, Switch, Visa

B&B per night:
S £335.00–£359.00
D £382.00–£405.00

HB per person:
DY £240.00–£280.00

OPEN All year round

℗
Utell International

Consistently ranked one of the world's best, this opulent 1931 hotel offers the friendliest, almost telepathic levels of service, an outstanding choice of restaurants and a glorious spa.

450

Rating Applied For

HOTEL LA PLACE

17 Nottingham Place, London, W1M 3FF
T: (020) 7486 2323
F: (020) 7486 4335
E: reservations@hotellaplace.com
I: www.hotellaplace.com

Bedrooms: 5 single, 3 double, 6 twin, 3 triple, 3 family rooms; suites available
Bathrooms: 20 en suite

Lunch available
EM 1800 (LO 2030)
CC: Amex, Barclaycard, Delta, Diners, Eurocard, JCB, Mastercard, Solo, Switch, Visa, Visa Electron

B&B per night:
S £90.00–£150.00
D £115.00–£160.00

HB per person:
DY £65.00–£160.00

OPEN All year round

Family-owned and managed, small, friendly townhouse hotel with a high proportion of repeat clientele. At Hotel La Place you are a person, not just a room number.

★★★★ Silver Award
Ad p15

THE SELFRIDGE, A THISTLE HOTEL

Orchard Street, London, W1H 0JS
T: (020) 7408 2080
F: (020) 7629 8849
E: markbarrett@thistle.co.uk
I: www.thistlehotels.co.uk

Bedrooms: 86 single, 62 double, 146 twin; suites available
Bathrooms: 294 en suite

Lunch available
EM 1800 (LO 2300)
CC: Amex, Barclaycard, Delta, Diners, Eurocard, JCB, Mastercard, Switch, Visa

B&B per night:
S £202.00–£228.00
D £227.00–£254.00

OPEN All year round

℗
Thistle Hotels/Utell International

A deluxe hotel in the centre of the capital. Situated just off Oxford Street, this is the ideal choice for business or pleasure.

200

★★★★ Silver Award
Ad p15

THISTLE MARBLE ARCH

Bryanston Street, Marble Arch, London, W1A 4UR
T: (020) 7629 8040
F: (020) 7499 7792
E: marble.arch@thistle.co.uk
I: www.thistlehotels.com

Bedrooms: 35 single, 153 double, 359 twin, 54 triple, 88 family rooms
Bathrooms: 689 en suite

Lunch available
EM 1800 (LO 0100)
CC: Amex, Barclaycard, Delta, Diners, Eurocard, JCB, Maestro, Mastercard, Solo, Switch, Visa, Visa Electron

B&B per night:
S £226.00–£262.00
D £226.00–£262.00

OPEN All year round

℗
Thistle Hotels/Utell International

In the heart of London's busy West End, overlooking Oxford Street; close to shops, theatres and nightclubs.

300

Rating Applied For
Ad p15

THISTLE PICCADILLY

39 Coventry Street, London, W1V 7FH
T: (020) 7930 4033
F: (020) 7925 2586
E: piccadilly@thistle.co.uk
I: www.thistlehotels.co.uk

Bedrooms: 15 single, 27 double, 44 twin, 5 triple
Bathrooms: 91 en suite

CC: Amex, Barclaycard, Delta, Diners, Eurocard, JCB, Mastercard, Switch, Visa

B&B per night:
S £181.00–£187.00
D £216.00–£243.00

OPEN All year round

℗
Thistle Hotels/Utell International

This traditional Victorian hotel is just yards from Piccadilly Circus. It provides easy access to all areas of the capital, great for business or pleasure.

16

LONDON W2

★★★★
Ad p15

THISTLE HYDE PARK

90–92 Lancaster Gate, London, W2 3NR
T: (020) 7262 2711
F: (020) 7262 2147
I: hyde.park@thistle.co.uk

Bedrooms: 10 single, 28 double, 16 twin; suites available
Bathrooms: 54 en suite

Lunch available
EM 1830 (LO 2230)
Parking for 25
CC: Amex, Barclaycard, Delta, Diners, Eurocard, Mastercard, Switch, Visa

B&B per night:
S £236.00–£263.00
D £287.00–£315.00

OPEN All year round

℗
Thistle Hotels/Utell International

Luxurious townhouse hotel overlooking Hyde Park and Kensington Gardens. Convenient for the West End and the shops of Bayswater and Notting Hill.

35

LONDON W2 continued

Rating Applied For Ad p15	**THISTLE KENSINGTON GARDENS** 104 Bayswater Road, London, W2 3HL T: (020) 7262 4461 F: (020) 7706 4560 I: kensington.gardens@thistle.co. uk	Bedrooms: 48 single, 81 double, 41 twin, 5 triple Bathrooms: 175 en suite	Lunch available EM 1800 (LO 2215) Parking for 80 CC: Amex, Barclaycard, Diners, Mastercard, Switch, Visa	B&B per night: S £151.00–£176.00 D £173.00–£228.00 OPEN All year round

Modern hotel overlooking Kensington Gardens and Hyde Park. Close to shops and tourist attractions. Car parking available, at a small fee.

Thistle Hotels/Utell International

🏨🕭📞🖨🛁🔧🍴⬆🈂🔆🗝🚪⬤🛗📶◐🍺🎯60 SC 🗝 SP 🌐

Rating Applied For Ad p15	**THISTLE LANCASTER GATE** 75-89 Lancaster Gate, London, W2 3NN T: (020) 7402 4272 F: (020) 7706 4156 E: lancaster.gate@thistle.co.uk I: www.thistlehotels.com	Bedrooms: 76 single, 74 double, 209 twin, 26 triple, 5 family rooms; suite available Bathrooms: 390 en suite	Lunch available EM 1700 (LO 2300) CC: Amex, Barclaycard, Delta, Diners, JCB, Mastercard, Switch, Visa	B&B per night: S £134.00–£158.00 D £153.00–£178.00 OPEN All year round

A modern hotel behind a gracious 19thC facade, opposite Kensington Gardens and Hyde Park. Within easy reach of Oxford Street and the West End.

Thistle Hotels/Utell International

🏨🕭🛁📞🖨🛁🔧🍴⬆🈂🔆🗝🚪⬤🛗📶🍴120 🌡 🗝 SP 🏠 T

★	**ACTON PARK HOTEL** 116 The Vale, Acton, London, W3 7JT T: (020) 8743 9417 F: (020) 8743 9417	Bedrooms: 7 single, 4 double, 8 twin, 2 triple Bathrooms: 21 en suite	Lunch available EM 1800 (LO 2200) Parking for 15 CC: Amex, Barclaycard, Delta, Diners, Eurocard, JCB, Maestro, Mastercard, Solo, Switch, Visa, Visa Electron	B&B per night: S £48.00–£64.00 D £59.00–£72.00 OPEN All year round

Small, friendly, family-run hotel, just off the North Circular Road. Between Heathrow and the West End, overlooking parkland. Ample parking.

🏨🕭🛁🛁📞🚪🔧🛁🗝🚪📺⬤🛗📶🍴40 🌡 SC 🗝 SP T

★★★

LONDON LODGE HOTEL
134-136 Lexham Gardens, London, W8 6JE
T: (020) 7244 8444
F: (020) 7373 6661
E: info@londonlodgehotel.com
I: www.londonlodgehotel.com

B&B per night:
S £95.00–£129.00
D £115.00–£169.00

HB per person:
DY £79.00–£105.00

OPEN All year round

Newly refurbished townhouse hotel, ideally situated in a quiet residential street in the heart of Kensington. Perfectly placed for business, shopping and seeing London. All rooms individually designed to reflect traditional English elegance. Modern facilities such as satellite television, PC modem lines, mini bar. Executive rooms have whirlpool bath and private safe.

Bedrooms: 7 single, 8 double, 12 twin, 1 triple Bathrooms: 28 en suite	Lunch available EM 1800 (LO 2230) CC: Amex, Delta, Diners, JCB, Mastercard, Solo, Switch, Visa, Visa Electron

🏨🕭🛁🛁📞🚪🔧🗝🚪◐⬤🛗📶🍴🍴✈ SC 🗝 SP T

Rating Applied For Ad p15	**THISTLE KENSINGTON PALACE** De Vere Gardens, London, W8 5AF T: (020) 7937 8121 F: (020) 7937 2816	Bedrooms: 65 single, 65 double, 140 twin, 6 triple, 22 family rooms; suite available Bathrooms: 298 en suite	Lunch available EM 1700 (LO 2330) CC: Amex, Barclaycard, Delta, Diners, Eurocard, JCB, Mastercard, Switch, Visa	B&B per night: S £139.00–£163.00 D £156.00–£210.00 OPEN All year round

Luxurious hotel overlooking Kensington Palace and its gardens. Very convenient for the shops of Kensington and Knightsbridge; the museums of Science, Natural History and the Victoria and Albert.

Thistle Hotels/Utell International

🏨🕭📞🛁📞🚪🔧🛁🗝🚪📺◐⬤🛗📶🍴180 ✈ SC 🗝 SP

LONDON W8 continued

★★★★
Ad p15·

THISTLE KENSINGTON PARK
16-32 De Vere Gardens, London,
W8 5AG
T: (020) 7937 8080
F: (020) 7937 7616

Bedrooms: 80 single,
92 double, 134 twin,
17 triple, 30 family
rooms; suites available
Bathrooms: 353 en suite

Lunch available
EM 1800 (LO 2300)
CC: Amex, Barclaycard,
Delta, Diners, Eurocard,
JCB, Mastercard, Switch,
Visa

B&B per night:
S £178.00–£203.00
D £213.00–£269.00

OPEN All year round

Ⓒⓡ
Thistle Hotels/Utell
International

Situated off Kensington High Street, the hotel offers guests luxury and comfort. Within easy reach of the city centre, Hyde Park and Knightsbridge shopping district.

Ⓜⓢⓔⓛ 120 ☆ ✕ ⓢⓟ

LONDON W14

★★★★
Silver
Award

THE KENSINGTON
Kensington House, Richmond Way,
London, W14 0AX
T: (020) 7674 1000
F: (020) 7674 1050
E: reservations@thekensington.co.uk
I: www.thekensington.co.uk

B&B per night:
S £104.00–£250.00
D £120.00–£250.00

OPEN All year round

A contemporary, urban-chic hotel, located just down the road from Notting Hill, West London. Uniquely designed, this hotel offers great value in terms of facilities, style, service and price with upgrades to suites, free car parking and free use of the stunning Kensington Spa and Health Club for all guests.

Bedrooms: 16 single,
60 double, 150 twin;
suites available
Bathrooms: 226 en suite

EM 1800 (LO 2200)
Parking for 28
CC: Amex, Barclaycard,
Delta, Diners, Eurocard,
JCB, Mastercard, Solo,
Switch, Visa

Ⓜⓢⓔ 26 ☆✕ ✕ ⓢⓟ Ⓣ

LONDON WC1

Rating
Applied For
Ad p15

BLOOMSBURY PARK HOTEL
126 Southampton Row, London,
WC1B 5AD
T: (020) 7430 0434
F: (020) 7242 0665

Bedrooms: 5 single,
44 double, 46 twin
Bathrooms: 95 en suite

Lunch available
EM 1800 (LO 2130)
CC: Amex, Barclaycard,
Delta, Diners, Mastercard,
Switch, Visa

B&B per night:
S £124.00–£148.00
D £139.00–£163.00

OPEN All year round

Ⓒⓡ
Thistle Hotels/Utell
International

Midway between the West End and the City and close to Covent Garden and the British Museum, the hotel is convenient for Euston, St Pancras and King's Cross stations.

Ⓜⓢⓔ 30 ✕ ⓢⓟ Ⓣ

Rating
Applied For
Ad p15

LONDON RYAN HOTEL
Gwynne Place, King's Cross Road,
King's Cross, London, WC1X 9QN
T: (020) 7278 2480
F: (020) 7837 3776
E: london.ryan@thistle.co.uk

Bedrooms: 30 single,
117 double, 46 twin,
18 triple
Bathrooms: 211 en suite

Lunch available
EM 1800 (LO 2200)
Parking for 26
CC: Amex, Barclaycard,
Delta, Diners, Eurocard,
JCB, Mastercard, Switch,
Visa

B&B per night:
S £128.00–£132.00
D £131.00–£155.00

OPEN All year round

Ⓒⓡ
Thistle Hotels/Utell
International

A modern hotel, between the City and the shops and theatres of the West End; convenient for King's Cross and Euston stations.

Ⓜⓢⓔ 88 ☆ ⓢⓟ Ⓣ

★★★★
Ad p15

THISTLE BLOOMSBURY
Bloomsbury Way, London,
WC1A 2SD
T: (020) 7242 5881
F: (020) 7831 0225
E: bloomsbury@thistle.co.uk
I: www.thistlehotels.com

Bedrooms: 8 single,
32 double, 79 twin,
14 triple, 5 family
rooms; suites available
Bathrooms: 138 en suite

Lunch available
EM 1730 (LO 2200)
CC: Amex, Barclaycard,
Delta, Diners, Eurocard,
JCB, Mastercard, Solo,
Switch, Visa

B&B per night:
S £167.00–£192.00
D £192.00–£217.00

OPEN All year round

Ⓒⓡ
Thistle Hotels/Utell
International

Edwardian hotel built in 1898 with traditional style decor. Kingsleytwo bar brasserie and full conference facilities. Just a short walk from Covent Garden and Trafalgar Square.

Ⓜⓢⓔ 100 ⓢⓟ 🏨 Ⓣ

WHERE TO STAY
Please mention this guide when making your booking.

LONDON WC1 continued

Rating Applied For Ad p15	**THISTLE KINGS CROSS** 100 King's Cross Road, London, WC1X 9DT T: (020) 7278 2434 F: (020) 7833 0798	Bedrooms: 29 single, 32 double, 261 twin, 29 triple Bathrooms: 351 en suite	Lunch available EM 1800 (LO 2145) Parking for 35 CC: Amex, Barclaycard, Delta, Diners, Maestro, Mastercard, Solo, Switch, Visa, Visa Electron	B&B per night: S £122.00–£146.00 D £140.00–£164.00 OPEN All year round ⊕ Thistle Hotels/Utell International

A few minutes from bustling King's Cross, this modern hotel is very convenient for both the City and the shops and entertainment of the West End.

⋀⅏㇏🖥️◻️↯⬀ⓈⓍ📺●⬆️🏭.☺⬛🍴150 ⬆️ SP 🀄

LONDON WC2

★★★★ Silver Award Ad p15	**THISTLE CHARING CROSS** Strand, London, WC2N 5HX T: (020) 7839 7282 F: (020) 7747 8454 E: charing.x@thistle.co.uk	Bedrooms: 200 twin, 38 triple Bathrooms: 238 en suite	Lunch available EM CC: Amex, Barclaycard, Delta, Diners, JCB, Mastercard, Switch, Visa	B&B per night: S £242.00–£279.00 D £242.00–£279.00 OPEN All year round ⊕ Thistle Hotels

Famous Victorian railway hotel at heart of the capital just minutes from Trafalgar Square and Covent Garden. Easy access to airports, trains and buses.

⋀⅏15 ↯🖥️◻️↯⬀Ⓢ Ⓧ📺●⬆️🏭.☺⬛🍴140 SC ⬆️ SP 🀄 T

Rating Applied For Ad p15	**THISTLE TRAFALGAR SQUARE** Whitcomb Street, London, WC2H 7HG T: (020) 7930 4477 F: (020) 7925 2149 E: trafalgar.square@thistle.co.uk I: www.thistlehotels.com	Bedrooms: 36 single, 40 double, 56 twin Bathrooms: 132 en suite	Lunch available EM 1700 (LO 2300) CC: Amex, Barclaycard, Delta, Diners, JCB, Mastercard, Switch, Visa	B&B per night: S £176.00–£201.00 D £210.00–£266.00 OPEN All year round ⊕ Thistle Hotels/Utell International

Located in the cultural heart of London between Trafalgar Square and Leicester Square. Ideal for theatreland, shopping, sightseeing and business.

⋀⅏㇏🖥️◻️↯Ⓢ Ⓧ⬀●⬆️🏭.⬛🍴8✕⬆️ SP T

OUTER LONDON
CROYDON *Tourist Information Centre Tel: (020) 8253 1009*

★★★★ Silver Award	**SELSDON PARK** Addington Road, Sanderstead, South Croydon, Surrey CR2 8YA T: (020) 8657 8811 F: (020) 8651 6171 E: caroline.chardon@ principalhotels.co.uk I: www.principalhotels.co.uk	Bedrooms: 49 single, 84 double, 62 twin, 4 family rooms; suites available Bathrooms: 199 en suite	Lunch available EM 1930 (LO 2200) Parking for 265 CC: Amex, Barclaycard, Delta, Diners, Eurocard, Mastercard, Solo, Switch, Visa	B&B per night: S £59.00–£99.00 D £118.00–£198.00 HB per person: DY £69.00–£99.00 OPEN All year round ⊕ Principal Hotels/Grand Heritage Hotels

Neo-Jacobean country house hotel, 10 minutes from the M25, 30 minutes from London and Gatwick, set in 200 acres of parkland. Special weekend rates.

⋀⅏♿🏨↯🖥️◻️↯Ⓢ Ⓧ⬀●⬆️🏭.⬛🍴200 ⬀✕⚡⚘🏹⚘∪▶☼⬆️ SP 🀄 T

ENFIELD

★★ Silver Award	**OAK LODGE HOTEL** 80 Village Road, Bush Hill Park, Enfield, Middlesex EN1 2EU T: (020) 8360 7082 I: www.oaklodgehotel.co.uk	Bedrooms: 4 double, 2 twin, 1 family room Bathrooms: 6 en suite, 1 private, 1 public	Lunch available EM 1950 (LO 2100) Parking for 6 CC: Amex, Barclaycard, Delta, Diners, Eurocard, Mastercard, Switch, Visa	B&B per night: S £69.50–£93.50 D £89.50–£130.00 HB per person: DY £75.00–£113.50 OPEN All year round

Award-winning country house hotel and candlelit restaurant set in leafy surroundings. Interior furnished with style, elegance and intimacy of an ocean-going yacht.

⅏♿🏨↯🖥️◻️↯Ⓢ Ⓧ●🏭.⬛🍴16▶☼🚐 SP T ◉

CREDIT CARD BOOKINGS
If you book by telephone and are asked for your credit card number it is advisable to check the proprietor's policy should you cancel your reservation.

HAMPTON COURT

★★★★

CARLTON MITRE HOTEL

Hampton Court Road, Hampton Court,
Surrey KT8 9BN
T: (020) 8979 9988
F: (020) 8979 9777
E: mitre@carltonhotels.co.uk
I: www.carltonhotels.co.uk

B&B per night:
S £130.00–£171.50
D £130.00–£183.00

HB per person:
DY £155.50–£197.00

OPEN All year round

Set on the banks of the River Thames and directly opposite Hampton Court Palace, this impressive 17thC hotel enjoys glorious views from every window. The individually furnished bedrooms reflect the tradition and service of the past three centuries, whilst offering modern facilities for today's discerning guest.

Bedrooms: 15 double, 20 twin, 1 triple; suite available
Bathrooms: 36 en suite

Lunch available
EM 1900 (LO 2130)
Parking for 30
CC: Amex, Barclaycard, Delta, Diners, Mastercard, Switch, Visa

---

HARROW *Tourist Information Centre Tel: (020) 8424 1103*

★★★★

GRIM'S DYKE HOTEL

Old Redding, Harrow Weald, Harrow,
Middlesex HA3 6SH
T: (020) 8954 4227 & 8385 3100
F: (020) 8954 4560
E: enquiries@grimsdyke.com
I: www.grimsdyke.com

B&B per night:
S Min £123.00
D Min £147.00

HB per person:
DY Min £145.00

OPEN All year round

Grand Heritage Hotels

Restored in 1996 and once home to WS Gilbert of Gilbert and Sullivan fame. You can enjoy excellent food, fine wines, cream teas, guided tours, murder-mystery dinners and Gilbert and Sullivan operettas with dinner. Set in acres of woodland and gardens, it is ideal for a relaxing weekend break.

Bedrooms: 30 double, 14 twin; suites available
Bathrooms: 44 en suite

Lunch available
EM 1900 (LO 2130)
Parking for 120
CC: Amex, Barclaycard, Delta, Diners, Mastercard, Switch, Visa

---

HEATHROW AIRPORT

See under West Drayton

KINGSTON UPON THAMES *Tourist Information Centre Tel: (020) 8547 5592*

★★

HOTEL ANTOINETTE OF KINGSTON

Beaufort Road, Kingston upon Thames,
Surrey KT1 2TQ
T: (020) 8546 1044
F: (020) 8547 2595
E: hotelantoinette@btinternet.com
I: www.hotelantoinette.co.uk

B&B per night:
S £52.00–£60.00
D £62.00–£68.00

OPEN All year round

Minotel

Friendly, comfortable hotel, offering excellent cuisine. Bar lounge with cable TV, gardens and large car park. Within easy reach of central London by road and rail, and close to many local attractions, such as Hampton Court, Kew Gardens and sporting venues such as Wimbledon, Epsom and Sandown Park.

Bedrooms: 25 single, 19 double, 24 twin, 5 triple, 26 family rooms
Bathrooms: 99 en suite

EM 1830 (LO 2115)
Parking for 100
CC: Amex, Barclaycard, Delta, Mastercard, Switch, Visa

HALF BOARD PRICES Half board prices are given per person, but in some cases these may be based on double/twin occupancy.

SUTTON

★★ **THATCHED HOUSE HOTEL**

135-141 Cheam Road, Sutton,	Bedrooms: 6 single,	Lunch available
Surrey SM1 2BN	18 double, 8 twin	EM 1900 (LO 2130)
T: (020) 8642 3131	Bathrooms: 29 en suite,	Parking for 30
F: (020) 8770 0684	3 private	CC: Barclaycard, Delta,
		Diners, JCB, Mastercard,
		Switch, Visa

B&B per night:
S £47.50–£75.00
D £55.00–£90.00

HB per person:
DY £57.50–£90.00

OPEN All year round

An old cottage-style thatched hotel, completely modernised. A few minutes from Sutton station and 20 minutes from central London.

🛏🏊♿🏩📞🖥🖵🚭🛎🔒🗝🛗🅿🍽♨50 ⛵🏌✳🚐🕱 SP

WEST DRAYTON

Rating
Applied For
Ad p15

HEATHROW PARK HOTEL

Bath Road, Longford, West Drayton,	Bedrooms: 135 double,	Lunch available
Middlesex UB7 0EQ	119 twin, 55 triple,	EM 1800 (LO 2330)
T: (020) 8759 2400	1 family room	Parking for 500
F: (020) 8759 5278	Bathrooms: 310 en suite	CC: Amex, Barclaycard,
E: heathrow.park@thistle.co.uk		Delta, Diners, JCB,
I: www.thistlehotels.com/		Mastercard, Solo, Switch,
heathrow_park/		Visa

B&B per night:
S £133.00–£157.00
D £133.00–£157.00

OPEN All year round

Ⓒ⃝

Thistle Hotels/Utell
International

Modern hotel with superb conference and training facilities. Offers car parking and easy access to all Heathrow terminals with regular shuttle bus.

📶🎠🛏🏊♿🏩📞🖥🖵🚭🖐🍴🔒🗝🚭🌙📧🅿🍽700 🛥🏋🎿🎣🛐🕱 SP Ⓣ

USE YOUR *i*s

There are more than 550 Tourist
Information Centres throughout
England offering friendly help with
accommodation and holiday ideas
as well as suggestions of places to
visit and things to do. There may well
be a centre in your home town which
can help you before you set out.
You'll find addresses in the
local Phone Book.

CUMBRIA

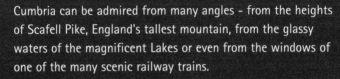

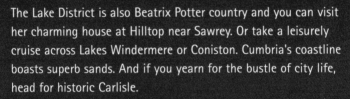

Cumbria can be admired from many angles - from the heights of Scafell Pike, England's tallest mountain, from the glassy waters of the magnificent Lakes or even from the windows of one of the many scenic railway trains.

The Lake District is also Beatrix Potter country and you can visit her charming house at Hilltop near Sawrey. Or take a leisurely cruise across Lakes Windermere or Coniston. Cumbria's coastline boasts superb sands. And if you yearn for the bustle of city life, head for historic Carlisle.

Fell racing attracts competitors from all over the world. It's a sprint to the top of a fell (or peak) and is nearly as exhausting to watch as to run!

The county of Cumbria

FOR MORE INFORMATION CONTACT:
Cumbria Tourist Board
Ashleigh, Holly Road, Windermere,
Cumbria LA23 2AQ
Tel: (015394) 44444
Fax: (015394) 44041
Email: mail@cumbria-tourist-board.co.uk
Internet: www.gocumbria.co.uk

The Pictures:
1 Walking at Wasdale;
2 Great Langdale;
3 Ullswater;
4 Derwentwater.

Where to Go in Cumbria - see pages 46-49
Where to Stay in Cumbria - see pages 50-68

Whilst in
CUMBRIA ...

You will find hundreds of interesting places to visit during your stay, just some of which are listed in these pages.

Contact any Tourist Information Centre in the region for more ideas on days out in Cumbria.

Appleby Castle
Appleby-in-Westmorland, Cumbria CA16 6XH
Tel: (017683) 51402
A beautiful castle with breathtaking views, steeped in history. The Great Hall is a must for anyone to see.

Aquarium of the Lakes
Newby Bridge, Ulverston, Cumbria LA12 8AS
Tel: (015395) 30153
Discover the UK's largest collection of freshwater fish in Britain's award-winning freshwater aquarium. Meet mischievous otters, diving ducks, sharks and rays.

Brantwood, Home of John Ruskin
Coniston, Cumbria LA21 8AD
Tel: (015394) 41396
Superb lake and mountain views. Works by Ruskin and contemporaries, memorabilia. Ruskin watercolours. Craft and picture gallery, gardens.

Brockhole Visitor Centre
National Park Authority, Windermere,
Cumbria LA23 1LJ
Tel: (015394) 46601
Interactive exhibitions, audio-visual show, shop, gardens, grounds, adventure playground, dry-stone walling area, trails, events and croquet. Cafe with home cooked food.

Cars of the Stars Motor Museum
Keswick, Cumbria CA12 5LS
Tel: (017687) 73757
Features TV and film vehicles including the Batmobile, Chitty Chitty Bang Bang, the James Bond collection, Herbie, FAB 1 plus many other famous cars and motorcycles.

The Dock Museum
Barrow-in-Furness, Cumbria LA14 2PW
Tel: (01229) 894444
The museum, which straddles a Victorian graving dock, presents the story of steel shipbuilding for which Barrow is famous. Interactive displays and nautical adventure playground.

Dove Cottage and Wordsworth Museum
Town End, Grasmere, Cumbria LA22 9SH
Tel: (015394) 35544
Wordsworth's home from 1799-1808. Poet's possessions, museum with manuscripts, farmhouse reconstruction, paintings and drawings. Special events throughout the year.

Eden Ostrich World
Langwathby, Penrith, Cumbria CA10 1LW
Tel: (01768) 881771
Working farm with lots of farm animals, some of them rare breeds. Covered and outdoor play areas, picnic areas, tearoom and craft shop.

Furness Abbey

Barrow-in-Furness, Cumbria LA13 0TJ
Tel: (01229) 823420
Ruins of a 12thC Cistercian abbey, the second wealthiest in England. Extensive remains include transepts, choir and west tower of church, canopied seats and arches.

Graythwaite Hall Gardens

Newby Bridge, Ulverston, Cumbria LA12 8BA
Tel: (015395) 31248
Rhododendrons, azaleas and flowering shrubs. Laid out by T Mawson, 1888-1890.

Heron Corn Mill and Museum of Papermaking

Waterhouse Mills, Beetha, Milnthorpe,
Cumbria LA7 7AR
Tel: (015395) 65027
Restored working corn mill featuring 4.9-metre (14ft) high breastshot waterwheel. The museum shows paper making both historic and modern with artefacts, displays and diagrams.

Hill Top

Near Sawrey, Ambleside, Cumbria LA22 0LF
Tel: (015394) 36269
Beatrix Potter wrote many of her popular Peter Rabbit stories and other books in this charming little house. It still contains her own china and furniture.

K Village Heritage Centre

Netherfield, Kendal, Cumbria LA9 7DA
Tel: (01539) 732363
Heritage centre within the 'K' Village where visitors can follow numbered exhibits detailing the history of K Shoes in Kendal and the Lake District since 1842.

Lakeland Motor Museum

Holker Hall, Cark in Cartmel,
Grange-over-Sands, Cumbria LA11 7PL
Tel: (015395) 58509
Over 10,000 exhibits including rare motoring automobilia. A 1930s garage recreation and the Campbell Legend Bluebird Exhibition.

Lakeland Sheep and Wool Centre

Cockermouth, Cumbria CA13 0QX
Tel: (01900) 822673
An all-weather attraction with live sheep shows including working dog demonstrations. Also large screen and other exhibitions on the area. Gift shop and cafe.

Lakeside and Haverthwaite Railway

Haverthwaite Station, Ulverston, Cumbria LA12 8AL
Tel: (015395) 31594
Standard gauge steam railway operating a daily seasonal service through the beautiful Leven Valley. Steam and diesel locomotives on display.

Levens Hall

Levens, Kendal, Cumbria LA8 0PD
Tel: (015395) 60321
Elizabethan mansion incorporating a pele tower. Famous topiary garden laid out in 1694, steam collection and plant centre. Shop, play area, picnic area.

Linton Tweeds

Shaddon Mills, Shaddon Gate, Carlisle, Cumbria CA2 5TZ
Tel: (01228) 527569
Centre shows history of weaving in Carlisle up to Linton's today. Visitors can try weaving and other hands-on activities.

Lowther Leisure and Wildlife Park

Hackthorpe, Penrith, Cumbria CA10 2HG
Tel: (01931) 712523
Attractions include exotic birds and animals, rides, miniature railway, boating lake, play areas, adventure fort, Tarzan trail, international circus and a puppet theatre.

Muncaster Castle, Gardens and Owl Centre

Ravenglass, Cumbria CA18 1RQ
Tel: (01229) 717614
The most beautifully situated Owl Centre in the world. See the birds fly, picnic in the gardens and visit the Pennington family home.

The Pictures:
1 Buttermere;
2 Carlisle Castle;
3 Watendlath Bridge;
4 Derwentwater;
5 Green Gable;
6 Kirkstile Inn.

CUMBRIA

Tullie House Museum and Art Gallery

Carlisle, Cumbria CA3 8TP
Tel: (01228) 534781
Major tourist complex housing museum, art gallery, education facility, lecture theatre, shops, herb garden restaurant and terrace bars.

Ravenglass and Eskdale Railway

Ravenglass, Cumbria CA18 1SW
Tel: (01229) 717171
England's oldest narrow-gauge railway runs for 11km (7 miles) through glorious scenery to the foot of England's highest hills. Most trains are steam hauled.

Ullswater Steamers

Kendal, Cumbria LA9 4QD
Tel: (017684) 82229
Relax and enjoy beautiful Ullswater combining a cruise with a visit to other local attractions. All boats have bar and toilet facilities.

Senhouse Roman Museum

The Battery Sea, Brows, Maryport, Cumbria CA15 6JD
Tel: (01900) 816168
Once the headquarters of Hadrian's Coastal Defence system. The UK's largest group of Roman altar stones and inscriptions from one site. Roman military equipment, stunning sculpture.

Windermere Steamboat Museum

Bowness-on-Windermere, Cumbria LA23 1BN
Tel: (015394) 45565
A wealth of interest and information about life on bygone Windermere. Regular steam launch trips, vintage vessels and classic motorboats. Model boat pond and lakeside picnic area.

Sizergh Castle

Kendal, Cumbria LA8 8AE
Tel: (015395) 60070
Strickland family home for 750 years, now National Trust owned. With 14thC pele tower, 15thC great hall, 16thC wings. Stuart connections. Rock garden, rose garden, daffodils.

The World of Beatrix Potter

Bowness-on-Windermere, Cumbria LA23 3BX
Tel: (015394) 88444
The life and works of Beatrix Potter presented on a 9-screen video-wall. Beautiful three dimensional scenes bring her stories to life.

South Lakes Wild Animal Park

Dalton-in-Furness, Cumbria LA15 8JR
Tel: (01229) 466086
Wild zoo park in over 17 acres of grounds. Over 120 species of animals from all around the world. Large waterfowl ponds, miniature railway, cafe.

Townend

Troutbeck, Windermere, Cumbria LA23 1LB
Tel: (015394) 32628
Typical Lakeland statesman farmer's house c1626. All original interiors, carved woodwork and domestic implements from the family who lived there for over three centuries.

Trotters World of Animals

Coalbeck Farm, Bassenthwaite, Cumbria CA12 4RE
Tel: (017687) 76239
Farm park with collection of rare and interesting farm animals, poultry and baby animals, reptile house and bird of prey centre.

The Pictures:
1 Shoreline, Derwantwater;
2 Windermere Steamer;
3 Maryport;
4 Brundholme Wood;
5 Lake Windermere;
6 Cycling at Coniston;
7 Holker Hall, Grange-over-Sands;
8 Muncaster Castle;
9 Loughrigg.

Find out more about
CUMBRIA ...

Further information about holidays and attractions in Cumbria is available from:

CUMBRIA TOURIST BOARD

Ashleigh, Holly Road, Windermere, Cumbria LA23 2AQ.

Tel:	(015394) 44444
Fax:	(015394) 44041
Email:	mail@cumbria-tourist-board.co.uk
Internet:	www.gocumbria.co.uk

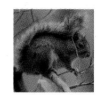

The following publications are available from Cumbria Tourist Board:

Cumbria Tourist Board Holiday Guide (free)
Tel: 08705 133059

Events Listings (free)

Cumbria The Lake District Touring Map
including tourist information and touring caravan and camping parks £3.95
Laminated Poster - £4.50

Getting to
CUMBRIA ...

BY ROAD: The M1/M6/M25/M40 provide a link with London and the South East and the M5/M6 provide access from the South West. The M62/M6 link Hull and Manchester with the region. Approximate journey time from London is 5 hours, from Manchester 2 hours.

BY RAIL: From London (Euston) to Oxenholme (Kendal) takes approximately 3 hours 30 minutes. From Oxenholme (connecting station for all main line trains) to Windermere takes approximately 20 minutes. From Carlisle to Barrow-in-Furness via the coastal route, with stops at many of the towns in between, takes approximately 2 hours. Trains from Edinburgh to Carlisle take 1 hour 45 minutes. The historic Settle-Carlisle line also runs through the county bringing passengers from Yorkshire via the Eden Valley.

www.travelcumbria.co.uk

Where to stay in
CUMBRIA

Accommodation entries in this region are listed in alphabetical order of place name, and then in alphabetical order of establishment.

Map references refer to the colour location maps at the front of this guide. The first number indicates the map to use; the letter and number which follow refer to the grid reference on the map.

At-a-glance symbols at the end of each accommodation entry give useful information about services and facilities. A key to symbols can be found inside the back cover flap. Keep this open for easy reference.

A brief description of the towns and villages offering accommodation in the entries which follow, can be found at the end of this section.

A complete listing of all English Tourism Council assessed hotels appears at the back of this guide.

AMBLESIDE, Cumbria Map ref 5A3 *Tourist Information Centre Tel: (015394) 32582*

★★★

THE AMBLESIDE SALUTATION HOTEL
Lake Road, Ambleside, LA22 9BX
T: (015394) 32244
F: (015394) 34157
E: reservations@hotelambleside.uk.com
I: www.hotelambleside.uk.com

In the heart of the Lake District, a traditional hotel overlooking village centre, beautifully refurbished to provide 42 en suite rooms (9 non-smoking) and many with jacuzzi baths. Comfortable lounge and extended restaurant serving dinners. Excellent bar food lunchtimes and evenings. Free membership of nearby luxury leisure club. A warm welcome assured.

Bedrooms: 3 single,
27 double, 8 twin,
2 triple, 2 family rooms
Bathrooms: 42 en suite

Lunch available
EM 1900 (LO 2100)
Parking for 49
CC: Amex, Barclaycard,
Diners, JCB, Mastercard,
Switch, Visa

B&B per night:
S £39.00–£52.00
D £78.00–£104.00

HB per person:
DY £53.00–£66.50

OPEN All year round

Best Western Hotels

Image symbols row

WELCOME HOST This is a nationally recognised customer care programme which aims to promote the highest standards of service and a warm welcome. Establishments taking part in this initiative are indicated by the ⊕ symbol.

AMBLESIDE continued

★★★ Silver Award
LANGDALE HOTEL AND COUNTRY CLUB
Great Langdale, Ambleside,
LA22 9JD
T: (015394) 37302
F: (015394) 37130
E: itsgreat@langdale.co.uk
I: www.langdale.co.uk

Bedrooms: 29 double,
23 twin, 13 family rooms
Bathrooms: 65 en suite

Lunch available
EM 1800 (LO 2145)
Parking for 65
CC: Amex, Barclaycard,
JCB, Mastercard, Switch,
Visa

B&B per night:
S £70.00–£130.00
D £70.00–£210.00

HB per person:
DY £95.00–£110.00

OPEN All year round

Winner of 1986 Civic Trust environmental award, in 35 acres of wooded grounds. Indoor country club, large pool, spa-bath, sports facilities, restaurants, bars. Minimum stay 2 nights.

★★
QUEENS HOTEL
Market Place, Ambleside, LA22 9BU
T: (015394) 32206
F: (015394) 32721
I: www.smoothhound.co.uk/hotels/
quecum.html

Bedrooms: 4 single,
14 double, 3 twin,
2 triple, 3 family rooms
Bathrooms: 26 en suite

Lunch available
EM 1900 (LO 2130)
Parking for 12
CC: Amex, Barclaycard,
Delta, Maestro,
Mastercard, Solo, Switch,
Visa

B&B per night:
S £25.00–£36.00
D £50.00–£72.00

OPEN All year round

In the heart of the Lakes and convenient for walking, climbing and other leisure activities. Two fully licensed bars, choice of restaurant or bar meals.

★★
ROTHAY GARTH HOTEL
Rothay Road, Ambleside, LA22 0EE
T: (015394) 32217
F: (015394) 34400
E: enquiries@rothay-garth.co.uk
I: www.rothay-garth.co.uk

Bedrooms: 1 single,
9 double, 2 twin, 2 triple,
1 family room; suite
available
Bathrooms: 14 en suite,
1 private

Lunch available
EM 1900 (LO 2030)
Parking for 20
CC: Barclaycard, Delta,
Diners, Eurocard, JCB,
Mastercard, Solo, Switch,
Visa, Visa Electron

B&B per night:
S £38.00–£43.00
D £76.00–£86.00

HB per person:
DY £58.00–£68.00

OPEN All year round

Distinctive Victorian country house with elegant Loughrigg restaurant overlooking lovely gardens and nearby mountains. Close to village centre and Lake Windermere. Great value all-season breaks.

★★★ Silver Award

ROTHAY MANOR HOTEL
Rothay Bridge, Ambleside, LA22 0EH
T: (015394) 33605
F: (015394) 33607
E: hotel@rothaymanor.co.uk
I: www.rothaymanor.co.uk

B&B per night:
S £75.00–£80.00
D £120.00–£140.00

HB per person:
DY £65.00–£100.00

OPEN Feb–Dec

Elegant Regency house standing in its own grounds, quarter mile from the head of Lake Windermere. Personally managed by the Nixon family, it still retains the comfortable, relaxed atmosphere of a private house. Internationally renowned for cuisine and ideally situated for local attractions and sightseeing. Free use of nearby leisure centre.

Bedrooms: 2 single,
5 double, 3 twin, 5 triple,
3 family rooms; suites
available
Bathrooms: 18 en suite

Lunch available
EM 1945 (LO 2100)
Parking for 50
CC: Amex, Barclaycard,
Delta, Diners, JCB,
Mastercard, Switch, Visa

ACCESSIBILITY
Look for the 🚻 symbols which indicate accessibility for wheelchair users. A list of establishments is at the front of this guide.

★★

A warm welcome, pleasant rooms, fresh home cooking and a friendly relaxed atmosphere await you here, surrounded by the well-renowned delights of the Lake District. Pets are welcome. Many owners prefer the freedom of our annexe rooms. Private car park. For a closer look, visit our website or ring for a brochure.

SMALLWOOD HOUSE HOTEL

Compston Road, Ambleside, LA22 9DJ
T: (015394) 32330
F: (015394) 33764
E: enq@smallwoodhotel.co.uk
I: www.smallwoodhotel.co.uk

Bedrooms: 2 single,
6 double, 3 twin, 2 triple
Bathrooms: 11 en suite,
1 public

EM 1800 (LO 2000)
Parking for 11

B&B per night:
S £25.00–£40.00
D £50.00–£70.00

HB per person:
DY £38.00–£50.00

OPEN All year round

★★★
Silver
Award

The family-run Wateredge Hotel has developed from two 17thC fisherman's cottages and is delightfully situated on the shores of Windermere with gardens to the lake edge. We offer quiet relaxation, elegant comfort, excellent cuisine, beautiful lake views and, above all, personal unobtrusive service. Log fires. Cosy bar. Private jetty.

WATEREDGE HOTEL

Waterhead Bay, Ambleside, LA22 0EP
T: (015394) 32332
F: (015394) 31878
E: contact@wateredgehotel.co.uk
I: www.wateredgehotel.co.uk

Bedrooms: 3 single,
12 double, 8 twin
Bathrooms: 23 en suite

Lunch available
EM 1900 (LO 2030)
Parking for 25
CC: Amex, Barclaycard,
Delta, JCB, Mastercard,
Switch, Visa

B&B per night:
S £48.00–£64.00
D £74.00–£156.00

HB per person:
DY £57.00–£98.00

OPEN All year round

★★★
Silver
Award

Pamper yourself at Appleby Manor, probably the most relaxing and friendly hotel in the world! You'll find beautiful, spotlessly-clean bedrooms, log fires, magnificent lounges, a delightful sunny conservatory, tasty and imaginative food in the award-winning restaurant and a relaxing leisure club. Enjoy all that the Lake District, North Pennines and Yorkshire Dales have to offer.

APPLEBY MANOR COUNTRY HOUSE HOTEL

Roman Road, Appleby-in-Westmorland,
CA16 6JB
T: (017683) 51571 & 51570
F: (017683) 52888
E: nswinscoe@bigfoot.com
I: www.applebymanor.co.uk

Bedrooms: 13 double,
8 twin, 1 triple, 8 family
rooms; suite available
Bathrooms: 30 en suite

Lunch available
EM 1900 (LO 2100)
Parking for 51
CC: Amex, Barclaycard,
Delta, Diners, Eurocard,
JCB, Maestro, Mastercard,
Solo, Switch, Visa, Visa
Electron

B&B per night:
S £72.00–£82.00
D £104.00–£124.00

HB per person:
DY £62.00–£85.00

OPEN All year round

Ⓒℝ
Best Western Hotels

QUALITY ASSURANCE SCHEME

Star ratings and awards were correct at the time of going to press but are subject to change. Please check at the time of booking.

BORROWDALE, Cumbria Map ref 5A3

★★ **MARY MOUNT HOTEL**
Borrowdale, Keswick, CA12 5UU
T: (017687) 77223 & 77381
E: marymount@bigfoot.com
I: visitweb.com/marymount

Bedrooms: 1 single, 5 double, 5 twin, 2 triple, 1 family room Bathrooms: 14 en suite	Lunch available EM 1830 (LO 2045) Parking for 40 CC: Barclaycard, Delta, Eurocard, Mastercard, Switch, Visa

B&B per night:
S £27.00–£32.00
D £54.00–£64.00

OPEN All year round

Set in 4.5 acres of gardens and woodlands on the shores of Derwentwater, 2.5 miles from Keswick. Views across lake to Catbells and Maiden Moor. Families and pets welcome.

BUTTERMERE, Cumbria Map ref 5A3

★★

BRIDGE HOTEL
Buttermere, Cockermouth, CA13 9UZ
T: (017687) 70252
F: (017687) 70215
E: enquiries@bridge-hotel.com
I: www.bridge-hotel.com

HB per person:
DY £50.00–£68.00

OPEN All year round

18thC coaching inn, beautifully situated between two lakes in Lakeland's loveliest valley. Superb unrestricted walking country and breathtaking scenery. Complimentary afternoon tea is served near the log fire in our very comfortable residents' lounge. Two well-stocked bars serve expertly kept real ales, 4-poster beds, dogs welcome, special breaks.

Bedrooms: 1 single, 14 double, 6 twin Bathrooms: 20 en suite, 1 private	Lunch available EM 1900 (LO 2100) Parking for 60 CC: Barclaycard, Mastercard, Switch, Visa

CARLISLE, Cumbria Map ref 5A2 *Tourist Information Centre Tel: (01228) 625600*

★★ **COUNTY HOTEL**
9 Botchergate, Carlisle, CA1 1QP
T: (01228) 531316
F: (01228) 401805
E: counth@cairn-hotels.co.uk
I: www.cairn-hotels.co.uk

Bedrooms: 14 single, 225 double, 27 twin, 4 triple, 4 family rooms Bathrooms: 274 en suite	Lunch available EM 1900 (LO 2145) Parking for 30 CC: Amex, Barclaycard, Delta, Diners, Mastercard, Solo, Switch, Visa

B&B per night:
S £39.95–£77.45
D £49.95–£84.95

HB per person:
DY £55.50–£60.50

OPEN All year round

Built in 1853 and extensively refurbished with every modern convenience. City centre location, adjacent to railway station. Parking on premises.

CARTMEL, Cumbria Map ref 5A3

★★
Silver
Award

AYNSOME MANOR HOTEL
Cartmel, Grange-over-Sands, LA11 6HH
T: (015395) 36653
F: (015395) 36016
E: info@aynsomemanorhotel.co.uk
I: www.aynsomemanorhotel.co.uk

B&B per night:
S £40.00–£50.00
D £60.00–£80.00

HB per person:
DY £45.00–£67.00

OPEN Feb–Dec

Lovely old manor house, nestling in the historic vale of Cartmel. Personally managed, for 20 years, by the Varley family. An award-winning Georgian dining room, open log fires and elegant lounges create the perfect atmosphere for relaxation. Ideal base for Lakeland and its peninsulas. Recommended in all leading guides.

Bedrooms: 6 double, 4 twin, 2 triple Bathrooms: 12 en suite, 1 public	EM 1900 (LO 2030) Parking for 20 CC: Amex, Barclaycard, Delta, Diners, Eurocard, JCB, Maestro, Mastercard, Solo, Visa

IDEAS For ideas on places to visit refer to the introduction at the beginning of this section.

CUMBRIA

★★ **ALLERDALE COURT HOTEL**
Market Square, Cockermouth,
CA13 9NQ
T: (01900) 823654
F: (01900) 823033
E: allerdalecourt@edirectory.co.uk
I: www.edirectory.co.uk/
allerdalecourt

Bedrooms: 10 single,
10 double, 4 twin
Bathrooms: 24 en suite

EM 1900 (LO 2130)
CC: Amex, Barclaycard,
Delta, Diners, Eurocard,
Mastercard, Solo, Switch,
Visa, Visa Electron

B&B per night:
D £66.00–£75.00

HB per person:
DY Min £45.00

OPEN All year round

Traditional 17thC building, oak beams. Family-run inn, offering excellent food in 2 renowned restaurants. Refurbished and comfortable en suite bedrooms, well stocked bar.

ᗰ➲🖼🕭🖳💻♿🔍🛈Ⓢ🅿🏛📶🍴60▶ SC 🐾 SP 🏨 T

★★★ **TROUT HOTEL**
Crown Street, Cockermouth,
CA13 0EJ
T: (01900) 823591
F: (01900) 827514
E: enquiries@trouthotel.co.uk
I: www.trouthotel.co.uk

Bedrooms: 1 single,
20 double, 7 twin,
1 triple
Bathrooms: 29 en suite

Lunch available
EM 1900 (LO 2130)
Parking for 50
CC: Amex, Barclaycard,
Delta, Mastercard, Switch,
Visa

B&B per night:
S £59.95–£109.00
D £89.95–£140.00

HB per person:
DY £59.95–£75.95

OPEN All year round

Attractive black and white listed building, dating from c 1670, on banks of River Derwent adjacent to own award-winning gardens. 12 miles west of Keswick off A66.

ᗰ➲🖼🕭🖳💻♿🔍🛈Ⓢ🖳🅾🌐🖳🍴50♫▶❄🐾 SP 🏨 T

★★

SUN HOTEL & 16TH CENTURY INN
Coniston, LA21 8HQ
T: (015394) 41248
F: (015394) 41219
E: the sun@hotelconiston.com
I: www.smoothhound.co.uk/hotels/sun.html

B&B per night:
S £35.00–£40.00
D £70.00–£80.00

OPEN All year round

Peaceful Edwardian 11-bedroom hotel with 16thC pub. Elevated location above Coniston Village with large garden, patio, car park, restaurant, lounge and conservatory. With 5 real ales, 35 wines and excellent menu, the pub (under new ownership) is being "unmodernised".

Bedrooms: 1 single,
7 double, 3 twin
Bathrooms: 9 en suite,
2 private

Lunch available
EM 1900 (LO 2045)
Parking for 20
CC: Amex, Barclaycard,
Delta, Mastercard, Switch,
Visa

ᗰ➲🖼🕭🖵♿🛈Ⓢ🔍🖳💻🖳🍴20∪❄🐾 SP 🏨 T

★★ **SHEPHERD'S ARMS HOTEL**
Ennerdale Bridge, Cleator,
CA23 3AR
T: (01946) 861249
F: (01946) 861249
E: enquiries@shepherdsarmshotel.
co.uk
I: shephardsarmshotel.co.uk

Bedrooms: 1 single,
3 double, 4 twin
Bathrooms: 6 en suite,
2 private

Lunch available
EM 1930 (LO 2130)
Parking for 8
CC: Barclaycard, Delta,
Mastercard, Solo, Switch,
Visa

B&B per night:
S Min £30.00
D Min £56.00

HB per person:
DY £42.00–£44.00

OPEN All year round

Small hotel with an informal and relaxed atmosphere, situated in the centre of Ennerdale Bridge. Bar and restaurant, open fires. Popular with walkers.

ᗰ➲🖵♿🛈Ⓢ🔍🖳🖳❄🌸 SP T

AT-A-GLANCE SYMBOLS
Symbols at the end of each accommodation entry give useful information about services and facilities. A key to symbols can be found inside the back cover flap. Keep this open for easy reference.

★★

BOWER HOUSE INN
Eskdale, CA19 1TD
T: (019467) 23244
F: (019467) 23308
E: info@bowerhouseinn.co.uk
I: bowerhousehotel.co.uk

B&B per night:
S £40.00–£55.00
D Max £78.00

HB per person:
DY £55.00–£64.00

OPEN All year round

A typical 17thC Lakeland inn set in its own secluded gardens. There is a lovely oak-beamed bar, candlelit restaurant, relaxing lounge and comfortable en suite accommodation. Noted for good food and an ideal centre for walking and touring the area, the inn is popular with locals and vistors.

Bedrooms: 3 single, 11 double, 7 twin, 3 triple
Bathrooms: 24 en suite

Lunch available
EM 1830 (LO 2130)
Parking for 60
CC: Amex, Barclaycard, Delta, Mastercard, Solo, Switch, Visa

★

CLARE HOUSE
Park Road, Grange-over-Sands, LA11 7HQ
T: (015395) 33026 & 34253

HB per person:
DY £48.00–£52.00

OPEN Apr–Nov

Charming hotel in its own grounds, with well appointed bedrooms, pleasant lounges and super bay views, offering peaceful holidays to those who wish to relax and be looked after. Delightful meals, prepared with care and pride from fresh, local produce, will contribute greatly to the enjoyment of your stay.

Bedrooms: 3 single, 2 double, 11 twin, 1 triple
Bathrooms: 16 en suite, 1 public

Lunch available
EM 1845 (LO 1915)
Parking for 16

★★

HAMPSFELL HOUSE HOTEL
Hampsfell Road, Grange-over-Sands, LA11 6BG
T: (015395) 32567
F: (015395) 35995
E: hampsfellhotel@msn.com

B&B per night:
S £31.00–£38.00
D £62.00–£70.00

HB per person:
DY £49.00–£53.00

OPEN All year round

Enjoy the pleasant tranquil setting of this Victorian hotel, set in its own private grounds surrounded by woodland away from busy roads. Relax in the comfortable lounges and enjoy the friendly atmosphere. The dining room serves freshly prepared 4-course evening dinner with fine wines. There's ample safe parking.

Bedrooms: 4 double, 4 twin, 1 triple
Bathrooms: 9 en suite

EM 1900 (LO 2000)
Parking for 12
CC: Amex, Barclaycard, Delta, Eurocard, JCB, Mastercard, Solo, Switch, Visa, Visa Electron

TOWN INDEX
This can be found at the back of this guide. If you know where you want to stay, the index will give you the page number listing accommodation in your chosen town, city or village.

GRANGE-OVER-SANDS continued

★★ KENTS BANK HOTEL

96 Kentsford Road, Kents Bank,
Grange-over-Sands, LA11 7BB
T: (015395) 32054

Bedrooms: 1 single,
3 double, 3 twin,
1 family room
Bathrooms: 8 en suite

Lunch available
EM 1900 (LO 2000)
Parking for 30
CC: Barclaycard, Eurocard,
Mastercard, Visa

B&B per night:
S £25.00–£28.00
D £50.00–£56.00

HB per person:
DY £35.00–£39.00

Small hotel in a residential area, overlooking Morecambe Bay and close to the Lake District. Licensed bar, beautiful views.

OPEN All year round

★★★ NETHERWOOD HOTEL

Grange-over-Sands, LA11 6ET
T: (015395) 32552
F: (015395) 34121
E: blawith@aol.com
I: www.netherwood-hotel.co.uk

Bedrooms: 3 single,
16 double, 4 twin,
2 triple, 3 family rooms
Bathrooms: 28 en suite,
2 public

Lunch available
EM 1900 (LO 2030)
Parking for 160
CC: Barclaycard, Delta,
Eurocard, Mastercard,
Solo, Switch, Visa, Visa
Electron

B&B per night:
S £55.00–£65.00
D £110.00–£130.00

HB per person:
DY £79.00–£92.00

Built in 1893 and a building of high architectural and historic interest, with superb oak panelling throughout, set in 14 acres of gardens, overlooking Morecambe Bay.

OPEN All year round

GRASMERE, Cumbria Map ref 5A3

★★ THE GRASMERE HOTEL

Broadgate, Grasmere, Ambleside,
LA22 9TA
T: (015394) 35277
F: (015394) 35277
E: enquiries@grasmerehotel.co.uk
I: www.grasmerehotel.co.uk

Bedrooms: 1 single,
9 double, 2 twin
Bathrooms: 12 en suite

EM 1930 (LO 2030)
Parking for 16
CC: Amex, Barclaycard,
Delta, JCB, Mastercard,
Solo, Switch, Visa, Visa
Electron

HB per person:
DY £40.00–£60.00

OPEN Feb–Dec

In the midst of beautiful mountain scenery, with award-winning restaurant overlooking secluded garden through which the River Rothay flows.

★★★

GRASMERE RED LION HOTEL

Red Lion Square, Grasmere, Ambleside,
LA22 9SS
T: (015394) 35456
F: (015394) 35579
E: enquiries@hotelgrasmere.uk.com
I: www.hotelgrasmere.uk.com

Village centre traditional coaching inn, refurbished to provide 47 delightful en suite rooms – including 12 additional non-smoking rooms built in 1999. Hairdressing salon, fitness centre, mini-gym and free leisure club membership. Enjoy good food served by friendly staff – lunch in the conservatory or dinner in the Courtyard Restaurant.

Bedrooms: 3 single,
28 double, 12 twin,
2 triple, 2 family rooms
Bathrooms: 47 en suite

Lunch available
EM 1900 (LO 2100)
Parking for 38
CC: Amex, Barclaycard,
Delta, Diners, Eurocard,
JCB, Mastercard, Switch,
Visa

B&B per night:
S £41.00–£55.50
D £82.00–£111.00

HB per person:
DY £55.00–£70.00

OPEN All year round

Best Western Hotels

★★ MOSS GROVE HOTEL

Grasmere, Ambleside, LA22 9SW
T: (015394) 35251
F: (015394) 35691
E: martinw@globalnet.co.uk
I: www.mossgrove.co.uk

Bedrooms: 1 single,
7 double, 3 twin, 1 triple,
1 family room
Bathrooms: 13 en suite,
1 public

Lunch available
EM 1930 (LO 2030)
Parking for 16
CC: Barclaycard, Delta,
JCB, Maestro, Mastercard,
Solo, Switch, Visa, Visa
Electron

B&B per night:
S £27.00–£55.00
D £54.00–£110.00

HB per person:
DY £36.00–£70.00

OPEN Feb–Nov

Minotel

Family-run, elegant Lakeland hotel, centrally situated. All bedrooms non-smoking, satellite TV, some 4-poster bedrooms. Delightful bar and conservatory. Free use of indoor pool.

PRICES
Please check prices and other details at the time of booking.

GRASMERE continued

Rating
Applied For
Ad p15

THISTLE GRASMERE
Keswick Road, Grasmere,
Ambleside, LA22 9PR
T: (015394) 35666
F: (015394) 35565
E: grasmere@thistle.co.uk

Bedrooms: 17 single,
14 double, 36 twin,
3 triple, 2 family rooms
Bathrooms: 72 en suite

Lunch available
EM 1900 (LO 2045)
Parking for 90
CC: Amex, Barclaycard,
Delta, Diners, Mastercard,
Switch, Visa

B&B per night:
S £100.00–£123.00
D £121.00–£144.00

OPEN All year round

Utell International/
Thistle Hotels

Standing on the shore of Lake Grasmere, in several ares of beautiful grounds, this hotel is an ideal base for exploring the Lake District.

Ⓜ ⅀ ♿ 🏨 ☎ ▤ ▢ ♨ ♞ 🛈 Ⓢ ⅄ ⑉ 📺 ◑ 🏧 ⌨ ⵔ ⏲100 ♦ ► ❄ ⚲ SP Ⓣ

HAWKSHEAD, Cumbria Map ref 5A3

★★
Silver
Award

QUEENS HEAD HOTEL
Main Street, Hawkshead, Ambleside,
LA22 0NS
T: (015394) 36271
F: (015394) 36722
E: enquiries@queensheadhotel.co.uk
I: www.queensheadhotel.co.uk

B&B per night:
S £42.00–£49.50
D £70.00–£79.00

OPEN All year round

The Queen's Head Hotel was built in the 16thC in the prettiest village in the Lake District. Low oak-beamed ceilings, panel walls and log fire. Most well known for the excellent cuisine and quality accommodation.

Bedrooms: 10 double,
1 twin, 2 triple
Bathrooms: 11 en suite,
2 private

Lunch available
EM 1815 (LO 2130)
CC: Barclaycard, Delta,
Eurocard, Mastercard,
Solo, Switch, Visa

Ⓜ ⅀ 🏨 ☎ ▤ ▢ ♨ ♞ 🛈 Ⓢ ⅄ ⵔ ⌨ ⏲ ♪ ♘ ⚲ SP 🏠 Ⓣ

KENDAL, Cumbria Map ref 5B3 *Tourist Information Centre Tel: (01539) 725758*

★★

GARDEN HOUSE
Fowl-Ing Lane, Kendal, LA9 6PH
T: (01539) 731131
F: (01539) 740064
E: gardenhouse.hotel@virgin.net
I: www.gardenhousehotel.co.uk

Bedrooms: 2 single,
4 double, 3 twin, 1 triple,
1 family room
Bathrooms: 11 en suite

EM 1900 (LO 2030)
Parking for 30
CC: Amex, Barclaycard,
Delta, Eurocard, JCB,
Mastercard, Switch, Visa,
Visa Electron

B&B per night:
S £49.50–£59.00
D £75.00–£79.00

HB per person:
DY £51.00–£57.00

OPEN All year round

Elegant country house offering personal service. Ideal touring base for Lakes and dales. Ample parking. 2-day breaks available. All rooms private facilities.

Ⓜ ⅀ ♿ 🏨 ☎ ▤ ▢ ♨ ♞ 🛈 Ⓢ ⅄ ⑉ ⌨ ⵔ ⏲40 ► ❄ ♘ SP Ⓣ

★

HEAVES HOTEL
Kendal, LA8 8EF
T: (015395) 60396
F: (015395) 60269
E: hotel@heaves.freeserve.co.uk

B&B per night:
S £32.00–£65.00
D £54.00–£65.00

HB per person:
DY £40.50–£47.50

OPEN All year round

A superb Georgian mansion, owned and run by successive generations of the same family for over 50 years. Set in 10 acres of formal gardens and woodland, 4 miles from exit 36 M6 and 4 miles from Kendal. Spacious en suite rooms, residents' bar, separate lounge, library and billiard room.

Bedrooms: 1 single,
6 double, 5 twin, 1 triple,
1 family room
Bathrooms: 14 en suite,
2 public

Lunch available
EM 1900 (LO 2000)
Parking for 24
CC: Amex, Barclaycard,
Delta, Diners, Eurocard,
JCB, Maestro, Mastercard,
Solo, Switch, Visa, Visa
Electron

Ⓜ ⅀ 🏨 ☎ ▢ ♨ ♞ 🛈 Ⓢ ⅄ ⑉ 📺 ⌨ ⵔ ⏲60 ∪ ► ❄ ⚲ SP 🏠 Ⓣ

CHECK THE MAPS
The colour maps at the front of this guide show all the cities, towns and villages for which you will find accommodation entries.
Refer to the town index to find the page on which they are listed.

KESWICK, Cumbria Map ref 5A3 *Tourist Information Centre Tel: (017687) 72645*

★★★
Silver
Award

BORROWDALE GATES COUNTRY HOUSE HOTEL AND RESTAURANT

Grange-in-Borrowdale, Keswick, CA12 5UQ
T: (017687) 77204
F: (017687) 77254
E: hotel@borrowdale-gates.com
I: www.borrowdale-gates.com

B&B per night:
S £47.50–£69.50
D £85.00–£130.00

HB per person:
DY £57.50–£85.00

OPEN Feb–Dec

Situated in a peaceful setting, amidst the breathtaking scenery of the Borrowdale Valley. This is arguably Lakeland's most beautiful and sought after destination. A charming and unpretentious hotel, which is owner managed. The hotel has gained an enviable reputation for hospitality, service and food in its acclaimed restaurant. Super base for walking and touring.

Bedrooms: 3 single,
13 double, 11 twin,
2 triple
Bathrooms: 29 en suite,
1 public

Lunch available
EM 1900 (LO 2045)
Parking for 40
CC: Amex, Barclaycard,
Delta, Eurocard,
Mastercard, Solo, Switch,
Visa, Visa Electron

★★★
Silver
Award

DERWENTWATER HOTEL

Portinscale, Keswick, CA12 5RE
T: (017687) 72538
F: (017687) 71002
E: reservations@derwentwater-hotel.co.uk
I: ds.dial.pipex.com/derwentwater.hotel

B&B per night:
S £75.00–£95.00
D £130.00–£190.00

HB per person:
DY £65.00–£95.00

OPEN All year round

Best Western Hotels

The epitome of a Lakeland country house hotel and enjoying an unrivalled location on the shores of Lake Derwentwater in 16 acres of conservation grounds. Refurbished to provide high standards of accommodation – sublimely comfortable without being pretentious. Award-winning hospitality and unique location for the perfect Lakeland retreat. Pets most welcome.

Bedrooms: 4 single,
20 double, 21 twin,
2 triple; suite available
Bathrooms: 47 en suite

EM 1900 (LO 2130)
Parking for 140
CC: Amex, Barclaycard,
Delta, JCB, Maestro,
Mastercard, Solo, Switch,
Visa, Visa Electron

★★★

THE KESWICK COUNTRY HOUSE HOTEL
Station Road, Keswick, CA12 4NQ
T: (017687) 72020
F: (017687) 71300

Bedrooms: 5 single,
28 double, 27 twin,
9 triple, 5 family rooms;
suite available
Bathrooms: 74 en suite

Lunch available
EM 1830 (LO 2115)
Parking for 120
CC: Amex, Barclaycard,
Delta, Diners, JCB,
Mastercard, Switch, Visa

B&B per night:
S £35.00–£100.00
D £60.00–£140.00

OPEN All year round

Principal Hotels/Utell International

Victorian hotel situated in 4 acres of award-winning gardens, only a stroll away from Keswick town centre.

QUALITY ASSURANCE SCHEME

For an explanation of the quality and facilities represented by the Stars please refer to the front of this guide. A more detailed explanation can be found in the information pages at the back.

★★

KING'S ARMS HOTEL

Main Street, Keswick, CA12 5BL

T: (017687) 72083 & 71108

F: (017687) 75550

E: info@kingsarmshotelkeswick.co.uk

I: www.kingsarmshotelkeswick.co.uk

B&B per night:
S £42.00–£47.00
D £64.00–£72.00

OPEN All year round

Charming 18thC coaching inn in the beautiful lake town of Keswick. Oak-beamed bar and lounges, lovely air-conditioned restaurant with superb home-cooking. Table d'hote, a la carte and 3-course Walkers' Special. Pizza and pasta restaurant in courtyard. Lively bar popular with locals. En suite bedrooms with colour TV/Sky, tea/coffee maker.

Bedrooms: 9 double, 4 twin
Bathrooms: 13 en suite

Lunch available
EM 1800 (LO 2200)
Parking for 7
CC: Barclaycard, Delta, JCB, Mastercard, Switch, Visa

★★★

KINGS HEAD HOTEL

Thirlspot, Keswick, CA12 4TN

T: (017687) 72393 (General enquiries) & 0500 600725 (Reservations)

F: (017687) 72309

I: www.lakelandsheart.demon.co.uk

B&B per night:
S £20.00–£40.00
D £40.00–£80.00

HB per person:
DY £37.00–£60.00

OPEN All year round

Located in the heart of the Lake District between Grasmere and Keswick, this 17thC former coaching inn is an ideal base for exploring the area. Beautifully furnished with period antiques and offering feature bedrooms, fine wines, real ales, restaurant and bar. Dining from quality menus, with attentive discreet service.

Bedrooms: 3 single, 10 double, 4 twin
Bathrooms: 17 en suite

Lunch available
EM 1800 (LO 2130)
Parking for 60
CC: Barclaycard, Delta, Eurocard, Mastercard, Switch, Visa

★★
Silver
Award

LAIRBECK HOTEL

Vicarage Hill, Keswick, CA12 5QB

T: (017687) 73373 (3 lines)

F: (017687) 73144

E: rogerc@lairbeck.demon.co.uk

I: www.lairbeck.demon.co.uk

B&B per night:
S £30.00–£38.00
D £60.00–£76.00

HB per person:
DY £46.00–£55.00

OPEN Feb–Dec

Lairbeck is a traditional country house hotel built of Lakeland stone, in a secluded setting with mountain views, just 10 minutes' walk from Keswick. Friendly, relaxed atmosphere with log fires, full central heating and ample parking. Excellent home cooking. All bedrooms are fully en suite and non-smoking. Special breaks.

Bedrooms: 4 single, 7 double, 2 twin, 1 family room
Bathrooms: 14 en suite

EM 1830 (LO 1930)
Parking for 15
CC: Barclaycard, Delta, Mastercard, Solo, Switch, Visa, Visa Electron

---

MAP REFERENCES The map references refer to the colour maps at the front of this guide. The first figure is the map number; the letter and figure which follow indicate the grid reference on the map.

★★★
Silver
Award

SKIDDAW HOTEL
Market Square, Keswick, CA12 5BN
T: (017687) 72071
F: (017687) 74850
E: info@skiddawhotel.co.uk
I: www.skiddawhotel.co.uk

B&B per night:
S £42.00–£53.00
D £78.00–£96.00

HB per person:
DY £51.50–£57.50

OPEN All year round

Family-owned and run hotel in picturesque market town, surrounded by the beauty and tranquillity of the mountains and lakes. Excellent value for money, in comfortable up-to-date surroundings with superb facilities. En suite bedrooms with colour TV/Sky channels, tea/coffee maker, telephone, hairdryer, trouser press. Superb restaurant with carvery.

Bedrooms: 7 single,
14 double, 11 twin,
8 triple
Bathrooms: 40 en suite

Lunch available
EM 1800 (LO 2200)
Parking for 8
CC: Amex, Barclaycard,
Delta, Mastercard, Switch,
Visa

🅰🐾🍴📞🖲📺⬜🎯💈§⚿🔌💷🕳💺🍽70🐾🔌👤🎿💥📶 SP T ⚙

★★

SWAN HOTEL AND COUNTRY INN
Thornthwaite, Keswick, CA12 5SQ
T: (017687) 78256
F: (017687) 78080
E: bestswan@aol.com
I: www.swan-hotel-keswick.co.uk

B&B per night:
S £29.00–£35.00
D £58.00–£70.00

HB per person:
DY £46.00–£52.00

OPEN Feb–Dec

The Swan Hotel is an attractive 17thC former coaching inn set amidst magnificent Lakeland scenery in a quiet, elevated position overlooking Skiddaw and the Derwent Valley. Rooms available in hotel or converted coach house.

Bedrooms: 9 double,
9 twin, 2 family rooms
Bathrooms: 20 en suite

Lunch available
EM (LO 2130)
Parking for 30
CC: Barclaycard,
Mastercard, Visa

🅰🐾🛄🍴🖲⬜♿§⚿🔌💷💺🍽120♦✳📶 SP 🏠 T

★
Gold
Award

SWINSIDE LODGE HOTEL
Grange Road, Newlands, Keswick,
CA12 5UE
T: (017687) 72948 &
07887 930998 (Mobile)
F: (017687) 72948
E: stay@swinsidelodge.fsbusiness.co.uk

B&B per night:
S £62.00–£70.00
D £94.00–£122.00

HB per person:
DY £87.00–£95.00

OPEN All year round

Beautifully situated in an idyllic location at the foot of Cat Bells and just 5 minutes' walk from Lake Derwentwater, Swinside Lodge offers peace and tranquillity. This informal, licensed, country-house hotel provides the highest standards of comfort, service and hospitality and is renowned, both locally and nationally, for its superb, award-winning cuisine.

Bedrooms: 5 double,
2 twin
Bathrooms: 7 en suite

EM 1930 (LO 2000)
Parking for 12
CC: Delta, Mastercard,
Switch, Visa

🅰🐾10🖲⬜♿§⚿🔌💷🍽✳🎿🚗📶 SP T

NB

IMPORTANT NOTE Information on accommodation listed in this guide has been supplied by the proprietors. As changes may occur you are advised to check details at the time of booking.

★★

THWAITE HOWE HOTEL
Thornthwaite, Keswick, CA12 5SA
T: (017687) 78281
F: (017687) 78529

B&B per night:
S £28.50–£57.00
D £57.00–£66.00

HB per person:
DY £46.00–£55.00

OPEN All year round

In 2 acres of garden with magnificent mountain views. Peaceful setting within easy reach of A66. We are a small, friendly country house specialising in delicious home cooking using local produce where possible. This is complemented by an excellent selection of fine wines.

Bedrooms: 5 double, 3 twin
Bathrooms: 8 en suite

EM 1900 (LO 1900)
Parking for 12
CC: Barclaycard, Delta, Eurocard, Mastercard, Solo, Switch, Visa

---

KIRKBY LONSDALE, Cumbria Map ref 5B3 *Tourist Information Centre Tel: (015242) 71437*

★★

PHEASANT INN
Casterton, Kirkby Lonsdale,
Carnforth, Lancashire LA6 2RX
T: (015242) 71230
F: (015242) 71230
E: pheasant.casterton@
eggconnnect.net
I: www.pheasantinn.co.uk

Bedrooms: 2 single,
7 double, 2 twin
Bathrooms: 11 en suite

Lunch available
EM 1830 (LO 2100)
Parking for 40
CC: Barclaycard, Delta, Diners, Eurocard, JCB, Mastercard, Switch, Visa

B&B per night:
S Max £40.00
D Max £72.00

OPEN All year round

Friendly country inn specialising in providing excellent food and accommodation. Ideal location for exploring the Lakes and dales. One mile from Kirkby Lonsdale.

★★

WHOOP HALL INN
Burrow with Burrow,
Kirkby Lonsdale, Carnforth,
Lancashire LA6 2HP
T: (01524) 271284
F: (01524) 272154
E: whoophall@cybernet.co.uk
I: www.whoophall.co.uk

Bedrooms: 3 single,
11 double, 3 twin,
2 triple, 1 family room;
suite available
Bathrooms: 20 en suite

Lunch available
EM 1800 (LO 2200)
Parking for 120
CC: Amex, Barclaycard, Delta, Diners, Eurocard, Mastercard, Solo, Switch, Visa

B&B per night:
S £45.00–£50.00
D £50.00–£75.00

HB per person:
DY £41.00–£48.00

OPEN All year round

Minotel/The
Independents

Renowned 17thC inn with oak beams, log fires and restaurant serving traditional food with local specialities. Ideal base for Lakes and Dales. Only 6 miles from M6 junction 36.

LANGDALE, Cumbria Map ref 5A3

★

BRITANNIA INN
Elterwater, Ambleside, LA22 9HP
T: (015394) 37210
F: (015394) 37311
E: info@britinn.co.uk
I: www.britinn.co.uk

Bedrooms: 4 single,
7 double, 2 twin
Bathrooms: 12 en suite,
1 private

Lunch available
EM 1830 (LO 2130)
Parking for 17
CC: Amex, Barclaycard, Delta, Eurocard, JCB, Maestro, Mastercard, Solo, Switch, Visa

B&B per night:
S £24.00–£39.00
D £48.00–£78.00

OPEN All year round

Ashley Courtenay

Traditional Lake District inn on a village green in the beautiful Langdale Valley. Cosy bars with log fires, home-cooked food and real ales. Attractive en suite accommodation.

CENTRAL RESERVATIONS OFFICES
The symbol ⓒⓡ and a group name in an entry indicate that bookings can be made through a central reservations office. These are listed in a separate section towards the back of this guide.

★★

THE PLOUGH HOTEL
Cow Brow, Lupton, LA6 1PJ
T: (015395) 67227
F: (015395) 67848

B&B per night:
S £25.00–£35.00
D £30.00–£65.00

HB per person:
DY £25.00–£45.00

OPEN All year round

Tastefully refurbished country inn renowned for the warmth of its welcome. Superb food, real ales and well-appointed rooms.

Bedrooms: 8 double,
1 triple, 1 family room;
suite available
Bathrooms: 10 en suite

Lunch available
EM 1800 (LO 2115)
Parking for 80
CC: Barclaycard, Delta,
Diners, Mastercard,
Switch, Visa

150

★★★

NEWBY BRIDGE HOTEL
Newby Bridge, Ulverston, LA12 8NA
T: (015395) 31222
F: (015395) 31868
E: newby.bridge.hotel@kencomp.net
I: www.newbybridgehotel.co.uk

B&B per night:
S £49.00–£59.00
D £66.00–£86.00

OPEN All year round

This elegant Georgian mansion is situated in a commanding position overlooking the southern shores of Lake Windermere. Individually styled bedrooms, many with 4-poster beds, jacuzzi bath and lake view. Cosy bar and lounges feature oak panelling and open log fires. Exclusive leisure facilities overlook the mature Roman garden.

Bedrooms: 21 double,
3 twin, 3 triple, 5 family
rooms
Bathrooms: 32 en suite

Lunch available
EM 1900 (LO 2130)
Parking for 60
CC: Amex, Barclaycard,
Delta, Mastercard, Switch,
Visa

130

★★★★

SWAN HOTEL
Newby Bridge, Ulverston, LA12 8NB
T: (015395) 31681
F: (015395) 31917
E: swanhotel@aol.com
I: www.swanhotel.com

B&B per night:
S £60.00–£115.00
D £110.00–£170.00

HB per person:
DY Min £75.00

OPEN All year round

Overlooking Lake Windermere, this beautifully renovated 17thC former coaching inn has become the premier Lake District venue for holiday and business visitors. Fantastic facilities include luxurious bedrooms and suites, stunning split-level restaurant, health and fitness spa with pool, spa bath, sauna and steam rooms, fitness room and beauty salon.

Bedrooms: 2 single,
38 double, 15 twin;
suites available
Bathrooms: 55 en suite

Lunch available
EM 1900 (LO 2130)
Parking for 100
CC: Amex, Barclaycard,
Delta, Eurocard,
Mastercard, Switch, Visa

90

CREDIT CARD BOOKINGS
If you book by telephone and are asked for your credit card number it is advisable to check the proprietor's policy should you cancel your reservation.

NEWBY BRIDGE continued

★★★

WHITEWATER HOTEL
The Lakeland Village, Newby Bridge,
LA12 8PX
T: (015395) 31133
F: (015395) 31881
E: smcintosh@btconnect.com
I: www.whitewater-hotel.co.uk

B&B per night:
S £70.00–£87.50
D £100.00–£145.00

HB per person:
DY £70.00–£80.00

OPEN All year round

The Whitewater's fantastic riverside setting, 5 minutes from Lake Windermere, and its superb leisure facilities make it the perfect setting for your relaxing break. On-site health and fitness club offers swimming pool, sauna, steam room, squash, tennis, jacuzzi, solaria, state-of-the-art gym and a full range of beauty treatments in our health spa.

Bedrooms: 2 single, 16 double, 5 twin, 10 triple, 2 family rooms
Bathrooms: 35 en suite

Lunch available
EM 1900 (LO 2100)
Parking for 50
CC: Amex, Barclaycard, Delta, Diners, Eurocard, JCB, Mastercard, Switch, Visa, Visa Electron

SAWREY, Cumbria Map ref 5A3

★★

SAWREY HOTEL
Far Sawrey, Ambleside, LA22 0LQ
T: (015394) 43425
F: (015394) 43425

B&B per night:
S £29.50–£32.00
D £59.00–£64.00

HB per person:
DY £38.00–£42.00

OPEN All year round

Country inn on the quieter side of Lake Windermere. One mile from the car ferry on the Hawkshead road B5285. It has been run by the Brayshaw family for over 30 years and a warm welcome awaits guests all year with special rates between November and March.

Bedrooms: 2 single, 9 double, 4 twin, 2 triple, 1 family room
Bathrooms: 18 en suite, 1 public

Lunch available
EM 1900 (LO 2045)
Parking for 30
CC: Barclaycard, Delta, Eurocard, JCB, Mastercard, Solo, Switch, Visa, Visa Electron

SHAP, Cumbria Map ref 5B3

★★★

SHAP WELLS HOTEL
Shap, Penrith, CA10 3QU
T: (01931) 716628
F: (01931) 716377
E: manager@shapwells.com
I: www.shapwells.com

Bedrooms: 14 single, 39 double, 36 twin, 5 triple, 4 family rooms; suites available
Bathrooms: 98 en suite, 1 public

Lunch available
EM 1900 (LO 2030)
Parking for 200
CC: Amex, Barclaycard, Delta, Diners, Eurocard, JCB, Maestro, Mastercard, Solo, Switch, Visa, Visa Electron

B&B per night:
S £55.00–£60.00
D £80.00–£90.00

OPEN Feb–Dec

The Independents

In a secluded valley in the Shap Fells. Ideal for exploring the Lakes, dales and Border country.

USE YOUR *i*s

There are more than 550 Tourist Information Centres throughout England offering friendly help with accommodation and holiday ideas as well as suggestions of places to visit and things to do. You'll find TIC addresses in the local Phone Book.

TROUTBECK, Cumbria Map ref 5A3

★★
Silver
Award

BROADOAKS COUNTRY HOUSE

Bridge Lane, Troutbeck, Windermere,
LA23 1LA
T: (015394) 45566
F: (015394) 88766
E: broadoaks.com@virgin.net
I: www.travel.to/broadoaks

Set in glorious countryside. This beautiful Victorian country house is perfect for a luxurious getaway, with jacuzzis, 4-poster and an award-winning dining room. Together with a bespoke civil wedding service available. It's simply "somewhere special".

Bedrooms: 10 double, 2 twin; suite available	Lunch available
Bathrooms: 12 en suite	EM 1900 (LO 2100)
	Parking for 40
	CC: Barclaycard, Delta, Eurocard, Mastercard, Visa

B&B per night:
S £65.00–£135.00
D £110.00–£210.00

HB per person:
DY £95.00–£140.00

OPEN All year round

★★

MORTAL MAN HOTEL
Troutbeck, Windermere, LA23 1PL
T: (015394) 33193
F: (015394) 31261
E: the-mortalman@btinternet.com
I: www.the_mortal_man_inns.com

Bedrooms: 6 double, 6 twin	Lunch available
Bathrooms: 12 en suite	EM 1930 (LO 2130)
	Parking for 30
	CC: Barclaycard, Delta, JCB, Mastercard, Solo, Switch, Visa, Visa Electron

B&B per night:
D £80.00–£100.00

OPEN All year round

Ideal centre for walking, touring or for a very quiet and restful holiday. Beautiful location with homely charm.

ULVERSTON, Cumbria Map ref 5A3 *Tourist Information Centre Tel: (01229) 587120*

Rating
Applied For

LONSDALE HOUSE HOTEL

11 Daltongate, Ulverston, LA12 7BD
T: (01229) 582598
F: (01229) 581260
E: lonsdale.house.hotel@kencomp.net
I: www.lonsdalehousehotel.co.uk

Perfectly situated in the heart of Ulverston's bustling market town, an ideal base for those wishing to explore the district. Enjoy dining in the wood-panelled restaurant complete with trompe d'oeil snug. Comfortable bedrooms, many featuring 4-poster beds and jacuzzi bath. Unlimited use of exclusive leisure facilities nearby.

Bedrooms: 1 single, 17 double, 3 triple	EM 1900 (LO 2100)
Bathrooms: 21 en suite	CC: Amex, Barclaycard, Delta, Mastercard, Switch, Visa

B&B per night:
S £45.00–£49.00
D £66.00–£86.00

OPEN All year round

WINDERMERE, Cumbria Map ref 5A3 *Tourist Information Centre Tel: (015394) 46499*

★★★
Ad IFC

THE BELSFIELD
Bowness-on-Windermere,
Windermere, LA23 3EL
T: (015394) 42448
F: (015394) 46397
E: belsfield@regalhotels.co.uk
I: www.corushotels.com

Bedrooms: 1 single, 31 double, 32 twin	Lunch available
Bathrooms: 64 en suite	EM 1900 (LO 2130)
	Parking for 50
	CC: Amex, Diners, Mastercard, Switch, Visa

B&B per night:
S £45.00–£60.00
D £90.00–£140.00

HB per person:
DY £55.00–£80.00

OPEN All year round

Corus & Regal Hotels

Attractively placed with splendid views over Lake Windermere and the Cumbrian mountains. Snooker room, heated indoor pool, sauna and pitch and putting green.

SYMBOLS
The symbols in each entry give information about services and facilities. A key to these symbols appears at the back of this guide.

★★★

BURNSIDE HOTEL
Kendal Road, Bowness-on-
Windermere, Windermere,
LA23 3EP
T: (015394) 42211 & 44530
F: (015394) 43824
E: stay@burnsidehotel.com
I: www.burnsidehotel.com

Bedrooms: 31 double,
11 twin, 11 triple,
4 family rooms; suites
available
Bathrooms: 57 en suite

Lunch available
EM 1830 (LO 2145)
Parking for 80
CC: Amex, Barclaycard,
Delta, Diners, Eurocard,
JCB, Maestro, Mastercard,
Solo, Switch, Visa, Visa
Electron

B&B per night:
S £73.00–£87.00
D £106.00–£134.00

HB per person:
DY £61.00–£82.00

OPEN All year round

*Set in gardens, views of Lake Windermere, 300 yards from village centre and steamer
piers. Full leisure facilities. Wedding ceremonies. Conference facilities. Self-catering
available.*

★★
Silver
Award

CEDAR MANOR HOTEL
Ambleside Road, Windermere, LA23 1AX
T: (015394) 43192
F: (015394) 45970
E: cedarmanor@fsbdial.co.uk
I: www.cedarmanor.co.uk

B&B per night:
S £32.00–£44.00
D £64.00–£86.00

HB per person:
DY £32.00–£61.00

OPEN All year round

*Situated close to Windermere village
and Lake, Cedar Manor is a haven for
food lovers and those who enjoy the
good things in life. The hotel has won
many awards for food and service.
For those who like to work off the
calories we have leisure facilities
nearby.*

Bedrooms: 9 double,
3 twin
Bathrooms: 12 en suite

Lunch available
EM 1930 (LO 2030)
Parking for 16
CC: Barclaycard,
Mastercard, Visa

★★
Silver
Award

CRAG BROW COTTAGE HOTEL
Helm Road, Bowness-on-Windermere,
LA23 3BU
T: (015394) 44080
F: (015394) 46003
E: cragbrow@aol.com

B&B per night:
S £45.00–£60.00
D £60.00–£90.00

HB per person:
DY £45.00–£60.00

OPEN All year round

*Situated in the heart of Bowness just
2 minutes' walk to lake shore. High
standard en suite rooms, beautiful
award-winning restaurant, extensive
wine list and well-stocked bar. Log
fire, ample parking in private car
park. Free membership of Parklands
leisure facilities for the duration of
your stay.*

Bedrooms: 10 double,
1 family room
Bathrooms: 11 en suite

Lunch available
EM 1800 (LO 2030)
Parking for 30
CC: Barclaycard, Delta,
Eurocard, Mastercard,
Switch, Visa

TOWN INDEX

This can be found at the back of the guide. If you
know where you want to stay, the index will give you
the page number listing accommodation in your
chosen town, city or village.

WINDERMERE continued

Rating
Applied For

DAMSON DENE HOTEL
Crosthwaite, Kendal, LA8 8JE
T: (015395) 68676
F: (015395) 68227
E: info@damsondene.co.uk
I: www.damsondene.co.uk

B&B per night:
S £49.00–£59.00
D £66.00–£86.00

OPEN All year round

The Damson Dene Hotel is located in the heart of beautiful Lyth Valley near Windermere. Set in mature landscaped gardens The hotel commands spectacular views of hills and fells beyond. Comfortable lounge with open log fire, many bedrooms featuring 4-poster beds and jacuzzi bath. Extensive leisure facilities.

Bedrooms: 2 single, 22 double, 9 twin, 2 triple
Bathrooms: 35 en suite

Lunch available
EM 1830 (LO 1900)
Parking for 52
CC: Amex, Barclaycard, Delta, Diners, Mastercard, Switch, Visa

★★★
Gold
Award

GILPIN LODGE COUNTRY HOUSE HOTEL AND RESTAURANT
Crook Road, Windermere, LA23 3NE
T: (015394) 88818
F: (015394) 88058
E: hotel@gilpin-lodge.co.uk
I: www.gilpin-lodge.co.uk

HB per person:
DY £60.00–£125.00

OPEN All year round

Elegant, friendly, relaxing, country house hotel and restaurant in 20 tranquil acres of woodland, moors and gardens 2 miles from Lake Windermere and 12 miles from M6. Sumptuous bedrooms, 4-posters, jacuzzi baths, etc. Award-winning food. See our comprehensive web site or phone for brochure.

Bedrooms: 9 double, 5 twin
Bathrooms: 14 en suite

Lunch available
EM 1900 (LO 2100)
Parking for 40
CC: Amex, Barclaycard, Delta, Diners, Eurocard, JCB, Maestro, Mastercard, Solo, Switch, Visa, Visa Electron

★★
HIDEAWAY HOTEL
Phoenix Way, Windermere, LA23 1DB
T: (015394) 43070
F: (015394) 48664

Bedrooms: 3 single, 7 double, 2 twin, 3 triple
Bathrooms: 15 en suite

EM 1930 (LO 2000)
Parking for 16
CC: Amex, Barclaycard, Delta, Eurocard, JCB, Maestro, Mastercard, Solo, Switch, Visa, Visa Electron

B&B per night:
S £30.00–£50.00
D £60.00–£120.00

HB per person:
DY £42.00–£75.00

OPEN Feb–Dec

Friendly, small hotel away from the main road, with a pleasant garden, well-trained chefs, open fires and well-equipped, comfortable en suite bedrooms.

★★★

HILLTHWAITE HOUSE
Thornbarrow Road, Windermere, LA23 2DF
T: (015394) 43636 & 46691
F: (015394) 88660
E: reception@hillthwaite.com
I: homepages.kencomp.net/hillthwaite/home.htm

B&B per night:
S £35.00–£55.00
D £70.00–£100.00

HB per person:
DY £47.50–£75.00

OPEN All year round

Extended country house overlooking lake and fells, nestling in 3 acres of gardens. Fine cuisine. Some 4-poster rooms with jacuzzi baths. Swimming pool, sauna, steam room. A warm welcome awaits you.

Bedrooms: 3 single, 17 double, 5 twin, 2 triple, 2 family rooms
Bathrooms: 29 en suite

Lunch available
EM 1900 (LO 2145)
Parking for 30
CC: Amex, Barclaycard, Delta, Eurocard, Mastercard, Switch, Visa

★★★
Silver
Award

LINDETH HOWE COUNTRY HOUSE HOTEL

Lindeth Drive, Longtail Hill, Bowness-on-Windermere, Windermere, LA23 3JF
T: (015394) 45759 (Main reception)
F: (015394) 46368
E: lindeth.howe@kencomp.net
I: www.lakes-pages.co.uk

A hotel for the new millennium. A quiet gem of a property formerly owned by Beatrix Potter. Completely redeveloped and extended during 1999 to provide an ideal country house with cosy lounges and great restaurant, set in 6 acres of gardens overlooking Windermere. 1.5 miles from golf club.

B&B per night:
S £45.00–£82.00
D £85.00–£160.00

HB per person:
DY £61.00–£98.50

OPEN All year round

Bedrooms: 5 single, 19 double, 9 twin, 3 triple
Bathrooms: 36 en suite

Lunch available
EM 1900 (LO 2030)
Parking for 50
CC: Barclaycard, Delta, JCB, Mastercard, Switch, Visa

★★★
Gold
Award

LINTHWAITE HOUSE HOTEL

Crook Road, Bowness-on-Windermere, Windermere, LA23 3JA
T: (015394) 88600
F: (015394) 88601
E: admin@linthwaite.com.
I: www.linthwaite.com

Spectacular views over Lake Windermere, friendly unstuffy staff, unwind and exercise your eyes. Attractions: wonderful hiking, golf, boating. Homes, houses and gardens: Beatrix Potter, Wordsworth, John Ruskin, Muncaster and Sizergh Castles, Levens and Holker Halls. Antiques, galleries, quality shopping widely available. Yorkshire Dales, Hadrian's Wall one hour.

B&B per night:
D £90.00–£250.00

HB per person:
DY £59.00–£160.00

OPEN All year round

CR
Grand Heritage Hotels

Bedrooms: 1 single, 21 double, 4 twin; suites available
Bathrooms: 26 en suite

Lunch available
EM 1915 (LO 2045)
Parking for 30
CC: Amex, Barclaycard, Delta, Diners, Mastercard, Solo, Switch, Visa

---

★★
Silver
Award

MEREWOOD COUNTRY HOUSE HOTEL

Ecclerigg, Windermere, LA23 1LH
T: (015394) 46484
F: (015394) 42128
E: merewood.hotel@impact-dtg.com

Creating the true country-house atmosphere. Set in a position of incomparable beauty, elevated with unrivalled views over Lake Windermere to the mountains beyond. Merewood has many features, from its oak-panelled glass-stained hall to its Edwardian conservatory bar. Specialises in civil weddings, groups and conferences or just relaxing breaks.

B&B per night:
S £60.00–£140.00
D £120.00–£140.00

HB per person:
DY £60.00–£190.00

OPEN All year round

Bedrooms: 20 twin
Bathrooms: 20 en suite

Lunch available
EM 1930 (LO 2045)
Parking for 70
CC: Amex, Barclaycard, Delta, Mastercard, Solo, Switch, Visa

WELCOME HOST This is a nationally recognised customer care programme which aims to promote the highest standards of service and a warm welcome. Establishments taking part in this initiative are indicated by the ⏣ symbol.

★★★

MOUNTAIN ASH HOTEL

Ambleside Road, Windermere, LA23 1AT
T: (015394) 43715
F: (015394) 88480
E: john_fawbert@msn.com
I: www.mountainashhotel.co.uk

B&B per night:
S £29.50–£55.00
D £50.00–£110.00

HB per person:
DY £33.00–£68.00

OPEN All year round

Lakeland-stone home, creatively refurbished to provide comfortable accommodation. Emphasis is on good, wholesome food, served by friendly staff in a relaxed atmosphere. Complimentary use of nearby leisure centre. Perfectly situated on the edge of the village for easy access to the South Lakes. Four-posters, spa baths.

Bedrooms: 1 single, 17 double, 1 twin, 3 family rooms
Bathrooms: 22 en suite

Lunch available
EM 1900 (LO 2030)
Parking for 30
CC: Barclaycard, Delta, Mastercard, Switch, Visa

★★

RAVENSWORTH HOTEL

Ambleside Road, Windermere, LA23 1BA
T: (015394) 43747
F: (015394) 43670
E: raveswth@aol.com
I: www.ravensworthhotel.co.uk

B&B per night:
S £24.50–£31.00
D £59.00–£76.00

HB per person:
DY £40.50–£54.00

OPEN All year round

Traditional Lakeland stone-built home form the late 19thC. Family-owned and run hotel offering a warm welcome, relaxed surroundings and excellent home-cooked food. Ideally situated with every access to all parts of the National Park and the many attractions on offer for all ages.

Bedrooms: 2 single, 9 double, 2 twin, 1 triple
Bathrooms: 14 en suite

Lunch available
EM 1830 (LO 2000)
Parking for 16
CC: Amex, Barclaycard, Delta, JCB, Maestro, Mastercard, Solo, Switch, Visa, Visa Electron

★

THE WILLOWSMERE HOTEL

Ambleside Road, Windermere, LA23 1ES
T: (015394) 43575 & 44962
F: (015394) 44962
E: willowsmerehotel@hotmail.com

Bedrooms: 2 single, 4 double, 1 twin, 6 triple
Bathrooms: 13 en suite

Lunch available
EM 1900 (LO 1900)
Parking for 40
CC: Amex, Barclaycard, Delta, Diners, JCB, Mastercard, Switch, Visa, Visa Electron

B&B per night:
S £25.00–£40.00
D £50.00–£80.00

HB per person:
DY £38.00–£50.00

OPEN Mar–Oct

Offers a comfortable and friendly atmosphere. Run by the fifth generation of local hoteliers. Varied food using fresh local produce.

CHECK THE MAPS

The colour maps at the front of this guide show all the cities, towns and villages for which you will find accommodation entries. Refer to the town index to find the page on which they are listed.

A brief guide to the main Towns and Villages offering accommodation in CUMBRIA

A AMBLESIDE, CUMBRIA - Market town situated at the head of Lake Windermere and surrounded by fells. The historic town centre is now a conservation area and the country around Ambleside is rich in historic and literary associations. Good centre for touring, walking and climbing.

● **APPLEBY-IN-WESTMORLAND, CUMBRIA** - Former county town of Westmorland, at the foot of the Pennines in the Eden Valley. The castle was rebuilt in the 17th C, except for its Norman keep, ditches and ramparts. It now houses a Rare Breeds Survival Trust Centre. Good centre for exploring the Eden Valley.

B BORROWDALE, CUMBRIA - Stretching south of Derwentwater to Seathwaite in the heart of the Lake District, the valley is walled by high fellsides. It can justly claim to be the most scenically impressive valley in the Lake District. Excellent centre for walking and climbing.

● **BUTTERMERE, CUMBRIA** - Small village surrounded by high mountains, between Buttermere Lake and Crummock Water. An ideal centre for walking and climbing the nearby peaks and for touring.

C CARLISLE, CUMBRIA - Cumbria's only city is rich in history. Attractions include the small red sandstone cathedral and 900-year-old castle with a magnificent view from the keep. Award-winning Tullie House Museum and Art Gallery brings 2,000 years of Border history dramatically to life. Excellent centre for shopping.

● **CARTMEL, CUMBRIA** - Picturesque conserved village based on a 12th C priory with a well-preserved church and gatehouse. Just half a mile outside the Lake District National Park, this is a peaceful base for walking and touring, with historic houses and beautiful scenery.

● **COCKERMOUTH, CUMBRIA** - Ancient market town at confluence of Rivers Cocker and Derwent. Birthplace of William Wordsworth in 1770. The house where he was born is at the end of the town's broad, tree-lined main street and is now owned by the National Trust. Good touring base for the Lakes.

● **CONISTON, CUMBRIA** - The 803m fell Coniston Old Man dominates the skyline to the east of this village at the northern end of Coniston Water. Arthur Ransome set his "Swallows and Amazons" stories here. Coniston's most famous resident was John Ruskin, whose home, Brantwood, is open to the public. Good centre for walking.

E ENNERDALE, CUMBRIA - The most western valley of the Lake District. The small village of Ennerdale Bridge is an ideal centre for walking and rock climbing and lies just one mile west of Ennerdale Water. Pillar and Pillar Rock, famous for its rock climbs, towers over the lake.

● **ESKDALE, CUMBRIA** - Several minor roads lead to the west end of this beautiful valley, or it can be approached via the east over the Hardknott Pass, the Lake District's steepest pass. Scafell Pike and Bow Fell lie to the north and a miniature railway links the Eskdale Valley with Ravenglass on the coast.

G GRANGE-OVER-SANDS, CUMBRIA - Set on the beautiful Cartmel Peninsula, this tranquil resort, known as Lakeland's Riviera, overlooks Morecambe Bay. Pleasant seafront walks and beautiful gardens. The bay attracts many species of wading birds.

● **GRASMERE, CUMBRIA** - Described by William Wordsworth as "the loveliest spot that man hath ever found", this village, famous for its gingerbread, is in a beautiful setting overlooked by Helm Crag. Wordsworth lived at Dove Cottage. The cottage and museum are open to the public.

H HAWKSHEAD, CUMBRIA - Lying near Esthwaite Water, this village has great charm and character. Its small squares are linked by flagged or cobbled alleys and the main square is dominated by the market house, or Shambles, where the butchers had their stalls in days gone by.

K KENDAL, CUMBRIA - The "Auld Grey Town" lies in the valley of the River Kent with a backcloth of limestone fells. Situated just outside the Lake District National Park, it is a good centre for touring the Lakes and surrounding country. Ruined castle, reputed birthplace of Catherine Parr.

● **KESWICK, CUMBRIA** - Beautifully positioned town beside Derwentwater and below the mountains of Skiddaw and Blencathra. Excellent base for walking, climbing, watersports and touring. Motor-launches operate on Derwentwater and motor boats, rowing boats and canoes can be hired.

● **KIRKBY LONSDALE, CUMBRIA** - Charming old town of narrow streets and Georgian buildings, set in the superb scenery of the Lune Valley. The Devil's Bridge over the River Lune is probably 13th C.

L LANGDALE, CUMBRIA - The two Langdale valleys (Great Langdale and Little Langdale) lie in the heart of beautiful mountain scenery. The craggy Langdale Pikes are almost 2500ft high. An ideal walking and climbing area and base for touring.

● **LUPTON, CUMBRIA** - Village divided by A65 between Kirkby Lonsdale and Kendal. Appears in the Domesday Book. Boasts many fine farmhouses dating back to the 17th C and a disused mill that has stood on Lupton beck for 700 years.'

N NEWBY BRIDGE, CUMBRIA - At the southern end of Windermere on the River Leven, this village has an unusual stone bridge with arches of unequal size. The Lakeside and Haverthwaite Railway has a stop here, and steamer cruises on Lake Windermere leave from nearby Lakeside.

S SAWREY, CUMBRIA - Far Sawrey and Near Sawrey lie near Esthwaite Water. Both villages are small but Near Sawrey is famous for Hill Top Farm, home of Beatrix Potter, now owned by the National Trust and open to the public.

● **SHAP, CUMBRIA** - Village lying nearly 1000ft above sea-level, amongst impressive moorland scenery. Shap Abbey, open to the public, is hidden in a valley nearby. Most of the ruins date from the early 13th C, but the tower is 16th C. The famous Shap granite and limestone quarries are nearby.

T TROUTBECK, CUMBRIA - Most of the houses in this picturesque village are 17th C, some retain their spinning galleries and oak-mullioned windows. At the south end of the village is Townend, owned by the National Trust and open to the public, an excellently preserved example of a yeoman farmer's or statesman's house.

U ULVERSTON, CUMBRIA - Market town lying between green fells and the sea. There is a replica of the Eddystone lighthouse on the Hoad which is a monument to Sir John Barrow, founder of the Royal Geographical Society. Birthplace of Stan Laurel, of Laurel and Hardy.

W WINDERMERE, CUMBRIA - Once a tiny hamlet before the introduction of the railway in 1847, now adjoins Bowness which is on the lakeside. Centre for sailing and boating. A good way to see the lake is a trip on a passenger steamer. Steamboat Museum has a fine collection of old boats.

CONFIRM YOUR BOOKING
You are advised to confirm your booking in writing.

Where to Stay

The official and best selling guides, offering the reassurance of quality assured accommodation

2001

Hotels, Townhouses and Travel Accommodation in England 2001	Guesthouses, Bed & Breakfast, Farmhouses and Inns in England 2001	Self Catering Holiday Homes in England 2001	Camping & Caravan Parks in Britain 2001
£10.99	£10.99	£9.99	£5.99

THE GUIDES INCLUDE

- Accommodation entries packed with information
- Full colour maps
- Places to visit
- Tourist Information Centres

Look out also for:

SOMEWHERE SPECIAL IN ENGLAND 2001

Accommodation achieving the highest standards in facilities and quality of service - the perfect guide for the discerning traveller

INFORMATIVE   EASY TO USE   GREAT VALUE FOR MONEY

NORTHUMBRIA

From the sublime to the magnificent, Northumbria is rich in variety with an enormous expanse of coastline, countryside and culture. Stately homes and castles, designer gardens and open air museums all wait to share their secrets.

Discover Durham with its imposing Cathedral where the Venerable Bede, England's first historian, is buried. And from the beautiful fishing village of Seahouses, nature lovers will enjoy the boat trip around the Farne Islands to see eider duck, puffins and grey seals.

On the last Saturday in June the week long medieval Alnwick Fair begins. Be sure to catch unique events such as dwyle flonking - hitting your opponent with a beer-soaked rag on a stick!

The counties of
County Durham, Northumberland,
Tees Valley and Tyne & Wear

FOR MORE INFORMATION CONTACT:
Northumbria Tourist Board
Aykley Heads, Durham DH1 5UX
Tel: (0191) 375 3000
Fax: (0191) 386 0899
Internet: www.ntb.org.uk

Where to Go in Northumbria - see pages 72-75
Where to Stay in Northumbria - see pages 76-83

The Pictures:
1   Hadrian's Wall, Northumberland;
2   Kielder Water, Northumberland;
3   Washington Old Hall,
     Tyne & Wear;
4   Durham Cathedral.

Whilst in
NORTHUMBRIA ○○○

You will find hundreds of interesting places to visit during your stay, just some of which are listed in these pages.

Contact any Tourist Information Centre in the region for more ideas on days out in Northumbria.

Auckland Castle

Bishop Auckland, County Durham DL14 7NR
Tel: (01388) 601627
Principal country residence of the Bishops of Durham since Norman times. The chapel and staterooms are open to the public.

Bamburgh Castle

Bamburgh, Northumberland NE69 7DF
Tel: (01668) 214515
Magnificent coastal castle completely restored in 1900. Collections of china, porcelain, furniture, paintings, arms and armour.

Bede's World

Jarrow, Tyne & Wear NE32 3DY
Tel: (0191) 489 2106
Discover the exciting world of the Venerable Bede, early medieval Europe's greatest scholar. Church, monastic site, museum with exhibitions and recreated Anglo-Saxon farm.

Belsay Hall, Castle and Gardens

Belsay, Newcastle upon Tyne NE20 0DX
Tel: (01661) 881636
House of the Middleton family for 600 years in 30 acres of landscaped gardens and winter garden. 14thC castle, ruined 17thC manor house and neo-classical hall.

Captain Cook Birthplace Museum

Marton, Middlesbrough, Cleveland TS7 6AS
Tel: (01642) 311211
Early life and voyages of Captain Cook and the countries he visited. Temporary exhibitions.

Cragside House, Gardens and Grounds

Rothbury, Morpeth, Northumberland NE65 7PX
Tel: (01669) 620333
House built 1864-1884 for the first Lord Armstrong, a Tyneside industrialist. Cragside was the first house to be lit by electricity generated by water power.

Discovery Museum

Blandford Square, Newcastle upon Tyne NE1 4JA
Tel: (0191) 232 6789
Discovery Museum offers a wide variety of experiences for all the family to enjoy. Visit the Science Factory, Great City, Fashion Works and maritime history.

Dunstanburgh Castle

Craster, Alnwick, Northumberland NE66 3TT
Tel: (01665) 576231
Romantic ruins of extensive 14thC castle in dramatic coastal situation on 30-metre (100ft) cliffs. Built by Thomas, Earl of Lancaster. Remains include gatehouse and curtain wall.

Durham Castle

Palace Green, Durham DH1 3RW
Tel: (0191) 374 3863
Castle founded in 1072, Norman chapel dating from 1080. Kitchens and great hall dated 1499 and 1284 respectively. Fine example of motte-and-bailey castle.

Gisborough Priory

Guisborough, Cleveland TS14 6HG
Tel: (01287) 633801
Remains of a priory founded by Robert de Brus in
AD1119 for Augustinian canons in the grounds of
Gisborough Hall. Main arch and window of east wall
virtually intact.

Hall Hill Farm

Lanchester, Durham DH7 0TA
Tel: (01388) 730300
Family fun set in attractive countryside. See and touch
the animals at close quarters. Farm trailer ride, riverside
walk, teashop and play area.

Hartlepool Historic Quay

Hartlepool, Cleveland TS24 0XZ
Tel: (01429) 860006
An exciting reconstruction of a seaport of the 1800s
with buildings and a lively quayside.

Housesteads Roman Fort

Haydon Bridge, Hadrian's Wall, Hexham,
Northumberland NE47 6NN
Tel: (01434) 344363
Best preserved and most impressive of the Roman forts.
Vercovicium was a 5-acre fort for an extensive 800 civil
settlement. Only example of a Roman hospital.

Josephine and John Bowes Museum

Barnard Castle, Durham DL12 8NP
Tel: (01833) 690606
French-style chateau housing art collections of national
importance plus archaeology of south west Durham.

Killhope, the North of England Lead Mining Museum

Cowshill, St John's Chapel, County Durham DL13 1AR
Tel: (01388) 537505
Most complete lead mining site in Great Britain. Mine
tours available, 10-metre (34ft) diameter waterwheel,
reconstruction of Victorian machinery, miners lodging
and woodland walks.

Life Interactive World

Times Square, Newcastle upon Tyne NE1 4EP
Tel: (0191) 261 6006
This remarkable visitor experience is at the heart of the
International Centre for Life, a £58 million landmark
Millennium project.

Lindisfarne Castle

Holy Island, Berwick-upon-Tweed,
Northumberland TD15 2SH
Tel: (01289) 389244
Fort converted into a private home for Edward Hudson
by the architect Sir Edwin Lutyens in 1903.

National Glass Centre

Sunderland, Tyne & Wear SR6 0GL
Tel: (0191) 515 5555
A large gallery presenting the best in contemporary
and historical glass. Master craftspeople demonstrate
glass-making techniques. Classes and workshops
available.

Natures World at the Botanic Centre

Acklam, Middlesbrough, Tees Valley TS5 7YN
Tel: (01642) 594895
Demonstration gardens, wildlife pond, gold medal-
winning white garden, environmental exhibition hall,
shop, tearoom and river Tees model.

Newcastle Cathedral

Church of St Nicholas, Newcastle upon Tyne NE1 1PF
Tel: (0191) 232 1939
13thC and 14thC church, added to in 18thC-20thC.
Famous lantern tower, pre-reformation font and font
cover, 15thC stained-glass roundel in the side chapel.

The Pictures:
1 The Angel of the North, Gateshead;
2 Boulby Cliff, Cleveland;
3 Tynemouth Priory and Castle, Tyne & Wear;
4 Dunstanburgh, Northumberland;
5 Alnwick, Northumberland;
6 Beamish, County Durham;
7 Bridges over the Tyne, Newcastle;
8 Bamburgh, Northumberland.

8

Thomas Bewick Birthplace Museum

Cherryburn, Mickley, Northumberland NE43 7DB
Tel: (01661) 843276
Birthplace cottage (1700) and farmyard. Printing house using original printing blocks. Introductory exhibition of the life, work and countryside.

Wallington House, Walled Garden and Grounds

Wallington Cambo, Morpeth,
Northumberland NE61 4AR
Tel: (01670) 774283
Built in 1688 on the site of an earlier medieval castle and altered in the 1740s. Interior has plasterwork, porcelain, furniture, pictures, needlework and a dolls house. Walled garden.

The North of England Open Air Museum

Beamish, County Durham DH9 0RG
Tel: (01207) 231811
Visit the town, colliery village, farm, railway station, Pockerley Manor and 1825 railway, recreating life in the North East in the early 1800s and 1900s.

Washington Old Hall

Washington, Tyne & Wear NE38 7LE
Tel: (0191) 416 6879
The home of George Washington's ancestors, from 1183-1288, remaining in the family until 1613. The manor, from which the family took its name, was restored in 1936.

Otter Trust's North Pennines Reserve

Vale House Farm, Bowes, County Durham DL12 9RH
Tel: (01833) 628339
A branch of the famous Otter Trust. Visitors can see Asian and British otters, red and fallow deer and several rare breeds of farm animals in this 230-acre wildlife reserve.

Wet 'N Wild

Royal Quays, North Shields NE29 6DA
Tel: (0191) 296 1333
Tropical indoor water park. A fun water playground providing the wildest and wettest indoor rapid experience. Whirlpools, slides and meandering lazy river.

Raby Castle

Staindrop, County Durham DL2 3AY
Tel: (01833) 660202
Medieval castle in 200-acre park. Includes a 600-year-old kitchen, carriage collection, walled gardens and deer park. Home of Lord Barnard's family for over 370 years.

Wildfowl and Wetlands Trust

Washington, Tyne & Wear NE38 8LE
Tel: (0191) 416 5454
Collection of 1,250 wildfowl of 108 varieties. Viewing gallery, picnic areas, hides and winter wild bird feeding station, flamingos and wild grey heron. Food available.

Sea Life Aquarium

Long Sands, Tynemouth, Tyne & Wear NE30 4JF
Tel: (0191) 257 6100
More than 30 hi-tech displays provide encounters with dozens of sea creatures. Journey beneath the North Sea and discover thousands of amazing creatures.

South Shields Museum and Art Gallery

Ocean Road, South Shields, Tyne & Wear NE33 2JA
Tel: (0191) 456 8740
Galleries of Catherine Cookson memorabilia and local history. Also an exciting programme of exhibitions and events.

The Pictures:
1 Freeborough Hill, Cleveland;
2 Roseberry Topping, Northumberland;
3 Cragside Estate, nr. Rothbury, Northumberland;
4 Alnwick Castle, Northumberland;
5 Bamburgh, Northumberland.

Find out more about
NORTHUMBRIA ...

Further information about holidays and
attractions in Northumbria is available from:

NORTHUMBRIA TOURIST BOARD
Aykley Heads, Durham DH1 5UX.
Tel: (0191) 375 3000
Fax: (0191) 386 0899
Internet: www.ntb.org.uk

*The following publications are available free from the
Northumbria Tourist Board, unless otherwise stated:*

Northumbria 2001

*information on the region, including hotels, bed and
breakfast and self-catering accommodation, caravan
and camping parks, attractions, shopping, eating and
drinking*

North of England Bed & Breakfast Map

*value for money bed and breakfast accommodation in
Northumbria and Yorkshire*

Going Places

*information on where to go, what to see and what to
do. Combined with the award-winning Powerpass
promotion which offers 2-for-1 entry into many of the
region's top attractions*

Group Travel Directory

*guide designed specifically for group organisers,
detailing group accommodation providers, places to
visit, suggested itineraries, coaching information and
events*

Educational Visits

*information to help plan educational visits within the
region. Uncover a wide variety of places to visit with
unique learning opportunities*

Discover Northumbria on two wheels

*information on cycling in the region including an order
form allowing the reader to order maps/leaflets from a
central ordering point*

Freedom

*caravan and camping guide to the North of England.
Available from Freedom Holidays, tel: 01202 252179*

Getting to
NORTHUMBRIA ...

BY ROAD: The north/south routes on the A1 and A19 thread the region as does the
A68. East/west routes like the A66 and A69 easily link with the western side of the
country. Within Northumbria you will find fast, modern interconnecting roads between
all the main centres, a vast network of scenic, traffic-free country roads to make
motoring a pleasure and frequent local bus services operating to all towns and villages.

BY RAIL: London to Edinburgh InterCity service stops at Darlington, Durham,
Newcastle and Berwick upon Tweed. 26 trains daily make the journey between
London and Newcastle in just under 3 hours. The London to Middlesbrough journey
takes 3 hours. Birmingham to Darlington 3 hours 15 minutes. Bristol to Durham
5 hours and Sheffield to Newcastle just over 2 hours. Direct services operate to
Newcastle from Liverpool, Manchester, Glasgow, Stranraer and Carlisle. Regional
services to areas of scenic beauty operate frequently, allowing the traveller easy
access. The Tyne & Wear Metro makes it possible to travel to many destinations
within the Tyneside area, such as Gateshead, South Shields, Whitley Bay and
Newcastle International Airport, in minutes.

Where to stay in
NORTHUMBRIA

Accommodation entries in this region are listed in alphabetical order of place name, and then in alphabetical order of establishment.

Map references refer to the colour location maps at the front of this guide. The first number indicates the map to use; the letter and number which follow refer to the grid reference on the map.

At-a-glance symbols at the end of each accommodation entry give useful information about services and facilities. A key to symbols can be found inside the back cover flap. Keep this open for easy reference.

A brief description of the towns and villages offering accommodation in the entries which follow, can be found at the end of this section.

A complete listing of all English Tourism Council assessed hotels appears at the back of this guide.

ALNMOUTH, Northumberland Map ref 5C1

★★ **SADDLE HOTEL**

24-25 Northumberland Street,
Alnmouth, Alnwick, NE66 2RA
T: (01665) 830476

Bedrooms: 3 double,
4 twin, 1 triple
Bathrooms: 8 en suite

Lunch available
EM 1830 (LO 2100)
CC: Barclaycard, Delta,
Eurocard, Mastercard,
Solo, Switch, Visa

B&B per night:
S £30.00–£36.00
D £50.00–£60.00

HB per person:
DY £36.00–£42.00

OPEN All year round

Personally supervised by owners and offering a high standard of accommodation. One of Alnmouth's premier eating houses, with many good food awards.

BAMBURGH, Northumberland Map ref 5C1

★★

VICTORIA HOTEL

Front Street, Bamburgh, NE69 7BP
T: (01668) 214431
F: (01668) 214404
E: victoria@bestwestern.co.uk
I: www.bestwestern.co.uk

B&B per night:
S £32.50–£45.00
D £75.00–£102.00

HB per person:
DY £42.50–£64.00

OPEN All year round

Set in the heart of the historic village of Bamburgh, dominated by its magnificent castle with Holy Island and the Farnes viewed from its ramparts. The stylish Brasserie has recently been awarded a rosette for culinary flair. Ideally located for exploring this stunning coastline with miles of sandy beaches.

Bedrooms: 6 single,
16 double, 6 twin,
1 triple, 1 family room
Bathrooms: 30 en suite

Lunch available
EM 1800 (LO 2130)
Parking for 6
CC: Amex, Barclaycard,
Delta, Diners, Mastercard,
Solo, Switch, Visa, Visa
Electron

BAMBURGH continued

★★★

WAREN HOUSE HOTEL
Waren Mill, Belford, NE70 7EE
T: (01668) 214581
F: (01668) 214484
E: enquiries@warenhousehotel.co.uk
I: www.warenhousehotel.co.uk

B&B per night:
S £50.50–£105.00
D £80.50–£185.00

HB per person:
DY £68.95–£123.45

OPEN All year round

Traditional, beautifully restored and renovated, award-winning country house hotel in 6 acres of wooded grounds and walled garden on edge of Budle Bay overlooking Holy Island. Superb accommodation, excellent food, choice of over 250 reasonably priced wines. Two miles Bamburgh Castle, 5 miles Farne Islands. Children over 14 welcome.

Bedrooms: 7 double, 3 twin; suites available
Bathrooms: 10 en suite

EM 1830 (LO 2030)
Parking for 14
CC: Amex, Barclaycard, Delta, Diners, JCB, Mastercard, Solo, Switch, Visa, Visa Electron

---

BARNARD CASTLE, Durham Map ref 5B3 *Tourist Information Centre Tel: (01833) 690909 or 630272*

★★★

JERSEY FARM HOTEL
Darlington Road, Barnard Castle, County Durham DL12 8TA
T: (01833) 638223
F: (01833) 631988
E: jerseyfarmhotel@enta.net
I: www.jerseyfarmhotel.enta.net

B&B per night:
S £55.00–£68.00
D £68.00–£88.00

HB per person:
DY £47.90–£57.90

OPEN All year round

One mile east of Barnard Castle in an Area of Outstanding Natural Beauty. The Watsons created the hotel in 1978 after previously farming the land. Comfortable rooms with panoramic views. The Meadow Restaurant famous for home cooking and carvery meals with plenty of it! Residents' lounge, bar and conservatory, all tastefully decorated.

Bedrooms: 1 single, 14 double, 1 twin, 2 triple, 2 family rooms; suites available
Bathrooms: 20 en suite

Lunch available
EM 1900 (LO 2100)
Parking for 100
CC: Barclaycard, Delta, Eurocard, Mastercard, Switch, Visa

BELLINGHAM, Northumberland Map ref 5B2 *Tourist Information Centre Tel: (01434) 220616*

★★

RIVERDALE HALL HOTEL
Bellingham, Hexham, NE48 2JT
T: (01434) 220254
F: (01434) 220457
E: iben@riverdalehall.demon.co.uk

B&B per night:
S £46.00–£48.00
D £69.00–£84.00

HB per person:
DY £49.50–£61.00

OPEN All year round

CR
The Independents

Spacious Victorian country hall in large grounds. All bedrooms en suite with TV, telephone and hospitality trays. Indoor swimming pool, sauna, fishing, cricket field and golf nearby. Award-winning restaurant. Kielder Water, Pennine Way and Hadrian's Wall nearby. The Cocker family's 22nd year.

Bedrooms: 3 single, 4 double, 9 twin, 4 triple
Bathrooms: 20 en suite, 2 public

Lunch available
EM 1830 (LO 2145)
Parking for 60
CC: Barclaycard, Delta, Diners, Mastercard, Switch, Visa

ACCESSIBILITY
Look for the 🛗 symbols which indicate accessibility for wheelchair users. A list of establishments is at the front of this guide.

CORNHILL–ON–TWEED, Northumberland Map ref 5B1

★★★
Silver
Award

Victorian country mansion set in 15 acres of natural woodland. Individually-styled en suite bedrooms. Enjoyable food, carefully prepared and reflecting a high level of culinary skills. Well stocked bar and cellar, restaurant and bistro. Fishing, clay pigeon shooting and golf by arrangement. Please book with accommodation.

TILLMOUTH PARK COUNTRY HOUSE HOTEL

Cornhill-on-Tweed, TD12 4UU
T: (01890) 882255
F: (01890) 882540
E: igl@tillmouthpark.force9.co.uk
I: www.tillmouthpark.co.uk

Bedrooms: 1 single, 6 double, 6 twin, 1 triple
Bathrooms: 14 en suite

Lunch available
EM 1900 (LO 2100)
Parking for 50
CC: Amex, Barclaycard, Delta, Diners, Maestro, Mastercard, Solo, Switch, Visa

B&B per night:
S £90.00–£125.00
D £130.00–£170.00

HB per person:
DY £90.00–£120.00

OPEN All year round

CR
Grand Heritage Hotels

CROOK, Durham Map ref 5C2

★★★

HELME PARK HALL HOTEL
Fir Tree, Crook, County Durham
DL13 4NW
T: (01388) 730970
F: (01388) 730970

Bedrooms: 2 single, 7 double, 4 twin
Bathrooms: 13 en suite

Lunch available
EM 1900 (LO 2100)
Parking for 70
CC: Amex, Barclaycard, Delta, Mastercard, Switch, Visa

B&B per night:
S £43.00–£43.00
D £70.00–£91.50

HB per person:
DY Min £45.80

OPEN All year round

Comfortable, fully refurbished hotel with open fires and warm, welcoming atmosphere. In 5 acres of grounds, with spectacular views over the dales. A haven of peace and tranquillity.

DARLINGTON, Durham Map ref 5C3 *Tourist Information Centre Tel: (01325) 388666*

★★★

Charming Jacobean mansion located in a picturesque hamlet in rural lower Teesdale. Set in 4 acres of formal gardens, the hotel offers high quality accommodation, a superb restaurant and leisure facilities including pool, sauna, tennis court and fishing. Conveniently located for the region's main towns and attractions.

HEADLAM HALL HOTEL

Headlam, Gainford, Darlington,
County Durham DL2 3HA
T: (01325) 730238
F: (01325) 730790
E: admin@headlamhall.co.uk
I: www.headlamhall.co.uk

Bedrooms: 21 double, 9 twin, 6 triple; suites available
Bathrooms: 34 en suite

Lunch available
EM 1930 (LO 2200)
Parking for 60
CC: Amex, Barclaycard, Delta, Diners, Eurocard, Mastercard, Switch, Visa

B&B per night:
S £65.00–£90.00
D £80.00–£105.00

HB per person:
DY £53.00–£85.00

OPEN All year round

DURHAM, Durham Map ref 5C2 *Tourist Information Centre Tel: (0191) 384 3720*

★★

KENSINGTON HALL HOTEL
Kensington Terrace, Willington,
Crook, County Durham DL15 0PJ
T: (01388) 745071
F: (01388) 745800
E: kensingtonhall@cs.com
I: ourworld.cs.com/kensingtonhall

Bedrooms: 3 double, 4 twin, 2 triple, 1 family room
Bathrooms: 10 en suite

Lunch available
EM 1900 (LO 2145)
Parking for 40
CC: Amex, Barclaycard, Delta, Diners, Eurocard, JCB, Mastercard, Solo, Switch, Visa, Visa Electron

B&B per night:
S £38.00–£40.00
D £48.00–£50.00

HB per person:
DY £50.00–£52.00

OPEN All year round

Comfortable family-run hotel, lounge bar, restaurant and function suite. Excellent meals. South-west of Durham on A690 to Crook. Easy access to Durham Cathedral, Beamish Museum and Weardale.

HAMSTERLEY FOREST, Durham

See under Barnard Castle, Crook

HEXHAM, Northumberland Map ref 5B2 *Tourist Information Centre Tel: (01434) 605225*

★★★

LANGLEY CASTLE
Langley-on-Tyne, Hexham, NE47 5LU
T: (01434) 688888
F: (01434) 684019
E: manager@langleycastle.com
I: www.langleycastle.com

B&B per night:
S £20.00–£23.00
D £40.00–£46.00

HB per person:
DY £27.00–£31.00

OPEN All year round

A genuine 14thC castle, set in own woodland estate. All rooms with private facilities, some with window seats set into 7ft thick walls, sauna and 4-poster beds. The magnificent drawing room, with blazing log fire, complements the intimate Josephine Restaurant. Perfect to explore Northumberland, Bamburgh Castle, Holy Island, the Borders.

Bedrooms: 16 double, 2 twin; suites available
Bathrooms: 18 en suite

Lunch available
EM 1900 (LO 2100)
Parking for 100
CC: Amex, Barclaycard, Delta, Diners, Mastercard, Switch, Visa

⚠️↘️🏡📞🍽️🖥️⬇️⚲📿✂️🏠🔼📺🖨️🛏️🍴160 🍵♿🅿️❄️✳️☀️ SP 🏨 T

HOLY ISLAND, Northumberland Map ref 5B1

★

LINDISFARNE HOTEL
Holy Island, Berwick-upon-Tweed, TD15 2SQ
T: (01289) 389273
F: (01289) 389284

Bedrooms: 2 single, 2 double, 1 twin, 2 triple
Bathrooms: 5 en suite, 1 public

Lunch available
EM 1900 (LO 2100)
Parking for 12
CC: Amex, Barclaycard, Delta, Diners, Eurocard, JCB, Mastercard, Solo, Switch, Visa, Visa Electron

HB per person:
DY £33.00–£45.00

OPEN All year round

Small, comfortable, family-run hotel providing coffees, lunches, afternoon teas and evening meals. An ideal place for ornithologists and within walking distance of Lindisfarne Castle and Priory.

⚠️↘️🏡📞🖥️⬇️⚲📿🅂🛏️✂️🏠🖨️♿🔍❄️✳️✈️↘️

LONGFRAMLINGTON, Northumberland Map ref 5C1

★★★

EMBLETON HALL
Longframlington, Morpeth, NE65 8DT
T: (01665) 570206 & 570249
F: (01665) 570056

Bedrooms: 2 single, 7 double, 4 twin
Bathrooms: 13 en suite

Lunch available
EM 1900 (LO 2130)
Parking for 44
CC: Amex, Barclaycard, Delta, Diners, Eurocard, Mastercard, Switch, Visa

B&B per night:
S £55.00–£55.00
D £85.00–£105.00

HB per person:
DY Max £76.00

OPEN All year round

Family-run country house hotel set in 5 acres of woodland and landscaped gardens. Specialises in home cooking using own produce.

⚠️↘️🔧🏡📞🖥️⬇️⚲📿🅂🖼️◐🍽️🛏️🍴40 🔍♿🅿️❤️✳️📍 SC ↘️ SP 🏨 T

MATFEN, Northumberland Map ref 5B2

★★★

MATFEN HALL
Matfen, Newcastle upon Tyne, NE20 0RH
T: (01661) 886500
F: (01661) 886055
E: info@matfenhall.com
I: www.matfenhall.com

B&B per night:
S £88.00–£128.00
D £126.00–£215.00

HB per person:
DY £79.00–£124.00

OPEN All year round

Built in the 1830s Matfen Hall has been lovingly restored into a luxurious hotel, which lies in the heart of Northumberland's most beautiful countryside. With panoramic views over its 18-hole golf course, the hotel offers splendid facilities, combining modern features with traditional opulence whilst retaining all its original character.

Bedrooms: 1 single, 23 double, 6 twin; suite available
Bathrooms: 30 en suite, 2 public

Lunch available
EM 1830 (LO 2145)
Parking for 150
CC: Amex, Barclaycard, Delta, Mastercard, Switch, Visa

⚠️↘️🔧🏡📞🖥️⬇️⚲📿🅂🖼️📺◐🍽️🛏️🍴100 📍✳️✈️↘️ SP 🏨 T

MIDDLESBROUGH, Tees Valley Map ref 5C3 Tourist Information Centre Tel: (01642) 243425 or 264330

★★★ BALTIMORE HOTEL

250 Marton Road, Middlesbrough,
Cleveland TS4 2EZ
T: (01642) 224111
F: (01642) 226156
E: info@lincoln-group.co.uk

Close to the heart of both commercial and residential Middlesbrough and 1 mile from the central station. Teesside Airport 18 miles.

Bedrooms: 18 single,
5 double, 7 twin, 1 triple;
suite available
Bathrooms: 31 en suite

Lunch available
EM 1830 (LO 2245)
Parking for 50
CC: Amex, Barclaycard,
Delta, Diners, Mastercard,
Switch, Visa

B&B per night:
S £29.50–£60.50
D £59.00–£72.00

OPEN All year round

(CR)
Utell International

★★★ TAD CENTRE

Ormesby Road, Middlesbrough,
Cleveland TS3 7SF
T: (01642) 203000
E: info@tad-centre.co.uk
I: www.tad-centre.co.uk

Modern, purpose-built training and conference centre. Spacious accommodation furnished to a comfortable standard, with bar and restaurant facilities for delegates.

Bedrooms: 40 double
Bathrooms: 40 en suite

Lunch available
EM 1800 (LO 2130)
Parking for 112
CC: Amex, Barclaycard,
Delta, JCB, Mastercard,
Switch, Visa

B&B per night:
S Min £55.00
D Min £67.00

HB per person:
DY Min £65.00

OPEN All year round

(CR)
The Independents

THISTLE MIDDLESBROUGH

Rating
Applied For
Ad p15

Fry Street, Middlesbrough,
Cleveland TS1 1JH
T: (01642) 232000
F: (01642) 232655

This brand new hotel offers luxury accommodation, ideally located within easy reach of the historic fishing towns of Whitby and Redcar. Car parking available.

Bedrooms: 100 single,
78 twin, 2 triple; suites
available
Bathrooms: 180 en suite

Lunch available
EM 1900 (LO 2200)
Parking for 40
CC: Amex, Barclaycard,
Delta, Diners, Eurocard,
Mastercard, Switch, Visa

B&B per night:
S £97.00–£120.00
D £97.00–£120.00

OPEN All year round

(CR)
Thistle Hotels/Utell
International

NEWCASTLE UPON TYNE, Tyne and Wear Map ref 5C2 Tourist Information Centre Tel: (0191) 277 8000 or 214 4422 (located in airport)

★★ CAIRN HOTEL

97-103 Osborne Road, Jesmond,
Newcastle upon Tyne, NE2 2TJ
T: (0191) 281 1358
F: (0191) 281 9031
E: arvanhanda@aol.com
I: www.cairn-hotels.co.uk

The Cairn is situated in select Jesmond, close to the Metro and bus route and near the city centre. All rooms are en suite. Ample parking.

Bedrooms: 6 single,
24 double, 14 twin,
6 triple
Bathrooms: 50 en suite

EM 1800 (LO 2115)
Parking for 17
CC: Amex, Barclaycard,
Delta, Diners, Eurocard,
Mastercard, Solo, Switch,
Visa, Visa Electron

B&B per night:
S £45.00–£59.00
D £55.00–£70.00

OPEN All year round

(CR)
The Independents

★★★★

THE COPTHORNE NEWCASTLE

The Close, Quayside, Newcastle upon Tyne,
Tyne & Wear NE1 3RT
T: (0191) 222 0333
F: (0191) 230 1111
E: sales.newcastle@mill-cop.com
I: www.stay.with-us.com

Situated on the banks of the Tyne, all 156 bedrooms, restaurants and bars boast superb views. Guests benefit from complimentary use of "Spirit" leisure club and free on-site car parking. Newcastle International Airport, railway station and motorway are all within easy reach.

Bedrooms: 131 double,
25 twin
Bathrooms: 156 en suite

Lunch available
EM 1830 (LO 2215)
Parking for 180
CC: Amex, Barclaycard,
Delta, Diners, Eurocard,
JCB, Mastercard, Switch,
Visa

B&B per night:
S £69.50–£193.50
D £99.00–£207.00

OPEN All year round

(CR)
Utell International

REGIONAL TOURIST BOARD The ⋀ symbol in an establishment entry indicates that it is a Regional Tourist Board member.

NEWCASTLE UPON TYNE continued

★★ **GROSVENOR HOTEL**

Grosvenor Road, Jesmond,
Newcastle upon Tyne, NE2 2RR
T: (0191) 281 0543
F: (0191) 281 9217
E: info@grosvenor-hotel.com
I: www.grosvenor-hotel.com

Bedrooms: 14 single,
11 double, 25 twin,
3 triple
Bathrooms: 51 en suite,
2 private, 1 public

Lunch available
EM 1730 (LO 2130)
Parking for 10
CC: Amex, Barclaycard,
Delta, Diners, Eurocard,
JCB, Maestro, Mastercard,
Switch, Visa

B&B per night:
S £30.00–£50.00
D £45.00–£70.00

HB per person:
DY £40.00–£60.00

OPEN All year round

Friendly hotel in quiet residential suburb, offering a wide range of facilities. Close to city centre. Bar restaurant, 24-hour service. Easy parking.

🄰🅋🦓⚄🔌📭☎🖥️🖐️🍷📶🛈Ⓢ✂️🅜📺🌙🍴🖨️🚪🍽️100 🐾 SP T

★

HADRIAN LODGE HOTEL

Hadrian Road, Wallsend,
Newcastle upon Tyne, Tyne & Wear
NE28 6HH
T: (0191) 262 7733
F: (0191) 263 0714
I: www.hadrianlodgehotel.co.uk

B&B per night:
S £39.00–£39.00
D £45.00–£45.00

OPEN All year round

ⓒⓡ
Minotel

Very friendly, comfortable hotel, close to the lively nightlife of Newcastle city centre and Whitley Bay. The superb Metro system is accessed opposite the hotel and we are next to the New Roman Fort visitors' centre at Segedunum.

Bedrooms: 8 single,
8 double, 7 twin, 1 triple
Bathrooms: 24 en suite

Lunch available
EM 1700 (LO 2130)
Parking for 60
CC: Amex, Barclaycard,
Delta, Eurocard, JCB,
Mastercard, Solo, Switch,
Visa, Visa Electron

🄰🅋🦓⚄☎🔌🖐️🍷🛈Ⓢ✂️🅜📺🌙🍴🖨️🚪🍽️10 🐾 🐕 🐎 🐾 SP T

★★ **OSBORNE HOTEL**

13-15 Osborne Road, Jesmond,
Newcastle upon Tyne, NE2 2AE
T: (0191) 281 3385
F: (0191) 281 7717

Bedrooms: 14 single,
4 double, 3 twin, 1 triple
Bathrooms: 22 en suite

EM 1700 (LO 2230)
Parking for 8
CC: Amex, Barclaycard,
Delta, JCB, Mastercard,
Solo, Switch, Visa

B&B per night:
S £35.00–£39.50
D £50.00–£59.50

OPEN All year round

Well-appointed owner-managed hotel, with emphasis on personal attention. Convenient for city centre, near Metro and bus services. En suite bedrooms, bar and restaurant.

🄰🅋🦓⚄☎📭🖐️🍷🛈Ⓢ✂️🅜📺🌙🍴🖨️SC 🐾 SP T

★★★
Silver
Award

SURTEES HOTEL

12-16 Dean Street,
Newcastle upon Tyne, NE1 1PG
T: (0191) 261 7771
F: (0191) 230 1322
I: www.scoot.co.uk/surteeshotel

Bedrooms: 12 single,
9 double, 6 twin
Bathrooms: 27 en suite

Lunch available
EM 1700 (LO 2230)
CC: Amex, Barclaycard,
Delta, Diners, Mastercard,
Switch, Visa

B&B per night:
S £59.50–£79.50
D £79.50–£89.50

OPEN All year round

City-centre hotel within walking distance of Eldon Square, the Quayside and station, with a 24-hour multi-storey car park adjacent. Cocktail and public bar, restaurant and nightclub.

🄰🅋🦓⚄☎📭🖐️🍷🛈Ⓢ🅜📺🌙📅🍴🖨️🚪🍽️120 🔆 🐎 🐾 SP T 🌐

Rating
Applied For
Ad p15

THISTLE NEWCASTLE

Neville Street,
Newcastle upon Tyne, NE99 1AH
T: (0191) 232 2471
F: (0191) 232 1285
E: newcastle@thistle.co.uk

Bedrooms: 54 single,
24 double, 36 twin,
1 triple
Bathrooms: 115 en suite

Lunch available
EM 1830 (LO 2145)
Parking for 25
CC: Amex, Barclaycard,
Delta, Diners, Eurocard,
JCB, Mastercard, Solo,
Switch, Visa

B&B per night:
S £111.00–£135.00
D £122.00–£145.00

OPEN All year round

ⓒⓡ
Thistle Hotels/Utell International

Recently restored 19thC hotel opposite the station. Wood-panelled restaurant and original decorative ceilings. Close to the city centre and shopping areas. Newcastle Airport, 8 miles.

🦓⚄☎📭🖐️🍷🛈📺🌙📅🍴🖨️🚪🍽️130 🐾 SP 🎹 🌐

QUALITY ASSURANCE SCHEME
Star ratings and awards are explained at the back of this guide.

OTTERBURN, Northumberland Map ref 5B1 *Tourist Information Centre Tel: (01830) 520093*

★★★
Silver
Award

THE TOWER

Otterburn, Newcastle upon Tyne,
NE19 1NS
T: (01830) 520620
F: (01830) 520620
E: reservations@otterburntower.co.
uk
I: www.otterburntower.co.uk

Bedrooms: 2 single,
10 double, 4 twin,
1 triple; suite available
Bathrooms: 17 en suite

Lunch available
EM 1900 (LO 2130)
Parking for 40
CC: Barclaycard, Delta,
Eurocard, JCB, Maestro,
Mastercard, Solo, Switch,
Visa, Visa Electron

B&B per night:
D £70.00–£85.00

OPEN All year round

Grade II Listed 13thC country house fronted by formal gardens and surrounded by pastures, rivers and woodland.

🅰🐎⚓🏨☎🖥📺♿🍴🛎🔥🏷⑮♿🎯◐🛏⑭📷🍴🍹100 ♦ ∪ ⤵ ► ❄ 🚗 🐾 SP 🎴

SEDGEFIELD, Durham Map ref 5C2

★★★

HARDWICK HALL HOTEL

Sedgefield, Stockton-on-Tees,
Cleveland TS21 2EH
T: (01740) 620253
F: (01740) 622771

Bedrooms: 16 double,
1 twin
Bathrooms: 17 en suite

Lunch available
EM 1930 (LO 2200)
Parking for 200
CC: Amex, Barclaycard,
Delta, Diners, Eurocard,
Mastercard, Solo, Switch,
Visa

B&B per night:
S Max £68.00
D Max £78.00

HB per person:
DY Max £48.00

OPEN All year round

The former home of Lord Boyne standing in 22 acres of lovely parkland. Extensive redevelopment due for completion June 2001 includes 36 additional luxury bedrooms.

🅰🐎🏨☎🖥📺♿🔥🏷⑮♿ TV 🖥📷🍴🍹100 ∪►✔❄🐾 SP 🎴 T

TYNEMOUTH, Tyne and Wear Map ref 5C2

★★★

GRAND HOTEL

Grand Parade, Tynemouth,
North Shields, Tyne and Wear
NE30 4ER
T: (0191) 293 6666
F: (0191) 293 6665
E: info@grand-hotel.demon.co.uk
I: www.grand-hotel.demon.co.uk

Bedrooms: 33 double,
1 twin, 10 triple, 1 family
room
Bathrooms: 45 en suite

Lunch available
EM 1830 (LO 2200)
Parking for 28
CC: Amex, Barclaycard,
Delta, Diners, Eurocard,
Mastercard, Switch, Visa

B&B per night:
S £60.00–£90.00
D £65.00–£160.00

HB per person:
DY £75.00–£100.00

OPEN All year round

Built in 1872 as a summer residence for the Duchess of Northumberland, this Victorian hotel is located on a cliff top overlooking Tynemouth Longsands beach.

🅰🐎🏨☎🖥📺♿🔥🏷⑮♿ TV ◐🛏📷📷🍴🍹150 🐕 ✈ 🐾 SP 🎴 T

WHITLEY BAY, Tyne and Wear Map ref 5C2 *Tourist Information Centre Tel: (0191) 200 8535*

★★

THE ESPLANADE HOTEL

The Esplanade, Whitley Bay, Tyne and Wear
NE26 2AW
T: (0191) 252 1111
F: (0191) 252 0101
E: esplanade.hotel@btinternet.com
I: www.esplanade-hotel.freeserve.co.uk

B&B per night:
S £45.00–£60.00
D £55.00–£70.00

OPEN All year round

Seafront hotel originally built in 1908 in Edwardian splendour. Interior recently completely refurbished to ultra-modern standards, with a Scandinavian blonde ash accent throughout. First floor seaview restaurant offering good food at reasonable prices. Excellent base for exploring Northumbria, whether for business or pleasure.

Bedrooms: 1 single,
15 double, 29 twin,
5 family rooms
Bathrooms: 50 en suite

Lunch available
EM 1800 (LO 2100)
CC: Amex, Barclaycard,
Delta, Diners, Eurocard,
Mastercard, Solo, Switch,
Visa

🅰🐎☎🖥📺♿🔥🏷⑮♿ TV ◐🛏📷🍴🍹30 SP T

QUALITY ASSURANCE SCHEME

Star ratings and awards were correct at the time of going to press but are subject to change. Please check at the time of booking.

WHITLEY BAY continued

★★★

REX HOTEL

The Promenade, Whitley Bay,
Tyne and Wear NE26 2RL
T: (0191) 252 3201
F: (0191) 251 4663
E: rex-hotel.freeserve.co.uk
I: www.rex-hotel.freeserve.co.uk

Bedrooms: 13 single, 20 double, 32 twin, 2 triple, 2 family rooms
Bathrooms: 69 en suite

Lunch available
EM 1900 (LO 2130)
Parking for 30
CC: Amex, Barclaycard, Delta, Diners, Eurocard, JCB, Mastercard, Solo, Switch, Visa

B&B per night:
S £39.00–£65.00
D £65.00–£75.00

HB per person:
DY £49.00–£85.00

OPEN All year round

Situated on the promenade with magnificent sea views. Fine restaurant and friendly service. Public bars and private residents' lounge.

150

★★★

WINDSOR HOTEL

South Parade, Whitley Bay,
Tyne and Wear NE26 2RF
T: (0191) 2518888
F: (0191) 2970272
E: info@windsor-hotel.demon.co.uk

Bedrooms: 3 single, 16 double, 43 twin
Bathrooms: 62 en suite

Lunch available
EM 1830 (LO 2200)
Parking for 20
CC: Amex, Barclaycard, Delta, Diners, Eurocard, Mastercard, Solo, Switch, Visa

B&B per night:
S £45.00–£65.00
D £55.00–£70.00

HB per person:
DY £43.00–£80.00

OPEN All year round

Privately owned hotel with beautifully appointed bedrooms, situated between the seafront and town centre. First choice for business or pleasure.

20

USE YOUR *i*s

There are more than 550 Tourist Information Centres throughout England offering friendly help with accommodation and holiday ideas as well as suggestions of places to visit and things to do. There may well be a centre in your home town which can help you before you set out. You'll find addresses in the local Phone Book.

*A brief guide to the main Towns and Villages
offering accommodation in* NORTHUMBRIA

A ALNMOUTH, NORTHUMBERLAND -
Quiet village with pleasant old buildings, at
the mouth of the River Aln where extensive
dunes and sands stretch along Alnmouth Bay.
18th C granaries, some converted to dwellings,
still stand.

B BAMBURGH, NORTHUMBERLAND -
Village with a spectacular red sandstone castle
standing 150ft above the sea. On the village
green the magnificent Norman church stands
opposite a museum containing mementoes of
the heroine Grace Darling.

● BARNARD CASTLE, DURHAM - High over
the Tees, a thriving market town with a busy
market square. Bernard Baliol's 12th C castle
(now ruins) stands nearby. The Bowes Museum,
housed in a grand 19th C French chateau,
holds fine paintings and furniture. Nearby are
some magnificent buildings.

● BELLINGHAM, NORTHUMBERLAND -
Set in the beautiful valley of the North Tyne
close to Kielder Forest, Kielder Water and
lonely moorland below the Cheviots. The
church has an ancient stone wagon roof
fortified in the 18th C with buttresses.

C CHOLLERFORD, NORTHUMBERLAND -
At the crossing of the military road and
Hadrian's Wall over the North Tyne River and
close to an important fort. Chesters Roman
fort with the remains of its bridge, its living
quarters and its bath houses stands in the park
of an 18th C mansion.

● CORNHILL-ON-TWEED,
NORTHUMBERLAND - Pretty border village on
the River Tweed which divides it from
Coldstream, of Regimental Guards fame. This
area is notable for its connections with the
Battle of Flodden Field, the last battle to be
fought between England and Scotland in 1513.

● CROOK, DURHAM - Pleasant market town
sometimes referred to as "the gateway to
Weardale". The town's shopping centre
surrounds a large, open green, attractively laid
out with lawns and flowerbeds around the
Devil's Stone, a relic from the Ice Age.

D DARLINGTON, DURHAM - Largest town in
County Durham, standing on the River Skerne
and home of the earliest passenger railway
which first ran to Stockton in 1825. Now the
home of a railway museum. Originally a
prosperous market town occupying the site of
an Anglo-Saxon settlement, it still holds an
open market.

● DURHAM, DURHAM - Ancient city with its
Norman castle and cathedral, now a World
Heritage site, set on a bluff high over the Wear.
A market and university town and regional
centre, spreading beyond the market-place on
both banks of the river.

H HEXHAM, NORTHUMBERLAND -
Old coaching and market town near Hadrian's
Wall. Since pre-Norman times a weekly market
has been held in the centre with its market-
place and abbey park, and the richly-furnished
12th C abbey church has a superb Anglo-
Saxon crypt.

● HOLY ISLAND, NORTHUMBERLAND -
Still an idyllic retreat, tiny island and fishing
village and cradle of northern Christianity. It is
approached from the mainland at low water by
a causeway. The clifftop castle (National Trust)
was restored by Sir Edwin Lutyens.

L LONGFRAMLINGTON,
NORTHUMBERLAND - Pleasant village with
an interesting church of the Transitional style.
On Hall Hill are the remains of a camp with
triple entrenchment. Brinkburn Priory is nearby.

M MIDDLESBROUGH, TEES VALLEY -
Boom-town of the mid 19th C, today's Teesside
industrial and conference town has a modern
shopping complex and predominantly modern
buildings. An engineering miracle of the early
20th C is the Transporter Bridge which
replaced an old ferry.

N NEWCASTLE UPON TYNE, TYNE AND
WEAR - Commercial and cultural centre of the
North East, with a large indoor shopping
centre, Quayside market, museums and
theatres which offer an annual 6 week season
by the Royal Shakespeare Company. Norman
castle keep, medieval alleys, old Guildhall.

O OTTERBURN, NORTHUMBERLAND -
Small village set at the meeting of the River
Rede with Otter Burn, the site of the Battle of
Otterburn in 1388. A peaceful tradition
continues in the sale of Otterburn tweeds in
this beautiful region, which is ideal for
exploring the Border country and the Cheviots.

R RUSHYFORD, DURHAM - Small village on
the old Great North Road.

S SEDGEFIELD, DURHAM - Ancient market
town, a centre for hunting and steeplechasing,
with a racecourse nearby. Handsome 18th C
buildings include the town council's former
Georgian mansion and the rectory. The church
with its magnificent spire has 17th C wood-
carvings by a local craftsman.

● STOCKTON-ON-TEES, TEES VALLEY -
Teesside town first developed in the 19th C
around the ancient market town with its broad
main street which has been the site of a
regular market since 1310. Green Dragon Yard
has a Georgian theatre and there is a railway
heritage trail around the town.

T TYNEMOUTH, TYNE AND WEAR -
At the mouth of the Tyne, old Tyneside resort
adjoining North Shields with its fish quay and
market. The pier is overlooked by the gaunt
ruins of a Benedictine priory and a castle.
Splendid sands, amusement centre and park.

W WHITLEY BAY, TYNE AND WEAR -
Traditional seaside resort with long beaches
of sand and rock and many pools to explore.
St Mary's lighthouse is open to the public.

CHECK THE MAPS

The colour maps at the front of this guide show
all the cities, towns and villages for which you will
find accommodation entries. Refer to the town
index to find the page on which they are listed.

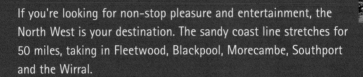
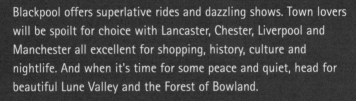

NORTH WEST

If you're looking for non-stop pleasure and entertainment, the North West is your destination. The sandy coast line stretches for 50 miles, taking in Fleetwood, Blackpool, Morecambe, Southport and the Wirral.

Blackpool offers superlative rides and dazzling shows. Town lovers will be spoilt for choice with Lancaster, Chester, Liverpool and Manchester all excellent for shopping, history, culture and nightlife. And when it's time for some peace and quiet, head for beautiful Lune Valley and the Forest of Bowland.

The annual Lancashire food festival in early March is an excellent opportunity to taste local delicacies, including Lancashire Hotpot and Black Pudding.

The counties of
Cheshire, Greater Manchester, Lancashire,
Merseyside and the High Peak District of
Derbyshire

FOR MORE INFORMATION CONTACT:
North West Tourist Board
Swan House, Swan Meadow Road,
Wigan Pier, Wigan WN3 5BB
Tel: (01942) 821222
Fax: (01942) 820002
Internet: www.visitnorthwest.com

The Pictures:
1 Blackpool Pleasure Beach;
2 Knowsley Safari Park,
   Merseyside;
3 Japanese Garden, Tatton Park.

Where to Go in the North West - see pages 86-89
Where to Stay in the North West - see pages 90-101

Whilst in the
NORTH WEST ...

You will find hundreds of interesting places to visit during your stay, just some of which are listed in these pages.

Contact any Tourist Information Centre in the region for more ideas on days out in the North West.

Arley Hall and Gardens

Arley, Northwich, Cheshire CW9 6NA
Tel: (01565) 777353
Early Victorian building set in 12 acres of magnificent gardens. 15thC tithe barn and a unique collection of watercolours of the area.

Astley Hall Museum and Art Gallery

Astley Park, Chorley, Lancashire PR7 1NP
Tel: (01257) 515555
Dates from 1580 with subsequent additions. Unique collections of furniture including a fine Elizabethan bed and the famous Shovel Board Table.

The Beatles Story

Albert Dock, Liverpool, Merseyside L3 4AA
Tel: (0151) 709 1963
Liverpool's award-winning visitor attraction with a replica of the original Cavern Club. Available for private parties.

Beeston Castle

Beeston, Tarporley, Cheshire CW6 9TX
Tel: (01829) 260464
A ruined 13thC castle situated on top of the Peckforton Hills, with views of the surrounding countryside. Exhibitions are held featuring the castle's history.

Blackpool Sea Life Centre

The Promenade, Blackpool, Lancashire FY1 5AA
Tel: (01253) 622445
Tropical sharks up to 2.5m (8ft) in length housed in a 100,000-gallon water display, with an underwater walkway. The new 'Lost City of Atlantis' is back.

Blackpool Tower

The Promenade, Blackpool, Lancashire FY1 4BJ
Tel: (01253) 622242
Inside the Tower you will find the Tower Ballroom, a circus, entertainment for the children, the Tower Top Ride and Undersea World.

Boat Museum

Ellesmere Port, Cheshire CH5 4FW
Tel: (0151) 355 5017
Over 50 historic craft, the largest floating collection in the world. Restored buildings, traditional cottages, workshops, steam engines, boat trips, shop and cafe.

CATALYST: The Museum of the Chemical Industry

Widnes, Cheshire WA8 0DF
Tel: (0151) 420 1121
Catalyst is the award-winning family day out where science and technology come alive.

Chester Zoo
Upton-by-Chester, Cheshire CH2 1LH
Tel: (01244) 380280
One of Europe's leading conservation zoos with over 5,000 animals in spacious and natural enclosures. Now featuring the new 'Twilight Zone'.

Croxteth Hall and Country Park
Liverpool, Merseyside L12 0HB
Tel: (0151) 228 5311
An Edwardian stately home set in 500 acres of countryside (woodlands and pasture), featuring a Victorian walled garden and animal collection.

Dunham Massey Hall Park and Garden
Altrincham, Cheshire WA14 4SJ
Tel: (0161) 941 1025
An 18thC mansion in a 250-acre wooded deer park. Over 30 rooms open to the public. Collections of furniture, paintings and silver. Restaurant and shop.

East Lancashire Railway
Bury, Greater Manchester BL9 0EY
Tel: (0161) 764 7790
Thirteen kilometres (8 miles) of preserved railway operated principally by steam. Traction Transport Museum close by.

Frontierland Western Theme Park
Promenade, Morecambe, Lancashire LA4 4DG
Tel: (01524) 410024
Over 40 thrilling rides and attractions including the Texas Tornado, Polo Tower, Perculator and Stampede rollercoaster. The indoor Fun House complex features live shows in summer.

Gawsworth Hall
Gawsworth, Macclesfield, Cheshire SK11 9RN
Tel: (01260) 223456
Beautiful Tudor half-timbered manor-house with tilting ground. Pictures, sculpture and furniture on display. Open-air theatre.

Granada Studios
Water Street, Manchester M60 9EA
Tel: (0161) 832 9090
Europe's only major television theme park, providing a unique insight into the fascinating world behind the television screen.

Jodrell Bank Science Centre, Planetarium and Arboretum
Lower Withington, Macclesfield, Cheshire SK11 9DL
Tel: (01477) 571339
Exhibition and interactive exhibits on astronomy, space, energy and the environment. Planetarium and the world-famous Lovell telescope, plus a 35-acre arboretum.

Knowsley Safari Park
Prescot, Merseyside L34 4AN
Tel: (0151) 430 9009
An 8km (5 mile) safari through 500 acres of rolling countryside. See the world's wildest animals roaming free. Picnic area, shops, cafeteria.

Lady Lever Art Gallery
Port Sunlight Village, Higher Bebington, Wirral CH62 5EQ
Tel: (0151) 478 4136
The first Lord Leverhulme's magnificent collection of British paintings dated 1750-1900. British furniture, Wedgwood pottery and oriental porcelain.

Lancaster Castle
Shire Hall, Castle Parade, Lancaster, Lancashire LA1 1YJ
Tel: (01524) 64998
Shire Hall has a collection of coats of arms, a crown court, a grand jury room, a 'drop room' and dungeons. External tour of the castle.

Lyme Park
Disley, Stockport, Greater Manchester SK12 2NX
Tel: (01663) 762023
A National Trust country estate set in 1,377 acres of moorland, woodland and park. This magnificent house has 17 acres of historic gardens.

The Pictures:
1 Little Moreton, Congleton, Cheshire;
2 Bridgewater Hall, Manchester;
3 Peckforton, Cheshire;
4 Blackpool Beach;
5 Rural Cheshire, Marbury;
6 Liverpool Football Club Stadium.

Southport Zoo and Conservation Park

Princes Park, Southport, Merseyside PR8 1RX
Tel: (01704) 538102
Lion, snow leopards, chimpanzees, monkeys, penguins, giant tortoise, reptile house, aquarium and much more. Snack bar, gift shop, picnic area.

Tate Gallery, Liverpool

Albert Dock, Liverpool, Merseyside L3 4BB
Tel: (0151) 702 7400
The National Collection of Modern Art is housed here in a converted warehouse.

Tatton Park

Knutsford, Cheshire WA16 6QN
Tel: (01625) 534400
Historic mansion with a 50-acre garden, traditional working farm, medieval manor-house and a 2,000 acre deer park. Sailing and outdoor centre, and an adventure playground.

Macclesfield Silk Museum

The Heritage Centre, Macclesfield, Cheshire SK11 6UT
Tel: (01625) 613210
Tells the story of the silk industry in Macclesfield. Features textiles, garments, models and room settings.

Merseyside Maritime Museum

Albert Dock, Liverpool, Merseyside L3 4AQ
Tel: (0151) 478 4499
Set in the heart of Liverpool's historic waterfront. The museum holds craft demonstrations, working displays and permanent galleries.

The Museum of Science & Industry in Manchester

Castlefield, Manchester M3 4FP
Tel: (0161) 832 2244
Based in the world's oldest passenger railway station with working exhibits which bring the past to life. The galleries will amaze, amuse and entertain.

Wigan Pier

Wallgate, Wigan, Lancashire WN3 4EF
Tel: (01942) 323666
Wigan Pier combines interaction with displays and reconstructions plus the Wigan Pier Theatre Company. Facilities include shops and a cafe.

Wildfowl and Wetland Trust

Martin Mere, Burscough, Lancashire L40 0TA
Tel: (01704) 895181
A 376-acre wild area, 20-acre lake and 45 acres of gardens. Rare and exotic ducks, geese, swans and flamingoes. Pantry, gift shop, art/craft gallery.

Norton Priory Museum and Gardens

Runcorn, Cheshire WA7 1SX
Tel: (01928) 569895
Medieval priory remains, purpose-built museum, St Christopher's statue, sculpture trail and award-winning walled garden, all set in 39 acres of beautiful gardens.

Rufford Old Hall

Rufford, Ormskirk, Lancashire L40 1SG
Tel: (01704) 821254
One of the finest 16thC buildings in Lancashire with a magnificent hall, particularly noted for its immense moveable screen.

Find out more about the
NORTH WEST ...

Further information about holidays and attractions
in the North West is available from:

NORTH WEST TOURIST BOARD

Swan House, Swan Meadow Road, Wigan Pier, Wigan WN3 5BB.

Tel: (01942) 821222

Fax: (01942) 820002

Internet: www.visitnorthwest.com

The following publications are available free from the North West Tourist Board:

Best of the North West

a guide to information on the region including hotels, self-catering establishments, caravan and camping parks. Also includes attractions, major events, shops and restaurants

Discovery Map

a non-accommodation guide, A1 folded to A4 map including list of visitor attractions, what to see and where to go

Bed and Breakfast Map

forming part of a family of maps for England, this guide provides information on bed and breakfast establishments in the North West region

Freedom

forming part of a family of publications about caravan and camping parks in the north of England

Stay on a Farm

a guide to farm accommodation in the north of England

Group Travel Planner

a guide to choosing the right accommodation, attraction or venue for group organisers

Venues

a 6-monthly newsletter about conference venues in the North West region

Schools Out

a 6-monthly newsletter aimed at schools providing information about where to go and what to see

The Pictures:
1 Healey Dell, Rochdale;
2 Pavilion Gardens, Buxton;
3 Bridgewater Canal, Manchester;
4 Lytham, Lancashire;
5 The Rows, Chester;
6 Barca Cafe Bar, Manchester;
7 Albert Dock, Liverpool.

Getting to the
NORTH WEST ...

BY ROAD:

Motorways intersect within the region which has the best road network in the country. Travelling north or south use the M6 and east or west the M62.

BY RAIL:

Most North West coastal resorts are connected to InterCity routes with trains from many parts of the country and there are through trains to major cities and towns.

Where to stay in the

NORTH WEST

Accommodation entries in this region are listed in alphabetical order of place name, and then in alphabetical order of establishment.

Map references refer to the colour location maps at the front of this guide. The first number indicates the map to use; the letter and number which follow refer to the grid reference on the map.

At-a-glance symbols at the end of each accommodation entry give useful information about services and facilities. A key to symbols can be found inside the back cover flap. Keep this open for easy reference.

A brief description of the towns and villages offering accommodation in the entries which follow, can be found at the end of this section.

A complete listing of all English Tourism Council assessed hotels appears at the back of this guide.

ALTRINCHAM, Greater Manchester Map ref 4A2 *Tourist Information Centre Tel: (0161) 912 5931*

★★

OASIS HOTEL

46-48 Barrington Road, Altrincham,
Cheshire WA14 1HN
T: (0161) 928 4523 & 929 9046
F: (0161) 928 1055
E: enquiries@oasishotel.co.uk
I: www.oasishotel.co.uk

B&B per night:
S £32.00–£38.00
D £42.00–£50.00

HB per person:
DY £25.00–£48.00

OPEN All year round

Independent hotel, ideally situated at Altrincham, within easy reach of Manchester Airport and city centre. Convenient for public transport (Metrolink) and motorways (M56, M6, M60). En suite rooms with colour TV, telephone and coffee-making facilities. Chinese restaurant providing high quality Chinese/ English meals. Lounge bar with Sky TV. Full English breakfast.

Bedrooms: 14 single,
10 double, 6 twin,
3 triple
Bathrooms: 32 en suite,
1 private

EM 1730 (LO 2230)
Parking for 25
CC: Amex, Barclaycard,
Delta, Diners, Mastercard,
Solo, Switch, Visa, Visa
Electron

🛇🐾♿🖥️🖵🖐️🍷ⓈⱮ📺🏧🅿🍽️150 ☼🛪🐾Ⓣ

TOWN INDEX

This can be found at the back of this guide. If you know where you want to stay, the index will give you the page number listing accommodation in your chosen town, city or village.

ALTRINCHAM continued

★★★

WOODLAND PARK HOTEL
Wellington Road, Timperley,
Altrincham, Cheshire WA15 7RG
T: (0161) 928 8631
F: (0161) 941 2821
E: info@woodlandpark.co.uk
I: www.woodlandpark.co.uk

Bedrooms: 14 single,
23 double, 7 twin,
1 triple, 1 family room
Bathrooms: 46 en suite

Lunch available
EM 1900 (LO 2200)
Parking for 150
CC: Amex, Barclaycard,
Delta, Diners, Eurocard,
Mastercard, Switch, Visa

B&B per night:
S £46.00–£90.00
D £62.00–£135.00

OPEN All year round

Elegant, family-owned country house hotel set in a secluded residential area of Altrincham. Refurbished to very high standards.

150

BLACKBURN, Lancashire Map ref 4A1 *Tourist Information Centre Tel: (01254) 53277*

★★★
Gold
Award

NORTHCOTE MANOR HOTEL
Northcote Road, Old Langho,
Blackburn, BB6 8BE
T: (01254) 240555
F: (01254) 246568
E: admin@ncotemanor.demon.co.
uk
I: ncotemanor.demon.co.uk

Bedrooms: 10 double,
4 twin
Bathrooms: 14 en suite

Lunch available
EM 1900 (LO 2130)
Parking for 50
CC: Amex, Barclaycard,
Delta, Mastercard, Switch,
Visa, Visa Electron

B&B per night:
S £80.00–£100.00
D £90.00–£130.00

OPEN All year round

Privately-owned refurbished manor house with outstanding restaurant, offering the best in hospitality. 9 miles from M6 junction 31, off A59. Special gourmet breaks.

50

BLACKPOOL, Lancashire Map ref 4A1 *Tourist Information Centre Tel: (01253) 478222*

★★

PARK HOUSE HOTEL
308 North Promenade, Blackpool,
FY1 2HA
T: (01253) 620081
F: (01253) 290181

Bedrooms: 13 single,
33 double, 35 twin,
14 triple, 8 family rooms
Bathrooms: 103 en suite,
3 public

Lunch available
EM 1800 (LO 2030)
Parking for 82
CC: Amex, Barclaycard,
Delta, Eurocard,
Mastercard, Switch, Visa

B&B per night:
S £26.00–£37.00
D £59.00–£87.00

HB per person:
DY £29.50–£41.00

OPEN All year round

Beautifully situated on promenade within easy reach of Winter Gardens, piers, golf-courses, town centre and Stanley Park.

160

CHESTER, Cheshire Map ref 4A2 *Tourist Information Centre Tel: (01244) 402111*

★★★★★
Gold
Award

THE CHESTER GROSVENOR
Eastgate, Chester, CH1 1LT
T: (01244) 324024 & 895614
F: (01244) 313246
E: chesgrov@chestergrosvenor.co.
uk
I: www.chestergrosvenor.co.uk

Bedrooms: 85 double;
suites available
Bathrooms: 85 en suite

Lunch available
EM 1800 (LO 2230)
Parking for 600
CC: Amex, Barclaycard,
Delta, Diners, Eurocard,
JCB, Mastercard, Switch,
Visa

B&B per night:
S £170.00–£200.00
D £265.00–£310.00

OPEN All year round

Small Luxury Hotels

De luxe city-centre hotel, owned by the Duke of Westminster. Two highly-acclaimed restaurants, leisure facilities and outstanding service. Ideal for touring North Wales.

220

★★★★
Silver
Award

Country-house hotel with 48 individually designed bedrooms, all en suite, and award-winning restaurant. £2 million leisure spa and beauty retreat. Mollington Grange Golf Club, only 100 yards from the hotel.

CRABWALL MANOR HOTEL AND RESTAURANT

Parkgate Road, Mollington, Chester,
CH1 6NE
T: (01244) 851666
F: (01244) 851400
E: louise@crabwall.com
I: www.crabwall.com

Bedrooms: 4 double,
44 twin; suites available
Bathrooms: 48 en suite

Lunch available
EM 1900 (LO 2130)
Parking for 120
CC: Amex, Barclaycard,
Delta, Diners, Eurocard,
JCB, Mastercard, Switch,
Visa

B&B per night:
S £125.00–£125.00
D £150.00–£150.00

HB per person:
DY £115.00–£170.00

OPEN All year round

100

★★

CURZON HOTEL

52-54 Hough Green, Chester, CH4 8JQ
T: (01244) 678581
F: (01244) 680866
E: curzon.chester@virgin.net
I: www.chestercurzonhotel.co.uk

B&B per night:
S £45.00–£50.00
D £60.00–£75.00

HB per person:
DY £45.00–£55.00

OPEN All year round

The Curzon is a family run Victorian townhouse hotel. Unwind in the lounge bar and sample our excellent cuisine in the splendid restaurant. Sleep peacefully in one of the 16 individually designed guest rooms. There is ample private parking and we are within easy reach of the city centre.

Bedrooms: 9 double, 5 triple, 2 family rooms
Bathrooms: 16 en suite

EM 1900 (LO 2100)
Parking for 19
CC: Amex, Barclaycard, Delta, Eurocard, Mastercard, Switch, Visa

---

★★

DENE HOTEL

Hoole Road, Chester, CH2 3ND
T: (01244) 321165
F: (01244) 350277
E: denehotel@btconnect.com
I: www.denehotel.com

Bedrooms: 7 single, 25 double, 12 twin, 3 triple, 2 family rooms
Bathrooms: 49 en suite

Lunch available
EM 1730 (LO 2200)
Parking for 51
CC: Amex, Barclaycard, Delta, Eurocard, Maestro, Mastercard, Switch, Visa

B&B per night:
S £40.00–£55.00
D £50.00–£65.00

HB per person:
DY £35.00–£44.00

OPEN All year round

In own grounds, adjacent to Alexandra Park and 1 mile from city centre. Rooms for non-smokers. New Francs Brasserie. Ample parking.

★★★
Silver
Award

GREEN BOUGH HOTEL AND RESTAURANT

60 Hoole Road, Chester, CH2 3NL
T: (01244) 326241 & 07710 353370
F: (01244) 326265
E: greenboughhotel@cwcom.net
I: www.smoothhound.co.uk/hotels/greenbo.html

B&B per night:
S £49.50–£79.50
D £55.00–£120.00

HB per person:
DY £67.00–£87.50

OPEN All year round

A de luxe, family-run fully refurbished Victorian hotel with friendly, relaxed atmosphere. The owners and their staff are dedicated to giving quality service to guests. The hotel and lodge are tastefully decorated with many antique furnishings. The award-winning Fleur de Lys Restaurant is a must.

Bedrooms: 17 double, 1 twin
Bathrooms: 18 en suite

Lunch available
EM 1900 (LO 2100)
Parking for 19
CC: Amex, Barclaycard, Diners, Mastercard, Switch, Visa

★★★

GROSVENOR-PULFORD HOTEL

Wrexham Road, Pulford, Chester, CH4 9DG
T: (01244) 570560
F: (01244) 570809
E: enquiries@grosvenorpulfordhotel.co.uk
I: www.grosvenorpulfordhotel.co.uk

B&B per night:
S £67.50–£77.50
D £85.00–£95.00

HB per person:
DY £60.00–£70.00

OPEN All year round

Ideally located only minutes from Chester but within easy access to Wales and Snowdonia. 68 en suite bedrooms. Magnificent leisure club includes 18m pool, whirlpool, steam and sauna rooms, gymnasium, solarium and snooker room. First class function suite. Bar and restaurant serving a wide range of food from bar snacks to a la carte.

Bedrooms: 4 single, 39 double, 18 twin, 5 triple, 2 family rooms; suites available
Bathrooms: 68 en suite

Lunch available
EM 1800 (LO 2200)
Parking for 200
CC: Amex, Barclaycard, Delta, Diners, Eurocard, Mastercard, Solo, Switch, Visa, Visa Electron

CHESTER continued

★★★★ **QUEEN HOTEL**

City Road, Chester, CH1 3AH
T: (01244) 305000
F: (01244) 318483
E: richard.hopson-cossey@
principalhotels.co.uk
I: www.principalhotels.co.uk

Bedrooms: 9 single,
48 double, 60 twin,
10 triple; suite available
Bathrooms: 127 en suite

Lunch available
EM 1830 (LO 2130)
Parking for 100
CC: Amex, Barclaycard,
Delta, Diners, Eurocard,
Maestro, Mastercard,
Solo, Switch, Visa, Visa
Electron

B&B per night:
S £60.00–£95.00
D £70.00–£120.00

HB per person:
DY £68.00–£110.00

OPEN All year round

Fully modernised hotel that still retains an elegant Victorian air. It is close to the station and all amenities.

⏣280 🅿 Principal Hotels/Utell International

CLITHEROE, Lancashire Map ref 4A1 *Tourist Information Centre Tel: (01200) 425566*

★★ **SHIREBURN ARMS HOTEL**

Whalley Road, Hurst Green,
Clitheroe, BB7 9QJ
T: (01254) 826518
F: (01254) 826208
E: sales@shireburn-hotel.co.uk
I: www.shireburn-hotel.co.uk

Bedrooms: 1 single,
11 double, 3 twin,
2 triple, 1 family room
Bathrooms: 18 en suite

Lunch available
EM 1730 (LO 2130)
Parking for 80
CC: Amex, Barclaycard,
Delta, Eurocard, JCB,
Mastercard, Solo, Switch,
Visa

B&B per night:
S £45.00–£55.00
D £65.00–£85.00

HB per person:
DY £35.00–£40.00

OPEN All year round

16thC family-run hotel, with unrivalled views, renowned for food and comfort, log fires, real ale, bar food. Within easy reach of the motorway network.

⏣80 🅿 Minotel

FRODSHAM, Cheshire Map ref 4A2

★★★ **FOREST HILLS HOTEL**

Overton Hill, Frodsham,
Warrington, WA6 6HH
T: (01928) 735255
F: (01928) 735517
E: info@foresthillshotel.com
I: www.foresthillshotel.com

Bedrooms: 26 double,
23 twin, 8 family rooms
Bathrooms: 57 en suite

Lunch available
EM 1900 (LO 2145)
Parking for 356
CC: Amex, Barclaycard,
Delta, Diners, Mastercard,
Switch, Visa

B&B per night:
S £88.50–£99.50
D £99.50–£109.00

HB per person:
DY £55.00–£60.00

OPEN All year round

Modern hotel, with leisure complex, situated on top of Overton Hill with panoramic views over the Cheshire countryside. Excellent base for touring Chester, Merseyside and North Wales.

⏣200 🅿

GARSTANG, Lancashire Map ref 4A1 *Tourist Information Centre Tel: (01995) 602125*

★★★ **CROFTERS HOTEL**

A6, Cabus, Garstang, Preston,
PR3 1PH
T: (01995) 604128
F: (01995) 601646

Bedrooms: 1 single,
5 double, 9 twin, 4 triple
Bathrooms: 19 en suite

Lunch available
EM 1900 (LO 2200)
Parking for 200
CC: Amex, Barclaycard,
Delta, Diners, Eurocard,
JCB, Maestro, Mastercard,
Solo, Switch, Visa, Visa
Electron

B&B per night:
S £46.00–£53.00
D £58.00–£64.00

HB per person:
DY £42.00–£52.00

OPEN All year round

Family-owned and managed hotel with all modern facilities, situated midway between Preston and Lancaster.

⏣200 🅿

HAYDOCK, Merseyside Map ref 4A1

★★★★ **THISTLE HAYDOCK**

Ad p15

Penny Lane, Haydock, St Helens,
WA11 9SG
T: (01942) 272000
F: (01942) 711092
E: haydock@thistle.co.uk
I: www.thistlehotels.com

Bedrooms: 2 single,
84 double, 40 twin,
13 triple; suites available
Bathrooms: 139 en suite

Lunch available
EM 1900 (LO 2200)
Parking for 180
CC: Amex, Barclaycard,
Delta, Diners, Eurocard,
JCB, Mastercard, Solo,
Switch, Visa, Visa Electron

B&B per night:
S £123.00–£126.00
D £138.00–£162.00

OPEN All year round

Utell International/
Thistle Hotels

This elegant Georgian-style hotel is set in 11 acres of formal gardens. Ideally located for both business and pleasure, it is found just minutes from the M6.

⏣300 🅿

MAP REFERENCES
Map references apply to the colour maps at the front of this guide.

★★

LONGVIEW HOTEL AND RESTAURANT

Manchester Road, Knutsford, WA16 0LX
T: (01565) 632119
F: (01565) 652402
E: longview_hotel@compuserve.com
I: www.longviewhotel@freeserve.com

B&B per night:
S £49.50–£79.50
D £68.50–£130.00

OPEN All year round

Friendly hotel of character, with cosy cellar bar, open log fires and high quality en suite bedrooms. Comfortable, relaxed dining room offers a value for money menu. Ideally situated overlooking heath, only a short stroll from Knutsford's many good restaurants and pubs. Close to Manchester, its airport and M6 motorway.

Bedrooms: 5 single, 17 double, 4 twin; suites available
Bathrooms: 26 en suite

EM 1830 (LO 2100)
Parking for 17
CC: Amex, Barclaycard, Diners, Mastercard, Visa

ⓐⓑⓒ 10 ⓓⓔ SP T

★★★★

MERE COURT HOTEL

Mere, Knutsford, WA16 0RW
T: (01565) 831000
F: (01565) 831001
E: sales@merecourt.co.uk
I: www.merecourt.co.uk

B&B per night:
S £60.00–£125.00
D £70.00–£140.00

OPEN All year round

Newly opened country house hotel. Built as a private residence in 1903 but now lovingly and skilfully restored to a fine country house hotel standing in 7 acres with a private lake. The main house offers 4-poster room and suites, some with double jacuzzi spa baths. Located 10 minutes from Manchester.

Bedrooms: 20 double, 14 twin; suites available
Bathrooms: 34 en suite

Lunch available
EM 1900 (LO 2200)
Parking for 150
CC: Amex, Barclaycard, Delta, Diners, JCB, Mastercard, Switch, Visa, Visa Electron

ⓐⓑⓒ 110 ⓤⓥ SP ⓦ T

★★★

MYTTON FOLD HOTEL AND GOLF COMPLEX

Whalley Road, Langho, Blackburn, BB6 8AB
T: (01254) 240662
F: (01254) 248119
E: mytton_fold.hotel@virgin.net
I: www.smoothhound.co.uk/hotels/mytton.html

Bedrooms: 13 double, 14 twin, 1 family room
Bathrooms: 28 en suite

Lunch available
EM 1830 (LO 2130)
Parking for 200
CC: Amex, Barclaycard, Delta, Mastercard, Solo, Switch, Visa, Visa Electron

B&B per night:
S £51.00–£51.00
D £74.00–£89.00

OPEN All year round

Mytton Fold, a tranquil, friendly oasis. Lovingly created colourful gardens. Private 18-hole golf course. 15 minutes M6, M65. 28 en suite rooms. Set amongst breathtaking scenery.

ⓐⓑⓒ 300 ⓧⓨ SP ⓦ T

★

ROCKLAND HOTEL

View Road, Rainhill, Prescot, L35 0LG
T: (0151) 426 4603
F: (0151) 426 0107

Bedrooms: 4 single, 2 double, 3 twin, 3 triple
Bathrooms: 10 en suite, 1 public

Lunch available
EM 1830 (LO 2030)
Parking for 30
CC: Amex, Barclaycard, Mastercard, Visa

B&B per night:
S £25.00–£34.50
D £35.00–£44.00

OPEN All year round

Georgian hotel set in own grounds in quiet suburban location. Easy access to motorway (1 mile) and 10 miles from Liverpool city centre.

ⓐⓑⓒ 50 ⓩ SP ⓦ T

COLOUR MAPS Colour maps at the front of this guide pinpoint all places under which you will find accommodation listed.

LIVERPOOL continued

Rating Applied For Ad p15	**THISTLE LIVERPOOL** Chapel Street, Liverpool, L3 9RE T: (0151) 227 4444 F: (0151) 236 3973 E: liverpool@cix.co.uk	Bedrooms: 121 double, 105 twin; suites available Bathrooms: 226 en suite	Lunch available EM 1900 (LO 2215) CC: Amex, Barclaycard, Diners, Eurocard, JCB, Maestro, Mastercard, Solo, Visa	B&B per night: **S £128.00–£152.00** **D £128.00–£152.00** OPEN All year round

A well known landmark, this modern hotel overlooks Liverpool's business quarter and has a magnificent view of the River Mersey from its rooms and celebrated restaurant.

(CR)
Thistle Hotels/Utell International

⌂🏠📞☎️🖥️◐🔌🍴💻 🔵📺110 🔍 SP 🏠 T ◎

LYTHAM ST ANNES, Lancashire Map ref 4A1 *Tourist Information Centre Tel: (01253) 725610*

★★★
Ad on this page

CHADWICK HOTEL
South Promenade, Lytham St Annes, FY8 1NP

T: (01253) 720061
F: (01253) 714455
E: sales@chadwickhotel.com
I: www.chadwickhotel.com

B&B per night:
S £40.00–£47.00
D £60.00–£66.00

HB per person:
DY £39.50–£44.50

OPEN All year round

Panoramic views across the Ribble estuary and Irish Sea. Award-winning family hotel provides excellent cuisine, comforts and facilities unsurpassed for value. Exclusive health and leisure suite. Children's soft play amenities. Great for relaxing short breaks or longer. Dinner dances and theme weekend parties. Truly a hotel for all seasons.

Bedrooms: 10 single,
11 double, 29 twin,
14 triple, 11 family
rooms
Bathrooms: 75 en suite

Lunch available
EM 1900 (LO 2030)
Parking for 40
CC: Amex, Barclaycard,
Delta, Diners, Eurocard,
Mastercard, Switch, Visa

🅐 ⌂♿🏠📞🖥️📺📺◐🔌🍴70 ♦🔍⚓U🏃❄️🎾 SP T

★★★
DALMENY HOTEL
19-33 South Promenade,
Lytham St Annes, FY8 1LX
T: (01253) 712236
F: (01253) 724447
E: info@dalmenyhotel.com
I: www.dalmenyhotel.com

Bedrooms: 1 single,
41 double, 3 triple,
65 family rooms
Bathrooms: 110 en suite

Lunch available
EM 1800 (LO 2230)
Parking for 115
CC: Amex, Barclaycard,
Delta, Diners, Mastercard,
Switch, Visa

B&B per night:
S £75.00–£90.00
D £100.00–£125.00

HB per person:
DY £67.00–£77.00

OPEN All year round

The Dalmeny is ideally situated on the seafront in St Annes, overlooking the promenade and gardens and within walking distance of the town centre.

🅐 ⌂♿🏠📞🖥️◐🔌🍴200 ♦🔍⚓🎾❄️ SP T ◎

ACCESSIBILITY

Look for the 🔷🔷🔷 symbols which indicate accessibility for wheelchair users. A list of establishments is at the front of this guide.

Chadwick Hotel
The

North West Tourism Awards 1999
SILVER AWARD WINNER

Enjoy the luxury of this modern family-run, seventy-bedroom hotel.

The hotel is renowned for good food and comfortable bedrooms, all of which have private facilities, colour television, satellite TV and telephone. Many rooms have spa bath and some have four poster beds. Other facilities include an indoor swimming pool designed on an Ancient Greek theme and also a jacuzzi, sauna, Turkish steam room and solarium. Games room, gym and soft adventure play area.

From £32 per person room and breakfast

South Promenade, Lytham St. Annes FY8 1NP
Tel: (01253) 720061 E-mail: sales@chadwickhotel.com

LYTHAM ST ANNES continued

★★ **ST IVES HOTEL**

7 South Promenade,
Lytham St Annes, FY8 1LS
T: (01253) 720011
F: (01253) 722873

Bedrooms: 1 single,
15 double, 6 twin,
22 triple, 21 family
rooms; suites available
Bathrooms: 65 en suite

Lunch available
EM 1700 (LO 2030)
Parking for 56
CC: Amex, Barclaycard,
Delta, Diners, Eurocard,
Mastercard, Solo, Switch,
Visa, Visa Electron

B&B per night:
S £30.00–£38.00
D £60.00–£68.00

HB per person:
DY £38.00–£48.00

OPEN All year round

Clean and child-friendly seafront hotel with a reputation for excellent food and entertainment facilities. Open all year and offering many special break packages for families and group bookings.

Ⓜ🐎♿🛏🔌🖐📱🍵📺🅟🍽️16 🛏🔑🐕🔍❄🚶🔥🎯🏹🐾 SP

MACCLESFIELD, Cheshire Map ref 4B2 *Tourist Information Centre Tel: (01625) 504114 or 504115*

★★★★ **SHRIGLEY HALL HOTEL GOLF AND COUNTRY CLUB**

Shrigley Park, Pott Shrigley,
Macclesfield, SK10 5SB
T: (01625) 575757
F: (01625) 573323
E: shrigleyhall@paramount-hotels.
co.uk
I: www.paramount-hotels.co.uk

Bedrooms: 23 single,
86 double, 34 twin,
5 triple; suite available
Bathrooms: 148 en suite

Lunch available
EM 1900 (LO 2145)
Parking for 300
CC: Barclaycard, Delta,
Eurocard, Mastercard,
Switch, Visa

B&B per night:
S Min £115.00
D Min £145.00

OPEN All year round

Country house hotel set in 262-acre estate of Shrigley Park. Overlooks the Cheshire plain. 18-hole golf-course and full leisure club. Tasteful bedrooms, award-winning restaurant.

Ⓜ🐎♿🏨🔌📧📱🍵🖐🇸🅟🍽️350 🛏🔑🐕🔍❄🔔🎯🐾 SP 🏠 T

MANCHESTER, Greater Manchester Map ref 4B1 *Tourist Information Centre Tel: (0161) 234 3157 or 234 3158*

★★

ALBANY HOTEL

21 Albany Road, Chorlton-cum-Hardy,
Manchester, M21 0AY
T: (0161) 881 6774
F: (0161) 862 9405

B&B per night:
S £39.50–£79.50
D £59.50–£89.50

HB per person:
DY £45.45–£61.45

OPEN All year round

Established in 1967, referred to as "The Hidden Gem" of Manchester hotels. A Victorian property, built in the 1860s, retaining the charm and character of a bygone era but with the facilities of a modern hotel. Individually appointed bedrooms and service only found in somewhere special. Licensed bar, restaurant.

Bedrooms: 1 single,
5 double, 4 twin, 4 triple
Bathrooms: 14 en suite

Lunch available
EM 1900 (LO 2200)
Parking for 8
CC: Amex, Barclaycard,
Delta, Diners, Eurocard,
Mastercard, Solo, Switch,
Visa, Visa Electron

Ⓜ🐎♿🏨🔌📧📱🖐🇸📺🍽️40 🔍❄🚿🐾 SP T

★★★★
Silver
Award

CROWNE PLAZA MANCHESTER–THE MIDLAND

Peter Street, Manchester, M60 2DS
T: (0161) 236 3333
F: (0161) 932 4100
E: sales@mhccl.demon.co.uk
I: www.crowneplaza.com

B&B per night:
S £99.00–£155.00
D £99.00–£155.00

HB per person:
DY £122.95–£178.95

OPEN All year round

Located in the heart of the city, this Edwardian hotel offers beautifully appointed bedrooms and suites with full air-conditioning. Within a short walk of the hotel are theatreland, Bridgewater Hall, Granada Studios, MEN arena and shopping areas. The hotel also offers 2 bars, 3 restaurants and a leisure club with pool.

Bedrooms: 241 double,
62 twin; suites available
Bathrooms: 303 en suite

Lunch available
EM 1830 (LO 2230)
CC: Amex, Barclaycard,
Delta, Diners, Eurocard,
JCB, Mastercard, Switch,
Visa, Visa Electron

Ⓜ🐎♿🏨🔌📧📱🖐🇸🔔🍽️650 🛏🔑🔍🌳 SC 🐾 SP 🏠 T ⓦ

★★★

GARDENS HOTEL
55 Piccadilly, Manchester, M1 2AP
T: (0161) 236 5155
F: (0161) 228 7287
E: gardens@hotmail.com

B&B per night:
S £49.00–£79.00
D £59.00–£99.00

OPEN All year round

This modern hotel, only 9 years old, is situated in the heart of the city, overlooking Piccadilly Gardens and a few minutes from Piccadilly railway station which has direct trains to the airport. All parts of the country can be easily accessed.

Bedrooms: 12 single,
47 double, 40 twin
Bathrooms: 99 en suite

Lunch available
EM 1830 (LO 2130)
CC: Amex, Barclaycard,
Delta, Diners, Eurocard,
Mastercard, Switch, Visa

70

★★★

JURYS MANCHESTER INN
56 Great Bridgewater Street, Manchester,
M1 5LE
T: (0161) 953 8888
F: (0161) 953 9090
I: www.jurys.com

B&B per night:
S £66.50–£72.00
D £74.00–£80.00

HB per person:
DY £82.50–£88.00

OPEN All year round

Utell International

A modern hotel located in the city centre, beside the Bridgewater Hall and the G-Mex. Each room can accommodate up to 3 adults or 2 adults and 2 children. All rooms have air conditioning, modem points, en suite bathrooms, satellite TV and tea/coffee-making facilities.

Bedrooms: 96 double,
2 twin, 101 triple,
66 family rooms
Bathrooms: 265 en suite

Lunch available
EM 1800 (LO 2130)
CC: Amex, Barclaycard,
Diners, Eurocard, JCB,
Mastercard, Switch, Visa

50

★★★

MANCHESTER CONFERENCE CENTRE AND HOTEL
The Weston Building,
Sackville Street, Manchester,
M1 3BB
T: (0161) 955 8000
F: (0161) 955 8050
E: weston@umist.ac.uk
I: www.meeting.co.uk

Bedrooms: 97 single,
1 double
Bathrooms: 98 en suite

Lunch available
EM 1830 (LO 2130)
Parking for 260
CC: Amex, Barclaycard,
Delta, Diners, Eurocard,
Mastercard, Solo, Switch,
Visa

B&B per night:
S £55.00–£85.00
D £65.00–£95.00

HB per person:
DY £65.00–£95.00

OPEN All year round

Modern building located within 10 minutes' walk of Piccadilly train and bus stations. Ample car parking available. 24-hour reception, room service, restaurant and bar.

300

★★★★

THE PALACE HOTEL
Oxford Street, Manchester, M60 7HA
T: (0161) 288 1111
F: (0161) 288 2222
I: www.principalhotels.co.uk

B&B per night:
S £95.00–£144.00
D £110.00–£144.00

HB per person:
DY £130.00–£174.00

OPEN All year round

Principal Hotels/Utell
International

A recent multi-million pound refurbishment has restored this Grade II terracotta building into a beautifully appointed hotel incorporating 252 executive standard bedrooms and ambassador rooms. Facilities include 9 state-of-the-art conference rooms and a magnificent ballroom, which accommodates up to 1,000 guests.

Bedrooms: 5 single,
120 double, 126 twin,
1 triple; suites available
Bathrooms: 252 en suite

Lunch available
EM 1900 (LO 2130)
CC: Amex, Barclaycard,
Delta, Diners, Mastercard,
Solo, Switch, Visa, Visa
Electron

1000

★★★★

RADISSON SAS HOTEL MANCHESTER AIRPORT

Chicago Avenue,
Manchester Airport, Manchester,
M90 3RA
T: (0161) 490 5000
F: (0161) 490 5100
E: sales@manzq.rdsas.com
I: www.radissonsas.com

Bedrooms: 225 double,
135 twin; suites
available
Bathrooms: 360 en suite

Lunch available
EM 1900 (LO 2230)
Parking for 180
CC: Amex, Barclaycard,
Delta, Diners, Eurocard,
JCB, Mastercard, Switch,
Visa, Visa Electron

B&B per night:
S £70.00–£155.00
D Min £80.00

HB per person:
DY Min £95.00

OPEN All year round

A new de luxe airport hotel and health club, with extensive conference and banqueting facilities, located between terminals 1 and 2 by the airport's "skylink".

★★★★
Ad p15

THISTLE MANCHESTER

3-5 Portland Street,
Piccadilly Gardens, Manchester,
M1 6DP
T: (0161) 228 3400
F: (0161) 228 6347
E: sales.manchester@thistle.co.uk
I: www.thistlehotels.com

Bedrooms: 76 single,
88 double, 29 twin,
12 triple; suites available
Bathrooms: 205 en suite

Lunch available
EM 1900 (LO 2200)
Parking for 50
CC: Amex, Barclaycard,
Delta, Diners, Eurocard,
JCB, Mastercard, Switch,
Visa

B&B per night:
S £127.00–£150.00
D £143.00–£167.00

OPEN All year round

Ⓒ®
Thistle Hotels

Traditional style hotel, combining old world charm with full modern facilities, including a leisure spa. Overlooks Piccadilly Gardens in the heart of the commercial and shopping area.

★★★

THE WATERSIDE HOTEL AND GALLEON LEISURE CLUB

Wilmslow Road, Didsbury, Manchester,
M20 5WZ
T: (0161) 445 0225

Set in peaceful surroundings and built to modern design, this privately owned hotel offers excellent facilities at good value prices, a warm welcome and unmistakable attention to detail. Luxury leisure club for residents' use. Good access to Manchester city centre and Manchester Airport.

F: (0161) 446 2090
E: office@watersidehotel.com.uk
I: www.watersidehotel.co.uk

Bedrooms: 1 single,
33 double, 10 twin,
1 triple, 1 family room
Bathrooms: 46 en suite

Lunch available
EM 1830 (LO 2130)
Parking for 250
CC: Amex, Barclaycard,
Delta, Diners, Mastercard,
Switch, Visa

B&B per night:
S £75.00–£79.00
D £94.00–£96.00

HB per person:
DY £93.00–£97.00

OPEN All year round

MANCHESTER AIRPORT

See under Altrincham, Knutsford, Manchester, Sale, Wilmslow

MAWDESLEY, Lancashire Map ref 4A1

★★★

MAWDSLEYS EATING HOUSE AND HOTEL

Hall Lane, Mawdesley, Ormskirk,
L40 2QZ
T: (01704) 822552 & 821874
F: (01704) 822096
E: mawdsleyeh@aol.com
I: www.mawdsleyeh.co.uk

Bedrooms: 11 single,
39 double, 6 twin
Bathrooms: 56 en suite

Lunch available
EM 1900 (LO 2200)
Parking for 100
CC: Amex, Barclaycard,
Delta, Diners, Mastercard,
Switch, Visa

B&B per night:
S £45.00–£47.50
D £50.00–£55.00

OPEN All year round

In the picturesque village of Mawdesley, which has been voted "best kept village". Its peaceful setting will be appreciated by business people and pleasure travellers alike.

MAP REFERENCES
The map references refer to the colour maps at the front of this guide. The first figure is the map number; the letter and figure which follow indicate the grid reference on the map.

MORETON, Merseyside Map ref 4A2

★★★ **LEASOWE CASTLE HOTEL**

Leasowe Road, Moreton, Wirral,
CH46 3RF
T: (0151) 606 9191
F: (0151) 678 5551
E: leasowe.castle@mail.cybase.co.
uk

Bedrooms: 24 double,
24 twin, 2 triple
Bathrooms: 50 en suite

Lunch available
EM 1900 (LO 2200)
Parking for 200
CC: Amex, Barclaycard,
Delta, Diners, Eurocard,
Mastercard, Switch, Visa

B&B per night:
S £45.00–£60.00
D £65.00–£78.00

HB per person:
DY £61.95–£76.95

OPEN All year round

16thC building converted to a hotel. All rooms en suite with direct-dial telephone, trouser press and hairdryer. 3 bars, health club, a la carte restaurant. Golf-course adjacent.

 240

PILLING, Lancashire Map ref 4A1

★★★ **SPRINGFIELD HOUSE HOTEL AND RESTAURANT**

Wheel Lane, Pilling, Preston,
PR3 6HL
T: (01253) 790301
F: (01253) 790907
E: recep@springfieldhouse.uk.com
I: www.springfieldhouse.uk.com

Bedrooms: 3 double,
1 twin, 3 triple, 1 family
room
Bathrooms: 8 en suite

Lunch available
EM 1900 (LO 2130)
Parking for 100
CC: Barclaycard, Delta,
Eurocard, JCB,
Mastercard, Solo, Switch,
Visa

B&B per night:
S £35.00–£40.00
D £59.50–£69.50

HB per person:
DY £46.50–£50.00

OPEN All year round

Manor house built in 1840, in its own grounds, renowned for superb food. Award-winning gardens, full facilities in all rooms. Enjoy the tranquillity of surrounding countryside.

100

RIBBLE VALLEY

See under Clitheroe, Langho

SADDLEWORTH, Greater Manchester Map ref 4B1 *Tourist Information Centre Tel: (01457) 870336*

★★★

A family-owned hotel set in one of Saddleworth's villages with picturesque surroundings of the Pennine Hills, yet only 5 minutes from M62 motorway. This ideal location together with our log fires and friendly atmosphere, is perfect for your stay. Our restaurant offers a la carte, home-made pizzas and bar snacks.

LA PERGOLA HOTEL AND RESTAURANT

Rochdale Road, Denshaw, Oldham,
OL3 5UE
T: (01457) 871040
F: (01457) 873804
E: reception@lapergola.freeserve.co.uk
I: www.hotel.restaurant.co.uk

Bedrooms: 2 single,
14 double, 7 twin,
1 triple, 3 family rooms;
suite available
Bathrooms: 27 en suite

Lunch available
EM 1800 (LO 2200)
Parking for 75
CC: Amex, Barclaycard,
Delta, Diners, Mastercard,
Switch, Visa

B&B per night:
S £37.50–£52.50
D £55.00–£65.00

OPEN All year round

The Independents

200

SALE, Greater Manchester Map ref 4A2

★★ **LENNOX LEA HOTEL**

Irlam Road, Sale, Cheshire M33 2BH
T: (0161) 973 1764
F: (0161) 969 6059
E: info@lennoxlea.co.uk
I: www.lennoxlea.co.uk

Bedrooms: 19 single,
6 double, 2 twin, 2 triple
Bathrooms: 29 en suite

EM 1830 (LO 2130)
CC: Amex, Barclaycard,
Diners, Eurocard,
Mastercard, Switch, Visa

B&B per night:
S £30.00–£52.95
D £40.00–£62.95

HB per person:
DY £44.05–£54.95

OPEN All year round

A small and friendly family-run hotel featuring the acclaimed Alexander's bistro. Close to M60, Manchester city centre/sports arenas/exhibition centres and Metrolink.

15

IMPORTANT NOTE Information on accommodation listed in this guide has been supplied by the proprietors. As changes may occur you are advised to check details at the time of booking.

SOUTHPORT, Merseyside Map ref 4A1 *Tourist Information Centre Tel: (01704) 533333*

★★ **METROPOLE HOTEL**

3 Portland Street, Southport,	Bedrooms: 11 single,	Lunch available	HB per person:
PR8 1LL	4 double, 4 twin, 4 triple	EM 1900 (LO 2030)	DY £34.00–£45.00
T: (01704) 536836	Bathrooms: 23 en suite,	Parking for 12	
F: (01704) 549041	1 public	CC: Amex, Barclaycard,	OPEN All year round
E: metropole.southport@		Delta, Eurocard, JCB,	
btinternet.com		Maestro, Mastercard,	
I: www.btinternet.com/~metropole.		Solo, Switch, Visa, Visa	
southport		Electron	

Fully licensed, centrally located, family-owned hotel offering traditional standards of comfort and courtesy. Fifty yards Lord Street shopping boulevard. Golf breaks a speciality.

🄰🄽 🏇 📞 🖃 ⌨ ♦ ♨ Ⓢ 🏠 TV 🛏 🚗 ▶ SC 🐾 SP T

★★★ **SCARISBRICK HOTEL**

239 Lord Street, Southport,	Bedrooms: 6 single,	Lunch available	B&B per night:
PR8 1NZ	53 double, 24 twin,	EM 1830 (LO 2130)	S £30.00–£77.00
T: (01704) 543000	6 triple; suite available	Parking for 65	D £60.00–£160.00
F: (01704) 533335	Bathrooms: 89 en suite	CC: Amex, Barclaycard,	
E: scarisbrickhotel@talk21.com		Delta, Diners, Mastercard,	HB per person:
I: www.scarisbrickhotel.com		Switch, Visa	DY £35.00–£94.00

Traditional hotel offering the highest standards of accommodation, cuisine and service. Two restaurants, several bars, conference and banqueting facilities. Leisure club including swimming pool and gym.

OPEN All year round

Ⓒⓡ

The Independents

🄰🄽 🏇 🛁 📞 🖃 ⌨ ♦ ♈ ♨ Ⓢ ⚥ 🛏 🌙 ⚒ 🏠 🚗 🍴 200 🐎 ☆ 🎯 ▶ 🐾 SP 🏛 T

TARPORLEY, Cheshire Map ref 4A2

★★★ **WILLINGTON HALL HOTEL**

Willington, Tarporley, CW6 0NB	Bedrooms: 2 single,	Lunch available	B&B per night:
T: (01829) 752321	3 double, 5 twin	EM 1930 (LO 2130)	S £67.50–£80.00
F: (01829) 752596	Bathrooms: 10 en suite,	Parking for 60	D £100.00–£120.00
E: enquiries@willingtonhall.co.uk	1 public	CC: Amex, Barclaycard,	
I: www.willingtonhall.co.uk		Mastercard, Switch, Visa	OPEN All year round

Country house hotel set in its own park with good views over surrounding countryside. Renowned for good food in restaurant and bar.

🄰🄽 🏇 5 🛁 📞 🖃 ⌨ ♦ ♨ Ⓢ 🛏 🏠 🚗 🍴 14 🐾 ☾ ✿ 🚲

URMSTON, Greater Manchester Map ref 4A2

★★ **MANOR HEY HOTEL**

130 Stretford Road, Urmston,	Bedrooms: 10 twin,	Lunch available	B&B per night:
Manchester, M41 9LT	3 triple	EM 1830 (LO 2000)	S £30.00–£49.50
T: (0161) 748 3896	Bathrooms: 12 en suite,	Parking for 50	D £45.00–£59.50
F: (0161) 746 7183	1 private	CC: Amex, Barclaycard,	
		Delta, Eurocard, Maestro,	OPEN All year round
		Mastercard, Solo, Switch,	
		Visa, Visa Electron	

Comfortable and friendly family-run hotel. Five minutes to Trafford Park, 15 minutes to Manchester Airport. Close to the Trafford Centre.

🏇 📞 🖃 ♦ ♨ Ⓢ TV 🏠 🚗 🍴 200 🚲 SP T

WADDINGTON, Lancashire Map ref 4A1

★★ **THE MOORCOCK INN**

Slaidburn Road, Waddington,	Bedrooms: 3 double,	Lunch available	B&B per night:
Clitheroe, BB7 3AA	8 twin	EM 1900 (LO 2200)	S £38.00–£40.00
T: (01200) 422333	Bathrooms: 10 en suite,	Parking for 250	D £60.00–£62.00
F: (01200) 429184	1 private	CC: Amex, Barclaycard,	
		Delta, Diners, Eurocard,	OPEN All year round
		JCB, Mastercard, Solo,	
		Switch, Visa, Visa Electron	

Friendly, family-run inn with panoramic views of Ribble Valley. En suite rooms. Fresh home-cooked food available in bar and restaurant. Banqueting facilities.

🄰🄽 🏇 🖃 ⌨ ♦ ♈ ♨ Ⓢ ⚥ 🛏 🏠 🚗 🍴 140 ☾ ▶ ✿ 🚲 SC SP T

CENTRAL RESERVATIONS OFFICES

The symbol Ⓒⓡ and a group name in an entry indicate that bookings can be made through a central reservations office. These are listed in a separate section towards the back of this guide.

WARRINGTON, Cheshire Map ref 4A2 *Tourist Information Centre Tel: (01925) 442180 or 442146*

★★★★

THE PARK ROYAL INTERNATIONAL HOTEL, HEALTH AND LEISURE SPA

Stretton Road, Stretton,
Warrington, Cheshire WA4 4NS
T: (01925) 730706
F: (01925) 730740
E: hotel@park-royal-int.co.uk

Bedrooms: 1 single,
81 double, 40 twin,
15 triple; suites available
Bathrooms: 137 en suite

Lunch available
EM 1900 (LO 2200)
Parking for 400
CC: Amex, Barclaycard,
Delta, Diners, Eurocard,
JCB, Mastercard, Solo,
Switch, Visa

B&B per night:
S £62.50–£101.50
D £72.50–£111.50

HB per person:
DY Min £52.50

OPEN All year round

Set in the heart of Cheshire, minutes from junction 10 M56. Exclusive health and leisure spa and beauty centre. Award-winning restaurant. Weekend rates available.

Best Western Hotels

WIGAN, Greater Manchester Map ref 4A1 *Tourist Information Centre Tel: (01942) 825677*

★★★

BURRIDGES HOTEL AND RESTAURANT

Standishgate, Wigan, Lancashire
WN1 1XA
T: (01942) 741674
F: (01942) 741683
E: info@burridges.co.uk
I: www.burridges.co.uk

Bedrooms: 9 double,
1 family room; suite
available
Bathrooms: 10 en suite

Lunch available
EM 1900 (LO 2200)
Parking for 24
CC: Amex, Barclaycard,
Delta, Diners, JCB,
Maestro, Mastercard,
Solo, Switch, Visa, Visa
Electron

B&B per night:
S £60.00–£70.00
D £60.00–£70.00

OPEN All year round

Former church built in 1902. First class restaurant offering an exciting range of modern dishes, created with the distinctive flair of our chef. High quality rooms.

WILMSLOW, Cheshire Map ref 4B2

★★★
Silver
Award

STANNEYLANDS HOTEL

Stanneylands Road, Wilmslow,
SK9 4EY
T: (01625) 525225
F: (01625) 537282
E: email@stanneylands.co.uk
I: www.stanneylandshotel.co.uk

Bedrooms: 7 single,
11 double, 13 twin; suite
available
Bathrooms: 31 en suite

Lunch available
EM 1900 (LO 2200)
Parking for 80
CC: Amex, Barclaycard,
Delta, Diners, Mastercard,
Switch, Visa

B&B per night:
S £95.50–£98.50

OPEN All year round

Utell International

The ideal blend of comfort and facilities makes Stanneylands a perfect setting for business meetings or entertaining in the exclusive restaurant. 3 miles from Manchester Airport and M56.

Rating
Applied For
Ad p15

THISTLE MANCHESTER AIRPORT

Wilmslow Road, Handforth,
Wilmslow, SK9 3LG
T: (01625) 529211
F: (01625) 536812

Bedrooms: 8 single,
7 double, 40 twin,
3 family rooms
Bathrooms: 58 private

Lunch available
EM 1900 (LO 2130)
Parking for 301
CC: Amex, Barclaycard,
Delta, Diners, Eurocard,
Mastercard, Switch, Visa

B&B per night:
S £115.00–£119.00
D £131.00–£135.00

OPEN All year round

Thistle Hotels/Utell
International

This Georgian hotel, set in attractive gardens, is within minutes of Manchester Airport. Ideal for visitors to the Peak District, Cheshire and Manchester city centre.

WIRRAL, Merseyside

See under Moreton

COUNTRY CODE Always follow the Country Code ❀ Enjoy the countryside and respect its life and work ❀ Guard against all risk of fire ❀ Fasten all gates ❀ Keep your dogs under close control ❀ Keep to public paths across farmland ❀ Use gates and stiles to cross fences, hedges and walls ❀ Leave livestock, crops and machinery alone ❀ Take your litter home ❀ Help to keep all water clean ❀ Protect wildlife, plants and trees ❀ Take special care on country roads ❀ Make no unnecessary noise

NORTH WEST

A brief guide to the main Towns and Villages offering accommodation in the

A **ALTRINCHAM, GREATER MANCHESTER -** Historic market town developed as a residential area in the 19th C. Preserves the best of the old at its fascinating Old Market Place, with the best of the new on pedestrianised George Street. International fashion and high style interior design rub shoulders with boutiques and speciality shops.

B **BLACKBURN, LANCASHIRE -** North East Lancashire town. Architecture reflects Victorian prosperity from the cotton industry. Daniel Thwaites, founder of Thwaites Brewery, is buried in St John's churchyard. Lewis Textile Museum is dedicated to the history of the textile industry.

● **BLACKPOOL -** Britain's largest fun resort, with Blackpool Pleasure Beach, 3 piers and the famous Tower. Host to the spectacular autumn illuminations - "the greatest free show on earth".

C **CHESTER, CHESHIRE -** Roman and medieval walled city rich in treasures. Black and white buildings are a hallmark, including "The Rows" - two-tier shopping galleries. 900-year-old cathedral and the famous Chester Zoo.

● **CLITHEROE, LANCASHIRE -** Ancient market town with an 800-year-old castle keep and a wide range of award-winning shops. Good base for touring Ribble Valley, Trough of Bowland and Pennine moorland. Country market on Tuesdays and Saturdays.

F **FRODSHAM, CHESHIRE -** Spacious tree-lined main street flanked by 17th, 18th and 19th C buildings. Near Delamere Forest and Sandstone Trail, close to the Mersey estuary and overlooked by Overton Hill.

G **GARSTANG, LANCASHIRE -** Picturesque country market town. The gateway to the fells, it stands on the Lancaster Canal and is a popular cruising centre. Close by are the remains of Greenhalgh Castle (no public access) and the Bleasdale Circle. Discovery Centre shows history of Over Wyre and Bowland fringe areas.

K **KNUTSFORD, CHESHIRE -** Delightful town with many buildings of architectural and historic interest. The setting of Elizabeth Gaskell's "Cranford". Annual May Day celebration and decorative "sanding" of the pavements are unique to the town. Popular Heritage Centre.

L **LANGHO, BLACKBURN WITH DARWEN -** This parish can trace its history back to Saxon times when in 798 AD a battle was fought at Billangohoh from which the names of Billington and Langho were derived. A flourishing community of mainly cattle farms, near both the River Ribble and the River Calder.

● **LIVERPOOL -** Vibrant city which became prominent in the 18th C as a result of its sugar, spice and tobacco trade with the Americas. Today the historic waterfront is a major attraction. Home to the Beatles, the Grand National and two 20th C cathedrals, as well as many museums and galleries.

● **LYTHAM ST ANNES, LANCASHIRE -** Pleasant resort famous for its championship golf-courses, notably the Royal Lytham and St Annes. Fine sands and attractive gardens. Some half-timbered buildings and an old restored windmill.

M **MACCLESFIELD, CHESHIRE -** Cobbled streets and quaint old buildings stand side by side with modern shops and three markets. Centuries of association with the silk industry; museums feature working exhibits and social history. Stunning views of the Peak District National Park.

● **MANCHESTER -** The Gateway to the North, offering one of Britain's largest selections of arts venues and theatre productions, a wide range of chain stores and specialist shops, a legendary, lively nightlife, spectacular architecture and a plethora of eating and drinking places.

● **MAWDESLEY, LANCASHIRE -** The picturesque village of Mawdesley lies amidst the fertile West Lancashire plain. Its traditional basket making industry survives today in the workshop of Cane Capital, and the historic Black Bull Inn is a superb local pub. A visit to Mawdesley must include Cedar Farm Galleries, a modern arts and crafts centre complete with tea room and farm animals.

P **PRESTON, LANCASHIRE -** Scene of decisive Royalist defeat by Cromwell in the Civil War and later of riots in the Industrial Revolution. Local history exhibited in Harris Museum. Famous for its Guild and the celebration that takes place every 20 years.

S **SADDLEWORTH, GREATER MANCHESTER** - The stone-built villages of Saddleworth are peppered with old mill buildings and possess a unique Pennine character. The superb scenery of Saddleworth Moor provides an ideal backdrop for canal trips, walking and outdoor pursuits.

● **SALE, GREATER MANCHESTER -** Located between Manchester and Altrincham, Sale owes its name to the 12th C landowner Thomas de Sale. It is now home to Trafford Water Sports Centre and Park which offers the best in aquatic leisure and countryside activities.

● **SOUTHPORT, MERSEYSIDE -** Delightful Victorian resort noted for gardens, sandy beaches and 6 golf-courses, particularly Royal Birkdale. Attractions include the Atkinson Art Gallery, Southport Railway Centre, Pleasureland and the annual Southport Flower Show. Excellent shopping, particularly in Lord Street's elegant boulevard.

T **TARPORLEY, CHESHIRE -** Old town with gabled houses and medieval church of St Helen containing monuments to the Done family, a historic name in this area. Spectacular ruins of 13th C Beeston Castle nearby.

W **WADDINGTON, LANCASHIRE -** One of the area's best-known villages, with a stream and public gardens gracing the main street.

● **WARRINGTON, CHESHIRE -** Has prehistoric and Roman origins. Once the "beer capital of Britain" because so much beer was brewed here. Developed in the 18th and 19th C as a commercial and industrial town. The cast-iron gates in front of the town hall were originally destined for Sandringham.

● **WIGAN, GREATER MANCHESTER -** Although a major industrial town, Wigan is an ancient settlement which received a royal charter in 1246. Famous for its pier distinguished in Orwell's "Road to Wigan Pier". The pier has now been developed as a major tourist attraction.

● **WILMSLOW, CHESHIRE -** Nestling in the valleys of the Rivers Bollin and Dane, Wilmslow retains an intimate village atmosphere. Easy to reach attractions include Quarry Bank Mill at Style. Lindow Man was discovered on a nearby common. Romany's caravan sits in a memorial garden.

YORKSHIRE

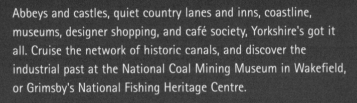

Yorkshire is the land of the white rose of England and traditional English fare - hearty roast beef and Yorkshire pudding. Boasting 1,000 square miles of National Parks, including the Dales, the Pennines and the northern Peak District, it's dotted with beauty spots.

Abbeys and castles, quiet country lanes and inns, coastline, museums, designer shopping, and café society, Yorkshire's got it all. Cruise the network of historic canals, and discover the industrial past at the National Coal Mining Museum in Wakefield, or Grimsby's National Fishing Heritage Centre.

The Egton Bridge Old Gooseberry Show on the first Tuesday in August is something different. It includes a competition to find the heaviest gooseberry.

The counties of
North, South, East and West Yorkshire and
Northern Lincolnshire

FOR MORE INFORMATION CONTACT:
Yorkshire Tourist Board
312 Tadcaster Road, York YO24 1GS
Tel: (01904) 707070 (24-hour brochure line)
Fax: (01904) 701414
Email: info@ytb.org.uk
Internet: www.yorkshirevisitor.com

Where to Go in Yorkshire - see pages 104-107
Where to Stay in Yorkshire - see pages 108-133

The Pictures:
1 Hull Fair;
2 Castle Howard, North Yorkshire;
3 Spurn Lighthouse, Holderness.

Whilst in
YORKSHIRE ...

You will find hundreds of interesting places to visit during your stay, just some of which are listed in these pages.

Contact any Tourist Information Centre in the region for more ideas on days out in Yorkshire.

Bolton Abbey Estate

Bolton Abbey, Skipton, North Yorkshire BD23 6EX
Tel: (01756) 710533
Ruins of a 12thC priory in a park setting by the river Wharfe. Tearooms, nature trails, fishing, fell-walking and picturesque countryside.

Cusworth Hall Museum of South Yorkshire Life

Cusworth Hall, Doncaster, South Yorkshire DN5 7TU
Tel: (01302) 782342
Georgian mansion in landscaped park containing Museum of South Yorkshire Life. Special educational facilities.

Deep Sea Experience Centre

Cleethorpes, North East Lincolnshire DN35 8SE
Tel: (01472) 290220
Touch the rays, watch the sharks being fed and see fish from coastal waters. Dine in the famous Shark Bite Restaurant or stroll around Davy Jones' gift shop.

Elsham Hall Country & Wildlife Park

Elsham, Brigg, North Lincolnshire DN20 0QZ
Tel: (01652) 688698
Trout and carp lakes, wild butterfly garden walkway, animal farm, pets' corner, adventure playground, new falconry centre, craft centre, art gallery and shop.

Eureka! The Museum for Children

Discovery Road, Halifax, West Yorkshire HX1 2NE
Tel: (01422) 330069
Eureka! is the first museum of its kind designed especially for children up to the age of 12 with over 400 hands-on exhibits.

Flamingo Land Theme Park, Zoo and Holiday Village

Kirby, Malton, North Yorkshire YO17 6UX
Tel: (01653) 668287
One-price family funpark with over 100 attractions and 8 shows. Europe's largest privately-owned zoo and its only triple looping coaster!

Fountains Abbey and Studley Royal

Studley Park, Ripon, North Yorkshire HG4 3DY
Tel: (01765) 608888
Largest monastic ruin in Britain, founded by Cistercian monks in 1132. Landscaped garden laid between 1720-1740 with lake, formal water garden, temples and deer park.

Helmsley Castle

Helmsley, York YO62 5AE
Tel: (01439) 770442
The great ruined keep dominates the town. Other remains include a 16thC domestic range with original panelling and plasterwork. Spectacular earthwork defences.

Jorvik Viking Centre

Coppergate, York YO1 9WT
Tel: (01904) 643211
Travel back in time in a 'time car' to a recreation of Viking York. See excavated remains of Viking houses and a display of objects found.

Last of the Summer Wine Exhibition (Compo's House)

30 Huddersfield Road, Holmfirth, Huddersfield HD6 1JS
Tel: (01484) 681408
Collection of photographs and memorabilia connected with the television series 'Last of the Summer Wine'.

Leeds City Art Gallery

The Headrow, Leeds LS1 3AA
Tel: (0113) 247 8248
British paintings, sculptures, prints and drawings of the 19thC and 20thC. Henry Moore gallery with permanent collection of 20thC sculpture.

Life Force - The National Millennium Faith Experience

St Peter's House, 8 Petergate, Bradford BD1 1DN
Tel: (01274) 224540
A unique interactive experience exploring the faiths and beliefs of different cultures, and how they have influenced some of Bradford's famous people, including the Bronte sisters. Exciting restaurant serving international cuisine.

Lightwater Valley Theme Park

North Stainley, Ripon, North Yorkshire HG4 3HT
Tel: (01765) 635321
Set in 175 acres of parkland, Lightwater Valley features a number of white-knuckle rides and children's rides along with shopping malls, a restaurant and picnic areas.

Mother Shipton's Cave & the Petrifying Well

High Bridge, Knaresborough, North Yorkshire HG5 8DD
Tel: (01423) 864600
The oldest tourist attractions in Britain, opened in 1630. Cave, well, museum, playground and 12 acres of riverside grounds.

The Pictures:
1 North Yorkshire Moors, Westerdale;
2 Countryside near Grimsby;
3 Keighley and Worth Valley Railway;
4 Felixkirk, North Yorkshire Moors;
5 The Humber Bridge;
6 Victoria Quarter, Leeds;
7 Nora Batty's Cottage, Holmfirth;
8 Skidby Windmill.

National Fishing Heritage Centre

Alexandra Dock, Grimsby,
North East Lincolnshire DN31 1UZ
Tel: (01472) 323345
A journey of discovery, experience the reality of life on a deep-sea trawler. Interactive games and displays. Children's area.

National Museum of Photography, Film & Television

Bradford, West Yorkshire BD1 1NQ
Tel: (01274) 202030
This fascinating and innovative museum houses the three types of media that have transformed the 20thC. Includes galleries dedicated to digital imaging, news, light and magic.

National Railway Museum

Leeman Road, York YO26 4XJ
Tel: (01904) 621261
From rocket to Eurostar, from giants of the steam age to a miniature railway ride — discover it all in a fun-packed family day.

Newby Hall & Gardens

Ripon, Yorkshire HG4 5AE
Tel: (01423) 322583
Late 17thC house with additions. Exceptional interior by Robert Adam. Classical sculpture, Gobelins tapestries, 25 acres of gardens, miniature railway and children's adventure garden.

North Yorkshire Moors Railway

Pickering, North Yorkshire YO18 7AJ
Tel: (01751) 472508
Evening and Sunday lunchtime dining service trains offer a unique and nostalgic experience with a wonderful selection of menus to suit all tastes.

Nunnington Hall

Nunnington, York YO62 5UY
Tel: (01439) 748283
Large 17thC manor house situated on the banks of the river Rye. Hall, bedrooms, nursery, maid's room (haunted) and Carlisle collection of miniature rooms. National Trust shop.

Sheffield Botanical Gardens

Clarkehouse Road, Sheffield S10 2LN
Tel: (0114) 250 0500
Extensive gardens with over 5,500 species of plants. Landscape by Robert Marnock, famous 19thC landscape designer.

Skipton Castle

Skipton, North Yorkshire BD23 1AQ
Tel: (01756) 792442
One of the most complete and well-preserved medieval castles in England. Civil War royalist stronghold.

Piece Hall

Halifax, West Yorkshire HX1 1RE
Tel: (01422) 358087
Built in 1779 and restored in 1976, this Grade I Listed building forms a unique and striking monument to the wealth and importance of the wool trade.

Wensleydale Cheese Visitor Centre

Gayle Lane, Hawes, North Yorkshire DL8 3RN
Tel: (01969) 667664
Museum, video and interpretation area, plus viewing gallery. Handmade Wensleydale cheese, licensed restaurant, specialist cheese shop, farm animals in a natural environment.

Pleasure Island Family Theme Park

Kings Road, Cleethorpes,
North East Lincolnshire DN35 0PL
Tel: (01472) 211511
The east coast's biggest fun day out, with over 50 rides and attractions. Whatever the weather, fun is guaranteed. Interactive play area, undercover attractions and shows from around the world.

Wigfield Farm

Worsbrough Bridge, Barnsley, South Yorkshire S70 5NQ
Tel: (01226) 733702
Open working farm with rare and commercial breeds of farm animals including pigs, cattle, sheep, goats, donkeys, ponies, small animals, snakes and other reptiles.

Ripley Castle

Ripley, Harrogate, North Yorkshire HG3 3AY
Te: (01423) 770152
Home to the Ingilby family for over 26 generations. Set in the heart of a delightful estate with Victorian walled gardens, deer park and pleasure grounds.

York Minster

Deangate, York YO1 7HH
Tel: (01904) 557200
The largest medieval Gothic cathedral in England. Museum of Saxon and Norman remains. Chapter house. Unrivalled views from the tower.

Ryedale Folk Museum

Hutton-le-Hole, York YO62 6UA
Tel: (01751) 417367
Reconstructed local buildings including cruck-framed long houses, Elizabethan manor house, furnished cottages, craftsmen's tools, household and agricultural implements.

Sea Life Centre

Scalby Mills, Scarborough, North Yorkshire YO12 6RP
Tel: (01723) 376125
Meet creatures that live in and around the oceans of the British Isles, ranging from starfish and crabs to rays and seals.

Find out more about
YORKSHIRE ...

Further information about holidays and attractions in the Yorkshire region is available from:

YORKSHIRE TOURIST BOARD

312 Tadcaster Road, York YO24 1GS.

Tel: (01904) 707070 (24-hour brochure line)
Fax: (01904) 701414
Email: info@ytb.org.uk
Internet: www.yorkshirevisitor.com

The following publications are available free from the Yorkshire Tourist Board:

Yorkshire Visitor Guide 2001
information on the region, including hotels, self-catering, caravan and camping parks. Also attractions, shops, restaurants and major events

Yorkshire - A Great Day Out
non-accommodation A5 guide listing where to go, what to see and where to eat, the list goes on! Including map

Bed & Breakfast Touring Map
forming part of a 'family' of maps covering England, this guide provides information on bed and breakfast establishments in the Yorkshire and Northumbria regions

What's On
listing of events. Published three times a year

Stay on a Farm in the North of England
farm holiday accommodation in the North of England

Freedom
caravan and camping guide to the North of England

Group Operators' Guide 2001
a guide to choosing the right venue for travel trade and group organisers including hotels, attractions and unusual venues

Conference and Venue Guide 2001
a full-colour, comprehensive guide to conference facilities in the region

The Pictures:
1 North Yorkshire Moors, Railway Steam Train;
2 Worsbrough Mill Museum, South Yorkshire;
3 York Minster;
4 Thixendale in the Wolds, East Yorkshire;
5 The beach at Bridlington, East Riding of Yorkshire;
6 Low Petergate and Minster Towers, York;
7 The Mills at Luddenden;
8 Flamborough, East Riding of Yorkshire.

Getting to
YORKSHIRE ...

BY ROAD: Motorways: M1, M62, M606, M621, M18, M180, M181, A1(M). Trunk roads: A1, A19, A57, A58, A59, A61, A62, A63, A64, A65, A66.

BY RAIL: InterCity services to Bradford, Doncaster, Harrogate, Kingston upon Hull, Leeds, Sheffield, Wakefield and York. Frequent regional railway services city centre to city centre including Manchester Airport service to Scarborough, York and Leeds.

Where to stay in
YORKSHIRE

Accommodation entries in this region are listed in alphabetical order of place name, and then in alphabetical order of establishment.

Map references refer to the colour location maps at the front of this guide. The first number indicates the map to use; the letter and number which follow refer to the grid reference on the map.

At-a-glance symbols at the end of each accommodation entry give useful information about services and facilities. A key to symbols can be found inside the back cover flap. Keep this open for easy reference.

A brief description of the towns and villages offering accommodation in the entries which follow, can be found at the end of this section.

A complete listing of all English Tourism Council assessed hotels appears at the back of this guide.

AYSGARTH, North Yorkshire Map ref 5B3

★★

THE GEORGE & DRAGON INN

Aysgarth, Leyburn, North Yorkshire
DL8 3AD
T: (01969) 663358
F: (01969) 663773

B&B per night:
S £32.00–£32.00
D £56.00–£56.00

HB per person:
DY £45.00–£45.00

OPEN All year round

Delightful 17thC inn, with old beams and antiques, in a pretty village amongst glorious scenery, perfectly situated for exploring the magnificent dales. Indulge in superb food, freshly prepared from local ingredients whenever possible, locally brewed ales, charming hospitality and beautiful, well-appointed bedrooms – all in a welcoming, congenial atmosphere.

Bedrooms: 3 double, 2 twin, 1 triple, 1 family room
Bathrooms: 7 en suite

Lunch available
EM 1800 (LO 2100)
Parking for 30
CC: Barclaycard, Delta, Eurocard, Maestro, Mastercard, Solo, Switch, Visa, Visa Electron

🅰 ≿ 📧 ⬜ ♨ ⬛ ⓢ 🛏 🖾 ▦ ⬛ ▼30 ✿ 🚿 SC ⬚ SP 🏠 T

CREDIT CARD BOOKINGS If you book by telephone and are asked for your credit card number it is advisable to check the proprietor's policy should you cancel your reservation.

BARNSLEY, South Yorkshire Map ref 4B1 *Tourist Information Centre Tel: (01226) 206757*

★★★
Silver
Award

ARDSLEY HOUSE HOTEL AND HEALTH CLUB
Doncaster Road, Ardsley, Barnsley,
South Yorkshire S71 5EH
T: (01226) 309955
F: (01226) 205374
E: sales@ardsley-house.co.uk
I: ardsley-house.co.uk

Bedrooms: 17 single,
23 double, 23 twin,
11 triple
Bathrooms: 74 en suite

Lunch available
EM 1900 (LO 2230)
Parking for 250
CC: Amex, Barclaycard,
Delta, Diners, Mastercard,
Solo, Switch, Visa

B&B per night:
S £70.00–£76.00
D £86.00–£92.00

HB per person:
DY £95.00–£104.25

OPEN All year round

18thC manor-house, tastefully converted to a private hotel. Extensive conference and banqueting facilities. French and English cooking. Full health and leisure facilities.

Ⓒ®
300 Best Western Hotels

BEDALE, North Yorkshire Map ref 5C3

★★

WHITE ROSE HOTEL
Bedale Road, Leeming Bar,
Northallerton, North Yorkshire
DL7 9AY
T: (01677) 422707 & 424941
F: (01677) 425123
E: royston@whiterosehotel.co.uk
I: www.whiterosehotel.co.uk

Bedrooms: 9 single,
2 double, 5 twin, 2 triple
Bathrooms: 18 en suite

Lunch available
EM 1900 (LO 2130)
Parking for 40
CC: Amex, Barclaycard,
Delta, Diners, Eurocard,
Mastercard, Switch, Visa

B&B per night:
S Min £38.00
D Min £48.00

OPEN All year round

Family-run private hotel half a mile from A1 in village on A684 – the road to the Dales. "Heartbeat" Country, historic city of York, coastal resorts within easy reach.

50

BOROUGHBRIDGE, North Yorkshire Map ref 5C3

★★★

CROWN HOTEL
Horsefair, Boroughbridge, York, YO51 9LB
T: (01423) 322328
F: (01423) 324512

B&B per night:
S £65.00–£80.00
D £80.00–£95.00

HB per person:
DY £57.50–£67.50

OPEN All year round

Based in the heart of North Yorkshire, the Crown really offers its guests something a little bit special. We have a fine a la carte restaurant, bars with real ales and fires and newly refurbished bedrooms. New leisure centre, pool, sauna, steam and jacuzzi, fitness suites. Make the Crown Hotel your first choice.

Bedrooms: 2 single,
16 double, 16 twin,
2 triple, 1 family room
Bathrooms: 37 en suite

Lunch available
EM 1900 (LO 2130)
Parking for 60
CC: Amex, Barclaycard,
Delta, Diners, Eurocard,
Mastercard, Switch, Visa

Ⓒ®
The Independents

160

BRADFORD, West Yorkshire Map ref 4B1 *Tourist Information Centre Tel: (01274) 753678*

★★★★
Silver
Award

The Cedar Court Hotel offers a unique mixture of modern design and friendly, quality service. Close to the dales and the many delights of Yorkshire, its location is ideal. Extensive leisure facilities, international restaurant and beautifully appointed bedrooms make the Cedar Court an excellent choice for your weekend break.

CEDAR COURT HOTEL BRADFORD
Mayo Avenue (top of the M606),
Off Rooley Lane, Bradford, West Yorkshire
BD5 8HZ
T: (01274) 406606
F: (01274) 406600
E: sales@cedarcourt-hotelbradford.co.uk
I: www.cedarcourt-hotel-bradford.co.uk.

B&B per night:
S £68.75–£108.75
D £78.50–£118.50

HB per person:
DY £45.00–£128.25

OPEN All year round

Bedrooms: 89 double,
35 twin, 7 triple; suites
available
Bathrooms: 131 en suite

Lunch available
EM 1800 (LO 2200)
Parking for 320
CC: Amex, Barclaycard,
Diners, Eurocard, JCB,
Mastercard, Switch, Visa

800

CONFIRM YOUR BOOKING
You are advised to confirm your booking in writing.

★★

PARK DRIVE HOTEL

12 Park Drive, Heaton, Bradford,
West Yorkshire BD9 4DR
T: (01274) 480194
F: (01274) 484869
E: sales@parkdrivehotel.co.uk
I: www.parkdrivehotel.co.uk

B&B per night:
S £35.00–£52.00
D £49.00–£62.00

HB per person:
DY £37.00–£44.00

OPEN All year round

"It's like staying in the country!" This elegant Victorian residence in its delightful woodland setting is just 1.5 miles from the city centre. Enjoy delicious home cooking, friendly personal service and a peaceful night's sleep. Visit Bronte Parsonage, National Museum of Photography, Yorkshire Dales, "Emmerdale", Salts Mill or Royal Armouries.

Bedrooms: 5 single,
3 double, 2 twin, 1 triple
Bathrooms: 11 en suite

EM 1900 (LO 2030)
Parking for 9
CC: Amex, Barclaycard,
Delta, Diners, Eurocard,
JCB, Maestro, Mastercard,
Solo, Switch, Visa, Visa
Electron

CR
The Independents

★★

PARK GROVE HOTEL AND RESTAURANT

Park Grove, Frizinghall, Bradford,
West Yorkshire BD9 4JY
T: (01274) 543444
F: (01274) 495619
E: enquiries@parkgrovehotel.co.uk
I: www.parkgrovehotel.co.uk

Bedrooms: 5 single,
7 double, 2 twin, 1 triple
Bathrooms: 15 en suite

EM 1900 (LO 2100)
Parking for 8
CC: Amex, Barclaycard,
Delta, Eurocard, JCB,
Maestro, Mastercard,
Solo, Switch, Visa, Visa
Electron

B&B per night:
S £25.00–£47.00
D £35.00–£62.00

HB per person:
DY £40.00–£60.00

OPEN All year round

CR
Minotel

Victorian establishment in a secluded preserved area of Bradford, 1.5 miles from the city centre. Gateway to the dales.

★★★

QUALITY VICTORIA HOTEL, BRADFORD

Bridge Street, Bradford,
West Yorkshire BD1 1JX
T: (01274) 728706
F: (01274) 736358
E: admin@gb654.u-net.com

Bedrooms: 13 single,
20 double, 23 twin,
4 triple; suites available
Bathrooms: 60 en suite

Lunch available
EM 1900 (LO 2200)
Parking for 80
CC: Amex, Barclaycard,
Delta, Diners, Eurocard,
Maestro, Mastercard,
Solo, Switch, Visa, Visa
Electron

B&B per night:
S £75.00–£80.00
D £90.00–£120.00

HB per person:
DY £85.00–£95.00

OPEN All year round

CR
Choice Hotels Europe

Historic building with an elegant interior, close to the railway, bus stations and main shopping centre. An ideal base for either business or leisure.

★★

BURTON LODGE HOTEL

Brandesburton, Driffield, East Yorkshire
YO25 8RU
T: (01964) 542847
F: (01964) 544771
E: burton@lodge5755.freeserve.co.uk

B&B per night:
S £34.00–£36.00
D £48.00–£52.00

HB per person:
DY £38.00–£47.00

OPEN All year round

Charming country hotel set in 2 acres of grounds adjoining Hainsworth Park Golf Course (18 holes and 1st tee from the hotel grounds). Nine en suite bedrooms including 2 family, and 2 ground floor bedrooms. Fine English cooking and carefully chosen wine list. Comfortable lounge/bar with open fire. Situated on the A165, 8 miles from Beverley.

Bedrooms: 1 single,
2 double, 4 twin, 2 triple
Bathrooms: 9 en suite

EM 1900 (LO 2100)
Parking for 15
CC: Amex, Barclaycard,
Delta, Eurocard, JCB,
Mastercard, Switch, Visa

★★★

EXPANSE HOTEL

North Marine Drive, Bridlington,
East Riding of Yorkshire YO15 2LS
T: (01262) 675347
F: (01262) 604928
E: expanse@brid.demon.co.uk
I: www.expanse.co.uk

B&B per night:
S £34.00–£60.00
D £62.00–£86.00

HB per person:
DY £40.00–£70.00

OPEN All year round

Overlooking the beach and sea, with panoramic views of the bay and Heritage Coast, together with easy access to coastal walks, the Expanse is an ideal hotel in which to relax or to use as a touring base.

Bedrooms: 13 single,
12 double, 19 twin,
4 triple
Bathrooms: 48 en suite

Lunch available
EM 1830 (LO 2100)
Parking for 24
CC: Amex, Barclaycard,
Delta, Eurocard,
Mastercard, Solo, Switch,
Visa

DEWSBURY, West Yorkshire Map ref 4B1

★★★

HEATH COTTAGE HOTEL & RESTAURANT

Wakefield Road, Dewsbury,
West Yorkshire WF12 8ET
T: (01924) 465399
F: (01924) 459405

Bedrooms: 9 single,
16 double, 1 twin,
3 triple
Bathrooms: 29 en suite

Lunch available
EM 1830 (LO 2130)
Parking for 65
CC: Barclaycard, Delta,
Eurocard, Mastercard,
Switch, Visa

B&B per night:
S £37.00–£50.00
D £62.00–£70.00

HB per person:
DY £37.00–£46.00

Impressive Victorian house in well-kept gardens. On the A638, 2.5 miles from M1 junction 40. Conference/banquet facilities. Large car park.

OPEN All year round

DONCASTER, South Yorkshire Map ref 4C1 *Tourist Information Centre Tel: (01302) 734309*

★★★

REGENT HOTEL

Regent Square, Doncaster, South Yorkshire
DN1 2DS
T: (01302) 364180 & 364336
F: (01302) 322331
E: admin@theregenthotel.co.uk
I: www.theregenthotel.co.uk

B&B per night:
S £58.00–£85.00
D £70.00–£90.00

HB per person:
DY £73.00–£110.00

OPEN All year round

A charming Victorian building overlooking a secluded regency park. Ideally situated within easy reach of Doncaster's vibrant town centre, business centres, market, historic racecourse and exhibition centre. Founded in 1935 and family-run since, the hotel has the distinctive air of "home from home", with a choice of public areas to suit.

Bedrooms: 21 single,
9 double, 15 twin,
5 triple
Bathrooms: 50 en suite

Lunch available
EM 1800 (LO 2200)
Parking for 26
CC: Amex, Barclaycard,
Delta, Diners, JCB,
Mastercard, Solo, Switch,
Visa

EASINGWOLD, North Yorkshire Map ref 5C3

★★

OLD FARMHOUSE COUNTRY HOTEL & RESTAURANT

Raskelf, York, YO61 3LF
T: (01347) 821971
F: (01347) 822392

Bedrooms: 6 double,
2 twin, 2 triple
Bathrooms: 10 en suite

EM 1930 (LO 2030)
Parking for 10
CC: Barclaycard, Delta,
Eurocard, JCB, Maestro,
Mastercard, Solo, Switch,
Visa, Visa Electron

B&B per night:
S £28.00–£35.00
D £60.00–£65.00

HB per person:
DY £45.00–£50.00

Former farmhouse, now a comfortable country hotel, offering award-winning 6-course evening meals, local cheeses. A true family-run concern. 15 miles from York.

OPEN Feb–Dec

WELCOME HOST
This is a nationally recognised customer care programme which aims to promote the highest standards of service and a warm welcome. Establishments taking part in this initiative are indicated by the ⊛ symbol.

GILLAMOOR, North Yorkshire Map ref 5C3

★★ **ROYAL OAK INN**
Gillamoor, York, YO62 7HX
T: (01751) 431414
F: (01751) 431414

Bedrooms: 5 double,
1 twin
Bathrooms: 6 en suite

Lunch available
EM 1900 (LO 2100)
Parking for 9
CC: Barclaycard, Eurocard,
Mastercard, Visa

B&B per night:
S £30.00-£38.00
D £40.00-£60.00

OPEN All year round

Old country inn on the edge of the North York Moors. Tastefully renovated, with plenty of character and charm. Open log fires.

GOATHLAND, North Yorkshire Map ref 5D3

★★ **MALLYAN SPOUT HOTEL**
The Common, Goathland, Whitby,
North Yorkshire YO22 5AN
T: (01947) 896486 & 896206
F: (01947) 896327
E: mallyan@ukgateway.net
I: www.mywebpage.net/
mallyanspout

Bedrooms: 4 single,
12 double, 7 twin
Bathrooms: 23 en suite

Lunch available
EM 1900 (LO 2100)
Parking for 100
CC: Amex, Barclaycard,
Delta, Mastercard, Solo,
Switch, Visa

B&B per night:
S £50.00-£80.00
D £70.00-£130.00

HB per person:
DY £50.00-£80.00

OPEN All year round

Comfortable hotel with old-fashioned comforts, welcoming log fires and good dining facilities. An ideal centre for walking the North York Moors. "Heartbeat" Country.

★★

WHITFIELD HOUSE HOTEL
Darnholm, Goathland, Whitby,
North Yorkshire YO22 5LA
T: (01947) 896215 & 896214

B&B per night:
S £30.00-£38.00
D £60.00-£60.00

HB per person:
DY £42.95-£46.00

OPEN All year round

Ⓒ
Guestaccom

17thC farmhouse providing modern comforts amidst old world charm. Peaceful location. Cottage-style en suite bedrooms (non-smoking) with every amenity. Special out-of-season breaks. Set in the heart of the North York Moors National Park, 250 metres from open moorland. Ideally situated for walking, touring or just relaxing in "Heartbeat Country".

Bedrooms: 1 single,
6 double, 2 triple
Bathrooms: 9 en suite

Lunch available
EM 1900 (LO 1730)
CC: Barclaycard, Delta,
JCB, Mastercard, Switch,
Visa

GOOLE, East Riding of Yorkshire Map ref 4C1

★★
Silver
Award

CLIFTON HOTEL
Boothferry Road, Goole,
East Riding of Yorkshire DN14 6AL
T: (01405) 761336
F: (01405) 762350
E: cliftonhotel@telinco.co.uk
I: www.s-h-systems.co.uk/hotels/
cliftong.html

Bedrooms: 4 single,
3 double, 1 twin,
1 family room
Bathrooms: 8 en suite,
1 private

EM 1900 (LO 2100)
Parking for 8
CC: Amex, Barclaycard,
Delta, Diners, Eurocard,
JCB, Maestro, Mastercard,
Solo, Switch, Visa, Visa
Electron

B&B per night:
S £30.00-£44.00
D £45.00-£52.00

OPEN All year round

Ⓒ
The Independents

Friendly and attentive service provided at this well-furnished and comfortable hotel. Restaurant menu includes healthy options.

GRASSINGTON, North Yorkshire Map ref 5B3

★★ **TENNANT ARMS HOTEL**
Kilnsey, Skipton, North Yorkshire
BD23 5PS
T: (01756) 752301

Bedrooms: 5 double,
3 twin, 2 triple
Bathrooms: 10 en suite

Lunch available
EM 1830 (LO 2130)
Parking for 40
CC: Barclaycard,
Mastercard, Visa

B&B per night:
S Min £35.00
D Min £55.00

HB per person:
DY Min £39.95

OPEN All year round

17thC coaching inn nestling alongside Kilnsey Crag, offering comfortable, attractive accommodation for those wishing to experience the beauty of Wharfedale.

GRIMSBY, North East Lincolnshire Map ref 4D1

★★★ MILLFIELDS

53 Bargate, Grimsby,
North East Lincolnshire DN34 5AD
T: (01472) 356068
F: (01472) 250286
E: info@millfieldshotel.co.uk
I: www.millfieldshotel.co.uk

Bedrooms: 17 double,
9 twin, 3 family rooms
Bathrooms: 29 en suite

Lunch available
EM 1900 (LO 2200)
Parking for 50
CC: Amex, Barclaycard,
Delta, Diners, Eurocard,
Mastercard, Solo, Switch,
Visa

B&B per night:
S £47.00–£67.00
D £62.50–£80.00

HB per person:
DY £62.50–£77.50

OPEN All year round

CR
Minotel

Exclusive yet competitively priced hotel with a wide range of leisure facilities, situated close to the commercial and retail centre of Grimsby.

HALIFAX, West Yorkshire Map ref 4B1 *Tourist Information Centre Tel: (01422) 368725*

★★★ ROCK INN HOTEL & CHURCHILLS RESTAURANT

Holywell Green, Halifax,
West Yorkshire HX4 9BS
T: (01422) 379721
F: (01422) 379110
E: therock@dial.pipex.com
I: www.rockinnhotel.com

Bedrooms: 24 double,
4 twin, 1 triple, 1 family
room; suites available
Bathrooms: 30 en suite

Lunch available
EM (LO 2200)
Parking for 125
CC: Amex, Barclaycard,
Delta, Diners, Mastercard,
Solo, Switch, Visa, Visa
Electron

B&B per night:
S £64.00–£85.00
D £67.00–£110.00

OPEN All year round

Privately-owned hostelry offering attractions of a wayside inn plus sophistication of a first class hotel and conference centre. Rural setting 1.5 miles junction 24 of M62.

HARROGATE, North Yorkshire Map ref 4B1 *Tourist Information Centre Tel: (01423) 537300*

★★
Silver
Award

ASCOT HOUSE HOTEL

53 Kings Road, Harrogate, North Yorkshire HG1 5HJ
T: (01423) 531005
F: (01423) 503523
E: admin@ascothouse.com
I: www.harrogate.com/ascot

B&B per night:
S £49.50–£59.50
D £75.00–£85.00

HB per person:
DY £49.00–£54.00

OPEN All year round

CR
Minotel

Delightful, refurbished hotel with lovely Victorian decorative features, within easy walking distance of Harrogate's renowned shops and gardens. Relax in our comfortable lounge bar. Enjoy quality cuisine and great value wines. All bedrooms en suite with telephone, TV, radio/alarm, hairdryer and tea/coffee facilities. Great selection of local attraction brochures. Car park.

Bedrooms: 4 single,
7 double, 7 twin, 1 triple
Bathrooms: 19 en suite

EM 1900 (LO 2030)
Parking for 14
CC: Amex, Barclaycard,
Delta, Diners, Eurocard,
Mastercard, Switch, Visa

★★★★ BALMORAL HOTEL

Franklin Mount, Harrogate,
North Yorkshire HG1 5EJ
T: (01423) 508208
F: (01423) 530652
E: info@balmoralhotel.co.uk
I: www.balmoralhotel.co.uk

Bedrooms: 3 single,
13 double, 4 twin; suites
available
Bathrooms: 20 en suite

Lunch available
EM 1800 (LO 2200)
Parking for 20
CC: Amex, Barclaycard,
Delta, Eurocard,
Mastercard, Solo, Switch,
Visa, Visa Electron

B&B per night:
S £59.00–£85.00
D £84.00–£169.00

HB per person:
DY Min £59.00

OPEN All year round

Exclusive townhouse with beautifully furnished rooms and a relaxed, tranquil ambience. Nine 4-poster rooms. Award-winning restaurant with modern English menu. Special weekend rates.

ACCESSIBILITY

Look for the symbols which indicate accessibility for wheelchair users. A list of establishments is at the front of this guide.

HARROGATE continued

★★★ HARROGATE SPA HOTEL

Prospect Place, West Park,
Harrogate, North Yorkshire
HG1 1LB
T: (01423) 564601
F: (01423) 507508

Bedrooms: 15 single,
9 double, 45 twin,
2 triple
Bathrooms: 71 en suite

Lunch available
EM 1830 (LO 2130)
Parking for 32
CC: Amex, Barclaycard,
Delta, Diners, Eurocard,
Mastercard, Switch, Visa

B&B per night:
S £35.00–£97.00
D £60.00–£108.00

HB per person:
DY £40.00–£65.00

OPEN All year round

Conveniently situated close to the town centre, Harrogate Conference Centre and overlooking "The Stray" parkland. We offer friendly service and traditional cuisine.

🄬
Utell International

★★★★ RUDDING PARK HOUSE AND HOTEL
Silver
Award

Rudding Park, Follifoot, Harrogate,
North Yorkshire HG3 1JH
T: (01423) 871350
F: (01423) 872286
E: sales@rudding-park.co.uk
I: www.rudding-park.co.uk

Bedrooms: 36 double,
12 twin, 2 family rooms;
suites available
Bathrooms: 50 en suite

Lunch available
EM 1900 (LO 2130)
Parking for 250
CC: Amex, Barclaycard,
Delta, Diners, Eurocard,
Mastercard, Switch, Visa

B&B per night:
S £115.00–£135.00
D £145.00–£165.00

HB per person:
DY Min £80.00

OPEN All year round

In its own 2000-acre estate, just 2 miles south of Harrogate, this contemporary hotel boasts the award-winning Clocktower restaurant and 18-hole parkland golf course.

🄬
Grand Heritage Hotels

HAWES, North Yorkshire Map ref 5B3

★★

STONE HOUSE HOTEL

Sedbusk, Hawes, North Yorkshire DL8 3PT
T: (01969) 667571
F: (01969) 667720
E: daleshotel@aol.com
I: www.stonehousehotel.com

B&B per night:
S £38.00–£89.00
D £63.00–£39.00

HB per person:
DY £51.00–£64.00

OPEN Feb–Dec

Fine Edwardian country house hotel set amidst beautiful gardens with panoramic views of upper Wensleydale. Well-appointed en suite bedrooms (5 with private conservatories on the ground floor). Delicious food, fine wines, log fires. Dogs welcome. Superb walking. This really is the perfect venue from which to explore the Dales!

Bedrooms: 1 single,
12 double, 8 twin,
1 triple; suites available
Bathrooms: 21 en suite,
1 private

EM 1900 (LO 2000)
Parking for 30
CC: Barclaycard, Delta,
Eurocard, Mastercard,
Solo, Switch, Visa, Visa
Electron

HAWORTH, West Yorkshire Map ref 4B1 *Tourist Information Centre Tel: (01535) 642329*

★★ OLD WHITE LION HOTEL

Main Street, Haworth, Keighley,
West Yorkshire BD22 8DU
T: (01535) 642313
F: (01535) 646222
E: enquiries@oldwhitelionhotel.
com
I: www.oldwhitelionhotel.com

Bedrooms: 3 single,
8 double, 1 twin, 2 triple
Bathrooms: 14 en suite

Lunch available
EM 1900 (LO 2130)
Parking for 8
CC: Amex, Barclaycard,
Delta, Diners, JCB,
Maestro, Mastercard,
Solo, Switch, Visa, Visa
Electron

B&B per night:
S £49.00–£55.00
D £65.00–£80.00

OPEN All year round

Family-run, centuries old coaching inn. Candlelit restaurant using local fresh produce. Old-world bars serving home-made bar meals and traditional ales. Special rates available all year.

QUALITY ASSURANCE SCHEME

Star ratings and awards were correct at the time of going to press but are subject to change. Please check at the time of booking.

HEBDEN BRIDGE, West Yorkshire Map ref 4B1 *Tourist Information Centre Tel: (01422) 843831*

★★★ **CARLTON HOTEL**

Albert Street, Hebden Bridge,
West Yorkshire HX7 8ES
T: (01422) 844400
F: (01422) 843117
E: ctonhotel@aol.com

Bedrooms: 3 single,
9 double, 4 twin
Bathrooms: 16 en suite

Lunch available
EM 1900 (LO 2130)
CC: Amex, Barclaycard,
Delta, Diners, Eurocard,
JCB, Maestro, Mastercard,
Solo, Switch, Visa, Visa
Electron

B&B per night:
S £46.00–£56.00
D £60.00–£85.00

OPEN All year round

Victorian emporium converted and lovingly restored to provide comfort and tranquillity from the town set below. Varied and interesting shops to hand and excellent walking nearby.

⋔⅍⊞📞🖥🖵♨🗘🅂⤬⊞🞀🖩🍴150 ▸ 🗲 🆂🅿 🆃

HELMSLEY, North Yorkshire Map ref 5C3

★★ **THE CROWN HOTEL**

Market Place, Helmsley, York,
YO62 5BJ
T: (01439) 770297
F: (01439) 771595

Bedrooms: 2 single,
4 double, 5 twin, 1 triple
Bathrooms: 12 en suite,
1 public

Lunch available
EM 1915 (LO 2000)
Parking for 15
CC: Barclaycard, Delta,
Mastercard, Solo, Switch,
Visa

B&B per night:
S £27.00–£35.00
D £54.00–£70.00

HB per person:
DY £39.00–£49.00

OPEN All year round

16thC inn with a Jacobean dining room offering traditional country cooking. Special breaks available. Dogs welcome. Run by the same family for 40 years.

⋔⅍♨📞🖥🖵♨🅂⤬🖩🍴🖱Ơ▸❋🗲🆂🅿🏨🆃

HOLMFIRTH, West Yorkshire Map ref 4B1 *Tourist Information Centre Tel: (01484) 222444*

★★★ **OLD BRIDGE HOTEL**

Off Victoria Street, Holmfirth,
Huddersfield, HD7 1DA
T: (01484) 681212
F: (01484) 687978
E: oldbridgehotel@enterprise.net
I: www.oldbridgehotel.co.uk

Bedrooms: 7 single,
11 double, 2 twin
Bathrooms: 20 en suite

Lunch available
EM 1900 (LO 2130)
Parking for 30
CC: Amex, Barclaycard,
Delta, Diners, Eurocard,
Mastercard, Switch, Visa

B&B per night:
S £25.00–£46.00
D £50.00–£57.00

OPEN All year round

Family-run hotel in riverside location. Real ales, bar meals, restaurant. Centre of "Summer Wine" Country. Superb walking and scenery.

⋔⅍⊞📞🖥🖵♨🗘🅂🖱🍴70 Ơ▸ 🆂🅲 🗲 🆂🅿 🏨 🆃

HOVINGHAM, North Yorkshire Map ref 5C3

★★★

WORSLEY ARMS HOTEL

Hovingham, York, YO62 4LA
T: (01653) 628234
F: (01653) 628130
E: worsleyarms@aol.com
I: fine-individual-hotels.co.uk

B&B per night:
S £65.00–£75.00
D £90.00–£100.00

HB per person:
DY £50.00–£70.00

OPEN All year round

Georgian coaching inn set in beautiful village, birthplace of the Duchess of Kent, Hovingham Hall. Hotel has relaxing lounges, log fires, comfortable rooms, elegant restaurant and informal Cricketer's Bar. Large gardens with wonderful walks nearby. Castle Howard 3 miles, Nunnington Hall 3 miles, golf courses nearby.

Bedrooms: 1 single,
8 double, 9 twin
Bathrooms: 18 en suite

Lunch available
EM 1900 (LO 2130)
Parking for 50
CC: Amex, Barclaycard,
Delta, Eurocard,
Mastercard, Solo, Switch,
Visa, Visa Electron

⋔⅍♨📞🖥🖵♨🗘🅂🖳🖩🍴50 ⚥♨Ơ▸🗲❋🗲🆂🅿🆃◉

HOWDEN, East Riding of Yorkshire Map ref 4C1

★ **WELLINGTON HOTEL**

31 Bridgegate, Howden,
East Yorkshire DN14 7JG
T: (01430) 430258 &
(01763) 287663
F: (01430) 432139

Bedrooms: 3 single,
3 double, 4 twin
Bathrooms: 8 en suite,
2 private

Lunch available
EM 1830 (LO 2200)
Parking for 60
CC: Amex, Barclaycard,
Delta, Mastercard, Solo,
Switch, Visa

B&B per night:
S £25.00–£35.00
D £35.00–£45.00

HB per person:
DY £27.50–£32.50

OPEN All year round

16thC coaching inn with modern facilities in historic market town. Popular restaurant, bars and beer garden. Warm, traditional welcome. Ideal for business or pleasure.

⋔⅍📞🖵♨🅂⤬🖩🍴60 ❋🗲🆂🅿🏨🆃

HUDDERSFIELD, West Yorkshire Map ref 4B1 *Tourist Information Centre Tel: (01484) 223200*

★★★ **BRIAR COURT HOTEL**

Halifax Road, Birchencliffe,
Huddersfield, HD3 3NT
T: (01484) 519902 &
519978 (Private line)
F: (01484) 431812
E: briarcourthotel@btconnect.com
I: www.briaracourthotel.co.uk

Bedrooms: 41 double,
5 twin, 1 triple, 1 family
room; suite available
Bathrooms: 48 en suite

Lunch available
EM 1800 (LO 2230)
Parking for 140
CC: Amex, Barclaycard,
Delta, Diners, Eurocard,
Mastercard, Solo, Switch,
Visa

B&B per night:
S £35.00–£59.00
D £45.00–£69.00

OPEN All year round

*Modern hotel combining professional yet friendly service with first class accommodation,
conference and wedding facilities. Home to popular Da Sandros pizzeria and easily
accessible from M62.*

⚙🐎⚓🛏🖥📠♿🎣ℹ️🆂✂🎪📺🅾🛏🛋🍽150 ✿ SP T

★★★ **THE GEORGE HOTEL**

St George's Square, Huddersfield,
HD1 1JA
T: (01484) 515444
F: (01484) 435056
E: stuart.mcmanus@
principal hotels.co.uk
I: www.principalhotels.co.uk

Bedrooms: 25 single,
19 double, 15 twin,
1 triple; suite available
Bathrooms: 60 en suite

Lunch available
EM 1900 (LO 2130)
Parking for 30
CC: Amex, Barclaycard,
Delta, Diners, Mastercard,
Solo, Switch, Visa

B&B per night:
S £60.00–£90.00
D £70.00–£90.00

HB per person:
DY £70.00–£90.00

OPEN All year round

CR

Principal Hotels/Utell
International

*This elegant town centre hotel has undergone a complete refurbishment. Located close to
shops and within easy reach of Peak District.*

⚙🐎⚓🛏🖥📠♿🎣ℹ️🆂🍽🅾🛏🛋🍽200 SC ✎ SP 🏨 T

★★★ **HUDDERSFIELD HOTEL AND ROSEMARY LANE BISTRO**

33-47 Kirkgate, Huddersfield,
HD1 1QT
T: (01484) 512111
F: (01484) 435262
E: enquiries@huddersfieldhotel.
com
I: www.huddersfieldhotel.com

Bedrooms: 14 single,
10 double, 24 twin,
3 family rooms
Bathrooms: 51 en suite

Lunch available
EM 1800 (LO 2200)
Parking for 120
CC: Amex, Barclaycard,
Delta, Diners, Eurocard,
JCB, Mastercard, Switch,
Visa

B&B per night:
S £39.00–£52.00
D £49.00–£70.00

HB per person:
DY £49.00–£65.00

OPEN All year round

*Past winner of "Yorkshire In Bloom". Free secure car park. Continental-style brasserie,
traditional pub and nightclub within the complex. Renowned for friendliness.*

⚙🐎🏨⚓🛏🖥♿🎣ℹ️🆂🍽📺🅾🛏🛋🛋🍷▶SC ✎ SP 🏨 T ⊛

HULL, Kingston upon Hull Map ref 4C1 *Tourist Information Centre Tel: (01482) 223559 (Paragon Street) or 702118
(King George Dock)*

★★★

*Set in attractive landscaped grounds,
5 miles from Hull/Beverley, ideally
situated for exploring East Yorkshire
coast and countryside. 103 en suite
bedrooms, tea and coffee-making
facilities, Sebastian Coe Health Club
with pool, gym, sauna, jacuzzi, steam
room, hair and beauty salon.
Friendly, informal surroundings in
the contemporary Arts Bar & Grill.*

JARVIS INTERNATIONAL HOTEL

Grange Park Lane, Willerby, Hull,
East Yorkshire HU10 6EA
T: (01482) 656488
F: (01482) 655848
I: www.jarvis.co.uk

Bedrooms: 53 double,
42 twin, 8 family rooms;
suites available
Bathrooms: 103 en suite

Lunch available
EM 1830 (LO 2230)
Parking for 600
CC: Barclaycard, Diners,
Eurocard, Mastercard,
Switch, Visa

B&B per night:
S £59.50–£70.00
D £100.00–£130.00

OPEN All year round

CR

Jarvis Hotels

⚙🐎⚓🏨⚓🛏🖥📠♿🎣ℹ️🆂🍽🅾🛏🛋🍽550 🛋✴🎣✿SC✎ SP T

TOWN INDEX

This can be found at the back of this guide. If you know where you want
to stay, the index will give you the page number listing accommodation
in your chosen town, city or village.

★★★
Silver
Award

ROMBALDS HOTEL AND RESTAURANT

West View, Wells Road, Ilkley,
West Yorkshire LS29 9JG
T: (01943) 603201
F: (01943) 816586
E: reception@rombalds.demon.co.uk
I: www.rombalds.co.uk

Standing on the face of Ilkley Moor, 600 yards from town centre, this elegantly furnished hotel provides very comfortable accommodation. The award-winning restaurant is a lovely setting in which to enjoy the well-produced food based on local produce. An ideal centre to tour England's North Country.

Bedrooms: 9 double,
5 twin, 1 triple; suites
available
Bathrooms: 15 en suite

Lunch available
EM 1830 (LO 2130)
Parking for 22
CC: Amex, Barclaycard,
Delta, Diners, Eurocard,
JCB, Mastercard, Solo,
Switch, Visa

B&B per night:
S £55.00–£99.50
D £80.00–£119.50

HB per person:
DY £52.50–£112.00

OPEN All year round

Best Western Hotels

♠️🐾📞🖥️🚲🎣👤Ⓢ🔁🖥️🛏️🍽️70 🔱⛵☀️🏴 SP 🎰 T

★★ **GEORGE & DRAGON HOTEL**

Market Place, Kirkbymoorside, York,
YO62 6AA
T: (01751) 433334
F: (01751) 432933

Bedrooms: 1 single,
12 double, 2 twin,
2 triple, 1 family room
Bathrooms: 18 en suite

Lunch available
EM 1830 (LO 2115)
Parking for 20
CC: Barclaycard, Delta,
Eurocard, Mastercard,
Solo, Switch, Visa

B&B per night:
S £49.00–£49.00
D £79.00–£90.00

OPEN All year round

Inn of character adjacent to the North York Moors. Extensively modernised bedrooms, all with colour TV, en suite bathrooms. Ideal touring location. Good Pub Guide "Newcomer of the Year Award 1995".

♠️🐾⛳🏨📞🖥️🚲🎣👤Ⓢ🗡️🖥️🛏️🍽️40 ✳️🔱☀️🏴 SP 🎰 T ♿

★★

ARAGON HOTEL

250 Stainbeck Lane, Meanwood, Leeds,
LS7 2PS
T: (0113) 275 9306
F: (0113) 275 7166

A quiet and peaceful late Victorian hotel set in an acre of garden. A non-smoking hotel with "Gold Award for Clean Air". All bedrooms en suite with TV, radio, telephone, hairdryer and hospitality tray. Two miles from city centre, 1 mile from Headingley and Boddington Hall, 2 miles from the university.

Bedrooms: 2 single,
7 double, 2 twin, 1 triple
Bathrooms: 12 en suite

EM 1900 (LO 2100)
Parking for 21
CC: Amex, Barclaycard,
Delta, Diners, Eurocard,
Mastercard, Solo, Switch,
Visa

B&B per night:
S £39.90–£44.90
D £49.90–£64.90

HB per person:
DY £49.90–£59.90

OPEN All year round

Ⓡ
The Independents

♠️🐾⛳📞🚲🎣🗡️🖥️🛏️🍽️16 ☀️✈️🚍 SP T

★★ **ASCOT GRANGE HOTEL**

126-130 Otley Road, Headingley,
Leeds, LS16 5JX
T: (0113) 293 4444
F: (0113) 293 5555

Bedrooms: 7 single,
11 double, 2 triple,
3 family rooms
Bathrooms: 23 en suite

Lunch available
EM 1900 (LO 2130)
Parking for 40
CC: Barclaycard, Delta,
Eurocard, Mastercard,
Switch, Visa

B&B per night:
S £40.00–£43.00
D £49.00–£52.00

HB per person:
DY £40.50–£50.50

OPEN All year round

Refurbished throughout to a high standard. Two miles from city centre, close to Beckets Park and Yorkshire County Cricket Ground. Warm welcome from friendly staff.

♠️🐾⛳🏨📞🖥️🚲👤Ⓢ📺🖥️🛏️🍽️80 ☀️✈️🏴 SP T ♿

RATING   All accommodation in this guide has been rated, or is awaiting a rating, by a trained English Tourism Council assessor.

LEEDS continued

★★★

JARVIS LEEDS NORTH
Ring Road, Mill Green View, Seacroft, Leeds, LS14 5QF
T: (0113) 273 2323
F: (0113) 232 3018
I: www.jarvis.co.uk

Bedrooms: 21 single, 32 double, 50 twin, 2 family rooms
Bathrooms: 105 en suite

Lunch available
EM 1900 (LO 2200)
Parking for 120
CC: Amex, Barclaycard, Delta, Diners, Eurocard, Mastercard, Switch, Visa

Ideal for both business and holiday makers. On the main Leeds to York road with easy access to the airport and motorways.

325

B&B per night:
S £32.50–£100.95
D £65.00–£119.90

HB per person:
DY £39.50–£149.80

OPEN All year round

CR
Jarvis Hotels

★★★

JARVIS PARKWAY HOTEL AND COUNTRY CLUB
Otley Road, Bramhope, Leeds, LS16 8AG
T: (0113) 269 9000
F: (0113) 267 4410
E: parkway@jarvis.co.uk
I: www.jarvis.co.uk

Bedrooms: 5 single, 86 double, 27 twin
Bathrooms: 118 en suite

Lunch available
EM 1900 (LO 2145)
Parking for 250
CC: Amex, Barclaycard, Delta, Diners, Eurocard, JCB, Mastercard, Switch, Visa

Mock-Tudor building in 2.5 acres of grounds, 6 miles from city centre on A660. Leisure centre. Special weekend rates.

300

B&B per night:
S £99.00–£119.00
D £109.00–£129.00

HB per person:
DY £53.00–£61.00

OPEN All year round

CR
Jarvis Hotels/Utell International

★★★★

THE HOTEL METROPOLE
King Street, Leeds, LS1 2HQ
T: (0113) 245 0841
F: (0113) 242 5156
I: www.principalhotels.co.uk

Bedrooms: 37 single, 51 double, 20 twin, 10 triple; suites available
Bathrooms: 118 en suite

Lunch available
EM 1900 (LO 2130)
Parking for 40
CC: Amex, Barclaycard, Delta, Diners, Eurocard, Maestro, Mastercard, Solo, Switch, Visa, Visa Electron

Traditional, spacious Victorian hotel situated in the city centre, close to rail, road and air links. Conference facilities for up to 250.

250

B&B per night:
S £40.00–£110.00
D £80.00–£120.00

HB per person:
DY £60.00–£127.00

OPEN All year round

CR
Principal Hotels/Utell International

★★★★★
Silver Award

DE VERE OULTON HALL
Rothwell Lane, Oulton, Woodlesford, Leeds, LS26 8HN
T: (0113) 282 1000
F: (0113) 282 8066
E: oulton.hall@devere-hotel.com
I: www.devereonline.co.uk

Fully renovated hall in the heart of Yorkshire, south-east of Leeds. Adjacent to a golf-course. Full leisure club including swimming pool, aerobics studio, beauty salon. Fine dining and informal restaurants available. Close to M62, M1 intersection and A1/M1 link road. Attractions include Royal Armouries, Harvey Nichols, York, Yorkshire Dales.

Bedrooms: 88 double, 64 twin; suites available
Bathrooms: 152 en suite

Lunch available
EM 1900 (LO 2200)
Parking for 220
CC: Amex, Barclaycard, Diners, Mastercard, Switch, Visa

350

B&B per night:
S Min £145.00
D Min £165.00

OPEN All year round

★★★★

WEETWOOD HALL
Otley Road, Headingley, Leeds, LS16 5PS
T: (0113) 230 6000
F: (0113) 230 6095
E: sales@weetwood.co.uk
I: www.weetwood.co.uk

Bedrooms: 41 single, 46 double, 19 twin
Bathrooms: 106 en suite

Lunch available
EM 1900 (LO 2130)
Parking for 150
CC: Amex, Barclaycard, Delta, Diners, Eurocard, JCB, Mastercard, Solo, Switch, Visa

Built around a Grade II Listed building. In 9.5 acres of beautiful wooded grounds, just 4 miles from Leeds city centre.

155

B&B per night:
S £42.50–£117.75
D £85.00–£138.50

HB per person:
DY £60.00–£135.25

OPEN All year round

LEEDS/BRADFORD AIRPORT

See under Bradford, Leeds

LEYBURN, North Yorkshire Map ref 5B3 *Tourist Information Centre Tel: (01969) 623069*

★

GOLDEN LION HOTEL & LICENSED RESTAURANT

Market Place, Leyburn,	Bedrooms: 2 single,	Lunch available	B&B per night:
North Yorkshire DL8 5AS	5 double, 3 twin, 4 triple	EM 1900 (LO 2100)	S £22.00–£32.00
T: (01969) 622161	Bathrooms: 14 en suite,	Parking for 12	D £44.00–£64.00
F: (01969) 623836	1 public	CC: Amex, Barclaycard,	
E: annegoldenlion@aol.com		Delta, Diners, Mastercard,	HB per person:
		Switch, Visa	DY £36.00–£44.00

Small family-run hotel in the market place of a busy dales town. A good base for touring the surrounding countryside. Special diets. Children/pets welcome.

OPEN All year round

LIVERSEDGE, West Yorkshire Map ref 4B1

★★

HEALDS HALL HOTEL
Leeds Road, Liversedge, West Yorkshire
WF15 6JA

T: (01924) 409112
F: (01924) 401895
E: healdshall@ndirect.co.uk

B&B per night:
S £40.00–£59.00
D £55.00–£80.00

HB per person:
DY £45.00–£80.00

OPEN All year round

18thC family-run hotel with	Bedrooms: 5 single,	Lunch available
nationally acclaimed award-winning	10 double, 6 twin,	EM 1900 (LO 2100)
restaurant, set in large established	3 triple	Parking for 80
gardens. Ideal venue for wedding	Bathrooms: 24 en suite	CC: Amex, Barclaycard,
receptions and conferences. On A62,		Delta, Diners, Eurocard,
near M1 and M62. Special weekend		JCB, Maestro, Mastercard,
breaks available, from £80 per		Solo, Switch, Visa, Visa
person, including meals. New bistro		Electron
open.		

MALTON, North Yorkshire Map ref 5D3 *Tourist Information Centre Tel: (01653) 600048*

★★

TALBOT HOTEL
Yorkersgate, Malton, North Yorkshire
YO17 7AJ

T: (01653) 694031
F: (01653) 693355
E: talbot@englishrosehotels.co.uk
I: www.englishrosehotels.co.uk

B&B per night:
S £49.50–£59.50
D £90.00–£110.00

HB per person:
DY £32.30–£47.50

OPEN All year round

An historic hotel in the centre of the	Bedrooms: 10 single,	Lunch available
bustling market town of Malton, just	15 double, 3 twin,	EM 1900 (LO 2115)
20 minutes from York. Boasting	3 family rooms; suite	Parking for 40
ample free parking and fine	available	CC: Amex, Barclaycard,
Yorkshire fare, this elegant hotel has	Bathrooms: 31 private	Delta, Diners, JCB,
delightful views over the Derwent		Mastercard, Switch, Visa
River and Howardian Hills. Famous		
Castle Howard is a short drive away.		

★

WENTWORTH ARMS HOTEL

Town Street, Old Malton, Malton,	Bedrooms: 3 double,	Lunch available	B&B per night:
North Yorkshire YO17 7HD	2 twin	EM 1800 (LO 2045)	S Min £25.00
T: (01653) 692618	Bathrooms: 4 en suite,	CC: Amex, Barclaycard,	D Min £50.00
	1 public	Delta, JCB, Maestro,	
		Mastercard, Solo, Switch,	OPEN All year round
		Visa, Visa Electron	

Former coaching inn, built early 1700s and run by the same family for 100 years. 20 miles from York. Excellent base for touring dales and moors.

WHERE TO STAY
Please mention this guide when making your booking.

★★

MILLERS HOUSE HOTEL

Middleham, Leyburn, North Yorkshire
DL8 4NR
T: (01969) 622630
F: (01969) 623570
E: hotel@millershouse.demon.co.uk
I: www.hotelwensleydale.com

B&B per night:
S Min £39.00
D £78.00–£92.00

HB per person:
DY £50.00–£66.00

OPEN Mar–Nov

Yorkshire's Hotel of the Year
runner-up 96/97. Elegant Georgian
country house in heart of dales.
Privately owned and run, offering a
warm welcome, quality and comfort.
All bedrooms are individually
furnished, en suite and non-smoking.
Restaurant renowned for its good
food and sensibly priced fine wines.
Twenty minutes from A1.

Bedrooms: 1 single,
3 double, 3 twin
Bathrooms: 6 en suite,
1 private

EM 1930 (LO 2000)
Parking for 8
CC: Barclaycard, Delta,
Mastercard, Solo, Switch,
Visa

⚠🐾10🏨📞🖥️🖂⬇️🔍🛡️S⤢🏃🖥️🚗🍴15⛵🅿️🌼✕🚲⚬SP🏛️

★★

THE OLD VICARAGE

Bruntcliffe Road, Morley, Leeds,
LS27 0JZ
T: (0113) 253 2174
F: (0113) 253 3549
E: oldvicarage@btinternet.com
I: www.oldvicaragehotel.co.uk

Bedrooms: 11 single,
7 double, 2 twin
Bathrooms: 20 en suite

EM 1800 (LO 1945)
Parking for 21
CC: Amex, Barclaycard,
Delta, Diners, Eurocard,
Maestro, Mastercard,
Solo, Switch, Visa, Visa
Electron

B&B per night:
S £34.00–£48.00
D £55.00–£62.00

HB per person:
DY £42.00–£58.95

OPEN All year round

Within minutes of motorways, the Old Vicarage is a friendly, family-run hotel featuring
beautiful antiques and Victoriana in an authentic setting. 75% no smoking.

⚠🐾🔧🏨📞🖥️⬇️🔍🛡️S⤢🏃📺🖥️🚗🍴10🌼✕🚲SP🏛️T

★★★

SOLBERGE HALL

Newby Wiske, Northallerton,
North Yorkshire DL7 9ER
T: (01609) 779191
F: (01609) 780472
E: hotel@solberge.freeserve.co.uk
I: www.smoothhound.com

Bedrooms: 4 single,
15 double, 5 twin
Bathrooms: 24 en suite

Lunch available
EM 1930 (LO 2130)
Parking for 80
CC: Amex, Barclaycard,
Delta, Diners, Eurocard,
JCB, Maestro, Mastercard,
Solo, Switch, Visa, Visa
Electron

B&B per night:
S £70.00–£70.00
D £90.00–£120.00

HB per person:
DY £70.00–£70.00

OPEN All year round

Ⓒ®
Best Western Hotels

Georgian country house in the heart of Herriot Country, convenient for the moors and
dales. Daily half-board prices based on 2-night stay.

⚠🐾🔧🏨📞🖥️⬇️🔍🛡️S⤢🏃🖥️🚗🍴100⛵🅿️✓🌼🚲SP🏛️T

★★

GRASSFIELDS COUNTRY HOUSE HOTEL

Low Wath Road, Pateley Bridge,
Harrogate, North Yorkshire
HG3 5HL
T: (01423) 711412 & 712844
F: (01423) 712844
E: grassfields@nidderdale.com.uk
I: www.nidderdale.co.uk

Bedrooms: 1 single,
4 double, 4 twin
Bathrooms: 9 en suite

Lunch available
EM 1900 (LO 2100)
Parking for 30
CC: Barclaycard, Delta,
Eurocard, Mastercard,
Switch, Visa

B&B per night:
S £25.00–£31.00
D £50.00–£75.00

HB per person:
DY £41.95–£46.45

OPEN All year round

Georgian building in 2 acres of lawns and trees, within level walking distance of Pateley
Bridge. A fine wine cellar and wholesome Yorkshire food.

⚠🐾🏨📞🖥️⬇️🔍🛡️S🏃🖥️🚗🍴100⛵🎣✓🌼🚲SP🏛️T⚬

CHECK THE MAPS

The colour maps at the front of this guide show all the cities, towns
and villages for which you will find accommodation entries.
Refer to the town index to find the page on which they are listed.

PATELEY BRIDGE continued

★★ SPORTSMANS ARMS HOTEL

Wath-in-Nidderdale,
Pateley Bridge, Harrogate,
North Yorkshire HG3 5PP
T: (01423) 711306
F: (01423) 712524

Bedrooms: 10 double,
3 twin
Bathrooms: 11 en suite,
2 private

Lunch available
EM 1900 (LO 2130)
Parking for 30
CC: Barclaycard, Delta,
Mastercard, Solo, Switch,
Visa

B&B per night:
S £45.00–£50.00
D £70.00–£90.00

HB per person:
DY £50.00–£70.00

17thC building set in its own grounds with magnificent views of Nidderdale. Tastefully decorated and furnished throughout. Wide range of fresh foods and a fine selection of wines.

OPEN All year round

ᴀ⅍♿⚬🕿🖵♨🍷î⑤✂🏖🍴🖳🖨☎30 ✈※🐾🚗 Ⓣ

PECKFIELD, A1 West Yorkshire Map ref 4C1

★★★ BEST WESTERN MILFORD LODGE HOTEL

A1 Great North Road,
Peckfield, Leeds, LS25 5LQ
T: (01977) 681800
F: (01977) 681245
E: enquiries@mlh.co.uk
I: www.mlh.co.uk

Bedrooms: 24 double,
13 twin, 10 family rooms
Bathrooms: 47 en suite

Lunch available
EM 1800 (LO 2200)
Parking for 80
CC: Amex, Barclaycard,
Diners, Mastercard,
Switch, Visa

B&B per night:
S £49.00–£59.00
D £49.00–£59.00

OPEN All year round

Ⓒⓡ
Best Western Hotels

Located on the A1 between York and Leeds. Modern hotel, recently refurbished and air conditioned. Unwind in the Watermill Restaurant which features a working waterwheel. Prices are for room only.

ᴀ⅍♿🕿🖵♨🕯î⑤✂📺◐🖳⊚☎🍴70 ✎ ⑤ⓅⒻⓉ

RICHMOND, North Yorkshire Map ref 5C3 *Tourist Information Centre Tel: (01748) 850252*

★★

BRIDGE HOUSE HOTEL

Catterick Bridge, Richmond,
North Yorkshire DL10 7PE
T: (01748) 818331
F: (01748) 818331
E: bridge_house@hotmail.com

B&B per night:
S Max £40.00
D Max £60.00

HB per person:
DY Max £45.00

OPEN All year round

Riverside coaching inn dating back to the 15thC. Easily accessible from the A1, situated midway between the dales and moors. The hotel boasts a beautiful restaurant overlooking the gardens and river. Fully licensed bar where we serve a comprehensive range of meals. Well-appointed en suite bedrooms.

Bedrooms: 3 single,
5 double, 5 twin, 2 triple
Bathrooms: 15 en suite,
1 public

Lunch available
EM 1830 (LO 2130)
Parking for 72
CC: Amex, Barclaycard,
Delta, Diners, Mastercard,
Switch, Visa

ᴀ⅍🎁🕿🖵♨î⑤🏖📺🖳☎🍴120 ✈▶※◎ ⓅⒻⓉ

★★

KING'S HEAD HOTEL

Market Place, Richmond, North Yorkshire
DL10 4HS
T: (01748) 850220
F: (01748) 850635
E: res@kingsheadrichmond.co.uk
I: www.kingsheadrichmond.co.uk

B&B per night:
S £59.00–£61.00
D £79.00–£120.00

HB per person:
DY £55.00–£75.00

OPEN All year round

Ⓒⓡ

The Independents

Refurbished Georgian hotel in the centre of this historic market town. Ideal for touring Herriot Country and the Yorkshire Dales. All rooms en suite with satellite TV, beverage trays, hairdryer, etc. Restaurant open every evening and Sunday lunch. Bar meals available every lunchtime and evening. Traditional beers, good wine.

Bedrooms: 5 single,
18 double, 7 twin
Bathrooms: 30 en suite

Lunch available
EM 1900 (LO 2115)
Parking for 25
CC: Amex, Barclaycard,
Delta, Diners, Eurocard,
JCB, Maestro, Mastercard,
Solo, Switch, Visa, Electron

ᴀ⅍🎁🕿🖵♨🕯î⑤✂🏖◐🖳☎🍴150▶◎ⓅⒻⓉ

HALF BOARD PRICES
Half board prices are given per person, but in some cases these may be based on double/twin occupancy.

★★★

RIPON SPA HOTEL

Park Street, Ripon, North Yorkshire
HG4 2BU

T: (01765) 602172
F: (01765) 690770
E: spahotel@bronco.co.uk
I: www.stemsys.co.uk/spa

Set in several acres of landscaped gardens within minutes from National Trust's "Jewel in the Crown", Fountains Abbey. Situated at one of the gateways to the Yorkshire Dales National Park. Traditional friendly hospitality, good Yorkshire food without frills. Spring and winter offers each year.

Bedrooms: 10 single,
12 double, 13 twin,
5 triple
Bathrooms: 40 en suite

Lunch available
EM 1900 (LO 2045)
Parking for 40
CC: Amex, Barclaycard,
Delta, Diners, Eurocard,
JCB, Mastercard, Switch,
Visa

B&B per night:
S £75.00–£90.00
D £84.00–£110.00

HB per person:
DY £60.00–£95.00

OPEN All year round

Best Western Hotels

▲⅍⌂⌖☎✆⊞▢♨♞🛈⒮🍴●⊞▦⚓🍽200◡►✿⃝ SC ⚘ SP Ⓣ◉

★★

UNICORN HOTEL
Market Place, Ripon,
North Yorkshire HG4 1BP
T: (01765) 602202
F: (01765) 690734
E: info@unicorn-hotel.co.uk
I: www.unicorn-hotel.co.uk

Bedrooms: 10 single,
8 double, 11 twin,
4 triple
Bathrooms: 33 en suite

Lunch available
EM 1900 (LO 2100)
Parking for 20
CC: Amex, Barclaycard,
Delta, Diners, Eurocard,
Maestro, Mastercard,
Solo, Switch, Visa, Visa
Electron

B&B per night:
S £48.00–£48.00
D £68.00–£68.00

HB per person:
DY £44.00–£49.00

OPEN All year round

400-year-old coaching inn in the market place. Renowned for its food and company and once patronised by HRH Prince of Wales (King Edward VII).

▲⅍✆⊞▢♨♞🛈🍴●⊞▦⚓🍽60►SP▦Ⓣ

★★★

BLACKSMITHS COUNTRY INN

Hartoft End, Rosedale Abbey, Pickering,
North Yorkshire YO18 8EN

T: (01751) 417331
F: (01751) 417167
E: blacksmiths.rosedale@virgin.net
I: www.blacksmithsinn-rosedale.co.uk

Bedrooms: 1 single,
12 double, 5 twin,
1 triple
Bathrooms: 19 en suite

Lunch available
EM 1800 (LO 2130)
Parking for 60
CC: Barclaycard, Delta,
Mastercard, Switch, Visa

B&B per night:
S £41.50–£47.50
D £63.00–£75.00

HB per person:
DY £47.50–£61.50

OPEN All year round

Family-owned country hotel in beautiful forest and moorland setting. Tastefully decorated restaurant with special emphasis on traditional English food and good wine. Quality en suite bedrooms, some ground floor. Cosy bars and lounges, log fires, period furniture and careful restoration combine to provide a hotel of exceptional character.

▲⅍✆⊞▢♨♞🛈🍴▦⚓🍴✿🚗⚘SP▦Ⓣ

★★★

BEST WESTERN ELTON HOTEL
Main Street, Bramley, Rotherham,
South Yorkshire S66 2SF
T: (01709) 545681
F: (01709) 549100
E: bestwestern.eltonhotel@
btinternet.com
I: www.bestwestern.co.uk

Bedrooms: 9 single,
16 double, 4 twin
Bathrooms: 29 en suite

Lunch available
EM 1900 (LO 2130)
Parking for 50
CC: Amex, Barclaycard,
Delta, Diners, Eurocard,
JCB, Maestro, Mastercard,
Solo, Switch, Visa, Visa
Electron

B&B per night:
S £40.00–£72.00
D £55.00–£80.00

HB per person:
DY £60.00–£92.00

OPEN All year round

Best Western Hotels

200-year-old, stone-built house with modern extension and restaurant. Half mile from M18, 2 miles M1. Minimum prices for one-day stays apply weekends only.

▲⅍⌂⌖☎✆⊞▢♨♞🛈✂🍴●⊞▦⚓🍽50✿ SC ⚘ SP▦Ⓣ

ROTHERHAM continued

★★★

CONSORT HOTEL
Brampton Road, Thurcroft, Rotherham, South Yorkshire S66 9JA
T: (01709) 530022
F: (01709) 531529
I: www.consorthotel.com

Bedrooms: 18 double, 7 twin, 2 family rooms; suites available
Bathrooms: 27 en suite

Lunch available
EM 1800 (LO 2130)
Parking for 96
CC: Amex, Barclaycard, Delta, Diners, Eurocard, JCB, Mastercard, Solo, Switch, Visa, Visa Electron

B&B per night:
S £42.00–£72.00
D £62.00–£82.00

OPEN All year round

Modern hotel, fully air-conditioned and decorated to a high standard throughout, at the junction of M1 and M18 (access exits 31 and 33 off M1 and exit 1 of M18).

300 SP T

SCARBOROUGH, North Yorkshire Map ref 5D3 *Tourist Information Centre Tel: (01723) 373333*

★★★

THE CLIFTON HOTEL

Queens Parade, North Cliff, Scarborough, North Yorkshire YO12 7HX
T: (01723) 375691
F: (01723) 364203
E: cliftonhotel@englishrosehotels.co.uk
I: www.englishrosehotels.co.uk

In a commanding position overlooking the beautiful North Bay with spectacular views of the castle headland. Major local attractions are within walking distance and the hotel has its own car park. Famous for the warmth of its welcome and the generous portions of excellent Yorkshire fare, The Clifton is always a popular choice.

Bedrooms: 18 single, 28 double, 15 twin, 7 triple, 3 family rooms; suites available
Bathrooms: 71 en suite

Lunch available
EM 1830 (LO 2100)
Parking for 40
CC: Amex, Barclaycard, Delta, Diners, Mastercard, Switch, Visa

B&B per night:
S £55.00–£65.00
D £90.00–£105.00

HB per person:
DY £35.50–£49.50

OPEN All year round

CR
The Independents

110 SC SP T

★★★

ESPLANADE HOTEL
Belmont Road, Scarborough, North Yorkshire YO11 2AA
T: (01723) 360382
F: (01723) 376137

Bedrooms: 17 single, 19 double, 26 twin, 8 triple, 2 family rooms
Bathrooms: 72 en suite

EM 1830 (LO 2100)
Parking for 24
CC: Amex, Barclaycard, Delta, Diners, Mastercard, Switch, Visa

B&B per night:
S £46.00–£46.00
D £88.00–£98.00

HB per person:
DY £52.00–£57.00

OPEN All year round

CR
The Independents

Welcoming period-style hotel in good position on Scarborough's South Cliff. Close to beach, spa and town centre. Landau restaurant, parlour bar and roof terrace.

TV 140 SP T

★★★

HACKNESS GRANGE COUNTRY HOUSE HOTEL

North York Moors National Park, Hackness, Scarborough, North Yorkshire YO13 0JW
T: (01723) 882345
F: (01723) 882391
E: hacknessgrange@englishrosehotels.co.uk
I: www.englishrosehotels.co.uk

A stunning setting in the North York Moors National Park best describes this exceptional hotel. Perfect for exploring on foot, by bike or car – the ultimate base. Award-winning cuisine and delightfully furnished accommodation combine with excellent leisure facilities including indoor pool, jacuzzi. For the energetic there's golf and tennis.

Bedrooms: 3 single, 16 double, 7 twin, 3 triple, 4 family rooms; suite available
Bathrooms: 33 en suite

Lunch available
EM 1900 (LO 2100)
Parking for 60
CC: Amex, Barclaycard, Delta, Diners, Eurocard, Mastercard, Switch, Visa

B&B per night:
S £77.50–£87.50
D £135.00–£160.00

HB per person:
DY £54.50–£77.50

OPEN All year round

CR
Best Western Hotels/
The Independents

TV 20 SP T

IDEAS For ideas on places to visit refer to the introduction at the beginning of this section.

★★

MANOR HEATH HOTEL

67 Northstead Manor Drive, Scarborough,
North Yorkshire YO12 6AF
T: (01723) 365720
F: (01723) 365720
E: enquiries@manorheath.freeserve.co.uk
I: www.manorheath.freeserve.co.uk

B&B per night:
S £20.00–£23.00
D £40.00–£46.00

HB per person:
DY £27.00–£31.00

OPEN All year round

Detached hotel offering five-course dinner with choice of menu. Overlooking Peasholm Park and the sea. All rooms en suite with colour TV, radio alarm, tea making facilities. Double glazed and centrally heated. Private car park and garden. Children's reductions. OAP reductions in early/late season. Close to beach. A warm welcome awaits.

Bedrooms: 1 single,
6 double, 2 triple,
5 family rooms
Bathrooms: 14 en suite,
1 public

EM 1800
Parking for 12
CC: Barclaycard, Delta,
Mastercard, Solo, Switch,
Visa

★★

RED LEA HOTEL

Prince of Wales Terrace,
Scarborough, North Yorkshire
YO11 2AJ
T: (01723) 362431
F: (01723) 371230
E: redlea@globalnet.co.uk
I: www.redleahotel.co.uk

Bedrooms: 19 single,
11 double, 26 twin,
9 triple, 3 family rooms
Bathrooms: 68 en suite

Lunch available
EM 1830 (LO 2000)
CC: Amex, Barclaycard,
Delta, Mastercard, Solo,
Switch, Visa

B&B per night:
S £35.00–£37.00
D £70.00–£74.00

HB per person:
DY £48.00–£50.00

OPEN All year round

Traditional hotel with sea views, close to the Spa Centre. Restaurant, bar, lounges, lift and colour TVs. Solarium and indoor heated swimming pool.

★★

RYNDLE COURT PRIVATE HOTEL

47 Northstead Manor Drive,
Scarborough, North Yorkshire
YO12 6AF
T: (01723) 375188 & 07860 711517
F: (01723) 375188
E: enquiries@ryndlecourt.co.uk
I: www.ryndlecourt.co.uk

Bedrooms: 1 single,
7 double, 3 twin, 2 triple,
1 family room
Bathrooms: 14 en suite

Lunch available
EM 1730 (LO 1700)
Parking for 10
CC: Amex, Barclaycard,
Delta, Diners, JCB,
Mastercard, Solo, Switch,
Visa, Visa Electron

B&B per night:
S £29.00–£37.00
D £58.00–£60.00

HB per person:
DY £37.00–£40.00

OPEN Feb–Dec

Pleasantly situated overlooking Peasholm Park and near the sea. All rooms en suite with TV and tea-making facilities. Residents' bar, car park.

★★

SUNNINGDALE HOTEL

105 Peasholm Drive, Scarborough,
North Yorkshire YO12 7NB
T: (01723) 372041 & 07850 784347
F: (01723) 354691
E: sunningdale@barclay.net
I: www.sunningdale-scarborough.
co.uk

Bedrooms: 1 single,
7 double, 1 twin, 1 triple,
1 family room
Bathrooms: 11 en suite,
1 public

EM 1800 (LO 1900)
CC: Amex, Barclaycard,
Delta, JCB, Mastercard,
Solo, Switch, Visa

B&B per night:
S £26.00–£28.00
D £52.00–£56.00

HB per person:
DY £34.00–£36.00

OPEN All year round

Modern, detached hotel facing Peasholm Park and close to all north side attractions. Short, level walk to North Beach. See our website.

MAP REFERENCES
The map references refer to the colour maps at the front of this guide. The first figure is the map number; the letter and figure which follow indicate the grid reference on the map.

★★★★
Silver
Award

Close to junction 4 M180, within easy reach Lincoln, Hull, York. This beautifully-appointed hotel, set in 190 acres of mature woodland with its own 27-hole championship golf course and health club, combined with the choice of exquisite food in the elegant restaurant or real ales in the cosy bars, offers the discerning guest unrivalled quality.

FOREST PINES HOTEL, GOLF COURSE AND SPA

Ermine Street, Broughton, Brigg,
North Lincolnshire DN20 0AQ
T: (01652) 650770 (24 hours) & 650756
F: (01652) 650495
E: enquiries@forestpines.co.uk
I: www.forestpines.co.uk

Bedrooms: 44 double,
40 twin; suites available
Bathrooms: 84 en suite

Lunch available
EM 1900 (LO 2200)
Parking for 300
CC: Amex, Barclaycard,
Delta, Diners, Mastercard,
Switch, Visa, Visa Electron

B&B per night:
S Min £88.00
D Min £96.00

HB per person:
DY Min £108.00

OPEN All year round

Best Western Hotels

250

★★★
Silver
Award

Nestling alongside the tranquil River Derwent, 5 minutes from the M62, 20 minutes' drive from York. Dating back to 1782, this family-run country house boasts superb French/English restaurant, lounges, bar, open fires, large satellite TVs, Chippendale 4-poster room, country views, small lake with wildfowl, riverside walks.

LOFTSOME BRIDGE COACHING HOUSE LTD

Loftsome Bridge, Wressle, Selby,
North Yorkshire YO8 6EN
T: (01757) 630070
F: (01757) 630070
E: reception@loftsomebridge.co.uk
I: www.loftsomebridge-hotel.co.uk

Bedrooms: 8 double,
4 twin, 5 family rooms;
suite available
Bathrooms: 17 en suite

Lunch available
EM 1900 (LO 2145)
Parking for 80
CC: Amex, Delta,
Eurocard, Mastercard,
Switch, Visa, Visa Electron

B&B per night:
S £42.00–£47.00
D £52.00–£57.00

HB per person:
DY £61.95–£66.95

OPEN All year round

★★★

FALCON MANOR HOTEL

Skipton Road, Settle,
North Yorkshire BD24 9BD
T: (01729) 823814
F: (01729) 822087
E: enquiries@thefalconmanor.com
I: www.thefalconmanor.com

Bedrooms: 12 double,
5 twin, 2 triple
Bathrooms: 19 en suite

Lunch available
EM 1900 (LO 2130)
Parking for 80
CC: Amex, Barclaycard,
Delta, Eurocard,
Mastercard, Switch, Visa

B&B per night:
S £55.00–£60.00
D £80.00–£90.00

HB per person:
DY £55.00–£60.00

OPEN All year round

Privately-owned country house hotel in the dales market town of Settle. Ideal base for walking, touring and the Settle to Carlisle Railway.

120

★★

CUTLERS HOTEL

George Street, Sheffield,
South Yorkshire S1 2PF
T: (0114) 273 9939
F: (0114) 276 8332
E: enquiries@cutlershotel.co.uk
I: www.cutlershotel.co.uk

Bedrooms: 10 single,
30 double, 10 twin
Bathrooms: 50 en suite

EM 1800 (LO 2130)
CC: Barclaycard, Delta,
Eurocard, JCB,
Mastercard, Switch, Visa

B&B per night:
S £43.50–£48.50
D £54.50–£59.50

OPEN All year round

Modern hotel superbly positioned in the city centre. Ideal location, friendly atmosphere. Recently refurbished, offering first class accommodation and a wide range of services.

★★★

CONISTON HALL LODGE AND RESTAURANT

Coniston Cold, Skipton, North Yorkshire
BD23 4EB
T: (01756) 748080
F: (01756) 749487
E: conistonhall@clara.net
I: www.conistonhall.co.uk

Delightful hotel, set in 1,200 acres of private Yorkshire Dales parkland, centred on a 24-acre lake. Ideal for walking and fishing holidays and as a base for exploring the dales. Public bar with log fire serving tapas dishes. En suite rooms, all with satellite TV. Superb cuisine and warm welcome guaranteed.

Bedrooms: 38 double, 2 twin
Bathrooms: 40 en suite

Lunch available
EM 1700 (LO 2100)
Parking for 50
CC: Amex, Barclaycard, Delta, Diners, Mastercard, Solo, Switch, Visa

B&B per night:
S £48.50–£70.00
D £57.00–£79.00

HB per person:
DY £54.00–£74.00

OPEN All year round

A 🎿 👪 ♿ 📞 🖥 ☐ 👆 ♨ ☎ S ⚓ ⛵ 📺 ◑ ⛱ ⚓ ⛳ 100 ∪ ⚓ ► ✦ SC ⚓ SP T

★★

UNICORN HOTEL

Devonshire Place, Keighley Road,
Skipton, North Yorkshire BD23 2LP
T: (01756) 794146 & 793376
F: (01756) 793376
E: christine@unicornhotel.
freeserve.co.uk

Centrally situated, with double-glazing to ensure peace and tranquillity. Ideal base for touring Bronte Country and the Yorkshire Dales. Refurbished to a high standard.

Bedrooms: 6 double,
1 twin, 1 triple, 1 family room
Bathrooms: 9 en suite

EM 1900 (LO 2100)
CC: Amex, Barclaycard, Delta, Eurocard, Mastercard, Solo, Switch, Visa

B&B per night:
S £35.00–£45.00
D £55.00–£65.00

HB per person:
DY Min £45.00

OPEN All year round

A 🎿 📞 🖥 ☐ 👆 ♨ S 📺 ☐ ⚓ ⛱ ⛳ SP T

★★

ANGEL INN

Long Street, Topcliffe, Thirsk,
North Yorkshire YO7 3RW
T: (01845) 577237
F: (01845) 578000

Well-appointed, attractive village inn, renowned for good food and traditional ales. Ideal centre for touring York and Herriot Country.

Bedrooms: 2 single,
8 double, 4 twin,
1 family room
Bathrooms: 15 en suite

Lunch available
EM 1830 (LO 2130)
Parking for 150
CC: Barclaycard, Delta, Eurocard, JCB, Mastercard, Switch, Visa

B&B per night:
S £44.50–£50.00
D £60.00–£70.00

HB per person:
DY £45.00–£55.00

OPEN All year round

A 🎿 📞 🖥 ☐ 👆 ♨ S 📺 ☐ ⚓ ⛱ 150 ⚓ ⚓ ✦ ✕ ⛳ SP T

★★
Silver Award

GOLDEN FLEECE

Market Place, Thirsk, North Yorkshire
YO7 1LL
T: (01845) 523108
F: (01845) 523996
I: www.@bestwestern.co.uk

This historic coaching inn has attractive newly refurbished bedrooms, including some superior and antique 4-poster rooms. The bar and restaurant serve good food and fine wines as well as locally brewed ales. Ideally placed between dales and moors, and within walking distance of the new "World of James Herriot" visitor centre.

Bedrooms: 1 single,
14 double, 2 twin,
1 triple
Bathrooms: 18 en suite

Lunch available
EM 1900 (LO 2100)
Parking for 30
CC: Amex, Barclaycard, Delta, Eurocard, Mastercard, Solo, Switch, Visa, Visa Electron

B&B per night:
S £65.00–£85.00
D £85.00–£105.00

HB per person:
DY £75.00–£85.00

OPEN All year round

A 🎿 🏠 📞 🖥 ☐ 👆 ♨ S ⚓ 📺 ☐ ⚓ ⛱ 110 ∪ ► ⚓ SP 🏨 T

IMPORTANT NOTE
Information on accommodation listed in this guide has been supplied by the proprietors. As changes may occur you are advised to check details at the time of booking.

THIRSK continued

★★ **SHEPPARDS HOTEL RESTAURANT AND BISTRO**

Front Street, Sowerby, Thirsk,	Bedrooms: 6 double,	Lunch available	B&B per night:
North Yorkshire YO7 1JF	2 twin	EM 1900 (LO 2200)	S £62.00–£62.00
T: (01845) 523655	Bathrooms: 8 en suite	Parking for 35	D £84.00–£84.00
F: (01845) 524720		CC: Barclaycard, Delta,	
E: sheppards@thirskny.freeserve.		Eurocard, Mastercard,	OPEN All year round
co.uk		Switch, Visa	

17thC building on the village green. Carefully developed, giving every comfort whilst maintaining its rural atmosphere. An ideal centre for touring Herriot's Yorkshire.

🐾10 🏠 📞 🖥 ▢ 🛁 🕿 🛎 🅂 ⊁ 🍴 🏬 ⬛ 🍽60 ✿ ✕ 🚗 SP T

THORNTON WATLASS, North Yorkshire Map ref 5C3

★

THE BUCK INN

Thornton Watlass, Ripon, North Yorkshire
HG4 4AH
T: (01677) 422461
F: (01677) 422447

B&B per night:
S Min £40.00
D Min £60.00

HB per person:
DY Min £45.00

OPEN All year round

Friendly village inn overlooking	Bedrooms: 1 single,	Lunch available
delightful cricket green in quiet	3 double, 2 twin, 1 triple	EM 1830 (LO 2130)
village. Just 5 minutes from A1. Relax	Bathrooms: 5 en suite,	Parking for 40
in our comfortable bedrooms. Enjoy	1 public	CC: Amex, Barclaycard,
our superb home cooked food and		Delta, Diners, Eurocard,
drink from our selection of real ales.		JCB, Maestro, Mastercard,
Large secluded garden with		Solo, Switch, Visa, Visa
children's play area. Private river fly		Electron
fishing. Ideal centre for exploring.		

🅰 🐾 ♨ 🖥 🛁 🅂 ⊁ 🍴 TV 🏬 ⬛ 🍽70 📞 ∪ ♪ ♣ ✿ SC 🐾 SP T

WAKEFIELD, West Yorkshire Map ref 4B1 *Tourist Information Centre Tel: (01924) 305000 or 305001*

★★

PARKLANDS HOTEL

143 Horbury Road, Wakefield,
West Yorkshire WF2 8TY
T: (01924) 377407
F: (01924) 290348
E: steve@parklands23.fsnet.co.uk

B&B per night:
S £36.50–£42.50
D £46.50–£52.00

HB per person:
DY Min £46.50

OPEN All year round

Old friends and new are always	Bedrooms: 8 single,	Lunch available
welcome at the Parklands Hotel and	3 double, 1 twin	EM 1845 (LO 2115)
St Michael's Restaurant. Elegant	Bathrooms: 11 en suite,	Parking for 20
Victorian former vicarage	1 private	CC: Amex, Barclaycard,
overlooking 680 acres of beautiful		Delta, Eurocard,
parkland. Family-run for over 35		Mastercard, Solo, Switch,
years, providing a high standard of		Visa, Visa Electron
service and cuisine and well-		
appointed en suite bedrooms. Self-		
catering cottages also available.		

🅰 🐾 🏠 📞 🖥 ▢ 🕿 🅂 ⊁ 🍴 TV 🏬 ⬛ 🍽40 ∪ ♣ ✿ SC 🐾 SP 🎱 T

WEST WITTON, North Yorkshire Map ref 5B3

★★ **WENSLEYDALE HEIFER**

West Witton, Leyburn,	Bedrooms: 8 double,	Lunch available	B&B per night:
North Yorkshire DL8 4LS	4 twin, 1 triple, 1 family	EM 1830 (LO 2130)	S £60.00–£65.00
T: (01969) 622322	room; suite available	Parking for 40	D £72.00–£100.00
F: (01969) 624183	Bathrooms: 14 en suite	CC: Amex, Barclaycard,	
E: info@wensleydaleheifer.co.uk		Delta, Diners, Eurocard,	HB per person:
I: www.wensleydaleheifer.co.uk		Mastercard, Switch, Visa	DY £46.00–£60.00

17thC inn situated in Yorkshire Dales National Park. Award-winning restaurant and bistro. Four-poster bedrooms. Special breaks. Dogs welcome. Rustic country cooking.

OPEN All year round

🅰 🐾 ♨ 🖥 📞 🖥 ▢ 🛁 🕿 🅂 🍴 🏬 ⬛ ∪ ♪ ♣ ✿ SC 🐾 SP 🎱 T

PRICES

Please check prices and other details at the time of booking.

★★

SAXONVILLE HOTEL
Ladysmith Avenue, Whitby,
North Yorkshire YO21 3HX
T: (01947) 602631 & 0800 019 1147
F: (01947) 820523
E: saxonville@onyxnet.co.uk
I: www.yorkshirenet.co.uk/saxonville

B&B per night:
S £40.00–£40.00
D £80.00–£80.00

HB per person:
DY £51.00–£52.50

OPEN Apr–Oct

Family-owned and run since 1946. The hotel is situated on the West Cliff just a short stroll from Whitby's narrow streets and winding alleys. Guests are assured of a warm, friendly welcome and a high standard of service. Private car park. No supplement on single rooms.

Bedrooms: 4 single,
5 double, 11 twin,
2 triple
Bathrooms: 22 en suite

Lunch available
EM 1900 (LO 2030)
Parking for 20
CC: Barclaycard, Delta,
Mastercard, Switch, Visa

★★
Silver
Award

STAKESBY MANOR
Manor Close, High Stakesby, Whitby,
North Yorkshire YO21 1HL
T: (01947) 602773
F: (01947) 602140
E: relax@stakesby-manor.co.uk
I: www.stakesby-manor.co.uk

B&B per night:
S £54.00–£54.00
D £74.00–£80.00

HB per person:
DY £45.00–£53.00

OPEN All year round

Ⓒ
Minotel

Georgian house dating back to 1710, in its own grounds, on the outskirts of Whitby in the North York Moors National Park. Atmospheric oak panelled dining room serving freshly prepared food. Some non-smoking rooms. Open fires in winter. Views over moors or the roof tops of Whitby.

Bedrooms: 10 double,
3 twin
Bathrooms: 13 en suite

Lunch available
EM 1900 (LO 2130)
Parking for 30
CC: Amex, Barclaycard,
Delta, Eurocard, JCB,
Mastercard, Switch, Visa

★★

ALHAMBRA COURT HOTEL
31 St Mary's, Bootham, York, YO30 7DD
T: (01904) 628474 & 647427 (Guests)
F: (01904) 610690

B&B per night:
S £35.00–£47.50
D £50.00–£75.00

OPEN All year round

Situated in one of the most popular locations, a family-run hotel in a quiet cul-de-sac, 5 minutes' walk from city centre. 24 bedrooms, all en suite with full facilities, comfortable lounges, cosy bar and non-smoking restaurant. Lift. Private car park. Midweek winter breaks from £68.00 per person for 2 nights' dinner, bed and breakfast.

Bedrooms: 3 single,
9 double, 7 twin, 4 triple,
1 family room
Bathrooms: 24 en suite

EM 1800 (LO 2030)
Parking for 20
CC: Barclaycard, Delta,
Maestro, Mastercard,
Solo, Switch, Visa, Visa
Electron

CENTRAL RESERVATIONS OFFICES
The symbol Ⓒ and a group name in an entry indicate that bookings can be made through a central reservations office. These are listed in a separate section towards the back of this guide.

★★★

AMBASSADOR

123-125 The Mount, York, YO24 1DU
T: (01904) 641316
F: (01904) 640259
E: stay@ambassadorhotel.co.uk
I: www.ambassadorhotel.co.uk

B&B per night:
S £90.00–£108.00
D £118.00–£128.00

OPEN All year round

CR
Best Western Hotels

Carefully created within this fine Georgian building, without sacrificing style or elegance, is the Ambassador Hotel. Beautiful bedrooms, the award-winning Grays restaurant, where the food is simple and delicious, the decor classic. Easy walk to the city centre or racecourse. Ample car parking in the grounds.

Bedrooms: 18 double, 7 twin
Bathrooms: 25 en suite

Lunch available
EM 1830 (LO 2130)
Parking for 38
CC: Amex, Barclaycard, Delta, Diners, Mastercard, Switch, Visa

---

★★

ASHCROFT HOTEL

294 Bishopthorpe Road, York, YO23 1LH
T: (01904) 659286 & 629543
F: (01904) 640107

B&B per night:
S £40.00–£48.00
D £55.00–£85.00

HB per person:
DY £40.00–£55.00

OPEN All year round

CR
Minotel

Victorian former mansion in 2 acres of wooded grounds overlooking the River Ouse, only 1 mile from the city centre. All bedrooms are en suite and have colour TV, radio, telephone, coffee/tea-making facilities, hairdryer and trouser press.

Bedrooms: 1 single, 7 double, 4 twin, 1 triple, 2 family rooms
Bathrooms: 15 en suite

Lunch available
EM 1900 (LO 2130)
Parking for 35
CC: Amex, Barclaycard, Delta, Diners, Eurocard, JCB, Mastercard, Solo, Switch, Visa, Visa Electron

---

★★

COTTAGE HOTEL

1 Clifton Green, York, YO30 6LH
T: (01904) 643711
F: (01904) 611230

B&B per night:
S £35.00–£45.00
D £45.00–£65.00

HB per person:
DY £29.50–£39.50

OPEN All year round

Enchanting, family-run hotel 10 minutes' walk from city centre, overlooking beautiful Clifton Green. Four-poster bedrooms available. Private car park. We offer dinner, bed and breakfast breaks at special rates. Brochure available on request.

Bedrooms: 2 single, 11 double, 5 twin, 2 triple
Bathrooms: 20 en suite

EM 1830 (LO 2030)
Parking for 12
CC: Amex, Barclaycard, Diners, Mastercard, Switch, Visa

AT-A-GLANCE SYMBOLS

Symbols at the end of each accommodation entry give useful information about services and facilities. A key to symbols can be found inside the back cover flap. Keep this open for easy reference.

★★★
Silver
Award

DEAN COURT HOTEL

Duncombe Place, York, YO1 7EF
T: (01904) 625082
F: (01904) 620305
E: info@deancourt-york.co.uk
I: www.deancourt-york.co.uk

B&B per night:
S £70.00–£95.00
D £95.00–£170.00

HB per person:
DY £70.00–£100.00

OPEN All year round

CR
Best Western Hotels

Superbly appointed hotel with unrivalled location opposite York Minster. All the historic attractions of York are within easy walking distance. All bedrooms and public areas have been tastefully refurbished 1998/99 and include 4 de-luxe rooms. Enjoy the award-winning food in the restaurant or cosy cafe conservatory. Secure car park and valet parking service.

Bedrooms: 9 single, 20 double, 6 twin, 2 triple, 2 family rooms; suite available
Bathrooms: 39 en suite

Lunch available
EM 1900 (LO 2130)
Parking for 30
CC: Amex, Barclaycard, Delta, Diners, Eurocard, JCB, Mastercard, Switch, Visa

---

★

GRANBY LODGE HOTEL

41-43 Scarcroft Road, York, YO24 1DB
T: (01904) 653291
F: (01904) 653291

B&B per night:
S £30.00–£35.00
D £60.00–£70.00

HB per person:
DY £40.00–£45.00

OPEN All year round

Victorian family hotel offering all modern comforts and a mezzanine bar-lounge. En suite bedrooms. Walking distance of city centre. Car park. Close to racecourse.

Bedrooms: 9 single, 15 double, 11 twin, 4 triple, 4 family rooms
Bathrooms: 41 en suite, 4 public

EM 1800 (LO 1900)
Parking for 30
CC: Amex, Barclaycard, Diners, Eurocard, Mastercard, Visa

★★★
Silver
Award

THE GRANGE HOTEL

1 Clifton, York, YO30 6AA
T: (01904) 644744
F: (01904) 612453
E: info@grangehotel.co.uk
I: www.grangehotel.co.uk

B&B per night:
S £99.00–£160.00
D £125.00–£215.00

HB per person:
DY £59.00–£112.00

OPEN All year round

Exclusive Regency townhouse of great charm and character just minutes from York Minster and city centre. Furnished in classic country-house style, this beautifully restored Listed building has 30 luxurious en suite bedrooms, 3 superb restaurants, award-winning food and first class service. Excellent conference and private dining facilities. Private car park.

Bedrooms: 3 single, 10 double, 16 twin, 1 family room; suite available
Bathrooms: 30 en suite

Lunch available
EM 1800 (LO 2200)
Parking for 26
CC: Amex, Barclaycard, Delta, Diners, Eurocard, JCB, Mastercard, Switch, Visa

---

CREDIT CARD BOOKINGS
If you book by telephone and are asked for your credit card number it is advisable to check the proprietor's policy should you cancel your reservation.

★★

HEDLEY HOUSE
3-4 Bootham Terrace, York,
North Yorkshire YO30 7DH

T: (01904) 637404
F: (01904) 639774
E: h.h@mcmail.com
I: www.hedleyhouse.com

B&B per night:
S £25.00–£46.00
D £48.00–£70.00

HB per person:
DY £35.00–£54.00

OPEN All year round

Family-run hotel in a quiet residential area within 10 minutes' walk of the city centre. All rooms have private bathroom, remote colour TV, telephone and hospitality tray. Vegetarian and special diets catered for. Off-street car park and lock-up garages available.

Bedrooms: 2 single,
5 double, 5 twin, 2 triple,
2 family rooms
Bathrooms: 16 en suite

Lunch available
EM 1830 (LO 1900)
Parking for 18
CC: Amex, Barclaycard,
Delta, Eurocard, JCB,
Mastercard, Solo, Switch,
Visa, Visa Electron

★★★
Silver
Award

JUDGES LODGING
9 Lendal, York, YO1 8AQ
T: (01904) 623587 & 638733
F: (01904) 679947
E: judgeshotel@aol.com

B&B per night:
S £75.00–£80.00
D £100.00–£175.00

HB per person:
DY £85.00–£185.00

OPEN All year round

Proprietor: Gerald C. Mason, MBE. Grade I Listed Georgian townhouse of exceptional historic importance. The most centrally located hotel in the city centre. Lavishly decorated and furnished, many 4-poster beds, spa baths. Private car parking.

Bedrooms: 2 single,
6 double, 4 twin, 3 triple;
suites available
Bathrooms: 15 en suite

Lunch available
EM 1700 (LO 2130)
Parking for 16
CC: Amex, Barclaycard,
Mastercard, Switch, Visa

★★

KILIMA HOTEL
129 Holgate Road, York, YO24 4AZ
T: (01904) 625787
F: (01904) 612083
E: sales@kilima.co.uk
I: www.kilima.co.uk

Bedrooms: 4 single,
7 double, 3 twin,
1 family room
Bathrooms: 15 en suite

Lunch available
EM 1830 (LO 2130)
Parking for 20
CC: Amex, Barclaycard,
Diners, Mastercard,
Switch, Visa

B&B per night:
S Min £58.00
D Min £86.00

HB per person:
DY Min £63.00

OPEN All year round

Lovingly furbished 19thC rectory with a fine restaurant serving a la carte and table d'hote. Walking distance to city centre. Private car park.

Best Western Hotels

★★

LADY ANNE MIDDLETON'S HOTEL
Skeldergate, York, YO1 6DS
T: (01904) 611570
F: (01904) 613043
E: bookings@ladyannes.co.uk
I: www.ladyannes.co.uk

B&B per night:
S £50.00–£80.00
D £80.00–£120.00

HB per person:
DY £60.00–£75.00

OPEN All year round

Collection of historic buildings in English courtyard gardens, close to the river and within city walls. Free car parking, short walk to all main attractions. Conservatory restaurant serves predominantly English dishes. Health club with fitness pool (not suitable for under 16s).

Bedrooms: 3 single,
31 double, 15 twin,
3 triple; suites available
Bathrooms: 52 en suite

Lunch available
EM 1800 (LO 2100)
Parking for 50
CC: Amex, Barclaycard,
Delta, Mastercard, Switch,
Visa

SYMBOLS The symbols in each entry give information about services and facilities. A key to these symbols appears at the back of this guide.

★★★

MONKBAR HOTEL
St Maurice's Road, York, YO31 7JA
T: (01904) 638086
F: (01904) 629195
E: colin-gardner@monkbar-york.freeserve.co.uk

B&B per night:
S £70.00–£89.00

HB per person:
DY £80.00–£99.00

OPEN All year round

CR
Best Western Hotels

A short walk from York Minster and all tourist attractions. Attractive bedrooms, 4-poster room, jacuzzi. Friendly hotel with award-winning food. Courtyard garden. Parking on site.

Bedrooms: 7 single,
32 double, 60 twin
Bathrooms: 99 en suite

Lunch available
EM 1800 (LO 2130)
Parking for 80
CC: Amex, Barclaycard,
Delta, Diners, Eurocard,
Maestro, Mastercard,
Switch, Visa

★★

NEWINGTON HOTEL
147-157 Mount Vale, York,
YO24 1DJ
T: (01904) 625173 & 623090
F: (01904) 679937
E: bookings@ladyannes.co.uk
I: www.ladyannes.co.uk

Bedrooms: 6 single,
19 double, 9 twin,
6 triple, 2 family rooms
Bathrooms: 42 en suite

Lunch available
EM 1800 (LO 2115)
CC: Amex, Barclaycard,
Mastercard, Switch, Visa

B&B per night:
S £50.00–£60.00
D £80.00–£110.00

HB per person:
DY £52.00–£62.00

OPEN All year round

Hotel in a fine Georgian terrace, next to York's famous racecourse and within walking distance of city centre. Car park, indoor swimming pool, sauna.

★★

ORCHARD COURT HOTEL
4 St Peter's Grove, Bootham, York,
YO30 6AQ
T: (01904) 653964
F: (01904) 653964

Bedrooms: 3 single,
5 double, 2 twin, 2 triple,
2 family rooms
Bathrooms: 12 en suite,
2 public

EM 1800 (LO 2000)
Parking for 14
CC: Amex, Barclaycard,
Delta, Diners, Eurocard,
JCB, Maestro, Mastercard,
Switch, Visa, Visa Electron

B&B per night:
S £25.00–£35.00
D £40.00–£60.00

HB per person:
DY £28.00–£38.00

OPEN All year round

Friendly, family-run Victorian hotel in quiet location within 10 minutes' walk of city centre and its historic attractions.

★★★

THE PARSONAGE COUNTRY HOUSE HOTEL
York Road, Escrick, York, YO19 6LF
T: (01904) 728111
F: (01904) 728151
E: reservations@parsonagehotel.co.uk
I: www.parsonagehotel.co.uk

B&B per night:
S £75.00–£95.00
D £95.00–£125.00

HB per person:
DY £60.00–£95.00

OPEN All year round

CR
Grand Heritage Hotels

The Parsonage Country House Hotel ia a Grade II Listed building set in 6.5 acres of woodland and gardens, offering peace and relaxation yet only minutes from York city centre. An award-winning restaurant complements luxurious accommodation with non-smoking and ground floor rooms available.

Bedrooms: 20 double,
1 twin; suite available
Bathrooms: 21 en suite

Lunch available
EM 1900 (LO 2130)
Parking for 120
CC: Amex, Barclaycard,
Delta, Diners, Eurocard,
Mastercard, Switch, Visa

WELCOME HOST This is a nationally recognised customer care programme which aims to promote the highest standards of service and a warm welcome. Establishments taking part in this initiative are indicated by the ⊛ symbol.

TRAVEL
ACCOMMODATION

QUEENS HOTEL

Queens Staith Road, Skeldergate, York,
YO32 5XF
T: (01904) 611321

B&B per night:
D Min £45.00

OPEN All year round

Tourist lodge on the banks of the River Ouse in the heart of the ancient city of York. All family rooms (1 – 4 persons) with en suite facilities, colour TV, tea/coffee-making facilities, hairdryers. Breakfast available.

Bedrooms: 80 family rooms
Bathrooms: 80 en suite

CC: Mastercard, Switch, Visa

★★★★

ROYAL YORK HOTEL

Station Road, York, YO24 1AA
T: (01904) 653681
F: (01904) 623503
E: julia.bodmer@principalhotels.co.uk
I: www.principalhotels.co.uk

Bedrooms: 28 single, 64 double, 56 twin, 6 triple, 4 family rooms; suites available
Bathrooms: 158 en suite

Lunch available
EM 1900 (LO 2145)
Parking for 120
CC: Amex, Barclaycard, Delta, Diners, JCB, Mastercard, Solo, Switch, Visa, Visa Electron

B&B per night:
S £74.00–£140.00

OPEN All year round

©®

Principal Hotels/Utell International

Set in 3 acres of private grounds, this magnificent Victorian hotel is in the centre of historic York. Prices are based on minimum 2-night stay.

★★

SAVAGES HOTEL

15 St Peter's Grove, Clifton, York,
YO30 6AQ
T: (01904) 610818
F: (01904) 627729

B&B per night:
S £24.50–£35.00
D £49.00–£70.00

HB per person:
DY £34.50–£45.00

OPEN All year round

A Victorian hotel, close to the city centre in peaceful tree-lined St Peter's Grove, Savages Hotel offers the comforts and services to make your stay a relaxing and memorable occasion. Comfortable, well-equipped bedrooms (some ground floor) and traditional restaurant serving fine food.

Bedrooms: 3 single, 9 double, 5 twin, 1 triple, 3 family rooms
Bathrooms: 21 en suite

EM 1800 (LO 2100)
Parking for 14
CC: Amex, Barclaycard, Delta, Diners, Maestro, Mastercard, Solo, Switch, Visa, Visa Electron

---

QUALITY ASSURANCE SCHEME

For an explanation of the quality and facilities represented by the Stars please refer to the front of this guide. A more detailed explanation can be found in the information pages at the back.

A brief guide to the main Towns and Villages offering accommodation in YORKSHIRE

B BARNSLEY, SOUTH YORKSHIRE -
Barnsley became rich through coal and glass.
It has Norman origins and the ruins of Monk
Bretton Priory include 13th C chapter house
and church. Attractions are Cooper Art Gallery,
Cannon Hall and Worsbrough Mill.

● **BEDALE, NORTH YORKSHIRE** -
Ancient church of St Gregory and Georgian
Bedale Hall occupy commanding positions over
this market town situated in good hunting
country. The hall, which contains interesting
architectural features including great ballroom
and flying-type staircase, now houses a library
and museum.

● **BOROUGHBRIDGE, NORTH YORKSHIRE** -
On the River Ure, Boroughbridge was once an
important coaching centre with 22 inns and in
the 18th C a port for Knaresborough's linens. It
has fine old houses, many trees and a cobbled
square with market cross. Nearby stand 3
megaliths known as the Devil's Arrows.

● **BRADFORD, WEST YORKSHIRE** -
City founded on wool, with fine Victorian and
modern buildings. Attractions include the
cathedral, city hall, Cartwright Hall, Lister Park,
Moorside Mills Industrial Museum and
National Museum of Photography, Film and
Television.

● **BRANDESBURTON, EAST RIDING OF
YORKSHIRE** - The village church retains work
from the Norman period through to the 15th
C, and the shaft of a medieval cross stands on
the village green.

● **BRIDLINGTON, EAST RIDING OF
YORKSHIRE** - Lively seaside resort with long
sandy beaches, Leisure World and busy harbour
with fishing trips in cobles. Priory church of
St Mary whose Bayle Gate is now a museum.
Mementoes of flying pioneer, Amy Johnson, in
Sewerby Hall. Harbour Museum and Aquarium.

D DEWSBURY, WEST YORKSHIRE -
Town most famous for woollen products, with
history going back to Saxon times. Robin Hood
is reputed to have died and been buried in the
Cistercian convent in Kirklees Park nearby. Old
custom of tolling the Devil's Knell on
Christmas Eve to remind the devil of his
defeat.

● **DONCASTER, SOUTH YORKSHIRE** -
Ancient Roman town famous for its heavy
industries, butterscotch and racecourse (St
Leger), also centre of agricultural area.
Attractions include 18th C Mansion House,
Cusworth Hall Museum, Doncaster Museum,
St George's Church, The Dome and Doncaster
Leisure Park.

E EASINGWOLD, NORTH YORKSHIRE -
Market town of charm and character with a
cobbled square and many fine Georgian
buildings.

G GILLAMOOR, NORTH YORKSHIRE -
Village much admired by photographers for its
views of Farndale, including "Surprise View"
from the churchyard.

● **GOATHLAND, NORTH YORKSHIRE** -
Spacious village with several large greens
grazed by sheep, an ideal centre for walking
the North York Moors. Nearby are several
waterfalls, among them Mallyan Spout. Plough
Monday celebrations held in January. Location
for filming of TV "Heartbeat" series.

● **GOOLE, NORTH LINCOLNSHIRE** - Busy
port on the River Ouse developed with the
opening of the Aire and Calder Canal in 1826
and reminiscent of the Netherlands with its
red brick buildings and flat, watery landscape.
Goole Museum houses Garside Local History
Collection.

● **GRASSINGTON, NORTH YORKSHIRE** -
Tourists visit this former lead-mining village
to see its "smiddy", antique and craft shops
and Upper Wharfedale Museum of country
trades. Popular with fishermen and walkers.
Cobbled market square, numerous prehistoric
sites. Grassington Feast in October. National
Park Centre.

● **GRIMSBY, NORTH EAST LINCOLNSHIRE** -
Founded 1,000 years ago by a Danish fisherman
named Grim, Grimsby is today a major fishing
port and docks. It has modern shopping
precincts and National Fishing Heritage Centre,
voted England's top tourist attraction in 1992.

H HALIFAX, WEST YORKSHIRE - Founded
on the cloth trade, and famous for its building
society, textiles, carpets and toffee. Most
notable landmark is Piece Hall where wool
merchants traded, now restored to house
shops, museums and art gallery. Home also
to Eureka! The Museum for Children.

● **HARROGATE, NORTH YORKSHIRE** -
Major conference, exhibition and shopping
centre, renowned for its spa heritage and
award-winning floral displays, spacious parks
and gardens. Famous for antiques, toffee, fine
shopping and excellent tea shops, also its
Royal Pump Rooms and Baths. Annual Great
Yorkshire Show in July.

● **HAWES, NORTH YORKSHIRE** - The capital
of Upper Wensleydale on the famous Pennine
Way, Yorkshire's highest market town and
renowned for great cheeses. Popular with
walkers. Dales National Park Information
Centre and Folk Museum. Nearby is spectacular
Hardraw Force waterfall.

● **HAWORTH, WEST YORKSHIRE** -
Famous since 1820 as home of the Bronte
family. The Parsonage is now a Bronte Museum
where furniture and possessions of the family
are displayed. Moors and Bronte waterfalls
nearby and steam trains on the Keighley and
Worth Valley Railway pass through.

● **HEBDEN BRIDGE, WEST YORKSHIRE** -
Originally a small town on packhorse route,
Hebden Bridge grew into a booming mill town
in the 18th C with rows of "up-and-down"
houses of several storeys built against hillsides.
Ancient "pace-egg play" custom held on
Good Friday.

● **HELMSLEY, NORTH YORKSHIRE** -
Delightful small market town with red roofs,
warm stone buildings and cobbled market
square, on the River Rye at the entrance to
Ryedale and the North York Moors. Remains
of 12th C castle, several inns and All Saints'
Church.

● **HOLMFIRTH, WEST YORKSHIRE** - Village
on the edge of the Peak District National Park,
famous as the location for the filming of the
TV series "Last of the Summer Wine".

● **HOVINGHAM, NORTH YORKSHIRE** -
Peaceful village of golden stone cottages,
below Hambleton Hills, clustering around
Hovingham Hall, home of Duchess of Kent's
family. Built by Sir Thomas Worsley in 1760,
the Hall is open to the public by appointment.

● **HOWDEN, EAST RIDING OF YORKSHIRE**
Small town near the River Ouse, dominated by
partly-ruined medieval church of St Peter's
which has ancient origins but has been rebuilt
in a range of architectural styles over the
centuries. The ruined choir and chapter house
are best seen from the picturesque market
place.

● **HUDDERSFIELD, WEST YORKSHIRE** -
Founded on wool and cloth, has a famous
choral society. Town centre redeveloped, but
several good Victorian buildings remain,
including railway station, St Peter's Church,
Tolson Memorial Museum, art gallery and
nearby Colne Valley Museum.

● **HULL** - Busy seaport with a modern city
centre and excellent shopping facilities.
Maritime traditions in the town, docks
museum, and the home of William Wilberforce,
the slavery abolitionist, whose house is now a
museum. The Humber Bridge is 5 miles west.

I ILKLEY, WEST YORKSHIRE - Former spa
with an elegant shopping centre and famous
for its ballad. The 16th C manor house, now a
museum, displays local prehistoric and Roman
relics. Popular walk leads up Heber's Ghyll to
Ilkley Moor, with the mysterious Swastika
Stone and White Wells, 18th C plunge baths.

CONFIRM YOUR BOOKING
You are advised to confirm your booking in writing.

K **KIRKBYMOORSIDE, NORTH YORKSHIRE** - Attractive market town with remains of Norman castle. Good centre for exploring moors. Nearby are wild daffodils of Farndale.

L **LEEDS, WEST YORKSHIRE** - Large city with excellent modern shopping centre and splendid Victorian architecture. Museums and galleries including Temple Newsam House (the Hampton Court of the North), Tetley's Brewery Wharf and the Royal Armouries Museum; also home of Opera North.

- **LEYBURN, NORTH YORKSHIRE** - Attractive dales market town where Mary Queen of Scots was reputedly captured after her escape from Bolton Castle. Fine views over Wensleydale from nearby.

- **LIVERSEDGE, WEST YORKSHIRE** - Typical West Yorkshire town 3 miles north-west of Dewsbury.

M **MALTON, NORTH YORKSHIRE** - Thriving farming town on the River Derwent with large livestock market. Famous for racehorse training. The local museum has Roman remains and the Eden Camp Modern History Theme Museum transports visitors back to wartime Britain. Castle Howard within easy reach.

- **MIDDLEHAM, NORTH YORKSHIRE** - Town famous for racehorse training, with cobbled squares and houses of local stone. Norman castle, once principal residence of Warwick the Kingmaker and later Richard III. Ancient stronghold of the Neville family was taken over by the Crown after the Battle of Barnet in 1471.

- **MORLEY, WEST YORKSHIRE** - On the outskirts of Leeds, just off the M62 and close to the M1. The Town Hall dominates the town. Textiles, engineering and coal-mining area.

N **NEWBY WISKE, NORTH YORKSHIRE** - Village on the River Wiske in the Vale of Mowbray.

P **PATELEY BRIDGE, NORTH YORKSHIRE** - Small market town at centre of Upper Nidderdale. Flax and linen industries once flourished in this remote and beautiful setting. Remains of Bronze Age settlements and disused lead mines.

R **RICHMOND, NORTH YORKSHIRE** - Market town on edge of Swaledale with 11th C castle, Georgian and Victorian buildings surrounding cobbled market-place. Green Howards' Museum is in the former Holy Trinity Church. Attractions include the Georgian Theatre, restored Theatre Royal, Richmondshire Museum, Easby Abbey.

- **RIPON, NORTH YORKSHIRE** - Small, ancient city with impressive cathedral containing Saxon crypt which houses church treasures from all over Yorkshire. Charter granted in 886 by Alfred the Great. "Setting the Watch" tradition kept nightly by horn-blower in Market Square. Fountains Abbey nearby.

- **ROSEDALE ABBEY, NORTH YORKSHIRE** - Sturdy hamlet built around Cistercian nunnery in the reign of Henry II, in the middle of Rosedale, largest of the moorland valleys. Remains of 12th C priory. Disused lead mines on the surrounding moors.

- **ROTHERHAM, SOUTH YORKSHIRE** - In the Don Valley, Rotherham became an important industrial town in the 19th C with discovery of coal and development of iron and steel industry by Joshua Walker who built Clifton House, now the town's museum. Magnificent 15th C All Saints Church is town's showpiece.

S **SCARBOROUGH, NORTH YORKSHIRE** - Large, popular East Coast seaside resort, formerly a spa town. Beautiful gardens and two splendid sandy beaches. Castle ruins date from 1100; fine Georgian and Victorian houses. Scarborough Millennium depicts 1,000 years of town's history. Sea Life Centre.

- **SCUNTHORPE, NORTH LINCOLNSHIRE** - Consisted of 5 small villages until 1860 when extensive ironstone beds were discovered. Today an industrial "garden town" with some interesting modern buildings. Nearby Normanby Hall contains fine examples of Regency furniture.

- **SELBY, NORTH YORKSHIRE** - Small market town on the River Ouse, believed to have been birthplace of Henry I, with a magnificent abbey containing much fine Norman and Early English architecture.

- **SETTLE, NORTH YORKSHIRE** - Town of narrow streets and Georgian houses in an area of great limestone hills and crags. Panoramic view from Castleberg Crag which stands 300ft above town.

- **SHEFFIELD, SOUTH YORKSHIRE** - Local iron ore and coal gave Sheffield its prosperous steel and cutlery industries. The modern city centre has many interesting buildings - Cathedral, Cutlers' Hall, Crucible Theatre, Graves and Mappin Art Galleries. Meadowhall Shopping Centre nearby.

- **SKIPTON, NORTH YORKSHIRE** - Pleasant market town at gateway to dales, with farming community atmosphere, a Palladian Town Hall, parish church and fully roofed castle at the top of the High Street. The Clifford family motto, "Desoramis" is sculpted in huge letters on the parapet over the castle gateway.

T **THIRSK, NORTH YORKSHIRE** - Thriving market town with cobbled square surrounded by old shops and inns. St Mary's Church is probably the best example of Perpendicular work in Yorkshire. House of Thomas Lord founder of Lord's Cricket Ground - is now a folk museum.

- **THORNTON WATLASS, NORTH YORKSHIRE** - Picturesque village in Lower Wensleydale.

W **WAKEFIELD, WEST YORKSHIRE** - Thriving city with cathedral church of All Saints boasting 247-ft spire. Old Bridge, a 9-arched structure, has fine medieval chantry chapels of St Mary's. Fine Georgian architecture and good shopping centre (The Ridings). National Coal Mining Museum for England nearby.

- **WEST WITTON, NORTH YORKSHIRE** - Popular Wensleydale village, where the burning of "Owd Bartle", effigy of an 18th C pig rustler, is held in August. John James, antiquary, was born and buried here.

- **WHITBY, NORTH YORKSHIRE** - Quaint holiday town with narrow streets and steep alleys at the mouth of the River Esk. Captain James Cook, the famous navigator, lived in Grape Lane. 199 steps lead to St Mary's Church and St Hilda's Abbey overlooking harbour. Dracula connections. Gothic weekend every April.

Y **YORK** - Ancient walled city nearly 2,000 years old, containing many well-preserved medieval buildings. Its Minster has over 100 stained glass windows and is the largest Gothic cathedral in England. Attractions include Castle Museum, National Railway Museum, Jorvik Viking Centre and York Dungeon.

Ratings you can trust

When you're looking for a place to stay, you need a rating system you can trust. The **English Tourism Council's** ratings are your clear guide to what to expect, in an easy-to-understand form. Properties are visited annually by our trained, impartial assessors, so you can have confidence that your accommodation has been thoroughly checked and rated for quality before you make a booking.

Based on the internationally recognised rating of One to Five Stars, the system puts great emphasis on quality and is based on research which shows exactly what consumers are looking for when choosing an hotel.

Ratings are awarded from One to Five Stars - the more Stars, the higher the quality and the greater the range of facilities and level of services provided.

Look out, too, for the English Tourism Council's Gold and Silver Awards, which are awarded to properties achieving the highest levels of quality within their Star rating. While the overall rating is based on a combination of facilities and quality, the Gold and Silver Awards are based solely on quality.

The ratings are your sign of quality assurance, giving you the confidence to book the accommodation that meets your expectations.

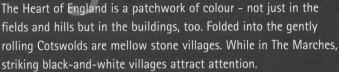

HEART OF ENGLAND

The Heart of England is a patchwork of colour - not just in the fields and hills but in the buildings, too. Folded into the gently rolling Cotswolds are mellow stone villages. While in The Marches, striking black-and-white villages attract attention.

The cosmopolitan cities of Birmingham and Coventry rub shoulders with classic spa and market towns. And the lively university city of Nottingham is filled with cinemas, wine bars, restaurants and clubs. This is Shakespeare country and it's also home to Althorp House, the resting place of Princess Diana.

If you happen to be in the Staffordshire village of Wetton, be sure to time your visit for the annual World Toe-Wrestling Championships in June!

The counties of
Derbyshire, Gloucestershire,
Herefordshire, Leicestershire, Lincolnshire
Northamptonshire, Nottinghamshire,
Rutland, Shropshire, Staffordshire,
Warwickshire, Worcestershire
and West Midlands

FOR MORE INFORMATION CONTACT:
Heart of England Tourist Board
Larkhill Road, Worcester WR5 2EZ
Tel: (01905) 761100
Fax: (01905) 763450

The Pictures:
1 Darwin Statue, Shrewsbury;
2 Anne Hathaway's Cottage,
   Warwickshire;
3 Warwick Castle.

Where to Go in the Heart of England - see pages 138-142
Where to Stay in the Heart of England - see pages 143-175

Whilst in the
HEART OF ENGLAND ...

You will find hundreds of interesting places to visit during your stay, just some of which are listed in these pages.

Contact any Tourist Information Centre in the region for more ideas on days out in the Heart of England.

Acton Scott Historic Working Farm
Acton Scott Church, Stretton, Warwickshire SY6 6QN
Tel: (01694) 781306
Demonstrates farming and rural life in south Shropshire at the close of the 19thC.

Alton Towers Theme Park
Alton, Stoke-on-Trent, Staffordshire ST10 4DB
Tel: 0870 5204060
Theme Park with over 125 rides and attractions including Oblivion, Nemesis, Haunted House, Runaway Mine Train, Congo River Rapids, Log Flume and many children's rides.

The American Adventure
Ilkeston, Derbyshire DE7 5SX
Tel: (01773) 531521
The American Adventure has action and entertainment for all ages. The Missile white-knuckle rollercoaster, Europe's tallest skycoaster and the world's wettest log flume.

Belton House, Park and Gardens
Belton, Grantham, Lincolnshire NG32 2LS
Tel: (01476) 566116
The crowning achievement of restoration country house architecture, built in 1685-1688 for Sir John Brownlow with alterations by James Wyatt in 1777.

Belvoir Castle
Belvoir, Grantham, Lincolnshire NG32 1PD
Tel: (01476) 870262
The present castle is the fourth to be built on this site and dates from 1816. Art treasures include works by Poussin, Rubens, Holbein and Reynolds. Queen's Royal Lancers display.

Birmingham Botanical Gardens and Glasshouses
Edgbaston, Birmingham, West Midlands B15 3TR
Tel: (0121) 454 1860
Fifteen acres of ornamental gardens and glasshouses. Widest range of plants in the Midlands from tropical rainforest to arid desert. Aviaries with exotic birds, child's play area.

Black Country Living Museum
Dudley, West Midlands DY1 4SQ
Tel: (0121) 557 9643
One of Britain's best open-air museums. Wander around original shops and houses, ride on fair attractions and take a look down a mine.

Museum of British Road Transport
Coventry, West Midlands CV1 1PN
Tel: (024) 7683 2425
Two hundred cars and commercial vehicles, 200 cycles and 75 motorcycles from the 19thC to date, plus the 'Thrust 2' land speed story.

Butlins Family Entertainment Resort
Roman Bank, Skegness, Lincolnshire PE25 1NJ
Tel: (01754) 762311
New skyline pavilion, toyland, sub tropical waterworld, tenpin bowling and entertainment's centre. Live shows.

Cadbury World
Bournville, Birmingham, West Midlands B30 2LD
Tel: (0121) 451 4180
The story of Cadbury's chocolate. Includes chocolate-making demonstration and childrens attractions.

Chatsworth House and Garden

Bakewell, Derbyshire DE45 1PP
Tel: (01246) 582204
Built in 1687-1707 with a collection of fine pictures, books, drawings and furniture. Garden laid out by 'Capability' Brown with fountains, cascades, a farmyard and playground.

Cotswold Farm Park

Guiting Power, Cheltenham, Gloucestershire GL54 5UG
Tel: (01451) 850307
Collection of rare breeds of British farm animals. Pets' corner, adventure playground, farm trail, picnic area, gift shop and cafe. Lambing and other seasonal farming displays.

Drayton Manor Family Theme Park

Tamworth, Staffordshire B78 3TW
Tel: (01827) 287979
A major theme park and zoo, with 100 rides and attractions. Set in 250 acres of countryside with lakes, nature trail, farmyard, restaurants and bars.

The Heights of Abraham Cable Cars, Caverns and Country Park

Matlock Bath, Matlock, Derbyshire DE4 3PD
Tel: (01629) 582365
A spectacular cable car ride takes you to the summit where there are a wide variety of attractions for young and old alike. Gift shop and coffee shop.

Ironbridge Gorge Museum

Ironbridge, Telford, Shropshire TF8 7AW
Tel: (01952) 433522
World's first cast-iron bridge. Museum of the River Visitor Centre, Tar Tunnel, Jackfield Tile Museum, Coalport China Museum, Rosehill House, Blists Hill Museum and Museum of Iron.

Lincoln Castle

Castle Hill, Lincoln, Lincolnshire LN1 3AA
Tel: (01522) 511068
A medieval castle including towers and ramparts with a Magna Carta exhibition, a prison chapel experience, reconstructed Westgate and popular events throughout the summer.

Midland Railway Centre

Butterley Station, Ripley, Derbyshire DE5 3QZ
Tel: (01773) 747674
Over 50 locomotives and over 100 items of historic rolling stock of Midland and LMS origin with a steam-hauled passenger service, a museum site, country and farm park.

National Sea Life Centre

Brindleyplace, Birmingham, West Midlands B1 2HL
Tel: (0121) 633 4700
Over 55 fascinating displays. The opportunity to come face-to-face with hundreds of sea creatures, from sharks to shrimps.

The National Tramway Museum

Crich, Matlock, Derbyshire DE4 5DP
Tel: (01773) 852565
A collection of over 70 trams from Britain and overseas dating from 1873-1957. Tram rides on a 1.6 km (1-mile) route, a period street scene, depots, a power station, workshops and exhibition.

The Pictures:
1 Rockingham Castle, Northamptonshire;
2 Chatsworth House, Derbyshire;
3 South Shropshire Hills;
4 New Place, Stratford-upon-Avon;
5 Brindley Place, Birmingham;
6 Robin Hood Statue, Nottingham;
7 Alderton, Gloucestershire;
8 Rutland Water.

Severn Valley Railway

Bewdley, Worcestershire DY12 1BG
Tel: (01299) 403816
Preserved standard gauge steam railway running 2.6 km (16 miles) between Kidderminster, Bewdley and Bridgnorth. Collection of locomotives and passenger coaches.

Shakespeare's Birthplace

Stratford-upon-Avon, Warwickshire CV37 6QW
Tel: (01789) 204016
The world famous house where William Shakespeare was born in 1564 and where he grew up. See the highly acclaimed exhibition 'Shakespeare's World'.

Nottingham Industrial Museum

Wollaton Park, Nottingham, Nottinghamshire NG8 2AE
Tel: (0115) 915 3910
An 18thC stables presenting the history of Nottingham's industries: printing, pharmacy, hosiery and lace. There is also a Victorian beam engine, a horse gin and transport.

Ye Olde Pork Pie Shoppe and the Sausage Shop

Melton Mowbray. Leicestershire LE13 1NW
Tel: (01664) 562341
Oldest and only remaining pork pie bakery producing authentic Melton Mowbray pork pies. Learn why Melton Mowbray became the original home to the pork pie industry. Demonstrations and tastings. Adjacent Dickinson & Morris Sausage Shop.

Peak District Mining Museum

Matlock Bath, Matlock, Derbyshire DE4 3NR
Tel: (01629) 583834
Explore 3,500 years of lead mining history with displays, hands-on exhibits and climbing shafts. Go underground and learn to pan for gold. Plus 'Hazards of Mining' display.

Rugby School Museum

Little Church Street, Rugby, Warwickshire CV21 3AW
Tel: (01788) 556109
Rugby School Museum tells the story of the school, scene of Tom Brown's Schooldays, and contains the earlier memorabilia of the game invented on the school close.

The Shrewsbury Quest

Abbey Foregate, Shrewsbury, Shropshire SY2 6AH
Tel: (01743) 243324
Twelfth-century medieval visitor attraction. Solve mysteries, create illuminated manuscripts, play medieval games and relax in the unique herb gardens. Gift shop and cafe.

Shugborough Estate

Shugborough, Milford, Staffordshire ST17 0XB
Tel: (01889) 881388
Eighteenth-century mansion house with fine collection of furniture. Gardens and park contain beautiful neo-classical monuments.

Skegness Natureland Seal Sanctuary

The Promenade, Skegnes, Lincolnshire PE25 1DB
Tel: (01754) 764345
Collection of performing seals, baby seals, penguins, aquarium, crocodiles, snakes, terrapins, scorpions, tropical birds, butterflies (May-October) and pets.

Snibston Discovery Park

Coalville, Leicester, Leicestershire LE67 3LN
Tel: (01530) 510851
An all-weather and award-winning science and industrial heritage museum.

Spode Visitor Centre

Spode, Stoke-on-Trent, Staffordshire ST4 1BX
Tel: (01782) 744011
Visitors are shown the various processes in the making of bone china. Samples can be bought at the Spode Shop.

The Tales of Robin Hood

Maid Marian Way, Nottingham NG1 6GF
Tel: (0115) 948 3284
Join the world's greatest medieval adventure. Ride through the magical green wood and play the Silver Arrow game, in the search for Robin Hood.

Three Choirs Vineyards

Baldwins Farm, Newent, Gloucestershire GL18 1LS
Tel: (01531) 890223
Internationally award-winning wines are available for tasting and for sale. Winery gallery shows you how wine is made. Restaurant with magnificent views of the vines. Peaceful ponds, plus vineyard walks.

Twycross Zoo

Twycross, Atherstone, Warwickshire CV9 3PX
Tel: (01827) 880250
Gorillas, orang-utans, chimpanzees, a modern gibbon complex, elephants, lions, giraffes, a reptile house, pets' corner and rides.

Walsall Arboretum

Lichfield Street, Walsall, West Midlands
Tel: (01922) 653148
Picturesque Victorian park with over 79 acres of gardens, lakes and parkland.

Warwick Castle

Warwick CV34 4QU
Tel: (01926) 406600
Set in 60 acres of grounds. State rooms, armoury, dungeon, torture chamber, clock tower. A Royal Weekend Party 1898, and Kingmaker – a preparation for battle attractions.

Wedgwood Visitor Centre

Barlaston, Stoke-on-Trent, Staffordshire ST12 9ES
Tel: (01782) 204141
The visitor centre is located in the Wedgwood factory which lies within a 500 acre country estate. You can see potters and decorators at work. Also museum and shop

The Wildfowl and Wetlands Trust

Slimbridge, Gloucester, Gloucestershire GL2 7BT
Tel: (01453) 890333
Tropical house, hides, heated observatory, exhibits, children's playground and pond zone. Shop and restaurant.

Worcester Cathedral

10A College Green, Worcester, Worcestershire WR1 2LH
Tel: (01905) 611002
Norman crypt and chapter house, King John's Tomb, Prince Arthur's Chantry, medieval cloisters and buildings. Touch and hearing control, visually impaired facilities available.

The Pictures:
1 Symonds Yat, Wye Valley;
2 Fords Hospital, Coventry;
3 Alford Craft Market, Lincolnshire;
4 Shrewsbury Castle;
5 River Avon and Warwick Castle, Warwick;
6 Stratford-upon-Avon;
7 Nr. Chapel-en-le-Frith, Peak District;
8 Lamport Hall, Northamptonshire.

Find out more about the
HEART OF ENGLAND ...

Further information about holidays and attractions
in the Heart of England is available from:

HEART OF ENGLAND TOURIST BOARD
Larkhill Road, Worcester WR5 2EZ.
Tel: (01905) 761100
Fax: (01905) 763450

The following publications are available free from the Heart of England Tourist Board:

Bed & Breakfast Touring Map including Caravan and Camping

Escape & Explore

Events list

Great Places to Visit

Activity Holidays in the Heart of England

Food & Drink

The Pictures:
1   Packwood House, Warwickshire;
2   Black Country Museum, Dudley;
3   Ye Olde Trip to Jerusalem Inn,
    Nottingham;
4   Mary Arden's house, Wilmcote;
5   Burghley Horse Trials, Stamford.

Getting to the
HEART OF ENGLAND ...

BY ROAD: Britain's main motorways (M1/M6/M5) meet in the Heart of England; the
M40 links with the M42 south of Birmingham while the M4 provides fast access from
London to the south of the region. These road links ensure that the Heart of England is
more accessible by road than any other region in the UK.

BY RAIL: The Heart of England lies at the centre of the country's rail network. There
are direct trains from London and other major cities to many towns and cities within
the region.

Where to stay in the
HEART OF ENGLAND

Accommodation entries in this region are listed in alphabetical order of place name, and then in alphabetical order of establishment. As West Oxfordshire and Cherwell are promoted in both Heart of England and South of England, places in these areas with accommodation are listed in this section. See South of England for full West Oxfordshire and Cherwell entries.

Map references refer to the colour location maps at the front of this guide. The first number indicates the map to use; the letter and number which follow refer to the grid reference on the map.

At-a-glance symbols at the end of each accommodation entry give useful information about services and facilities. A key to symbols can be found inside the back cover flap. Keep this open for easy reference.

A brief description of the towns and villages offering accommodation in the entries which follow, can be found at the end of this section.

A complete listing of all English Tourism Council assessed hotels appears at the back of this guide.

ALCESTER, Warwickshire Map ref 2B1

★★★ **KINGS COURT HOTEL**

Kings Coughton, Stratford-upon-Avon, B49 5QQ	Bedrooms: 6 single, 18 double, 17 twin, 1 triple	Lunch available EM 1900 (LO 2200) Parking for 100	B&B per night: **S Min £56.00** **D Min £82.00**
T: (01789) 763111	Bathrooms: 42 en suite	CC: Amex, Barclaycard,	
F: (01789) 400242		Delta, Maestro,	OPEN All year round
E: info@kingscourthotel.co.uk		Mastercard, Solo, Switch,	
I: www.kingscourthotel.co.uk		Visa, Visa Electron	

Delightful bedrooms set around main part of the hotel, which is a listed Tudor farmhouse. Excellent home-cooked bar and restaurant meals. Close to Stratford-upon-Avon and the Cotswolds.

⋔ 🏠 ⅃ & 🖃 ❑ 🕯 🔧 🛈 ⑤ 🗡 🏵 📺 ▥ 🎿 ⌺ 80 ✿ 🗝 SP 🏠 T

ALREWAS, Staffordshire Map ref 4B3

★★ **CLAYMAR HOTEL AND RESTAURANT**

118a Main Street, Alrewas, Burton upon Trent, DE13 7AE	Bedrooms: 2 single, 10 double, 4 twin, 2 triple, 2 family rooms	Lunch available EM 1900 (LO 2130) Parking for 30	B&B per night: **S Min £42.00** **D Min £52.00**
T: (01283) 790202 & 791281	Bathrooms: 19 en suite, 1 private	CC: Barclaycard, Delta, Eurocard, Mastercard,	
F: (01283) 791465		Visa	OPEN All year round

Privately-run hotel and restaurant. Interesting menu at realistic prices. Bar and children's menu available. Reservations required for Sunday lunch. Convenient for all Staffordshire attractions.

⋔ 🏠 ⅃ & 🖃 ❑ 🕯 🔧 🛈 ⑤ 🏵 📺 ◐ ▥ 🎿 ⌺ ✿ 🚗 🗝 SP T

REGIONAL TOURIST BOARD The ⋔ symbol in an
establishment entry indicates that it is a Regional Tourist Board member.

★

THE BENTLEY BROOK INN AND FENNY'S RESTAURANT

Fenny Bentley, Ashbourne, DE6 1LF
T: (01335) 350278
F: (01335) 350422
E: all@bentleybrookinn.co.uk
I: www.bentleybrookinn.co.uk

A great place to stay for holidays or business trips; a traditional, family-run, busy country inn with large garden. Open all day. Close to Tissington Trail, Carsington Water, Dovedale, Chatsworth, Alton Towers. Good home-cooked food served in both bar and restaurant. Real ales from our on-site brewery.

Bedrooms: 1 single,
5 double, 3 twin
Bathrooms: 6 en suite,
1 private, 2 public

Lunch available
EM 1900 (LO 2130)
Parking for 60
CC: Amex, Barclaycard,
Delta, Diners, Mastercard,
Switch, Visa

B&B per night:
S £40.00–£45.00
D £50.00–£65.00

HB per person:
DY £31.50–£40.00

OPEN All year round

🅐🗝🕭🌣📧📠💻🛈💲🕭🎞️📠🍴20 ♨ 🎿🌳 🐾 🚲 SP T

★★★
Silver
Award

EAST LODGE COUNTRY HOUSE HOTEL AND RESTAURANT

Rowsley, Matlock, DE4 2EF
T: (01629) 734474
F: (01629) 733949
E: info@eastlodge.com
I: www.eastlodge.com

Bedrooms: 9 double,
6 twin
Bathrooms: 15 en suite

Lunch available
EM 1900 (LO 2100)
Parking for 30
CC: Amex, Barclaycard,
Mastercard, Switch, Visa

B&B per night:
S £75.00–£95.00
D £95.00–£125.00

HB per person:
DY £47.50–£67.50

OPEN All year round

Tastefully furnished country house hotel and restaurant, set in 10 acres of grounds close to Chatsworth, Haddon Hall and the market town of Bakewell.

🅐🗝🕭🌣📧📠💻🛈💲🎞️📠🍴70 ♨ 🎿🌳 🐾 🚲 SP 🏨 T

★★
Silver
Award

YORKSHIRE BRIDGE INN

Ashopton Road, Bamford, Hope Valley,
S33 0AZ
T: (01433) 651361
F: (01433) 651361
E: mr@ybridge.force9.co.uk
I: www.yorkshire-bridge.co.uk

This famous inn enjoys an idyllic setting by the beautiful reservoirs of Ladybower, Derwent and Howden in the Peak District. Chosen by "Publican" magazine 2000 awards as one of the top six freehouses of the year for all round excellence. Superb en suite rooms, lovely bar areas and a warm welcome all year.

Bedrooms: 9 double,
2 twin, 3 triple
Bathrooms: 14 en suite

Lunch available
EM 1800 (LO 2100)
Parking for 30
CC: Barclaycard, Delta,
Eurocard, JCB, Maestro,
Mastercard, Solo, Switch,
Visa, Visa Electron

B&B per night:
S £39.00–£43.00
D £52.00–£60.00

HB per person:
DY £41.00–£45.00

OPEN All year round

🅐🗝🕭🌣📧📠💻🛈💲🎞️📠🍴20 ♨ 🎿🌳 🐾 🚲 SP 🏨 T

★★

NEWPORT TOWERS HOTEL

Newport, Berkeley, GL13 9PX
T: (01453) 810575
F: (01453) 511062

Bedrooms: 1 single,
9 double, 43 twin,
2 triple
Bathrooms: 55 en suite

Lunch available
EM 1800 (LO 2130)
Parking for 200
CC: Amex, Barclaycard,
Delta, Diners, Eurocard,
JCB, Maestro, Mastercard,
Solo, Switch, Visa, Visa
Electron

B&B per night:
S £39.00–£41.00
D £45.00–£46.00

HB per person:
DY £27.00–£50.00

OPEN All year round

Budget hotel within a short drive of the picturesque villages of the Cotswolds. Other local attractions include Berkeley Castle and Slimbridge Wildfowl Trust.

🅐🗝🕭🌣📧💻🛈💲🎞️📺🍴150 🍴 🎿 🐾 🐾 🚲 SP T

QUALITY ASSURANCE SCHEME

Star ratings and awards are explained at the back of this guide.

★★

BIGGIN HALL

Biggin-by-Hartington, Buxton, SK17 0DH
T: (01298) 84451
F: (01298) 84681
E: bigginhall@compuserve.com
I: www.bigginhall.co.uk

B&B per night:
S £45.00–£75.00
D £50.00–£90.00

HB per person:
DY £35.00–£55.00

OPEN All year round

17thC hall, Grade II* Listed, 1,000 feet up in tranquil countryside in Peak District National Park. Sympathetically modernised. Fresh home cooking and comforts. Beautiful, uncrowded walks from the grounds. Close to Chatsworth, Haddon Hall, Dovedale, etc.

Bedrooms: 7 double, 7 twin, 3 triple, 2 family rooms
Bathrooms: 19 en suite

EM 1900 (LO 1900)
Parking for 30
CC: Amex, Barclaycard, Delta, Eurocard, Mastercard, Solo, Switch, Visa, Visa Electron

ⓜ🖐12♨🏠🍴🖵♿🎣👜Ⓢⅇ🅟🖵ⅉ☎20✾👟🐾ⓈⓅ🏠Ⓣ

★★

SHERIDEN HOUSE HOTEL

82 Handsworth Wood Road,
Handsworth Wood, Birmingham, B20 2PL
T: (0121) 523 5960 & 554 2185
F: (0121) 551 4761
E: g.f.harmon@btinternet.com
I: www.SmoothHound.co.uk/hotels/sheriden.html

B&B per night:
S £34.00–£40.00
D £46.00–£56.00

HB per person:
DY £49.00–£55.00

OPEN All year round

Approximately 3 miles north of Birmingham city centre on B4124, 5 minutes junction 7 M6, junction 1 M5, 20 minutes from the NEC. Ideal for Birmingham's ICC, NIA, UCE, Perry Barr, Aston University, Alexander Stadium. En suite bedrooms, telephone, TV, tea/coffee facilities. Licensed restaurant. Bar. Brochure/map on request. Car park. Weekend rates.

Bedrooms: 2 single, 3 double, 5 twin
Bathrooms: 10 en suite, 1 public

Lunch available
EM 1830 (LO 2100)
Parking for 30
CC: Amex, Barclaycard, Delta, Eurocard, JCB, Mastercard, Solo, Switch, Visa, Visa Electron

ⓜ🖐🏠🍴🖵♿🎣Ⓢⅇ🅟🖵ⅉ☎30✾👟🐾ⓈⓅⓉ

Rating Applied For Ad p15	THISTLE BIRMINGHAM CITY			
	St Chad's, Queensway, Birmingham, B4 6HY T: (0121) 236 4211 F: (0121) 233 2195	Bedrooms: 36 single, 59 double, 36 twin, 2 triple Bathrooms: 133 en suite	Lunch available EM 1800 (LO 2200) Parking for 600 CC: Amex, Barclaycard, Delta, Diners, Eurocard, Mastercard, Solo, Switch, Visa	B&B per night: S £118.00–£142.00 D £133.00–£157.00 OPEN All year round ⒸⓇ Thistle Hotels/Utell International

City centre location and close to shopping areas, this modern hotel offers a relaxed ambience for both business and pleasure. Minutes from National Exhibition Centre.

ⓜ🖐🍴🖵♿🎣Ⓢⅇ🅟🖵ⅉ☎180🐾ⓈⓅⓉ⊛

Rating Applied for Ad p15	THISTLE BIRMINGHAM EDGBASTON			
	225 Hagley Road, Edgbaston, Birmingham, B16 9RY T: (0121) 455 9777 F: (0121) 454 9432 E: birmingham.edgbaston@thistle.co.uk I: www.thistlehotels.com	Bedrooms: 86 single, 23 double, 39 twin, 3 family rooms; suites available Bathrooms: 151 en suite	Lunch available EM 1830 (LO 2200) Parking for 200 CC: Amex, Barclaycard, Delta, Diners, Eurocard, JCB, Mastercard, Solo, Switch, Visa	B&B per night: S £116.00–£140.00 D £128.00–£152.00 OPEN All year round ⒸⓇ Thistle Hotels/Utell International

Excellent amenities complement this hotel's prime location close to the city centre, Cadbury World and the Sea Life Centre. Car parking available.

ⓜ🖐🍴🖵♿🎣Ⓢⅇ🅟🖵ⅉ☎170🐾ⓈⓅⓉ

See under Birmingham, Coventry

BOURTON-ON-THE-WATER, Gloucestershire Map ref 2B1 *Tourist Information Centre Tel: (01451) 820211*

★★
Silver
Award

DIAL HOUSE

The Chestnuts, High Street, Bourton-on-the-Water, Cheltenham, GL54 2AN
T: (01451) 822244
F: (01451) 810126
E: info@dialhousehotel.com
I: www.dialhousehotel.com

Built in 1698 of Cotswold stone, the hotel nestles peacefully in village centre within 1.5 acres of walled gardens. All rooms are individually decorated, some with 4-posters. The Inglenook Restaurant has been awarded rosettes for excellent cuisine. Comfortable lounge with log fire. Bargain breaks available all year.

Bedrooms: 1 single,
7 double, 3 twin,
1 family room
Bathrooms: 11 en suite,
1 private

Lunch available
EM 1900 (LO 2100)
Parking for 18
CC: Amex, Barclaycard,
Delta, Maestro,
Mastercard, Switch, Visa,
Visa Electron

B&B per night:
S £35.00–£67.00
D £70.00–£129.00

HB per person:
DY £67.50–£85.00

OPEN All year round

BRIDGNORTH, Shropshire Map ref 4A3 *Tourist Information Centre Tel: (01746) 763257*

★

THE CROFT HOTEL
St. Mary's Street, Bridgnorth,
WV16 4DW
T: (01746) 762416 & 767155
F: (01746) 767431

Listed building with a wealth of oak beams, in an old street. Family-run and an ideal centre for exploring the delightful Shropshire countryside.

Bedrooms: 3 single,
4 double, 1 twin, 4 triple
Bathrooms: 10 en suite,
1 public

Lunch available
EM 1800 (LO 2030)
CC: Amex, Barclaycard,
Mastercard, Visa

B&B per night:
S £25.00–£41.00
D £40.00–£50.00

HB per person:
DY £34.50–£57.90

OPEN All year round

Guestaccom

★★★
Gold
Award

OLD VICARAGE HOTEL

Worfield, Bridgnorth, WV15 5JZ
T: (01746) 716497 & 0800 0968010
F: (01746) 716552
E: admin@the-old-vicarage.demon.co.uk
I: www.oldvicarageworfield.com

Luxury country house hotel in the peaceful hamlet of Worfield. The restaurant boasts many awards with menus sourcing fresh local ingredients. Ideal location for business or pleasure. Within easy reach of motorway routes. Local attractions include Severn Valley Railway and Ironbridge Gorge. HB prices based on two-night stay.

Bedrooms: 8 double,
5 twin, 1 triple; suite
available
Bathrooms: 14 en suite

Lunch available
EM 1900 (LO 2100)
Parking for 30
CC: Amex, Barclaycard,
Delta, Mastercard, Visa,
Visa Electron

B&B per night:
S £75.00–£110.00
D £115.00–£175.00

HB per person:
DY £75.00–£107.50

OPEN All year round

BROADWAY, Worcestershire Map ref 2B1

★★★
Silver
Award

BROADWAY HOTEL
The Green, Broadway, WR12 7AA
T: (01386) 852401 (Daytime upto 10pm)
F: (01386) 853879
E: Bookings@
cotswold-inns-hotels.co.uk
I: www.cotswold-inns-hotel.co.uk

Grade II Listed 17thC hotel in the heart of picturesque village. Newly refurbished, combining stylish modern fabrics and decoration with antique furniture.

Bedrooms: 3 single,
11 double, 6 twin
Bathrooms: 20 en suite

Lunch available
EM 1900 (LO 2130)
Parking for 20
CC: Amex, Barclaycard,
Delta, JCB, Mastercard,
Switch, Visa

B&B per night:
S Min £68.50
D Min £110.00

HB per person:
DY Min £72.00

OPEN All year round

Cotswolds Inns &
Hotels

MAP REFERENCES
Map references apply to the colour maps at the front of this guide.

★★

COLLIN HOUSE HOTEL & RESTAURANT

Collin Lane, Broadway, WR12 7PB
T: (01386) 858354
F: (01386) 858697
E: collin.house@virgin.net
I: www.broadway-cotswolds.co.uk/collin.html

A small, intimate 17thC country house. Built in mellow Cotswold stone, this lovely old building is set in 2 acres of mature gardens. Enjoy a relaxing break, have a drink in the bar around an imposing fireplace and dine by candlelight in our award-winning, beamed dining room.

Bedrooms: 3 double, 3 twin
Bathrooms: 6 en suite

Lunch available
EM 1900 (LO 2100)
Parking for 30
CC: Barclaycard, Eurocard, Mastercard, Solo, Switch, Visa, Visa Electron

B&B per night:
S £69.00–£69.00
D £92.00–£120.00

HB per person:
DY £67.00–£86.00

OPEN All year round

★★★★
Gold
Award

THE LYGON ARMS
Broadway, WR12 7DU
T: (01386) 852255
F: (01386) 854470
E: info@the-lygon-arms.co.uk
I: www.savoy-group.co.uk

Bedrooms: 2 single, 48 double, 9 twin, 6 triple
Bathrooms: 65 en suite

Lunch available
EM 1930 (LO 2115)
Parking for 153
CC: Amex, Barclaycard, Delta, Diners, Eurocard, JCB, Mastercard, Switch, Visa

B&B per night:
S Min £130.00
D Min £180.00

HB per person:
DY Min £145.00

OPEN All year round

16thC coaching inn set in the heart of the Cotswolds, with all the comforts of the 20thC. Well situated for touring the Cotswolds and Shakespeare Country.

★★★★

PINE LODGE HOTEL

Kidderminster Road, Bromsgrove, B61 9AB
T: (01527) 576600
F: (01527) 878981
E: enquiries@pine-lodge-hotel.co.uk

B&B per night:
S £37.00–£125.00
D £74.00–£140.00

HB per person:
DY £55.00–£140.00

OPEN All year round

Set in the Heart of England countryside, this modern Mediterranean-style hotel is within easy reach of the motorway network. Facilities include Parador Restaurant and Cafe, bar, conference and banquets for 200 people, civil wedding licence. Studio 4 health club including indoor pool, steam/sauna, gym, snooker and beauty treatments.

Bedrooms: 12 single, 70 double, 12 twin, 17 triple; suites available
Bathrooms: 111 en suite

Lunch available
EM 1900 (LO 2200)
Parking for 250
CC: Amex, Barclaycard, Delta, Diners, Mastercard, Switch, Visa

---

The Bay Tree
See South of England region for full entry details

ACCESSIBILITY

Look for the ♿🦽🚶 symbols which indicate accessibility for wheelchair users. A list of establishments is at the front of this guide.

★★★

DONINGTON MANOR HOTEL

High Street, Castle Donington, Derby, DE74 2PP
T: (01332) 810253
F: (01332) 850330
E: cngrist@dmhgrist.demon.co.uk
I: www.doningtonmanorhotel.co.uk

B&B per night:
S £66.00–£84.00
D £80.00–£100.00

OPEN All year round

This 18thC coaching inn retains many of its original features and all of its relaxed Regency elegance. The hotel has been considerably extended, achieving a harmonious blend of old and new. Excellent restaurant with classic Anglo-French cuisine. Two miles from the M1, junction 24, and close to Donington Park motor circuit and East Midlands Airport.

Bedrooms: 2 single, 14 double, 11 twin, 1 family room	Lunch available
	EM 1900 (LO 2130)
	Parking for 60
Bathrooms: 28 en suite	CC: Amex, Barclaycard, Delta, Diners, Eurocard, Mastercard, Switch, Visa

---

Rating
Applied For
Ad p15

THISTLE EAST MIDLANDS AIRPORT
East Midlands Airport,
Castle Donington, Derby, DE74 2SH
T: (01332) 850700
F: (01332) 850823
E: east.midlandsairport@thistle.co.uk
I: www.thistlehotels.com

Convenient for Derby and Nottingham. Nearby attractions include the Peak District, Sherwood Forest and Alton Towers. Car parking available.

Bedrooms: 48 double, 58 twin, 4 family rooms	Lunch available
	EM 1900 (LO 2200)
Bathrooms: 110 en suite	Parking for 180
	CC: Amex, Barclaycard, Delta, Diners, JCB, Mastercard, Solo, Switch, Visa, Visa Electron

B&B per night:
S £150.00–£175.00
D £150.00–£175.00

OPEN All year round

Thistle Hotels/Utell International

★★★
Gold
Award

BROCKENCOTE HALL

Chaddesley Corbett, Kidderminster, DY10 4PY
T: (01562) 777876
F: (01562) 777872
E: info@brockencotehall.com
I: www.brockencotehall.com

B&B per night:
S £110.00–£130.00
D £135.00–£170.00

HB per person:
DY £95.00–£157.50

OPEN All year round

Country house hotel set in 70 acres of parkland, offering traditional French cooking in an elegant and relaxed atmosphere. Heart of England Tourist Board Independent Hotel of the Year 1998.

Bedrooms: 13 double, 3 twin, 1 triple	Lunch available
	EM 1900 (LO 2130)
Bathrooms: 17 en suite	Parking for 50
	CC: Amex, Barclaycard, Delta, Diners, Eurocard, Mastercard, Switch, Visa

---

★★★

CARLTON HOTEL
Parabola Road, Cheltenham, GL50 3AQ
T: (01242) 514453
F: (01242) 226487

Bedrooms: 16 single, 16 double, 43 twin	Lunch available
	EM 1900 (LO 2130)
Bathrooms: 75 en suite	Parking for 85
	CC: Amex, Barclaycard, Delta, Diners, Eurocard, JCB, Maestro, Mastercard, Solo, Switch, Visa, Visa Electron

B&B per night:
S £47.00–£68.00
D £72.00–£86.00

HB per person:
DY £41.00–£48.50

OPEN All year round

In quiet position, 250 yards from Promenade. Emphasis on traditional friendly service. Tasteful bedrooms. Excellent restaurant/bar facilities. Half board prices apply weekends only.

COLOUR MAPS
Colour maps at the front of this guide pinpoint all places under which you will find accommodation listed.

★★★
Silver
Award

CHARLTON KINGS HOTEL

London Road, Charlton Kings, Cheltenham, GL52 6UU
T: (01242) 231061
F: (01242) 241900

B&B per night:
S £53.00–£81.50
D £68.00–£106.00

HB per person:
DY £48.00–£98.65

OPEN All year round

A pretty Victorian property, set in an acre of award-winning gardens, situated on the outskirts of Cheltenham. All rooms are beautifully furnished, with en suite bath/shower room. The restaurant provides interesting and varied menus. Light snacks can be enjoyed in the conservatory. Informally run but with high standards throughout.

Bedrooms: 2 single, 8 double, 2 twin, 1 triple, 1 family room
Bathrooms: 14 en suite

Lunch available
EM 1900 (LO 2045)
Parking for 26
CC: Amex, Barclaycard, Delta, Eurocard, JCB, Mastercard, Solo, Switch, Visa

---

★★★★
Silver
Award

THE CHELTENHAM PARK HOTEL

Cirencester Road, Charlton Kings, Cheltenham, GL53 8EA
T: (01242) 222021
F: (01242) 254880
E: cheltenhampark@paramount-hotels.co.uk
I: www.paramount-hotels.co.uk

B&B per night:
S £76.00–£112.00
D £120.00–£150.00

HB per person:
DY £72.00–£82.00

OPEN All year round

Stylish Regency hotel in own gardens in heart of Cotswolds. On the edge of Cheltenham, the hotel enjoys splendid views over golf course and Cotswold Hills. Use of the leisure club is included in your stay. For a day at the races, shopping or a visit to the Cotswolds, it's the ideal venue.

Bedrooms: 17 single, 67 double, 57 twin, 2 family rooms; suite available
Bathrooms: 143 en suite

Lunch available
EM 1930 (LO 2145)
Parking for 200
CC: Amex, Barclaycard, Delta, Diners, Maestro, Mastercard, Switch, Visa, Visa Electron

---

★★★

DUMBLETON HALL HOTEL
Dumbleton, Evesham, Worcestershire WR11 6TS
T: (01386) 881240
F: (01386) 882142
E: reception@dumbletonhallforce9.co.uk
I: www.dumbletonhallforce9.co.uk

Bedrooms: 5 single, 18 double, 7 twin, 7 triple, 2 family rooms; suites available
Bathrooms: 39 en suite

Lunch available
EM 1830 (LO 2130)
Parking for 80
CC: Amex, Barclaycard, Delta, Diners, Eurocard, Mastercard, Switch, Visa

B&B per night:
S £40.00–£80.00
D £50.00–£110.00

HB per person:
DY £50.00–£140.00

OPEN All year round

Cotswold-stone mansion, built c1830, in 19 acres. En suite bedrooms, conference rooms and elegant lounges. Ideal venue for weddings and celebrations. Midway between Cheltenham and Evesham.

USE YOUR *i*s

There are more than 550 Tourist Information Centres throughout England offering friendly help with accommodation and holiday ideas as well as suggestions of places to visit and things to do. You'll find TIC addresses in the local Phone Book.

★★★

300-year-old country manor-house hotel, set in 5 acres of secluded grounds only 1 mile from the centre of Regency Cheltenham. Acclaimed restaurant, en suite character bedrooms, 4-posters, log fires. Excellent walking. Ideal base for Warwick, Bath and Oxford. Special Cotswold Breaks offer.

THE PRESTBURY HOUSE HOTEL AND RESTAURANT

The Burgage, Prestbury, Cheltenham, GL52 3DN
T: (01242) 529533 (24 hours)
F: (01242) 227076
I: www.smoothhound.co.uk/hotels/prestbur.html

Bedrooms: 1 single, 11 double, 5 twin
Bathrooms: 17 en suite

Lunch available
EM 1900 (LO 2100)
Parking for 50
CC: Amex, Barclaycard, Diners, Mastercard, Switch, Visa

B&B per night:
S £45.00–£66.00
D £48.00–£80.00

OPEN All year round

 70 ⓤ ... SC SP T

Rating
Applied For
Ad p15

THISTLE CHELTENHAM
Gloucester Road, Cheltenham, GL51 0TS
T: (01242) 232 691
F: (01242) 221846
E: cheltenham@Thistle.co.uk
I: www.thistlehotels.com

In a quiet rural setting minutes from the centre of Cheltenham, the hotel is an ideal base from which to explore the Cotswolds. Ample car parking.

Bedrooms: 98 double, 15 twin, 9 triple; suites available
Bathrooms: 122 en suite

Lunch available
EM 1900 (LO 2145)
Parking for 250
CC: Amex, Barclaycard, Delta, Diners, JCB, Mastercard, Solo, Switch, Visa, Visa Electron

B&B per night:
S £122.00–£145.00
D £122.00–£145.00

OPEN All year round

CR
Thistle Hotels/Utell International

400 ... SP T

Bignell Park Hotel
See South of England region for full entry details

★★★

NOEL ARMS HOTEL
High Street, Chipping Campden, GL55 6AT
T: (01386) 840317
F: (01386) 841136
E: bookings@cotswold-inns-hotels.co.uk
I: www.cotswold-inns-hotels.co.uk

14thC coaching inn set in beautiful Cotswold countryside. Oak-panelled restaurant. Traditional ales and meals served in Dovers Bar.

Bedrooms: 12 double, 13 twin, 1 family room
Bathrooms: 26 en suite

Lunch available
EM 1900 (LO 2130)
Parking for 30
CC: Amex, Barclaycard, Delta, Diners, Eurocard, JCB, Mastercard, Solo, Switch, Visa

B&B per night:
S Min £75.00
D Min £110.00

HB per person:
DY Min £70.00

OPEN All year round

CR
Cotswolds Inns & Hotels

50 ... SP T

TOWN INDEX
This can be found at the back of the guide. If you know where you want to stay, the index will give you the page number listing accommodation in your chosen town, city or village.

★★★

THREE WAYS HOUSE
Chapel Lane, Mickleton,
Chipping Campden, GL55 6SB
T: (01386) 438429
F: (01386) 438118
E: threeways@puddingclub.com
I: www.puddingclub.com

B&B per night:
S £67.00–£82.00
D £97.00–£125.00

HB per person:
DY £65.00–£85.00

OPEN All year round

Cotswold village hotel close to Chipping Campden, Broadway and Stratford-upon-Avon. Comfortable bedrooms, some with pudding themes, cosy bar, good food and attentive service. Seen many times on TV as 'Home of the Pudding Club' where meetings of pudding lovers occur regularly. New, stylish and air conditioned restaurant.

Bedrooms: 3 single,
14 double, 19 twin,
3 triple, 2 family rooms
Bathrooms: 41 en suite

Lunch available
EM 1900 (LO 2130)
Parking for 40
CC: Amex, Barclaycard,
Delta, Diners, Mastercard,
Switch, Visa

The Circle

CHURCH STRETTON, Shropshire Map ref 4A3

★★★ **LONGMYND HOTEL**

Cunnery Road, Church Stretton,
SY6 6AG
T: (01694) 722244
F: (01694) 722718
E: reservations@longmynd.co.uk
I: www.longmynd.co.uk

Bedrooms: 6 single,
22 double, 13 twin,
6 triple, 3 family rooms
Bathrooms: 50 en suite,
2 public

Lunch available
EM 1845 (LO 2100)
Parking for 100
CC: Amex, Barclaycard,
Delta, Diners, Mastercard,
Switch, Visa

B&B per night:
S £55.00–£65.00
D £100.00–£130.00

HB per person:
DY £55.00–£65.00

OPEN All year round

Family-run country hotel commanding panoramic views of the south Shropshire highlands. Situated in an Area of Outstanding Natural Beauty. Self-catering lodges available.

★★ **MYND HOUSE HOTEL**

Ludlow Road, Little Stretton,
Church Stretton, SY6 6RB
T: (01694) 722212
F: (01694) 724180
E: myndhouse@goz.co.uk
I: www.goz.co.uk/myndhouse

Bedrooms: 1 single,
4 double, 2 twin; suites
available
Bathrooms: 7 en suite,
1 public

Lunch available
EM 1930 (LO 2115)
Parking for 16
CC: Amex, Barclaycard,
Delta, Eurocard,
Mastercard, Solo, Switch,
Visa, Visa Electron

B&B per night:
S £40.00–£55.00
D £60.00–£120.00

HB per person:
DY £45.00–£65.00

OPEN Feb–Dec

In a quiet village at the foot of Long Mynd. A small Edwardian country hotel offering comfortable accommodation, good food and walks from the door.

CIRENCESTER, Gloucestershire Map ref 2B1 *Tourist Information Centre Tel: (01285) 654180*

★★★

CROWN OF CRUCIS
Ampney Crucis, Cirencester, GL7 5RS
T: (01285) 851806
F: (01285) 851735
E: info@thecrownofcrucis
I: www.thecrownofcrucis.co.uk

B&B per night:
S £44.00–£62.00
D £62.00–£88.00

HB per person:
DY £54.00–£74.00

OPEN All year round

Delightful, privately owned 16thC Cotswold hotel and coaching inn with elegant fully en suite bedrooms overlooking continental-style courtyard and village cricket pitch. Excellent local reputation for quality food and friendly service. Award-winning restaurant and traditional Cotswold bar both with extensive and varied menu. Quiet riverside location 2.5 miles east of Cirencester.

Bedrooms: 9 double,
16 twin
Bathrooms: 25 en suite

Lunch available
EM 1800 (LO 2200)
Parking for 80
CC: Amex, Barclaycard,
Delta, Diners, Eurocard,
Maestro, Mastercard,
Solo, Switch, Visa, Visa
Electron

CLEARWELL, Gloucestershire Map ref 2A1

★★★
Silver
Award

WYNDHAM ARMS

Clearwell, Coleford, GL16 8JT
T: (01594) 833666
F: (01594) 836450

Bedrooms: 2 single,	Lunch available	B&B per night:
4 double, 9 twin, 2 triple,	EM 1845 (LO 2130)	S £52.50–£58.50
1 family room	Parking for 52	D £50.00–£100.00
Bathrooms: 18 en suite	CC: Amex, Barclaycard,	
	Delta, Diners, Eurocard,	HB per person:
	JCB, Mastercard, Solo,	DY £47.50–£76.00
	Switch, Visa, Visa Electron	

Stay free on Sundays in this historic hotel. Under the competent management of the Stanford family since 1973, chef de cuisine Paul Cooke since 1977. Minimum double price for 6 nights.

OPEN All year round

 56 ✦ ✸ SP ⌂ T

CLEOBURY MORTIMER, Shropshire Map ref 4A3

★★

THE REDFERN HOTEL

Cleobury Mortimer, Kidderminster,
Worcestershire DY14 8AA
T: (01299) 270395
F: (01299) 271011
E: jon@redfern-hotel.co.uk
I: www.redfern-hotel.co.uk

Bedrooms: 5 double,	Lunch available	B&B per night:
5 twin, 1 triple	EM 1930 (LO 2200)	S £53.00–£68.00
Bathrooms: 11 en suite	Parking for 20	D £80.00–£104.00
	CC: Amex, Barclaycard,	
	Delta, Diners, Eurocard,	HB per person:
	Mastercard, Switch, Visa	DY £56.00–£76.00

18thC stone-built hotel in ancient market town, bordering 6,000-acre Forest of Wyre. Conservation area. Four-poster bed and room with whirlpool bathroom available.

OPEN All year round

🄰🄽 ♨ ⚡ ☎ ▣ ❒ ♨ ⚟ 🛈 S ⧖ 🅟 TV ⊞ ⚓ ☎ 30 ∪ ♪ ✝ 🚗 ✸ SP ⌂ T

COTSWOLDS

See under Berkeley, Bourton-on-the-Water, Broadway, Cheltenham, Chipping Campden, Cirencester, Fairford, Gloucester, Lower Slaughter, Painswick, Stow-on-the-Wold, Stroud See also Cotswolds in South of England region.

COVENTRY, West Midlands Map ref 4B3 *Tourist Information Centre Tel: (02476) 832303 or 832304*

★★

MERRICK LODGE HOTEL

80-82 St Nicholas Street, Coventry,
CV1 4BP
T: (024) 7655 3940
F: (024) 7655 0112
I: www.merricklodge.co.uk

Bedrooms: 4 single,	Lunch available	B&B per night:
8 double, 9 twin, 4 triple,	EM 1830 (LO 2300)	S £40.00–£80.00
1 family room	Parking for 60	D £50.00–£90.00
Bathrooms: 25 en suite,	CC: Amex, Barclaycard,	
1 private shower	Delta, Diners, Eurocard,	HB per person:
	JCB, Mastercard, Solo,	DY £42.50–£97.50
	Switch, Visa	

Former manor-house, 5 minutes' walk from city centre. Table d'hote and a la carte restaurant, 3 bars. Comfortable, well-equipped bedrooms. Superb base for visiting the area.

OPEN All year round

🄰🄽 ♨ ⚡ ☎ ❒ ♨ ⚟ 🛈 S ☷ TV ◐ ⊞ ⚓ ☎ 180 🅟 ✸ SC ✸ SP T

DEDDINGTON, Oxfordshire

Holcombe Hotel & Restaurant See South of England region for full entry details

DERBY, Derbyshire Map ref 4B2 *Tourist Information Centre Tel: (01332) 255802*

★★★

INTERNATIONAL HOTEL & RESTAURANT

Burton Road (A5250), Derby,
DE23 6AD
T: (01332) 369321
F: (01332) 294430

Bedrooms: 12 single,	Lunch available	B&B per night:
40 double, 6 twin,	EM 1900 (LO 2215)	S £41.00–£55.00
4 triple	Parking for 120	D £46.00–£76.50
Bathrooms: 62 en suite	CC: Amex, Barclaycard,	
	Delta, Diners, Eurocard,	OPEN All year round
	Mastercard, Switch, Visa	

Situated close to the city centre, this privately owned hotel makes an excellent base from which to explore the Peak District Park. Good quality restaurant offers an extensive selection of fare.

🄰🄽 ♨ ⚡ ☎ ❒ ♨ ⚟ 🛈 S ☷ ◐ ⊞ ⚓ ☎ 60 🅟 SC ✸ SP T

QUALITY ASSURANCE SCHEME

Star ratings and awards were correct at the time of going to press but are subject to change. Please check at the time of booking.

★★★
Silver
Award

THE MILL AT HARVINGTON

Anchor Lane, Harvington, Evesham,
WR11 5NR
T: (01386) 870688
F: (01386) 870688

B&B per night:
S £63.00–£75.00
D £103.00–£141.00

HB per person:
DY £45.00–£72.00

OPEN All year round

Peaceful, owner-run, riverside hotel tastefully converted from beautiful house and mill. In acres of gardens, quarter mile Evesham to Stratford road. Old world hospitality and young, friendly staff who care, fresh local ingredients to create and serve meals you will remember. Half board prices based on minimum 2-night stay.

Bedrooms: 16 double,
5 twin
Bathrooms: 21 en suite

Lunch available
EM 1900 (LO 2045)
Parking for 45
CC: Amex, Barclaycard,
Delta, Diners, JCB,
Maestro, Mastercard,
Solo, Switch, Visa, Visa
Electron

★★★

THE WATERSIDE HOTEL
56 Waterside, Evesham, WR11 6JZ
T: (01386) 442420
F: (01386) 446272

Bedrooms: 2 single,
8 double, 4 twin, 1 triple
Bathrooms: 15 en suite,
1 public

Lunch available
EM 1830 (LO 2130)
Parking for 30
CC: Amex, Barclaycard,
Delta, Eurocard,
Mastercard, Switch, Visa

B&B per night:
S £56.50–£63.80
D £67.60–£82.50

HB per person:
DY £49.00–£66.00

OPEN All year round

Designer bedrooms, super beds. Evesham's premier restaurant, huge choice of menu, cooked fresh, personal service. Daily half board prices based on minimum 2-night stay.

★★★★
Gold
Award

WOOD NORTON HALL AND CONFERENCE CENTRE
Evesham, WR11 4YB
T: (01386) 420007 & 420000
F: (01386) 420190
E: woodnortonhall@bbc.co.uk
I: www.woodnortonhall.co.uk

Bedrooms: 38 double,
7 twin; suites available
Bathrooms: 45 en suite

Lunch available
EM 1900 (LO 2200)
Parking for 250
CC: Amex, Barclaycard,
Diners, Eurocard,
Mastercard, Switch, Visa

B&B per night:
S £80.00–£115.00
D £125.00–£220.00

HB per person:
DY £60.00–£90.00

OPEN All year round

Formerly home to French royalty, lovingly restored, this Victorian mansion offers stunning views over the Vale of Evesham.

Grand Heritage Hotels

★★

BULL HOTEL

Market Place, Fairford, GL7 4AA
T: (01285) 712535 & 712217
F: (01285) 713782
E: mashd@markdudley.freeserve.co.uk
I: www.smoothhound.co.uk/

B&B per night:
S £47.50–£69.50
D £56.50–£89.50

HB per person:
DY £38.25–£60.00

OPEN All year round

Historic 15thC family-run hotel in Fairford's famous market square. Restaurant offers full a la carte menu and fresh local produce. Home-cooked bar food and range of good beers. Good base for Cotswolds. Wedding and conference facilities. Enjoy the charm of this ancient Cotswold inn. 1.5 miles of private fishing on River Coln.

Bedrooms: 5 single,
11 double, 5 twin,
1 family room
Bathrooms: 20 en suite,
2 private, 2 public

Lunch available
EM 1800 (LO 2115)
Parking for 20
CC: Amex, Barclaycard,
Delta, Mastercard, Switch,
Visa

CONFIRM YOUR BOOKING
You are advised to confirm your booking in writing.

FINEDON, Northamptonshire Map ref 3A2

★★

TUDOR GATE HOTEL
35 High Street, Finedon,
Wellingborough, NN9 5JN
T: (01933) 680408
F: (01933) 680745
E: info@tudorgate-hotel.co.uk
I: www.tudorgate-hotel.co.uk

Bedrooms: 13 single,
11 double, 3 twin
Bathrooms: 27 en suite

Lunch available
EM 1830 (LO 2145)
Parking for 40
CC: Amex, Barclaycard,
Delta, Diners, Eurocard,
Maestro, Mastercard,
Solo, Switch, Visa

B&B per night:
S £49.00–£82.00
D £58.00–£110.00

HB per person:
DY £69.00–£107.00

OPEN All year round

Converted from a 17thC farmhouse, with 3 4-poster beds. Close to new A1/M1 link. 30 antique businesses within walking distance, wide range of leisure activities locally.

FOREST OF DEAN

See under Clearwell

FOWNHOPE, Herefordshire Map ref 2A1

★★

GREEN MAN INN
Fownhope, Hereford, HR1 4PE
T: (01432) 860243 (24 hours)
F: (01432) 860207
I: www.smoothhound.co.uk/Hotels/
Greenman.html

Bedrooms: 1 single,
13 double, 1 twin,
5 triple; suites available
Bathrooms: 20 en suite

Lunch available
EM 1900 (LO 2100)
Parking for 80
CC: Amex, Barclaycard,
Delta, Diners, Eurocard,
Mastercard, Solo, Switch,
Visa, Visa Electron

B&B per night:
S £37.50–£38.95
D £62.00–£64.00

HB per person:
DY £43.90–£46.50

OPEN All year round

15thC black and white coaching inn, midway between Ross-on-Wye and Hereford, in picturesque village of Fownhope. On B4224, close to River Wye in the beautiful Wye Valley.

GAINSBOROUGH, Lincolnshire Map ref 4C2

★

WHITE HART HOTEL
Lord Street, Gainsborough,
DN21 2DD
T: (01427) 612018
F: (01427) 811756
E: white.hart@tesco.net

Bedrooms: 5 single,
3 double, 5 twin,
1 family room
Bathrooms: 14 en suite

Lunch available
EM 1900 (LO 2100)
Parking for 20
CC: Barclaycard, Delta,
Mastercard, Switch, Visa

B&B per night:
S £30.00–£37.50
D £50.00–£57.50

OPEN All year round

Family-run hotel within town centre pedestrianisation. Restaurant, bars, room for weddings and seminars. Bar snacks, table d'hote menus. Lively weekends. Two minutes from Old Hall.

GLOSSOP, Derbyshire Map ref 4B2 *Tourist Information Centre Tel: (01457) 855920*

★★
Silver
Award

WIND IN THE WILLOWS HOTEL
Derbyshire Level, off Sheffield Road,
(A57), Glossop, SK13 7PT
T: (01457) 868001
F: (01457) 853354
E: info@windinthewillows.co.uk
I: www.windinthewillows.co.uk

Bedrooms: 9 double,
3 twin; suite available
Bathrooms: 12 en suite

EM 1930 (LO 1945)
Parking for 20
CC: Amex, Barclaycard,
Delta, Diners, Eurocard,
Mastercard, Solo, Switch,
Visa, Visa Electron

B&B per night:
S £74.00–£92.00
D £99.00–£119.00

OPEN All year round

Friendly country house hotel with log fires, home cooking, peace and relaxation. Views over the Peak District National Park. Adjacent golf-course, in excellent walking country.

GLOUCESTER, Gloucestershire Map ref 2B1 *Tourist Information Centre Tel: (01452) 421188*

★★

EDWARD HOTEL
88 London Road, Gloucester,
GL1 3PG
T: (01452) 525865
F: (01452) 302165

Bedrooms: 3 single,
5 double, 10 twin
Bathrooms: 18 en suite,
1 public

EM 1800 (LO 1930)
Parking for 25
CC: Barclaycard, Delta,
Eurocard, JCB,
Mastercard, Solo, Switch,
Visa

B&B per night:
S £35.00–£45.00
D £45.00–£60.00

OPEN All year round

Grade II Victorian terrace, large car park, short stroll to city. Freshly decorated bedrooms, bar, "chesterfield" lounge with log fire, and a gallery of Edwards!

RATING All accommodation in this guide has been rated, or is awaiting a rating, by a trained English Tourism Council assessor.

GLOUCESTER continued

★★★

NEW COUNTY HOTEL
44 Southgate Street, Gloucester, GL1 2DU
T: (01452) 307000
F: (01452) 500487
E: newcountry@meridianleisure.com
I: www.meridianleisure.com

B&B per night:
S £42.50–£55.00
D £60.00–£65.00

HB per person:
DY £55.00–£67.50

OPEN All year round

Ideally situated in the heart of Gloucester City, this 19thC hotel combines many original features with all modern amenities to create a fine, modern day hotel. All bedrooms are en suite and decorated to the highest standards. Free car parking adjacent. Ideal base for exploring the Cotswolds and nearby Cheltenham.

Bedrooms: 18 single,
12 double, 3 twin,
6 triple
Bathrooms: 39 en suite

Lunch available
EM 1900 (LO 2130)
Parking for 50
CC: Amex, Barclaycard,
Delta, Diners, Mastercard,
Switch, Visa

⋔☆⌕🖥☐✦🍷⌕⑤🗝🔌◐Ⅲ🖪♈140▸🖐SP🏛Ⅳ🌐

GOODRICH, Herefordshire Map ref 2A1

★★

YE HOSTELRIE HOTEL
Goodrich, Ross-on-Wye, Herefordshire
HR9 6HX
T: (01600) 890241
F: (01600) 890838
E: ye-hostelrie@lineone.net
I: ye-hostelrie.8k.com

B&B per night:
S £31.00–£33.00
D £48.00–£50.00

HB per person:
DY £29.95–£35.95

OPEN All year round

Picturesque family-run hotel, in the heart of the Wye Valley, close to Goodrich Castle and the Forest of Dean, Ye Hostelrie offers very comfortable en suite accommodation, excellent home-cooked food and real ales. Attractive patio and garden, secure parking. Pets are welcome in the bedrooms at no charge.

Bedrooms: 3 double,
2 twin, 1 triple
Bathrooms: 6 en suite

Lunch available
EM 1900 (LO 2130)
Parking for 33
CC: Amex, Barclaycard,
Delta, Mastercard, Solo,
Switch, Visa, Visa Electron

⋔☆🖥☐✦⑤🗝🔌⑰Ⅲ🖪♈60▸✣🚲🐾🏛

GRINDLEFORD, Derbyshire Map ref 4B2

★★★

MAYNARD ARMS HOTEL
Main Road, Grindleford,
Hope Valley, S32 2HE
T: (01433) 630321
F: (01433) 630445

Bedrooms: 8 double,
2 twin; suites available
Bathrooms: 10 en suite

Lunch available
EM 1900 (LO 2130)
Parking for 60
CC: Amex, Barclaycard,
Delta, Eurocard,
Mastercard, Switch, Visa

B&B per night:
S £69.00–£89.00
D £79.00–£99.00

HB per person:
DY £49.50–£59.50

OPEN All year round

Established hotel with a relaxed, friendly atmosphere and extensive facilities. Picturesque gardens with lovely views of Hope Valley and Peak Park. Excellent walking country.

⋔☆🐴⌕🖥☐✦🍷⑤🗝⑰Ⅲ🖪♈140✣🚲🐾SP🏛Ⅳ

HEREFORD, Herefordshire Map ref 2A1 *Tourist Information Centre Tel: (01432) 268430*

★★★

BELMONT LODGE AND GOLF COURSE
Belmont, Hereford, HR2 9SA
T: (01432) 352666
F: (01432) 358090
E: info@belmontlodge.co.uk
I: www.belmontlodge.co.uk

Bedrooms: 26 twin,
4 triple
Bathrooms: 30 en suite,
2 public

Lunch available
EM 1900 (LO 2130)
Parking for 120
CC: Amex, Barclaycard,
Delta, Mastercard, Solo,
Switch, Visa

B&B per night:
S £35.00–£49.50
D £60.00–£67.50

HB per person:
DY £48.00–£62.50

OPEN All year round

Comfortable hotel situated off the A465, 2 miles south of Hereford city centre. Overlooking the River Wye and Herefordshire countryside, offering beautiful views.

⋔☆🏌⌕🖥☐✦🍷⑤🗝⑰◐Ⅲ🖪♈60♣🗝♪▸✣🚲🐾SP🏛Ⅳ

WHERE TO STAY
Please mention this guide when making your booking.

★

THE NEW PRIORY HOTEL
Stretton Sugwas, Hereford,
HR4 7AR
T: (01432) 760264 & 760183
F: (01432) 761809

Bedrooms: 1 single,
4 double, 1 twin, 1 triple
Bathrooms: 6 en suite,
1 private

Lunch available
EM 1900 (LO 2145)
Parking for 60
CC: Barclaycard, Delta,
JCB, Mastercard, Solo,
Switch, Visa, Visa Electron

B&B per night:
S £30.00–£40.00
D £50.00–£70.00

HB per person:
DY £37.50–£45.00

Friendly family hotel in pleasant, peaceful surroundings, 2 miles from centre of Hereford. Good home-cooked food. En suite 4-poster rooms. Former monastery with lots of historic interest.

OPEN All year round

ⅢⅢⅢⅢ100 ⅢⅢ SP Ⅲ

★★★

THREE COUNTIES HOTEL
Belmont Road, Hereford, HR2 7BP
T: (01432) 299955
F: (01432) 275114
E: threecountieshotel@hotmail.
com

Bedrooms: 17 double,
43 twin
Bathrooms: 60 en suite

EM 1900 (LO 2115)
Parking for 250
CC: Amex, Barclaycard,
Delta, Diners, Maestro,
Mastercard, Solo, Switch,
Visa

B&B per night:
S £38.50–£59.50
D £57.00–£78.00

OPEN All year round

Excellently appointed hotel set in 3.5 acres. Emphasis on traditional, friendly service. Tasteful bedrooms, restaurant and bar offer today's guests all modern comforts. Town centre 1 mile.

ⅢⅢⅢⅢ400 ⅢⅢ SP T

★★★
Gold
Award

NUTHURST GRANGE COUNTRY HOUSE HOTEL AND RESTAURANT

Nuthurst Grange Lane, Hockley Heath,
Warwickshire B94 5NL
T: (01564) 783972

Nuthurst Grange nestles in 7.5 acres of landscaped gardens and woodlands. Relax and be pampered in one of our 15 luxurious bedrooms, enjoy a superb meal in our award-winning restaurant. We are perfectly placed in the heart of England close to National Trust attractions and market towns. Also an ideal venue for parties, wedding receptions, meetings and conferences.

F: (01564) 783919
E: info@nuthurst-grange.co.uk
I: www.theaa.co.uk/hotels

Bedrooms: 10 double,
5 twin; suite available
Bathrooms: 15 en suite

Lunch available
EM 1900 (LO 2130)
Parking for 88
CC: Amex, Barclaycard,
Delta, Diners, Maestro,
Mastercard, Solo, Switch,
Visa, Visa Electron

B&B per night:
S £125.00–£135.00
D £155.00–£185.00

OPEN All year round

ⅢⅢⅢⅢ80 ⅢⅢ SP T

★★

ADMIRAL RODNEY HOTEL
North Street, Horncastle, LN9 5DX
T: (01507) 523131
F: (01507) 523104
E: admiralrodney@bestwestern.co.
uk

Bedrooms: 19 double,
9 twin, 1 triple, 2 family
rooms
Bathrooms: 31 en suite

Lunch available
EM 1900 (LO 2130)
Parking for 70
CC: Amex, Barclaycard,
Delta, Diners, Maestro,
Mastercard, Solo, Switch,
Visa, Visa Electron

B&B per night:
S £45.00–£54.00
D £58.00–£76.00

HB per person:
DY £39.00–£64.00

OPEN All year round

Located in pleasant market town just off main Lincoln to Skegness road – ideal touring base. Large car park, en suite bedrooms, fine restaurant.

Best Western Hotels

ⅢⅢⅢⅢ120 ⅢⅢ SP T

TOWN INDEX

This can be found at the back of this guide. If you know where you want to stay, the index will give you the page number listing accommodation in your chosen town, city or village.

★★★ **THE BEST WESTERN VALLEY HOTEL**

Ironbridge, Telford, TF8 7DW	Bedrooms: 9 single,	Lunch available
T: (01952) 432247	23 double, 3 twin	EM 1900 (LO 2200)
F: (01952) 432308	Bathrooms: 35 en suite	Parking for 100
E: valley.hotel@ironbridge.fsnet.co.uk		CC: Amex, Barclaycard, Diners, Eurocard, Mastercard, Visa
I: www.bestwestern.co.uk		

B&B per night:
S £90.00–£100.00
D £110.00–£120.00

HB per person:
DY £76.00–£81.00

OPEN All year round

Georgian Listed building situated in World Heritage Site of Ironbridge. Riverside location with large car park. All Ironbridge Gorge Museum attractions within walking distance.

(CR)
Best Western Hotels

★★★ **CLARENDON HOUSE BAR-BRASSERIE HOTEL**

Old High Street, Kenilworth,	Bedrooms: 16 single,	Lunch available
CV8 1LZ	9 double, 5 twin, 1 triple	EM 1900 (LO 2200)
T: (01926) 857668	Bathrooms: 31 en suite	Parking for 34
F: (01926) 850669		CC: Amex, Barclaycard,
E: info@clarendonhousehotel.com		Delta, Diners, Eurocard,
I: www.clarendonhousehotel.com		JCB, Maestro, Mastercard, Solo, Switch, Visa

B&B per night:
S £49.50–£55.00
D £75.00–£90.00

HB per person:
DY £45.00–£45.00

OPEN All year round

Unique, historic inn dating from 1430, still supported by the old oak tree around which the former "Castle Tavern" was built. Own 16thC well from which they drew water is still open in the bar.

★★★

THE PEACOCK HOTEL

149 Warwick Road, Kenilworth, CV8 1HY
T: (01926) 851156 & 964500
F: (01926) 864644
E: peacockhotel@rafflesmalaysian.com
I: www.peacockhotel.com

B&B per night:
S £40.00–£70.00
D £50.00–£85.00

HB per person:
DY £59.00–£89.00

OPEN All year round

Small and luxurious hotel committed to providing outstanding quality and first class service at reasonable prices. Ideally located for meetings and conferences. Choice of 3 elegant restaurants, contemporary bar, gardens and ample parking. Optional tours and an "in-house" coach service available.	Bedrooms: 5 single, 8 double, 2 twin; suites available	Lunch available
	Bathrooms: 15 en suite	EM 1800 (LO 2230) Parking for 17 CC: Amex, Barclaycard, Delta, Diners, Eurocard, JCB, Maestro, Mastercard, Solo, Switch, Visa, Visa Electron

---

★★ **CEDARS HOTEL**

Mason Road, Kidderminster,	Bedrooms: 2 single,	EM 1900 (LO 2030)
DY11 6AG	8 double, 6 twin, 3 triple,	Parking for 23
T: (01562) 515595	2 family rooms	CC: Amex, Barclaycard,
F: (01562) 751103	Bathrooms: 21 en suite	Delta, Diners, Mastercard,
E: reservations@cedars-hotel.co.uk		Switch, Visa

B&B per night:
S £41.00–£58.00
D £56.00–£72.00

HB per person:
DY £58.00–£72.00

OPEN All year round

Charming conversion of a Georgian building close to the River Severn, Severn Valley Railway and Worcestershire countryside. 15 minutes from M5.

(CR)
Minotel

CHECK THE MAPS

The colour maps at the front of this guide show all the cities, towns and villages for which you will find accommodation entries.
Refer to the town index to find the page on which they are listed.

KIDDERMINSTER continued

★★★

THE GRANARY HOTEL AND RESTAURANT

Heath Lane, Shenstone, Kidderminster, DY10 4BS
T: (01562) 777535
F: (01562) 777722

B&B per night:
S £58.00–£65.50
D £68.00–£83.00

HB per person:
DY Min £73.50

OPEN All year round

In lovely, peaceful surroundings, amid some of Worcestershire's most beautiful countryside, The Granary Hotel boasts 18 luxury en suite bedrooms along with a stylishly redesigned restaurant, and 3 superior conference/banqueting suites with licence for civil ceremonies.

Bedrooms: 5 double, 12 twin, 1 triple
Bathrooms: 18 en suite

Lunch available
EM 1900 (LO 2130)
Parking for 95
CC: Amex, Barclaycard, Delta, Diners, Eurocard, Mastercard, Switch, Visa

The Independents

120

LANGAR, Nottinghamshire Map ref 4C2

★★★
Silver Award

LANGAR HALL
Langar, Nottingham, NG13 9HG
T: (01949) 860559
F: (01949) 861045
E: langarhall-hotel@ndirect.co.uk
I: www.langarhall.com

Bedrooms: 9 double, 2 twin
Bathrooms: 11 en suite

Lunch available
EM 1900 (LO 2130)
Parking for 20
CC: Amex, Barclaycard, Delta, Diners, JCB, Mastercard, Solo, Switch, Visa

B&B per night:
S £75.00–£95.00
D £100.00–£150.00

OPEN All year round

Charming small hotel in peaceful rural setting, 12 miles south-east of Nottingham. Central for touring or as a stop-off for travellers between north and south.

20

LEAMINGTON SPA, Warwickshire Map ref 4B3 *Tourist Information Centre Tel: (01926) 742762*

★★★

ANGEL HOTEL
143 Regent Street, Leamington Spa, CV32 4NZ
T: (01926) 881296
F: (01926) 881296

Bedrooms: 10 single, 22 double, 16 twin, 2 family rooms
Bathrooms: 50 en suite

Lunch available
EM 1900 (LO 2230)
Parking for 33
CC: Amex, Barclaycard, Delta, Diners, Mastercard, Switch, Visa

B&B per night:
S £35.00–£50.00
D £50.00–£65.00

OPEN All year round

The Angel Hotel is located in central Royal Leamington Spa, with en suite bedrooms, restaurant, bar, conference and function rooms.

40

★★★

EATON COURT HOTEL
1-7 St Marks Road, Leamington Spa, CV32 6DL
T: (01926) 885848
F: (01926) 885848
E: eatoncourt@cascade-uk.net

Bedrooms: 10 single, 12 double, 10 twin, 2 triple, 2 family rooms
Bathrooms: 36 en suite

Lunch available
EM 1900 (LO 2130)
Parking for 36
CC: Amex, Barclaycard, Diners, Mastercard, Visa

B&B per night:
S £40.00–£55.00
D £65.00–£75.00

HB per person:
DY £55.00–£70.00

OPEN All year round

Friendly privately owned and run hotel near town centre. Spacious en suite rooms with comfortable facilities, function rooms, licensed restaurant and secluded garden.

100

CHECK THE MAPS

The colour maps at the front of this guide show all the cities, towns and villages for which you will find accommodation entries. Refer to the town index to find the page on which they are listed.

★★

LEADON HOUSE HOTEL
Ross Road, Ledbury, Herefordshire HR8 2LP
T: (01531) 631199 & 632880
F: (01531) 631476
E: leadonho@lineone.net

B&B per night:
S £33.00–£47.00
D £51.00–£64.00

HB per person:
DY £38.00–£44.50

OPEN All year round

Graceful Edwardian family-run hotel. Recent quality refurbishment with period decor and furnishings. Set in open countryside about a mile from town centre. A warm welcome, good food, spacious and comfortable accommodation – the ideal base to explore the many attractions of "England's most rural county" and Heart of England. Restricted smoking.

Bedrooms: 1 single,
2 double, 1 twin,
2 family rooms
Bathrooms: 6 en suite

EM 1830 (LO 1930)
Parking for 8
CC: Amex, Barclaycard,
Delta, Eurocard,
Mastercard, Solo, Switch,
Visa, Visa Electron

★★ **THREE HORSESHOES INN AND RESTAURANT**

Buxton Road, Blackshaw Moor,
Leek, ST13 8TW
T: (01538) 300296
F: (01538) 300320

Bedrooms: 4 double,
2 twin
Bathrooms: 6 en suite

Lunch available
EM 1900 (LO 2100)
Parking for 100
CC: Amex, Barclaycard,
Delta, Eurocard, JCB,
Maestro, Mastercard,
Solo, Switch, Visa, Visa
Electron

B&B per night:
S £45.00–£55.00
D £55.00–£75.00

HB per person:
DY £40.00–£50.00

OPEN All year round

Traditional country inn with oak and pine beams, excellent restaurant with fine cuisine and a traditional bar carvery. 240 wines. Log fire.

★★

OAKLEIGH HOUSE HOTEL
25 St. Chad's Road, Lichfield, WS13 7LZ
T: (01543) 262688 & 255573
F: (01543) 418556
E: info@oakleighhouse.co.uk
I: www.oakleighhouse.co.uk

B&B per night:
S £45.00–£55.00
D £65.00–£75.00

HB per person:
DY £50.00–£80.00

OPEN All year round

Family-run, friendly, comfortable, licensed hotel. Edwardian house with garden overlooking a lake, 5 minutes' walk from city centre and cathedral. Restaurant, open to non-residents, has good reputation for serving delicious food using fresh local ingredients. Specialises in rare breed meat.

Bedrooms: 5 single,
3 double, 3 twin
Bathrooms: 10 en suite,
1 private, 1 public

Lunch available
EM 1900 (LO 2100)
Parking for 20
CC: Barclaycard, Delta,
Eurocard, Mastercard,
Switch, Visa

★★★ **THE BENTLEY HOTEL & LEISURE CLUB**

Newark Road, South Hykeham,
Lincoln, LN6 9NH
T: (01522) 878000
F: (01522) 878001
I: www.thebentleyhotel.uk.com

Bedrooms: 31 double,
22 twin; suite available
Bathrooms: 53 en suite

Lunch available
EM
Parking for 140
CC: Amex, Barclaycard,
Delta, Diners, Mastercard,
Solo, Switch, Visa, Visa
Electron

B&B per night:
S £62.00–£78.00
D £77.00–£87.00

HB per person:
DY £49.00–£57.00

OPEN All year round

Lincoln's newest and most modern hotel with leisure club. Beauty salon, conference centre, restaurant and bars.

Best Western Hotels

★★★

BRANSTON HALL HOTEL

Lincoln Road, Branston, Lincoln, LN4 1PD
T: (01522) 793305
F: (01522) 790549
E: brahal@enterprise.net
I: www.mercuryin.es/branston

B&B per night:
S £49.00–£69.50
D £63.00–£129.50

HB per person:
DY £60.00–£154.50

OPEN All year round

Elegant country house in beautiful grounds yet only 5 minutes from Lincoln city centre. All rooms are en suite and beautifully furnished. Our new leisure facilities include heated indoor pool, fully-equipped gymnasium, sauna and jacuzzi.

Bedrooms: 4 single, 33 double, 4 twin, 1 triple, 1 family room; suite available
Bathrooms: 43 en suite

Lunch available
EM 1900 (LO 2145)
Parking for 70
CC: Amex, Barclaycard, Delta, Eurocard, JCB, Mastercard, Solo, Switch, Visa, Visa Electron

---

★★

CASTLE HOTEL
Westgate, Lincoln, LN1 3AS
T: (01522) 538801
F: (01522) 575457

Bedrooms: 3 single, 11 double, 5 twin, 1 triple; suite available
Bathrooms: 20 en suite

EM 1900 (LO 2130)
CC: Barclaycard, Delta, Diners, Eurocard, JCB, Mastercard, Solo, Switch, Visa, Visa Electron

B&B per night:
S £62.00–£79.00
D £79.00–£125.00

HB per person:
DY £54.50–£77.50

OPEN All year round

Located amid Lincoln's historic heart, a very comfortable traditional English hotel offering hospitality at its best. Also featuring "Knights", an award-winning seafood and game restaurant.

Minotel

★★★

GRAND HOTEL
St Mary's Street, Lincoln, LN5 7EP
T: (01522) 524211
F: (01522) 537661
I: www.thegrandhotel.com

Bedrooms: 17 single, 14 double, 13 twin, 2 triple
Bathrooms: 46 en suite

Lunch available
EM 1900 (LO 2100)
Parking for 30
CC: Amex, Barclaycard, Delta, Diners, Mastercard, Solo, Switch, Visa

B&B per night:
S £54.00–£69.00
D £69.00–£79.00

HB per person:
DY £47.50–£56.00

OPEN All year round

Family-owned hotel, in the centre of beautiful historic city. Getaway breaks available throughout the year. Half board prices are based on a minimum 2-night stay.

The Independents/Best Western Hotels

LOUTH, Lincolnshire Map ref 4D2 *Tourist Information Centre Tel: (01507) 609289*

★★★

BRACKENBOROUGH ARMS HOTEL & RESTAURANT

Cordeaux Corner, Brackenborough, Louth, LN11 0SZ
T: (01507) 609169
F: (01507) 609413
E: info@brackenborough.co.uk
I: www.brackenborough.co.uk

B&B per night:
S £58.95–£62.00
D £70.00–£75.00

HB per person:
DY £42.50–£47.50

OPEN All year round

A purpose-built, country house hotel set in 7 acres, operating to high standards, being privately owned and family run. Most popular hotel and restaurant in the area, also offering casual dining in the lounge bar. Set back off the A16 Louth to Grimsby road, approximately 2 miles from Louth. Reduced price weekend breaks available.

Bedrooms: 2 single, 14 double, 7 twin, 1 triple
Bathrooms: 24 en suite

Lunch available
EM 1700 (LO 2200)
Parking for 90
CC: Amex, Barclaycard, Delta, Diners, Eurocard, Mastercard, Switch, Visa

---

HALF BOARD PRICES Half board prices are given per person, but in some cases these may be based on double/twin occupancy.

LOWER SLAUGHTER, Gloucestershire Map ref 2B1

★★★
Silver
Award

WASHBOURNE COURT HOTEL

Lower Slaughter, Cheltenham, GL54 2HS
T: (01451) 822143
F: (01451) 821045
E: washbourne@msn.com

B&B per night:
S £130.00–£200.00
D £145.00–£215.00

HB per person:
DY £87.50–£130.00

OPEN All year round

If you are in search of peace, tranquillity and the epitome of English country life, you need look no further than Washbourne Court. Set in the heart of the beautiful Cotswold countryside on the banks of the River Eye in the enchanting village of Lower Slaughter.

Bedrooms: 18 double, 6 twin, 4 triple; suites available
Bathrooms: 28 en suite

Lunch available
EM 1930 (LO 2130)
Parking for 50
CC: Amex, Barclaycard, Delta, Diners, Eurocard, Mastercard, Switch, Visa

♠♥12 ♦♣ ℮ ▢ ◊ 🆖 S ✂ ♨ 🏛 ⊿ 🍴20 ♋ ♉ ⊫ ☼ 🐾 🐎 ⬥ SP 🎗 T

MALVERN, Worcestershire Map ref 2B1 *Tourist Information Centre Tel: (01684) 892289*

★★★
Gold
Award

COLWALL PARK HOTEL
Walwyn Road, Colwall, Malvern, WR13 6QG
T: (01684) 540206 & 541033
F: (01684) 540847
E: hotel@colwall.com
I: www.colwall.com

Bedrooms: 3 single, 9 double, 7 twin, 2 triple, 2 family rooms; suites available
Bathrooms: 23 en suite

Lunch available
EM 1930 (LO 2100)
Parking for 40
CC: Amex, Barclaycard, Delta, Diners, JCB, Mastercard, Solo, Switch, Visa, Visa Electron

B&B per night:
S £64.50–£80.00
D £105.00–£150.00

HB per person:
DY £70.00–£92.50

OPEN All year round

Ⓒ
Best Western Hotels

Charming country house hotel on the western side of the Malvern Hills. Good views of the hills and mature hotel garden. Award-winning cuisine in relaxing, comfortable surroundings.

♠♥ ℮ ▢ ◊ 🆖 S ✂ ♨ TV ◐ 🏛 ⊿ 🍴120 ♉ ⊫ ☼ ⬥ SP T ◉

★★

COTFORD HOTEL

Graham Road, Malvern, WR14 2HU
T: (01684) 572427
F: (01684) 572952

B&B per night:
S £50.00–£60.00
D £70.00–£80.00

HB per person:
DY £53.00–£68.00

OPEN All year round

Beautiful Victorian hotel, built in 1851 reputedly for the Bishop of Worcester. All rooms en suite with satellite TV, telephone, radio and tea-making facilities. Complimentary use of Malvern Splash swimming pool and sauna. Close to town centre, theatre and hills but set in its own mature gardens to add peace and tranquillity to your stay.

Bedrooms: 9 single, 4 double, 1 twin, 3 triple
Bathrooms: 17 en suite

Lunch available
EM 1900 (LO 2100)
Parking for 14
CC: Amex, Barclaycard, Delta, Diners, Eurocard, Mastercard, Switch, Visa, Visa Electron

♠♥♦♣ ℮ ▢ ◊ 🆖 S ✂ ♨ 🏛 ⊿ 🍴14 ☼ ⬥ SP 🎗 T

COUNTRY CODE Always follow the Country Code ✿ Enjoy the countryside and respect its life and work ✿ Guard against all risk of fire ✿ Fasten all gates ✿ Keep your dogs under close control ✿ Keep to public paths across farmland ✿ Use gates and stiles to cross fences, hedges and walls ✿ Leave livestock, crops and machinery alone ✿ Take your litter home ✿ Help to keep all water clean ✿ Protect wildlife, plants and trees ✿ Take special care on country roads ✿ Make no unnecessary noise

★★★
Silver
Award

Set high on the Malvern Hills with 30-mile views to the Cotswolds. "The best view in England" – Daily Mail. All en suite. Family owned and run. Exceptional food. Daily half board prices based on minimum 2-night stay. Weekly is 7 nights for price of 6. Breaks available all week, all year.

THE COTTAGE IN THE WOOD HOTEL

Holywell Road, Malvern Wells, Malvern, WR14 4LG
T: (01684) 575859 (Manned 7am to midnight)
F: (01684) 560662
E: proprietor@cottageinthewood.co.uk
I: www.cottageinthewood.co.uk

Bedrooms: 16 double, 4 twin.
Bathrooms: 20 en suite

Lunch available
EM 1900 (LO 2100)
Parking for 40
CC: Amex, Barclaycard, Delta, Eurocard, JCB, Mastercard, Switch, Visa, Visa Electron

B&B per night:
S £75.00–£85.00
D £89.50–£145.00

HB per person:
DY £62.00–£98.00

OPEN All year round

®
Best Western Hotels

★★
Silver
Award

Enchanting wisteria covered country house hotel nestling into the foot of the Malvern Hills. Award-winning restaurant, pretty en suite bedrooms, log fires, personal care and service and a wonderfully warm and relaxing atmosphere. Away Breaks available all week, all year. Children and pets welcome.

HOLDFAST COTTAGE HOTEL

Marlbank Road, Little Malvern, Malvern, WR13 6NA
T: (01684) 310288
F: (01684) 311117
E: holdcothot@aol.com
I: www.holdfast-cottage.co.uk

Bedrooms: 1 single, 5 double, 2 twin
Bathrooms: 8 en suite, 1 public

EM 1900 (LO 2100)
Parking for 20
CC: Barclaycard, Delta, Mastercard, Solo, Switch, Visa, Visa Electron

B&B per night:
S Min £48.00
D Min £90.00

HB per person:
DY £64.00–£66.00

OPEN All year round

★★

Straddling the Herefordshire/ Worcestershire county border at British Camp (the Herefordshire Beacon) on the A449 midway between Malvern and Ledbury, the site of the hotel has provided a hostelry for travellers for more than 500 years. Walks with breathtaking views, excellent bar food, real ales, elegant restaurant and extensive wine list. Pets welcome.

MALVERN HILLS HOTEL

Wynds Point, British Camp, Malvern, WR13 6DW
T: (01684) 540690
F: (01684) 540327
E: malhilhotl@aol.com

Bedrooms: 2 single, 7 double, 3 twin, 3 triple
Bathrooms: 14 en suite, 1 private

Lunch available
EM 1900 (LO 2130)
Parking for 30
CC: Amex, Barclaycard, Delta, Diners, Eurocard, Mastercard, Solo, Switch, Visa

B&B per night:
S £40.00–£50.00
D £75.00–£85.00

HB per person:
DY £57.50–£62.50

OPEN All year round

MAP REFERENCES
The map references refer to the colour maps at the front of this guide. The first figure is the map number; the letter and figure which follow indicate the grid reference on the map.

MANSFIELD, Nottinghamshire Map ref 4C2

★★ **PINE LODGE HOTEL**

281-283 Nottingham Road, Mansfield, NG18 4SE T: (01623) 622308 F: (01623) 656819 E: plhotel@aol.com	Bedrooms: 5 single, 5 double, 7 twin, 2 triple Bathrooms: 19 en suite	Lunch available EM 1900 (LO 2100) Parking for 35 CC: Amex, Barclaycard, Delta, Diners, Eurocard, Mastercard, Solo, Switch, Visa

B&B per night:
S £35.00–£55.00
D £50.00–£65.00

HB per person:
DY £32.50–£45.50

OPEN All year round

Friendly and informal. Good food, good value, excellent service. Ideally situated close to many of Nottinghamshire's tourist and leisure attractions.

☊ ♞ ☎ 🖥 ▢ ⌖ ▢ Ⓢ ᛈ ⓉⓋ ◑ 🎱 ☕ ☎ 40 ᗌ ⊩ ❋ ✈ ↘ ⓈⓅ Ⓣ

MARKET DRAYTON, Shropshire Map ref 4A2 *Tourist Information Centre Tel: (01630) 652139*

★★ **THE BEAR HOTEL**

Hodnet, Market Drayton, TF9 3NH T: (01630) 685214 & 685788 F: (01630) 685787	Bedrooms: 1 single, 3 double, 2 twin, 1 triple, 1 family room Bathrooms: 8 en suite	Lunch available EM 1900 (LO 2145) Parking for 100 CC: Amex, Barclaycard, Delta, Eurocard, JCB, Mastercard, Solo, Switch, Visa

B&B per night:
S £40.00–£45.00
D £60.00–£70.00

OPEN All year round

Privately owned 16thC inn, with the character of a bygone age but 20thC comfort, and a warm and friendly atmosphere. Oak-beamed, open fires.

☊ ♞ 🚗 ☎ 🖥 ▢ ⌖ ᛈ Ⓢ ⌖ ⓉⓋ 🎱 ☕ ☎ 100 ❀ ∪ ⊩ ❋ ✈ 🚐 ↘ ⓈⓅ 🎰 Ⓣ

★★

ROSEHILL MANOR HOTEL & RESTAURANT

Tern Hill, Market Drayton, TF9 2JF
T: (01630) 638532 & 637000
F: (01630) 637008

B&B per night:
S Max £50.00
D Max £70.00

HB per person:
DY Max £55.00

OPEN All year round

Set in 1.5 acres of mature gardens, this Georgian house hotel has all the comforts you would expect. Easy to find as located on the A41 Chester road. The recently added garden conservatory and open fires in the 16thC lounge provide the perfect setting for that special occasion.	Bedrooms: 1 single, 5 double, 3 triple Bathrooms: 9 en suite	Lunch available EM 1900 (LO 2130) Parking for 60 CC: Amex, Barclaycard, Delta, Mastercard, Switch, Visa

☊ ♞ ☎ 🖥 ▢ ⌖ ᛉ Ⓢ ⌖ ᛈ ⓉⓋ 🎱 ☕ ❋ 🚐

MATLOCK, Derbyshire Map ref 4B2 *Tourist Information Centre Tel: (01629) 583388*

★★★
Silver
Award

RIBER HALL

Riber, Matlock, DE4 5JU T: (01629) 582795 F: (01629) 580475 E: info@riber-hall.co.uk I: www.riber-hall.co.uk	Bedrooms: 12 double, 2 twin Bathrooms: 14 en suite	Lunch available EM 1900 (LO 2130) Parking for 50 CC: Amex, Barclaycard, Delta, Diners, Eurocard, JCB, Mastercard, Switch, Visa

B&B per night:
S £95.00–£109.00
D £123.00–£143.00

HB per person:
DY £115.00–£157.00

OPEN All year round

Relax in this tranquil historic country house with old walled garden – visit the beautiful Peak National Park and its many stately homes, including Chatsworth.

☊ ♞ 10 ♨ 🚗 ☎ 🖥 ▢ ⌖ ᛉ ᛈ Ⓢ ⌖ ᛈ 🎱 ☕ ☎ 20 ◖ ❋ 🚐 Ⓢ🅒 ↘ ⓈⓅ 🎰 Ⓣ

AT-A-GLANCE SYMBOLS

Symbols at the end of each accommodation entry give useful information about services and facilities. A key to symbols can be found inside the back cover flap. Keep this open for easy reference.

163

★★

QUORN LODGE HOTEL
46 Asfordby Road, Melton Mowbray,
LE13 0HR
T: (01664) 566660 & 562590
F: (01664) 480660
E: quornlodge@aol.com
I: www.quornlodge.co.uk

B&B per night:
S £45.00–£51.50
D £59.50–£75.00

HB per person:
DY £42.25–£67.50

OPEN All year round

Original hunting lodge, few minutes' walk from town centre. The hotel is privately owned and is deservedly popular with its home-from-home atmosphere. Two 4-poster rooms for that special occasion. Ground floor rooms available. Special weekend rates. Be assured of excellent service with first class cuisine in our Laurels restaurant.

Bedrooms: 6 single, 7 double, 4 twin, 2 triple; suites available
Bathrooms: 19 en suite

Lunch available
EM 1900 (LO 2100)
Parking for 33
CC: Amex, Barclaycard, Delta, Eurocard, Mastercard, Switch, Visa

🛆🖧🏨📞🖼️🖵👌🔧🛎️⑤⚡🦮📺🖥️🍴100 ∪ ✻🏹🐾 SP T

★★★

SYSONBY KNOLL HOTEL
Asfordby Road, Melton Mowbray,
LE13 0HP
T: (01664) 563563
F: (01664) 410364
E: sysonby.knoll@btinternet.com
I: www.sysonby.knoll.btinternet.co.uk

B&B per night:
S £44.00–£61.00
D £61.00–£77.50

HB per person:
DY Min £41.50

OPEN All year round

Privately owned hotel within walking distance of town centre, standing in 4-acre grounds with river frontage. Lively restaurant is locally popular and our reputation for good food and exceptional hospitality gives us a loyal following of regular guests. Weekend breaks and 4-posters available. Pets welcome. Half board prices are for a minimum 2-night weekend stay.

Bedrooms: 7 single, 10 double, 6 twin, 1 triple
Bathrooms: 24 en suite

Lunch available
EM 1900 (LO 2100)
Parking for 30
CC: Amex, Barclaycard, Delta, Diners, Eurocard, JCB, Mastercard, Solo, Switch, Visa, Visa Electron

🄰🛆🖧🏨📞🖵👌🔧⑤🖥️🍴35 ⟲∪♿✻ SP T

★★★

BROOMHILL COUNTRY HOUSE HOTEL AND RESTAURANT
Holdenby Road, Spratton,
Northampton, NN6 8LD
T: (01604) 845959
F: (01604) 845834

Bedrooms: 2 single, 4 double, 7 twin
Bathrooms: 13 en suite

Lunch available
EM 1900 (LO 2145)
Parking for 100
CC: Amex, Barclaycard, Delta, Diners, Eurocard, Mastercard, Switch, Visa, Visa Electron

B&B per night:
S £70.00–£70.00
D £80.00–£90.00

OPEN All year round

Converted Victorian country house with splendid views. You will be offered relaxed, old-fashioned hospitality, while chef will tempt you with interesting and varied menus.

🄰🛆📞🖵👌⑤🖥️🍴45 ⟲♿∪➤✻🚪 SP T ◉

QUALITY ASSURANCE SCHEME
For an explanation of the quality and facilities represented by the Stars please refer to the front of this guide. A more detailed explanation can be found in the information pages at the back.

NORTHAMPTON continued

★★★
Silver
Award

LIME TREES HOTEL

8 Langham Place, Barrack Road,
Northampton, NN2 6AA
T: (01604) 632188
F: (01604) 233012
E: info@limetreeshotel.co.uk
I: www.limetreeshotel.co.uk

B&B per night:
S £45.00–£72.00
D £65.00–£85.00

HB per person:
DY £60.00–£87.00

OPEN All year round

Lime Trees is perfectly situated half a mile form the town centre. As a result of the personal attention from the owners the hotel has a strong local reputation for high standards in service, accommodation and restaurant. A converted stable block to the rear overlooks the courtyard which offers secure parking.

Bedrooms: 7 single,
14 double, 2 twin,
4 triple
Bathrooms: 27 en suite,
1 public

Lunch available
EM 1900 (LO 2100)
Parking for 24
CC: Amex, Barclaycard,
Delta, Diners, Eurocard,
Mastercard, Solo, Switch,
Visa, Visa Electron

 60

NOTTINGHAM, Nottinghamshire Map ref 4C2 *Tourist Information Centre Tel: (0115) 915 5330*

★★★

THE NOTTINGHAM GATEWAY HOTEL

Nuthall Road, Nottingham, NG8 6AZ
T: (0115) 979 4949
F: (0115) 979 4744
E: nottmgateway@btconnect.com

B&B per night:
S £40.00–£90.00
D £50.00–£100.00

HB per person:
DY £37.00–£105.50

OPEN All year round

Modern and conveniently located hotel enjoying a large and impressive glass architectural reception area, which permits you to relax in natural daylight all year round whatever the weather outside. Free on-site car parking. Carvery restaurant offering traditional English food, a la carte and Thai food cooked by our own Thai chef Lec.

Bedrooms: 69 double,
31 twin, 8 triple
Bathrooms: 108 en suite

Lunch available
EM 1830 (LO 2230)
Parking for 250
CC: Amex, Barclaycard,
Delta, Diners, Eurocard,
Mastercard, Solo, Switch,
Visa

300

★★★

SWANS HOTEL AND RESTAURANT
84-90 Radcliffe Road,
West Bridgford, Nottingham,
NG2 5HH
T: (0115) 981 4042
F: (0115) 945 5745
E: swanshotel@aol.com
I: www.smoothhound.co.uk/

Bedrooms: 5 single,
19 double, 4 twin,
1 triple, 1 family room;
suite available
Bathrooms: 30 en suite

Lunch available
EM 1900 (LO 2100)
Parking for 30
CC: Amex, Barclaycard,
Delta, Diners, Eurocard,
Mastercard, Solo, Switch,
Visa

B&B per night:
S £40.00–£58.00
D £55.00–£68.00

HB per person:
DY £32.00–£48.00

OPEN All year round

Ideally placed for all Nottingham's major sporting facilities. Good value, excellent service, wonderful food.

50

USE YOUR *i*s

There are more than 550 Tourist Information Centres throughout England offering friendly help with accommodation and holiday ideas as well as suggestions of places to visit and things to do. You'll find TIC addresses in the local Phone Book.

★★★
Silver
Award

BARNSDALE LODGE HOTEL

The Avenue, Rutland Water, Exton,
Oakham, Leicestershire LE15 8AH
T: (01572) 724678
F: (01572) 724961

B&B per night:
S Max £65.00
D Max £89.00

OPEN All year round

Traditional English fare in Edwardian-style dining rooms. Afternoon teas, elevenses and buttery menus complement the beautifully appointed surroundings. Enjoy panoramic views across Rutland Water and relax in this ideal retreat, or take a theatre, garden or golfing break. Special events individually catered for. We welcome you to the heart of Rutland.

Bedrooms: 8 single,
27 double, 8 twin,
2 triple; suites available
Bathrooms: 45 en suite

Lunch available
EM 1900 (LO 2145)
Parking for 220
CC: Amex, Barclaycard,
Delta, Diners, Eurocard,
Mastercard, Switch, Visa

⊞彡⇘綱☎📠❑✦🐾î§⚲🏊♨◑🖫🔌🍴250 ∪♪▸✎❋🔊 SP 🏮 T

★★★

BOULTONS COUNTRY TOWN HOUSE HOTEL AND RESTAURANTS

4 Catmos Street, Oakham, Leicestershire
LE15 6HW
T: (01572) 722844
F: (01572) 724473

B&B per night:
S £35.00–£60.00
D £70.00–£80.00

HB per person:
DY £45.00–£55.00

OPEN All year round

In Rutland, the heart of the English shires. Ideal base for touring the rolling countryside, picturesque villages and a variety of attractions, including Barnsdale Gardens and Rutland Water. A welcoming country-house ambience and "The Cottage" (circa 1604) lounge bar and restaurant provide an intimate setting for relaxation.

Bedrooms: 7 single,
12 double, 6 twin
Bathrooms: 25 en suite

Lunch available
EM 1900 (LO 2100)
Parking for 15
CC: Amex, Barclaycard,
Delta, Diners, Maestro,
Mastercard, Switch, Visa,
Visa Electron

⊞彡⇘綱☎📠❑✦🐾î§⚲🏊🔌🍴100 ∪▸✎ SP 🏮 T ◉

★★★
Silver
Award

PEN-Y-DYFFRYN COUNTRY HOTEL
Rhyd-y-Croesau, Oswestry,
SY10 7JD
T: (01691) 653700
F: (01691) 650066
E: peny.d@virginnet.co.uk
I: www.go2.co.uk/penydyffryn

Bedrooms: 1 single,
4 double, 4 twin,
1 family room
Bathrooms: 10 en suite

EM 1900 (LO 2030)
Parking for 15
CC: Amex, Barclaycard,
Delta, Mastercard, Solo,
Switch, Visa

B&B per night:
S £60.00–£63.00
D £78.00–£96.00

HB per person:
DY £57.00–£66.00

OPEN Feb–Dec

Peaceful, Georgian former rectory in 5 acres of grounds in Shropshire/Welsh border hills. Fully licensed, noted restaurant. Informal atmosphere, pets welcome. 30 minutes Shrewsbury and Chester.

⊞彡⇘綱☎📠❑✦🐾î§⚲🏊🔌🍴∪♪▸✎❋🐾🔊 SP 🏮 T

★★

THE FALCON HOTEL
New Street, Painswick, Stroud,
GL6 6UN
T: (01452) 814222 & 812228
F: (01452) 813377
E: bleninns@clara.net
I: www.poinswick.co.uk

Bedrooms: 5 double,
3 twin, 4 triple
Bathrooms: 12 en suite

Lunch available
EM 1900 (LO 2130)
Parking for 32
CC: Amex, Barclaycard,
Delta, Diners, Eurocard,
JCB, Mastercard, Solo,
Switch, Visa

B&B per night:
S £39.50–£45.00
D £59.00–£75.00

HB per person:
DY £40.00–£49.00

OPEN All year round

Famous old coaching inn dating from 1554, in the heart of Painswick. Refurbished to very high standards, with antique furniture and original oil paintings. Renowned restaurant.

⊞彡⇘綱☎📠❑✦🐾î§⚲🏊🔌🍴50 ❋🔊 SP 🏮 T

PAINSWICK continued

★★★ Silver Award

PAINSWICK HOTEL
Kemps Lane, Painswick, Stroud,
GL6 6YB
T: (01452) 812160
F: (01452) 814059
E: reservations@painswickhotel.
com
I: www.painswickhotel.com

Bedrooms: 2 single,
10 double, 5 twin,
2 triple
Bathrooms: 19 en suite

Lunch available
EM 1900 (LO 2130)
Parking for 40
CC: Amex, Barclaycard,
Delta, Eurocard, JCB,
Mastercard, Solo, Switch,
Visa, Visa Electron

B&B per night:
S £85.00–£145.00
D £120.00–£185.00

OPEN All year round

Situated in the beautiful Cotswold village of Painswick. The hotel offers friendly service, award-winning cuisine and luxurious bedrooms. Children and dogs most welcome.

🏟🐎♿🛋📞🖥📺🎯📶🔌🍴50 ∪ ⻌ ✿ 🏳 SP 🏨 T

PEAK DISTRICT

See under Ashbourne, Bakewell, Bamford, Biggin-by-Hartington, Glossop, Grindleford

ROSS-ON-WYE, Herefordshire Map ref 2A1 *Tourist Information Centre Tel: (01989) 562768*

★★

BRIDGE HOUSE HOTEL
Wilton, Ross-on-Wye,
Herefordshire HR9 6AA
T: (01989) 562655
F: (01989) 567652
E: alison@bhhotel.fsnet.co.uk

Bedrooms: 4 double,
3 twin, 1 triple
Bathrooms: 8 en suite

EM 1800 (LO 2000)
Parking for 12
CC: Barclaycard, Delta,
Mastercard, Switch, Visa

B&B per night:
S £36.00–£37.50
D £55.00–£56.00

HB per person:
DY £43.00–£53.00

OPEN All year round

Riverside hotel with panoramic views from the gardens and pride in its comfort and cuisine. All rooms en suite. Break terms available.

🏟🐎10📞🖥🔌📶🎯📺📺🔌🍴✿🏳📶 SP T

★★★ Silver Award

THE CHASE HOTEL
Gloucester Road, Ross-on-Wye,
Herefordshire HR9 5LH
T: (01989) 763161
F: (01989) 768330
E: info@chasehotel.co.uk
I: www.chasehotel.co.uk

Bedrooms: 16 double,
21 twin, 1 triple
Bathrooms: 38 en suite

Lunch available
EM 1900 (LO 2145)
Parking for 200
CC: Barclaycard, Delta,
Mastercard, Switch, Visa

B&B per night:
S £60.00–£85.00
D £75.00–£100.00

HB per person:
DY £45.00–£65.00

OPEN All year round

Georgian country house in 11 acres of beautiful grounds. Short walk town centre. Enthusiastic staff provide a professional service in a friendly, relaxed atmosphere. Ideal touring centre.

🏟🐎♿📞🛋📺🔌📶🖥📺📺⊙🍴300 ∪ ⻌ ✿ 🏳📶 SP 🏨 T ✹

★★★

THE ROYAL

Palace Pound, Ross-on-Wye, Herefordshire
HR9 5HZ
T: (01989) 565105
F: (01989) 768058

B&B per night:
S £50.00–£58.00
D £80.00–£100.00

OPEN All year round

This magnificent Victorian hotel, with superb views over the Wye Valley, is ideally located close to A40/M50 yet just a minute's walk to the centre of Ross-on-Wye. With modern amenities, superb cuisine (and now privately owned), The Royal provides an ideal base from which to tour this stunning region.

Bedrooms: 4 single,
20 double, 15 twin,
1 family room
Bathrooms: 40 en suite

Lunch available
EM 1900 (LO 2130)
Parking for 38
CC: Amex, Barclaycard,
Delta, Diners, Eurocard,
JCB, Maestro, Mastercard,
Solo, Switch, Visa, Visa
Electron

🏟🐎♿🛋📞🖥🔌📶🖥📺📺⊙🍴80 ⻌ ✿ SC 📶 SP 🏨 T

RUGBY, Warwickshire Map ref 4C3 *Tourist Information Centre Tel: (01788) 534970 or 534975*

★★

THE GROSVENOR HOTEL
81-87 Clifton Road, Rugby,
CV21 3QQ
T: (01788) 535686
F: (01788) 541297
E: therugbygrosvenorhotel@
freeserve.co.uk

Bedrooms: 9 single,
15 double, 2 twin; suite
available
Bathrooms: 26 en suite

Lunch available
EM 1900 (LO 2200)
Parking for 40
CC: Amex, Barclaycard,
Delta, Diners, Mastercard,
Switch

B&B per night:
S £51.50–£81.00
D £71.00–£97.50

HB per person:
DY £70.50–£100.00

OPEN All year round

Privately-owned hotel, sympathetically renovated and restored and ideally situated close to the town centre and main station. Indoor swimming pool and sauna.

🐎📞🛋🔌📶🖥📺⊙📺🎯🍴50 ♨ ⊰ ⻌ ✿ 📶 SP T

RUTLAND WATER Tourist Information Centre Tel: (01572) 653026

See under Oakham

SHERWOOD FOREST

See under Mansfield

SPALDING, Lincolnshire Map ref 3A1 *Tourist Information Centre Tel: (01775) 725468*

★★ **CLEY HALL HOTEL**

22 High Street, Spalding, PE11 1TX	Bedrooms: 6 single,	Lunch available	B&B per night:
T: (01775) 725157	4 double, 2 twin	EM 1900 (LO 2130)	S £45.00–£65.00
F: (01775) 710785	Bathrooms: 12 en suite	Parking for 20	D £65.00–£85.00
E: cleyhall@enterprise.net		CC: Amex, Barclaycard,	
I: homepages.enterprise.net/cleyhall		Delta, Diners, Eurocard,	HB per person:
		JCB, Mastercard, Solo,	DY £65.00–£80.00
		Switch, Visa, Visa Electron	
			OPEN All year round

18thC Georgian manor-house by the River Welland, 500 metres from town centre, with award-winning restaurant.

⚑🐕🏧🐾📞📠🖥↧🏵🛈⟁✂🅟🖨◐🏨🚗🍴40 ♨ ☀ ✿ 🐾 🐎🅣🛈

STAMFORD, Lincolnshire Map ref 3A1 *Tourist Information Centre Tel: (01780) 755611*

★★★ **GARDEN HOUSE HOTEL**

St Martins, Stamford, PE9 2LP	Bedrooms: 2 single,	Lunch available	B&B per night:
T: (01780) 763359	9 double, 8 twin,	EM 1900 (LO 2130)	S £50.00–£68.00
F: (01780) 763339	1 family room	Parking for 25	D £78.00–£95.00
E: gardenhousehotel@stamford60.	Bathrooms: 20 en suite	CC: Amex, Barclaycard,	
freeserve.co.uk		JCB, Mastercard, Solo,	HB per person:
I: stamford.co.uk		Switch, Visa	DY £45.00–£53.00

Charming 18thC townhouse converted to a hotel, where guests are treated as such by their hosts. Features a conservatory full of floral extravaganza and a meandering garden of 1 acre.

OPEN All year round

Ⓒ Minotel

⚑🐕🏧🐾📞📠🖥↧🏵🛈⟁🏨🚗🍴40 🅟 ☀ ✿ 🐾 🆂🅟🅣🛈

★★★ **GEORGE OF STAMFORD**
Silver Award

71 St Martins, Stamford, PE9 2LB	Bedrooms: 10 single,	Lunch available	B&B per night:
T: (01780) 750750 &	17 double, 9 twin,	EM 1800 (LO 2230)	S £78.00–£105.00
750700 (Reservations)	11 triple; suite available	Parking for 120	D £103.00–£220.00
F: (01780) 750701	Bathrooms: 47 en suite	CC: Amex, Barclaycard,	
E: reservations@		Delta, Diners, Eurocard,	OPEN All year round
georgehotelofstamford.com		Mastercard, Switch, Visa	
I: www.georgehotelofstamford.com			

Full of antique furniture, oak panelling and log fires, this historic inn is one of England's most famous resting places. Popular restaurant, more informal garden lounge.

⚑🐕🏧🐾📞📠🖥🏵🛈⟁🏨◐🖨🚗🍴50 🅟 ☀ ✿ 🐾 🆂🅟🅣🛈

STEEPLE ASTON, Oxfordshire

The Holt Hotel
See South of England region for full entry details

STOKE-ON-TRENT, Stoke-on-Trent Map ref 4B2 *Tourist Information Centre Tel: (01782) 236000*

★★★ **GEORGE HOTEL**
Silver Award

Swan Square, Burslem, Stoke-on-	Bedrooms: 9 single,	Lunch available	B&B per night:
Trent, ST6 2AE	15 double, 11 twin,	EM 1900 (LO 2130)	S £45.00–£70.00
T: (01782) 577544	4 triple	Parking for 22	D £65.00–£90.00
F: (01782) 837496	Bathrooms: 39 en suite	CC: Amex, Barclaycard,	
E: georgestoke@btinternet.com		Delta, Diners, Eurocard,	OPEN All year round
I: www.georgehotelstoke.cwc.net		JCB, Mastercard, Switch,	
		Visa	

Attractive neo-Georgian building. Conveniently situated between the Midlands, Liverpool and Manchester. Award-winning restaurant. Good centre for exploring the multitude of pottery outlets.

🐕📞📠🖥↧🏵🛈⟁🅟◐🏨🖨🚗🍴200 🎿 🐾 🆂🅟🅣

IMPORTANT NOTE Information on accommodation listed in this guide has been supplied by the proprietors. As changes may occur you are advised to check details at the time of booking.

STOKE-ON-TRENT continued

★★★ THE NORTH STAFFORD

Station Road, Stoke-on-Trent,
ST4 2AE
T: (01782) 744477
F: (01782) 744580
E: claireportas@principalhotels.co.uk
I: www.principalhotels.co.uk

Bedrooms: 27 single,
29 double, 21 twin,
2 triple, 1 family room
Bathrooms: 80 en suite

Lunch available
EM 1900 (LO 2200)
Parking for 200
CC: Amex, Barclaycard,
Delta, Mastercard, Switch,
Visa

B&B per night:
S £40.00–£95.00
D £70.00–£98.00

HB per person:
DY £45.00–£55.00

OPEN All year round

Classical and spacious, the North Stafford is situated opposite Stoke railway station and 10 miles from junction 16 of M6. Alton Towers 14 miles away.

ⒸⓇ
Principal Hotels/Utell
International

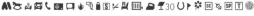

Rating Applied For — THE PLOUGH MOTEL AND RESTAURANT

Campbell Road, Stoke-on-Trent,
ST4 4EN
T: (01782) 414685
F: (01782) 414669
E: info@ploughmotel.co.uk
I: www.ploughmotel.co.uk

Bedrooms: 2 double,
12 twin, 2 triple, 4 family
rooms
Bathrooms: 20 en suite

Lunch available
EM 1800 (LO 2130)
Parking for 60
CC: Amex, Barclaycard,
Delta, Eurocard, JCB,
Maestro, Mastercard,
Solo, Switch, Visa, Visa
Electron

B&B per night:
S £29.50–£42.50
D £39.50–£49.50

OPEN All year round

Twenty bedroom en suite motel with family rooms. Restaurant and bar facilities, open to non-residents. Ideal starting point for Alton Towers and Staffordshire moorlands. Special short breaks.

STOW-ON-THE-WOLD, Gloucestershire Map ref 2B1 *Tourist Information Centre Tel: (01451) 831082*

★★ AULD STOCKS HOTEL

The Square, Stow-on-the-Wold,
Cheltenham, GL54 1AF
T: (01451) 830666
F: (01451) 870014

Bedrooms: 1 single,
14 double, 2 twin,
1 triple
Bathrooms: 18 en suite

Lunch available
EM 1900 (LO 2130)
Parking for 14
CC: Barclaycard, Delta,
JCB, Mastercard, Solo,
Switch, Visa, Visa Electron

B&B per night:
S Min £40.00
D Min £80.00

HB per person:
DY Min £57.50

OPEN All year round

17thC Grade II Listed hotel facing village green. Refurbished to combine modern comforts with original charm and character. Ideal base for exploring the Cotswolds.

ⒸⓇ
The Independents

★★★ Silver Award — FOSSE MANOR HOTEL

Stow-on-the-Wold, Cheltenham,
GL54 1JX
T: (01451) 830354
F: (01451) 832486
E: fossemanor@bestwestern.co.uk

Bedrooms: 3 single,
10 double, 4 twin,
3 triple; suite available
Bathrooms: 19 en suite,
1 private

Lunch available
EM 1900 (LO 2130)
Parking for 55
CC: Amex, Barclaycard,
Delta, Diners, Eurocard,
JCB, Mastercard, Solo,
Switch, Visa, Visa Electron

B&B per night:
S £55.00–£75.00
D £100.00–£170.00

HB per person:
DY £68.00–£101.00

OPEN All year round

ⒸⓇ
Best Western Hotels

Rurally located Cotswold manor house in beautiful gardens. Tastefully decorated throughout. Elegant restaurant serving traditional and continental cuisine. Central to all Cotswold attractions.

TOWN INDEX

This can be found at the back of the guide. If you know where you want to stay, the index will give you the page number listing accommodation in your chosen town, city or village.

STOW-ON-THE-WOLD continued

★★★
Silver
Award

GRAPEVINE HOTEL
Sheep Street, Stow-on-the-Wold,
GL54 1AU
T: (01451) 830344
F: (01451) 832278
E: wts@vines.co.uk
I: www.vines.co.uk/

B&B per night:
S Min £73.50
D Min £110.00

HB per person:
DY Min £151.00

OPEN All year round

"The Grapevine should be National Treasure". This unpretentious 17thC market town hotel, exuding warmth and hospitality, has a magnificent historic vine crowning its romantic conservatory restaurant. Beautiful furnishings and fine food are complemented by caring staff for whom nothing is too much trouble. Explore Oxford, Stratford and picturesque villages in mellow Cotswold stone.

Bedrooms: 12 double,
10 twin, 2 triple
Bathrooms: 24 en suite

Lunch available
EM 1900 (LO 2130)
Parking for 23
CC: Amex, Barclaycard,
Diners, JCB, Mastercard,
Visa

℻
Best Western Hotels

★★★

STOW LODGE HOTEL
The Square, Stow-on-the-Wold,
Cheltenham, GL54 1AB
T: (01451) 830485
F: (01451) 831671
E: chris@stowlodge.com
I: www.stowlodge.com

B&B per night:
S £60.00–£110.00
D £70.00–£120.00

OPEN Feb–Dec

A friendly family-run Cotswold manor-house hotel set in its own pretty gardens overlooking the market square of this picturesque hilltop town. The hotel is totally non-smoking and offers comfortable en suite bedrooms, an open fire in the lounge and a varied menu in the restaurant or bar.

Bedrooms: 1 single,
10 double, 9 twin,
1 triple
Bathrooms: 21 en suite

EM 1900 (LO 2100)
Parking for 30
CC: Barclaycard, Delta,
Diners, Eurocard, JCB,
Mastercard, Switch, Visa

★★★ **THE UNICORN HOTEL**
Sheep Street, Stow-on-the-Wold,
Cheltenham, GL54 1HQ
T: (01451) 830257
F: (01451) 831090

Bedrooms: 2 single,
14 double, 4 twin
Bathrooms: 20 en suite

Lunch available
EM 1900 (LO 2130)
Parking for 60
CC: Amex, Barclaycard,
Delta, Diners, Eurocard,
JCB, Mastercard, Switch,
Visa

B&B per night:
S Min £60.00
D Min £105.00

HB per person:
DY Min £68.00

OPEN All year round

℻
Cotswolds Inns &
Hotels

17thC coaching inn, well placed for touring Cotswolds. Recently refurbished. Its honey-stoned walls and flower boxes are as typical of the Cotswolds as the warm welcome inside.

STRATFORD-UPON-AVON, Warwickshire Map ref 2B1 *Tourist Information Centre Tel: (01789) 293127*

★★★ **CHARLECOTE PHEASANT COUNTRY HOTEL**
Ad IFC
Charlecote, CV35 9EW
T: (01789) 279954
F: (01789) 470222
E: www.corushotels.com

Bedrooms: 5 single,
19 double, 6 twin,
40 triple; suites available
Bathrooms: 70 en suite

Lunch available
EM 1900 (LO 2200)
Parking for 130
CC: Amex, Barclaycard,
Diners, Mastercard, Visa

B&B per night:
S £72.00–£95.00
D £98.00–£125.00

OPEN All year round

℻
Utell International

19thC farmhouse converted into a comfortable hotel, opposite Charlecote Park. Set in beautiful Warwickshire countryside, 4 miles from Stratford-upon-Avon and Warwick.

IDEAS
For ideas on places to visit refer to the introduction at the beginning of this section.

STRATFORD-UPON-AVON continued

★★★
Ad IFC

FALCON HOTEL
Chapel Street, Stratford-upon-Avon, CV37 6HA
T: (01789) 279953 (24 hours)
F: (01789) 414260
E: www.corushotels.com

Bedrooms: 4 single, 38 double, 32 twin, 9 triple, 1 family room; suite available
Bathrooms: 84 en suite

Lunch available
EM 1800 (LO 2100)
Parking for 124
CC: Amex, Barclaycard, Delta, Diners, Mastercard, Switch, Visa

B&B per night:
S £99.00–£105.00
D £115.00–£135.00

HB per person:
DY £58.00–£68.00

OPEN All year round

A magnificently preserved 16thC timbered inn, with a skilfully blended modern extension, large enclosed garden and ample car parking, situated in the heart of Stratford.

ⓒⓇ
Corus & Regal Hotels/ Utell International

♦♦ ☆ ♦ ✆ 🖂 ☐ ♦ ☜ 🛈 ⓢ ⤢ ☒ 📺 🌓 🖩 🛁 🍴200 ► ❄ SC ✂ SP 🏨 Ⓣ

★★★★
Silver Award

STRATFORD VICTORIA
Arden Street, Stratford-upon-Avon, CV37 6QQ
T: (01789) 271000
F: (01789) 271001
E: stratfordvictoria@compuserve.com
I: www.stratfordvictoria.co.uk

Bedrooms: 10 single, 37 double, 2 twin, 9 triple, 42 family rooms; suite available
Bathrooms: 100 en suite

Lunch available
EM 1800 (LO 2200)
Parking for 95
CC: Amex, Barclaycard, Delta, Diners, Eurocard, Mastercard, Switch, Visa

B&B per night:
S £99.00–£119.00
D £137.00–£185.00

HB per person:
DY £69.50–£89.50

OPEN All year round

Modern, Victorian-style hotel close to the centre of Stratford-upon-Avon. Restaurant, bar, gym, beauty salon, whirlpool spa and conference facilities.

♦♦ ☆ ♦ ♿ ☆ ✆ 🖂 ☐ ♦ ☜ 🛈 ⓢ ⤢ 🌓 🖩 🛁 🍴140 ⚒ ☀ ⚓ ❄ ✂ SP Ⓣ

Rating Applied for
Ad p15

THISTLE STRATFORD-UPON-AVON
Waterside, Stratford-upon-Avon, CV37 6BA
T: (01789) 294949 (switchboard)
F: (01789) 415874
E: stratford.uponavon@thistle.co.uk
I: www.demon.co.uk/quinsolve/arden/htm

Bedrooms: 8 single, 19 double, 34 twin, 2 triple
Bathrooms: 63 en suite

Lunch available
EM 1745 (LO 2130)
Parking for 60
CC: Amex, Barclaycard, Delta, Diners, Eurocard, JCB, Mastercard, Solo, Switch, Visa

B&B per night:
S £120.00–£143.00
D £147.00–£172.00

OPEN All year round

ⓒⓇ
Thistle Hotels

Ideally located in the heart of Stratford, opposite the Royal Shakespeare and Swan Theatres. This hotel has all the charm and comfort of an English country house.

♦♦ ☆ ♦ ♿ ☆ ✆ 🖂 ☐ ♦ ☜ 🛈 ⓢ ⤢ 🌓 🖩 🛁 🍴50 ► ❄ ✂ SP 🏨 Ⓣ ⊕

★★★★
Silver Award

🧍

WELCOMBE HOTEL AND GOLF COURSE
Warwick Road, Stratford-upon-Avon, CV37 0NR
T: (01789) 295252
F: (01789) 414666
E: sales@welcombe.co.uk
I: www.welcombe.co.uk

Bedrooms: 1 single, 49 double, 15 twin; suites available
Bathrooms: 65 en suite

Lunch available
EM 1800 (LO 2130)
Parking for 120
CC: Amex, Barclaycard, Diners, Mastercard, Switch, Visa

B&B per night:
S £120.00–£155.00
D £185.00–£310.00

OPEN All year round

ⓒⓇ
Small Luxury Hotels

Jacobean-style mansion set in 157 acres, 18-hole golf-course, tennis courts and large formal gardens with waterfall. Health and beauty salon.

♦♦ ☆ ♦ ♿ ☆ ✆ 🖂 ☐ ☜ 🌓 🖩 🛁 🍴100 ⚒ ⚔ ⚓ ☀ ⚙ ► ❄ ⚒ ✂ SP 🏨 Ⓣ ⊕

STROUD, Gloucestershire Map ref 2B1 *Tourist Information Centre Tel: (01453) 765768*

★★★

BEAR OF RODBOROUGH HOTEL
Rodborough Common, Stroud, GL5 5DE
T: (01453) 878522
F: (01453) 872523
E: bookings@cotswold-inns-hotels.co.uk
I: www.cotswold-inns-hotels.co.uk

Bedrooms: 6 single, 24 double, 16 twin
Bathrooms: 38 en suite

Lunch available
EM 1900 (LO 2130)
Parking for 120
CC: Amex, Barclaycard, Delta, Diners, Mastercard, Switch, Visa

B&B per night:
S Min £65.00
D Min £110.00

HB per person:
DY Min £71.00

OPEN All year round

ⓒⓇ
Cotswolds Inns & Hotels

Newly refurbished 17thC country hotel with log fires and oak beams set in 600 acres of National Trust land. Between Stroud and Minchinhampton.

♦♦ ☆ ♦ ✆ 🖂 ☐ ♦ ☜ 🛈 ⓢ ⤢ 🌓 🖩 🛁 🍴60 ⚓ ► ❄ ✂ SP 🏨 Ⓣ

ⓒⓇ
CENTRAL RESERVATIONS OFFICES

The symbol ⓒⓇ and a group name in an entry indicate that bookings can be made through a central reservations office. These are listed in a separate section towards the back of this guide.

SUTTON COLDFIELD, West Midlands Map ref 4B3

Rating Applied For
Ad p15

NEW HALL (A THISTLE COUNTRY HOUSE HOTEL)
Walmley Road, Sutton Coldfield,
West Midlands B76 1QX
T: (0121) 378 2442
F: (0121) 378 4637
E: new.hall@thistle.co.uk

Bedrooms: 4 single,
40 double, 16 twin;
suites available
Bathrooms: 60 en suite

Lunch available
EM 1900 (LO 2200)
Parking for 70
CC: Amex, Barclaycard,
Delta, Diners, Mastercard,
Switch, Visa

B&B per night:
S £153.00–£158.00
D £185.00–£211.00

OPEN All year round

Ⓒ
Thistle Hotels/Utell
International/Small
Luxury Hotels

Set in 25 acres of attractive grounds, this is the oldest inhabited moated manor house in England. Well-appointed accommodation, gourmet cuisine and first class leisure facilities.

[icons] 8 ... 45 ...

SWINSCOE, Staffordshire Map ref 4B2

★★

THE DOG AND PARTRIDGE COUNTRY INN WITH ROOMS IN THE GROUNDS
Swinscoe, Ashbourne, Derbyshire
DE6 2HS
T: (01335) 343183
F: (01335) 342742

Bedrooms: 6 double,
2 twin, 4 triple, 17 family
rooms; suites available
Bathrooms: 29 en suite

Lunch available
EM 1730 (LO 2300)
Parking for 100
CC: Amex, Barclaycard,
Delta, Diners, Maestro,
Mastercard, Solo, Switch,
Visa, Visa Electron

B&B per night:
S £30.00–£70.00
D £50.00–£80.00

HB per person:
DY £35.00–£60.00

OPEN All year round

A 17thC Inn with purpose built rooms in the grounds. Log fires. Real ales, good food. Pets and children welcome.

[icons] 24 ...

TELFORD, Shropshire Map ref 4A3 *Tourist Information Centre Tel: (01952) 238008*

★★

ARLESTON INN HOTEL
Arleston Lane, Wellington, Telford,
Shropshire TF1 2LA
T: (01952) 501881
F: (01952) 506429

Bedrooms: 2 single,
4 double, 1 twin
Bathrooms: 7 en suite

Lunch available
EM 1800 (LO 2200)
Parking for 40
CC: Barclaycard, Delta,
Eurocard, Mastercard,
Visa

B&B per night:
S Min £40.00
D Min £50.00

OPEN All year round

Tudor-style building with many exposed beamed ceilings. M54, 5 minutes from junction 6. A la carte and bar menus.

[icons]

★★

THE OAKS AT REDHILL
Redhill, St Georges, Telford,
Shropshire TF2 9NZ
T: (01952) 620126
F: (01952) 620257
I: www.scoot.oaks/uk.co

Bedrooms: 5 single,
3 double, 2 twin, 3 triple
Bathrooms: 13 en suite

Lunch available
EM 1900 (LO 2130)
Parking for 40
CC: Amex, Barclaycard,
Delta, Diners, Eurocard,
Mastercard, Solo, Switch,
Visa, Visa Electron

B&B per night:
S Max £48.00
D Max £55.00

OPEN All year round

Family-owned hotel, 2.5 miles from Telford town centre. Restaurant, public bar. En suite bedrooms with telephone, colour TV, tea/coffee facilities.

[icons] 40 ...

TUTBURY, Staffordshire Map ref 4B3

★★★

YE OLDE DOG & PARTRIDGE HOTEL

High Street, Tutbury, Burton upon Trent,
DE13 9LS
T: (01283) 813030
F: (01283) 813178

B&B per night:
S £45.00–£75.00
D £50.00–£99.00

HB per person:
DY £55.00–£120.00

OPEN All year round

One of England's oldest and finest 15thC coaching inns, situated in the historic village of Tutbury. This warm and friendly hotel offers luxury accommodation and excellent dining facilities in both the carvery and brasserie restaurants. The bedrooms are all individually designed and furnished to the highest standards.

Bedrooms: 5 single,
12 double, 2 twin,
1 triple
Bathrooms: 20 en suite

Lunch available
EM 1800 (LO 2145)
Parking for 100
CC: Amex, Barclaycard,
Mastercard, Solo, Switch,
Visa, Visa Electron

[icons]

UPPINGHAM, Rutland Map ref 4C3

★★
Silver
Award

LAKE ISLE HOTEL
16 High Street East, Uppingham,
Oakham, Leicestershire LE15 9PZ
T: (01572) 822951
F: (01572) 822951

Bedrooms: 1 single,
9 double, 2 twin; suites
available
Bathrooms: 12 en suite

Lunch available
EM 1930 (LO 2130)
Parking for 7
CC: Amex, Barclaycard,
Mastercard, Visa

B&B per night:
S £45.00–£52.00
D £65.00–£80.00

HB per person:
DY £54.00–£61.50

OPEN All year round

This 18thC hotel absorbs more than a little of Uppingham's charm. The personal touch will make your stay extra special with weekly changing menus and a list of over 300 wines.

WARWICK, Warwickshire Map ref 2C1 *Tourist Information Centre Tel: (01926) 492212*

★★★

Recently refurbished hotel. All 154 executive and standard bedrooms are en suite, many with views overlooking private grounds, which lead down to the River Avon. All bedrooms are well designed for the business and leisure guest. Only 10 minutes to Warwick centre, 20 minutes to Stratford-upon-Avon.

CHESFORD GRANGE HOTEL
Chesford Bridge, Kenilworth, Warwick,
CV8 2LD
T: (01926) 859331
F: (01926) 859075
E: samanthabrown@principalhotels.co.uk
I: www.principalhotels.co.uk

Bedrooms: 11 single,
71 double, 59 twin,
13 triple
Bathrooms: 154 en suite

Lunch available
EM 1900 (LO 2145)
Parking for 500
CC: Amex, Barclaycard,
Eurocard, Mastercard,
Visa

B&B per night:
S £60.00–£115.00
D £80.00–£130.00

HB per person:
DY £45.00–£75.00

OPEN All year round

CR
Principal Hotels/Utell
International

WEEDON, Northamptonshire Map ref 2C1

★★

GLOBE HOTEL
High Street, Weedon, Northampton,
NN7 4QD
T: (01327) 340336
F: (01327) 349058
E: llct@tinyworld.co.uk
I: www.djl-hotel.co.uk

Bedrooms: 4 single,
6 double, 5 twin, 3 triple
Bathrooms: 18 en suite

Lunch available
EM (LO 2200)
Parking for 40
CC: Amex, Barclaycard,
Delta, Eurocard, JCB,
Mastercard, Solo, Switch,
Visa, Visa Electron

B&B per night:
S £50.00–£55.00
D £55.00–£65.00

OPEN All year round

19thC countryside inn. Old world atmosphere and freehouse hospitality with excellent home-cooked food, available all day. Close to M1 and Stratford. Send for information pack.

WELLINGBOROUGH, Northamptonshire Map ref 3A2 *Tourist Information Centre Tel: (01933) 276412*

★★

HIGH VIEW HOTEL
156 Midland Road, Wellingborough,
NN8 1NG
T: (01933) 278733
F: (01933) 225948

Bedrooms: 5 single,
3 double, 4 twin, 2 triple
Bathrooms: 14 en suite,
1 public

EM 1830 (LO 2030)
Parking for 10
CC: Amex, Barclaycard,
Delta, Diners, JCB,
Mastercard, Solo, Switch,
Visa

B&B per night:
S £29.00–£45.00
D £39.00–£56.00

HB per person:
DY £25.00–£33.00

OPEN All year round

Large, detached, modernised building with pleasant gardens. In quiet tree-lined area near town centre and railway station. All rooms en suite.

WITNEY, Oxfordshire

*The Marlborough Hotel
See South of England region for full entry details*

CREDIT CARD BOOKINGS
If you book by telephone and are asked for your credit card number it is advisable to check the proprietor's policy should you cancel your reservation.

173

WOLVERHAMPTON, West Midlands Map ref 4B3 *Tourist Information Centre Tel: (01902) 556110*

★★ FOX HOTEL (WOLVERHAMPTON)

118 School Street, Wolverhampton, WV3 0NR T: (01902) 421680 F: (01902) 711654 E: sales@foxhotel.co.uk I: www.foxhotel.co.uk	Bedrooms: 26 single, 6 double Bathrooms: 32 en suite	Lunch available EM 1800 (LO 2200) Parking for 20 CC: Amex, Barclaycard, Delta, Diners, Eurocard, JCB, Maestro, Mastercard, Solo, Switch, Visa, Visa Electron

B&B per night:
S £35.00–£39.00
D £49.00–£59.00

HB per person:
DY £45.00–£55.00

OPEN All year round

Town centre, free parking, nearby shopping. All rooms en suite (1 spa room), satellite TV, direct-dial telephone. Bar, restaurant and conference room. Walking distance from railway station, football stadium.

ᴀ ⌖ ⊞ ⌕ ⊞ ▢ ♿ ⌕ ⓘ ⑤ ⌕ ⍥ ⊡ ◑ ⊞ ⌷ ✆ 60 ⑤ᶜ ⚲ ⑤ᴾ ⊤

★★★ PARK HALL HOTEL AND CONFERENCE CENTRE

Park Drive, Goldthorn Park, Wolverhampton, WV4 5AJ T: (01902) 331121 F: (01902) 344760 E: enquiries@parkhallhotel.co.uk I: www.parkhallhotel.co.uk	Bedrooms: 9 single, 9 double, 33 twin, 1 triple Bathrooms: 52 private	Lunch available EM 1900 (LO 2130) Parking for 200 CC: Amex, Barclaycard, Delta, Mastercard, Switch, Visa

B&B per night:
S £39.00–£59.00
D £49.00–£64.00

HB per person:
DY £39.00–£44.00

OPEN All year round

An elegant Georgian building set in its own beautifully kept gardens only 3 miles from town centre. Modernised, and in keeping with its period.

ᴀ ⌖ ⌕ ⊞ ▢ ♿ ⌕ ⓘ ⑤ ⌕ ⍥ ⊡ ◑ ⊞ ⌷ ✆ 400 ✿ ⚲ ⑤ᴾ ⊞ ⊤

Ⓒᴿ
Best Western Hotels

★★★ PATSHULL PARK HOTEL, GOLF AND COUNTRY CLUB

Patshull Park, Pattingham, Wolverhampton, WV6 7HR T: (01902) 700100 F: (01902) 700874 E: sales@patshull-park.co.uk I: www.patshull-park.co.uk	Bedrooms: 7 double, 38 twin, 4 triple; suite available Bathrooms: 49 en suite	Lunch available EM 1900 (LO 2130) Parking for 250 CC: Amex, Barclaycard, Delta, Diners, Eurocard, JCB, Mastercard, Solo, Switch, Visa, Visa Electron

B&B per night:
S £85.00–£105.00
D £90.00–£110.00

HB per person:
DY £49.50–£70.00

OPEN All year round

Modern hotel nestling sympathetically in the midst of this beautiful Capability Brown designed country estate. Own golf course, fishing lakes and extensive leisure complex.

ᴀ ⌖ ⌕ ⌕ ⊞ ▢ ♿ ⌕ ⓘ ⑤ ⌕ ⊡ ◑ ⊞ ⌷ ✆ 220 ⛳ ⚹ ⟲ ♨ ⌁ ⚲ ⑤ᴾ ⊞ ⊤

WOODHALL SPA, Lincolnshire Map ref 4D2

★★ EAGLE LODGE HOTEL

The Broadway, Woodhall Spa, LN10 6ST T: (01526) 353231 F: (01526) 352797	Bedrooms: 4 single, 7 double, 10 twin, 1 triple, 2 family rooms Bathrooms: 23 en suite, 1 private, 1 public	Lunch available EM 1900 (LO 2130) Parking for 50 CC: Amex, Barclaycard, Delta, Diners, Mastercard, Switch, Visa

B&B per night:
S £45.00–£45.00
D £65.00–£70.00

HB per person:
DY £45.00–£58.00

OPEN All year round

Mock-Tudor country house hotel in centre of Victorian spa village. Close to both Woodhall Spa golf-courses. Excellent food, real ales, friendly atmosphere.

ᴀ ⌖ ⌕ ⊞ ⌕ ⊞ ▢ ♿ ⌕ ⓘ ⑤ ⍥ ⊡ ⊞ ⌷ ✆ 50 ⟲ ♨ ✿ ⚲ ⑤ᴾ ⊤

★★★ THE GOLF HOTEL

The Broadway, Woodhall Spa, LN10 6SG T: (01526) 353535 F: (01526) 353096 I: www.principalhotels.co.uk	Bedrooms: 6 single, 16 double, 28 twin Bathrooms: 50 en suite	Lunch available EM 1930 (LO 2130) Parking for 100 CC: Amex, Barclaycard, Delta, Diners, Mastercard, Switch, Visa, Visa Electron

B&B per night:
S £35.00–£65.00
D £70.00–£85.00

HB per person:
DY £52.00–£77.00

OPEN All year round

Delightful half-timbered hotel set in 7 acres of gardens near famous Woodhall Spa golf-course. A short drive to the historic city of Lincoln.

ᴀ ⌖ ⌕ ⊞ ▢ ♿ ⌕ ⓘ ⑤ ⌕ ⍥ ⊡ ◑ ⊞ ⌷ ✆ 150 ♨ ⚲ ⟲ ♨ ✿ ⑤ᶜ ⚲ ⑤ᴾ ⊞ ⊤

Ⓒᴿ
Principal Hotels/Utell International

WELCOME HOST This is a nationally recognised customer care programme which aims to promote the highest standards of service and a warm welcome. Establishments taking part in this initiative are indicated by the ⊛ symbol.

WOODHALL SPA continued

★★★

PETWOOD HOTEL
Stixwould Road, Woodhall Spa,
LN10 6QF
T: (01526) 352411
F: (01526) 353473
E: reception@petwood.co.uk
I: www.petwood.co.uk

Bedrooms: 6 single,
30 double, 14 twin; suite
available
Bathrooms: 50 en suite

Lunch available
EM 1900 (LO 2100)
Parking for 70
CC: Amex, Barclaycard,
Delta, Diners, Eurocard,
JCB, Maestro, Mastercard,
Solo, Switch, Visa, Visa
Electron

B&B per night:
S £78.00–£88.00
D £105.00–£115.00

HB per person:
DY Min £67.50

OPEN All year round

Country house with superb restaurant, set in 30 acres of formal gardens and woodland. Putting green, croquet, snooker room. Former officers' mess of the famous Dambusters Squadron.

⋔🐾⛳🏨📞🖥️🖨️♿♨️🅿️💲✂️🔌◑🚻🖥️🛏️📺🍴150 🔱▶️❄️🐾SP🎱🈂️🌐

WYE VALLEY

See under Fownhope, Goodrich, Hereford, Ross-on-Wye

COUNTRY CODE
Always follow the Country Code 🌳
Enjoy the countryside and respect
its life and work 🌳 Guard against
all risk of fire 🌳 Fasten all gates
🌳 Keep your dogs under close control
🌳 Keep to public paths across
farmland 🌳 Use gates and stiles to
cross fences, hedges and walls 🌳
Leave livestock, crops and machinery
alone 🌳 Take your litter home 🌳
Help to keep all water clean 🌳
Protect wildlife, plants and trees 🌳
Take special care on country roads 🌳
Make no unnecessary noise 🌳

A brief guide to the main Towns and Villages offering
accommodation in the HEART OF ENGLAND

A ALCESTER, WARWICKSHIRE - Town has
Roman origins and many old buildings around
the High Street. It is close to Ragley Hall, the
18th C Palladian mansion with its magnificent
baroque Great Hall.

● **ALREWAS, STAFFORDSHIRE** - Delightful
village of black and white cottages, past which
the willow-fringed Trent runs. The Trent and
Mersey Canal enhances the scene and Fradley
Junction, a mile away, is one of the most
charming inland waterway locations in the
country.

● **ASHBOURNE, DERBYSHIRE** - Market town
on the edge of the Peak District National Park
and an excellent centre for walking. Its
impressive church with 212-ft spire stands in an
unspoilt old street. Ashbourne is well-known for
gingerbread and its Shrovetide football match.

B BAKEWELL, DERBYSHIRE - Pleasant
market town, famous for its pudding. It is set
in beautiful countryside on the River Wye and
is an excellent centre for exploring the
Derbyshire Dales, the Peak District National
Park, Chatsworth and Haddon Hall.

● **BAMFORD, DERBYSHIRE** - Village in the
Peak District near the Upper Derwent
Reservoirs of Ladybower, Derwent and
Howden. An excellent centre for walking.

● **BERKELEY, GLOUCESTERSHIRE** - Town
dominated by the castle where Edward II was
murdered. Dating from Norman times, it is still
the home of the Berkeley family and is open to
the public April to September Tuesday to
Sunday and October Sundays. The Jenner
Museum is here and Slimbridge Wildfowl Trust
is nearby.

● **BIGGIN-BY-HARTINGTON, DERBYSHIRE** -
Tiny village high in the Peak District above the
River Dove approx. 6 miles equidistant from
Bakewell and Matlock. Excellent area for
walking and exploring attractions nearby.

● **BIRMINGHAM, WEST MIDLANDS** -
Britain's second city, whose attractions include
Centenary Square and the ICC with Symphony
Hall, the NEC, the City Art Gallery, Barber
Institute of Fine Arts, 17th C Aston Hall,
science and railway museums, Jewellery
Quarter, Cadbury World, 2 cathedrals and
Botanical Gardens.

● **BOURTON-ON-THE-WATER
GLOUCESTERSHIRE** - The River Windrush
flows through this famous Cotswold village
which has a green, and cottages and houses of
Cotswold stone. Its many attractions include a
model village, Birdland, a Motor Museum and
the Cotswold Perfumery.

● **BRIDGNORTH, SHROPSHIRE** -
Red sandstone riverside town in 2 parts - High
and Low - linked by a cliff railway. Much of
interest including a ruined Norman keep, half-
timbered 16th C houses, Midland Motor
Museum and Severn Valley Railway.

● **BROADWAY, WORCESTERSHIRE** -
Beautiful Cotswold village called the "Show
village of England", with 16th C stone houses
and cottages. Near the village is Broadway
Tower with magnificent views over 12 counties
and a country park with nature trails and
adventure playground.

● **BROMSGROVE, WORCESTERSHIRE** -
This market town near the Lickey Hills has
an interesting museum and craft centre with
14th C church with fine tombs and a Carillon
tower. The Avoncroft Museum of Buildings is
nearby where many old buildings have been
re-assembled, having been saved from
destruction.

C CASTLE DONINGTON, LEICESTERSHIRE -
A Norman castle once stood here. The world's
largest collection of single-seater racing cars
is displayed at Donington Park alongside the
racing circuit, and an Aeropark Visitor Centre
can be seen at nearby East Midlands
International Airport.

● **CHADDESLEY CORBETT,
WORCESTERSHIRE** - An attractive village
with a blend of Georgian and timber framed
buildings. One mile west is the moated
Harvington Hall and 4 miles, the carpet town
of Kidderminster.

● **CHELTENHAM, GLOUCESTERSHIRE** -
Cheltenham was developed as a spa town in
the 18th C and has some beautiful Regency
architecture, in particular the Pittville Pump
Room. It holds international music and
literature festivals and is also famous for its
race meetings and cricket.

● **CHIPPING CAMPDEN, GLOUCESTERSHIRE**
- Outstanding Cotswold wool town with many
old stone gabled houses, a splendid church and
17th C almshouses. Nearby are Kiftsgate Court
Gardens and Hidcote Manor Gardens (National
Trust).

● **CHURCH STRETTON, SHROPSHIRE** -
Church Stretton lies under the eastern slope of
the Longmynd surrounded by hills. It is ideal
for walkers, with marvellous views, golf and
gliding. Wenlock Edge is not far away.

● **CIRENCESTER, GLOUCESTERSHIRE** -
"Capital of the Cotswolds", Cirencester was
Britain's second most important Roman town
with many finds housed in the Corinium
Museum. It has a very fine Perpendicular
church and old houses around the market
place.

● **CLEARWELL, GLOUCESTERSHIRE** -
Attractive village in the Forest of Dean, noted
for its castle, built in 1735 and one of the
oldest Georgian Gothic houses in England.
The old mines in Clearwell Caves are open to
the public.

● **CLEOBURY MORTIMER, SHROPSHIRE** -
Village with attractive timbered and Georgian
houses and a church with a wooden spire. It is
close to the Clee Hills with marvellous views.

● **COVENTRY, WEST MIDLANDS** - Modern
city with a long history. It has many places of
interest including the post-war and ruined
medieval cathedrals, art gallery and museums,
some 16th C almshouses, St Mary's Guildhall,
Lunt Roman fort and the Belgrade Theatre.

D DERBY, DERBYSHIRE - Modern industrial
city but with ancient origins. There is a wide
range of attractions including several
museums (notably Royal Crown Derby), a
theatre, a concert hall, and the cathedral with
fine ironwork and Bess of Hardwick's tomb.

E EVESHAM, WORCESTERSHIRE - Market
town in the centre of a fruit-growing area.
There are pleasant walks along the River Avon
and many old houses and inns. A fine 16th C
bell tower stands between 2 churches near the
medieval Almonry Museum.

F FAIRFORD, GLOUCESTERSHIRE - Small
town with a 15th C wool church famous for
its complete 15th C stained glass windows,
interesting carvings and original wall
paintings. It is an excellent touring centre and
the Cotswolds Wildlife Park is nearby.

● **FINEDON, NORTHAMPTONSHIRE** -
Large ironstone village with interesting
Victorian houses and a fine 14th C church. The
inn claims to be the oldest in England.

● **FOWNHOPE, HEREFORDSHIRE** -
Attractive village close to the River Wye with
black and white cottages and other interesting
houses. It has a large church with a Norman
tower and a 14th C spire.

G GAINSBOROUGH, LINCOLNSHIRE -
Britain's most inland port has strong
connections with the Pilgrim Fathers.
Gainsborough Old Hall, where they worshipped,
boasts a 15th C manor house with complete
kitchens.

● **GLOSSOP, LINCOLNSHIRE** - Town in
dramatic moorland surroundings with views
over the High Peak. The settlement can be
traced back to Roman times but expanded
during the Industrial Revolution.

● **GLOUCESTER, GLOUCESTERSHIRE** - A
Roman city and inland port, its cathedral is one
of the most beautiful in Britain. Gloucester's
many attractions include museums and the
restored warehouses in the Victorian docks
containing the National Waterways Museum,
Robert Opie Packaging Collection and other
attractions.

● **GOODRICH, GLOUCESTERSHIRE** -
Village standing above the River Wye with the
magnificent ruins of a red sandstone castle high
above it, now in the care of English Heritage.

● **GRINDLEFORD, DERBYSHIRE** - Good
centre for walking, at the eastern end of the
Hope Valley. Longshaw Estate is nearby with
1500 acres of moorland and woodland.

H HEREFORD, HEREFORDSHIRE - Agricultural county town, its cathedral containing much Norman work, a large chained library and the world-famous Mappa Mundi exhibition. Among the city's varied attractions are several museums including the Cider Museum and the Old House.

● **HOCKLEY HEATH, WEST MIDLANDS -** Village near the National Trust property of Packwood House, with its well-known yew garden, and Kenilworth.

● **HORNCASTLE, LINCOLNSHIRE -** Pleasant market town near the Lincolnshire Wolds, which was once a walled Roman settlement. It was the scene of a decisive Civil War battle, relics of which can be seen in the church. Tennyson's bride lived here.

I IRONBRIDGE, SHROPSHIRE - Small town on the Severn where the Industrial Revolution began. It has the world's first iron bridge built in 1779. The Ironbridge Gorge Museum, of exceptional interest, comprises a rebuilt turn-of-the-century town and sites spread over 6 square miles.

K KENILWORTH, WARWICKSHIRE - The main feature of the town is the ruined 12th C castle. It has many royal associations but was damaged by Cromwell. A good base for visiting Coventry, Leamington Spa and Warwick.

● **KIDDERMINSTER, WORCESTERSHIRE -** The town is the centre for carpet manufacturing. It has a medieval church with good monuments and a statue of Sir Rowland Hill, a native of the town and founder of the penny post. West Midlands Safari Park is nearby. Severn Valley Railway station.

L LANGAR, NOTTINGHAMSHIRE - Small village standing on a small escarpment. Has a fine, Early English style church and a strong village atmosphere.

● **LEAMINGTON SPA, WARWICKSHIRE -** 18th C spa town with many fine Georgian and Regency houses. The refurbished 19th C Pump Rooms with Heritage Centre. The attractive Jephson Gardens are laid out alongside the river.

● **LEDBURY, HEREFORDSHIRE -** Town with cobbled streets and many black and white timbered houses, including the 17th C market house and old inns. In attractive countryside nearby is Eastnor Castle, a venue for many events, with an interesting collection of tapestries and armour.

● **LEEK, STAFFORDSHIRE -** Old silk and textile town, with some interesting buildings and a number of inns dating from the 17th C. Its art gallery has displays of embroidery. Brindley Mill, designed by James Brindley, has been restored as a museum.

● **LICHFIELD, STAFFORDSHIRE -** Lichfield is Dr Samuel Johnson's birthplace and commemorates him with a museum and statue. The 13th C cathedral has 3 spires and the west front is full of statues. Among the attractive town buildings is the Heritage Centre. The Regimental Museum is in Whittington Barracks.

● **LINCOLN, LINCOLNSHIRE -** Ancient city dominated by the magnificent 11th C cathedral with its triple towers. A Roman gateway is still used and there are medieval houses lining narrow, cobbled streets. Other attractions include the Norman castle, several museums and the Usher Gallery.

● **LOUTH, LINCOLNSHIRE -** Attractive old market town set on the eastern edge of the Lincolnshire Wolds. St James's Church has an impressive tower and spire and there are the remains of a Cistercian abbey. The museum contains an interesting collection of local material.

● **LOWER SLAUGHTER, GLOUCESTERSHIRE -** Pretty Cotswold village of stone cottages with a river running through the main street.

M MALVERN, WORCESTERSHIRE - Spa town in Victorian times, its water is today bottled and sold worldwide. 6 resorts, set on the slopes of the Hills, form part of Malvern. Great Malvern Priory has splendid 15th C windows. It is an excellent walking centre.

● **MANSFIELD, NOTTINGHAMSHIRE -** Ancient town, now an industrial and shopping centre, with a popular market, in the heart of Robin Hood country. There is an impressive 19th C railway viaduct, 2 interesting churches, an 18th C Moot Hall and a museum and art gallery.

● **MARKET DRAYTON, SHROPSHIRE -** Old market town with black and white buildings and 17th C houses, also acclaimed for its gingerbread. Hodnet Hall is in the vicinity with its beautiful landscaped gardens covering 60 acres.

● **MATLOCK, DERBYSHIRE -** The town lies beside the narrow valley of the River Derwent surrounded by steep wooded hills. Good centre for exploring Derbyshire's best scenery.

● **MELTON MOWBRAY, LEICESTERSHIRE -** Close to the attractive Vale of Belvoir and famous for its pork pies and Stilton cheese which are the subjects of special displays in the museum. It has a beautiful church with a tower 100ft high.

N NORTHAMPTON, NORTHAMPTONSHIRE - A bustling town and a shoe manufacturing centre, with excellent shopping facilities, several museums and parks, a theatre and a concert hall. Several old churches include 1 of only 4 round churches in Britain.

● **NOTTINGHAM -** Attractive modern city with a rich history. Outside its castle, now a museum, is Robin Hood's statue. Attractions include "The Tales of Robin Hood"; the Lace Hall; Wollaton Hall; museums and excellent facilities for shopping, sports and entertainment.

O OAKHAM, RUTLAND - Pleasant former county town of Rutland. Fine 12th C Great Hall, part of its castle, with a historic collection of horseshoes. An octagonal Butter Cross stands in the market-place and Rutland County Museum, Rutland Farm Park and Rutland Water are of interest.

● **OSWESTRY, SHROPSHIRE -** Town close to the Welsh border, the scene of many battles. To the north are the remains of a large Iron Age hill fort. An excellent centre for exploring Shropshire and Offa's Dyke.

P PAINSWICK, GLOUCESTERSHIRE - Picturesque wool town with inns and houses dating from the 14th C. Painswick Rococo Garden is open to visitors from January to November, and the house is a Palladian mansion. The churchyard is famous for its yew trees.

R ROSS-ON-WYE, HEREFORDSHIRE - Attractive market town with a 17th C market hall, set above the River Wye. There are lovely views over the surrounding countryside from the Prospect and the town is close to Goodrich Castle and the Welsh border.

● **RUGBY, WARWICKSHIRE -** Town famous for its public school which gave its name to Rugby Union football and which featured in "Tom Brown's Schooldays".

S SPALDING, LINCOLNSHIRE - Fenland town famous for its bulbfields. A spectaclular Flower Parade takes place at the beginning of May each year and the tulips at Springfields show gardens are followed by displays of roses and bedding plants in summer. Interesting local museum.

● **STAMFORD, LINCOLNSHIRE -** Exceptionally beautiful and historic town with many houses of architectural interest, several notable churches and other public buildings all in the local stone. Burghley House, built by William Cecil, is a magnificent Tudor mansion on the edge of the town.

● **STOKE-ON-TRENT -** Famous for its pottery. Factories of several famous makers, including Josiah Wedgwood, can be visited. The City Museum has one of the finest pottery and porcelain collections in the world.

● **STOW-ON-THE-WOLD, GLOUCESTERSHIRE -** Attractive Cotswold wool town with a large market-place and some fine houses, especially the old grammar school. There is an interesting church dating from Norman times. Stow-on-the-Wold is surrounded by lovely countryside and Cotswold villages.

● **STRATFORD-UPON-AVON, WARWICKSHIRE -** Famous as Shakespeare's home town, Stratford's many attractions include his birthplace, New Place where he died, the Royal Shakespeare Theatre and Gallery and Hall's Croft (his daughter's house).

● **STROUD, GLOUCESTERSHIRE -** This old town, surrounded by attractive hilly country, has been producing broadcloth for centuries, the local museum has an interesting display on the subject. Many of the mills have been converted into craft centres and for other uses.

● **SUTTON COLDFIELD, WEST MIDLANDS -** Old market town, now part of the conurbation of Birmingham. The 2400-acre Sutton Park has facilities for golf, fishing and riding, with walks around the woodlands and lakes.

● **SWINSCOE, STAFFORDSHIRE** - Hamlet close to Alton Towers with its many attractions and to the beautiful scenery of Dovedale.

▣ **TELFORD, TELFORD & WREKIN** - New Town named after Thomas Telford, the famous engineer who designed many of the country's canals, bridges and viaducts. It is close to Ironbridge with its monuments and museums to the Industrial Revolution, including restored 18th C buildings.

● **TUTBURY, STAFFORDSHIRE** - Small town on the River Dove with an attractive High Street, old houses and the remains of the castle where Mary Queen of Scots was imprisoned.

▣ **UPPINGHAM, RUTLAND** - Quiet market town dominated by its famous public school which was founded in 1584. It has many stone houses and is surrounded by attractive countryside.

▣ **WARWICK, WARWICKSHIRE** - Castle rising above the River Avon, 15th C Beauchamp Chapel attached to St Mary's Church, medieval Lord Leycester's Hospital almshouses and several museums. Nearby is Ashorne Hall Nickelodeon and the National Heritage museum at Gaydon.

● **WEEDON, NORTHAMPTONSHIRE** - Old village steeped in history, with thatched cottages and several antique shops.

● **WELLINGBOROUGH, NORTHAMPTONSHIRE** - Manufacturing town, mentioned in the Domesday Book, with some old buildings and inns, in one of which Cromwell stayed on his way to Naseby. It has attractive gardens in the centre of the town and 2 interesting churches.

● **WOLVERHAMPTON, WEST MIDLANDS** - Modern industrial town with a long history, a fine parish church and an excellent art gallery. There are several places of interest in the vicinity including Moseley Old Hall and Wightwick Manor with its William Morris influence.

● **WOODHALL SPA, LINCOLNSHIRE** - Attractive town which was formerly a spa. It has excellent sporting facilities with a championship golf-course and is surrounded by pine woods.

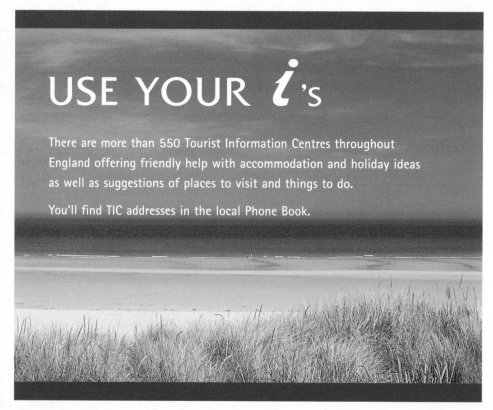

USE YOUR *i*'s

There are more than 550 Tourist Information Centres throughout England offering friendly help with accommodation and holiday ideas as well as suggestions of places to visit and things to do.

You'll find TIC addresses in the local Phone Book.

EAST OF ENGLAND

Open skies, rich Fenland, gorgeous villages and miles of sandy beaches - welcome to the East of England where life ticks slowly by.

Barge your way through the Norfolk Broads, punt along the River Cam, or walk over water on the pier at Southend.

Woburn Abbey, Sandringham and Kentwell Hall are just a few of the fabulous houses and gardens in the area. And if you fancy a day at the races, you can bet on Newmarket.

Graceful cathedrals pierce the skies at Ely, Norwich, Cambridge and Colchester. While beautiful Walsingham is dubbed 'England's Nazareth' and attracts an annual Pilgrimage in the remains of the Medieval Priory.

The counties of
Bedfordshire, Cambridgeshire,
Essex, Hertfordshire, Norfolk and Suffolk

FOR MORE INFORMATION CONTACT:
East of England Tourist Board
Toppesfield Hall, Hadleigh, Suffolk IP7 5DN
Tel: (01473) 822922
Fax: (01473) 823063
Email: eastofenglandtouristboard@compuserve.com
Internet: www.visitbritain.com/east-of-england/

Where to Go in the East of England - see pages 180-184
Where to Stay in the East of England - see pages 185-206

The Pictures:
1 Hunstanton, Norfolk;
2 King's College, Cambridge.

Whilst in the
EAST OF ENGLAND ○○○

You will find hundreds of interesting places to visit during your stay, just some of which are listed in these pages.

Contact any Tourist Information Centre in the region for more ideas on days out in the East of England.

Audley End House and Park

Audley End, Saffron Walden, Essex CB11 4JF
Tel: (01799) 522399
Palatial Jacobean house remodelled in the 18th-19thC. Magnificent Great Hall with 17thC plaster ceilings. Rooms and furniture by Robert Adam and park by 'Capability' Brown.

Banham Zoo

The Grove, Banham, Norwich, Norfolk NR16 2HE
Tel: (01953) 887771
Wildlife spectacular which will take you on a journey to experience at close quarters some of the world's most exotic, rare and endangered animals.

Barleylands Farm Museum and Visitor Centre

Billericay, Essex CM11 2UD
Tel: (01268) 532253
Visitor centre with a rural museum, animal centre, craft studios, blacksmith's shop, glass-blowing studio with viewing gallery, miniature steam railway. Restaurant.

Blickling Hall

Blickling, Norwich, Norfolk NR11 6NF
Tel: (01263) 738030
Jacobean redbrick mansion with garden, orangery, parkland and lake. Displays of fine tapestries and furniture. Picnic area, shop, restaurant and plant centre.

Bressingham Steam Museum and Gardens

Bressingham, Diss, Norfolk IP22 2AB
Tel: (01379) 687386
Steam rides through 8 km (5 miles) of woodland. Mainline locomotives, the Victorian Gallopers and over 50 steam engines. Plant centre.

Bure Valley Railway

Aylsham, Norwich, Norfolk NR11 6BW
Tel: (01263) 733858
A 15 inch narrow-gauge steam railway covering 14.4 km (9 miles) of track from Wroxham in the heart of the Norfolk Broads to Aylsham, a bustling market town.

Colchester Castle

Colchester, Essex CO1 1TJ
Tel: (01206) 282931
A Norman keep on the foundations of a Roman temple. The archaeological material includes much on Roman Colchester (Camulodunum).

Colchester Zoo

Stanway, Colchester, Essex CO3 5SL
Tel: (01206) 331292
Zoo with 200 species and some of the best cat collections in the UK, 40 acres of gardens and lakes, plus award-winning animal enclosures. Picnic areas, road train and four play areas.

Ely Cathedral

Ely, Cambridgeshire CB7 4DL
Tel: (01353) 667735
One of England's finest cathedrals. Monastic precinct, brass rubbing centre and stained glass museum. Guided tours.

Fritton Lake Country World

Fritton, Great Yarmouth, Norfolk NR31 9HA
Tel: (01493) 488208
A 250-acre centre with children's assault course, putting, an adventure playground, golf, fishing, boating, wildfowl, heavy horses, cart rides, falconry and flying displays.

The Gardens of the Rose

The Royal National Rose Society, Chiswell Green,
St Albans, Hertfordshire AL2 3NR
Tel: (01727) 850461
The Royal National Rose Society's Garden with 27 acres of garden and trial grounds for new varieties of rose. Roses of all types displayed with 1,700 different varieties.

Hatfield House and Gardens

Hatfield, Hertfordshire AL9 5NQ
Tel: (01707) 262823
Magnificent Jacobean house, home of the Marquess of Salisbury. Exquisite gardens, model soldiers and park trails. Childhood home of Queen Elizabeth I.

Hedingham Castle

Castle Hedingham, Halstead, Essex CO9 3DJ
Tel: (01787) 460261
The finest Norman keep in England, built in 1140 by the deVeres, Earls of Oxford. Visited by Kings Henry VII and VIII and Queen Elizabeth I. Besieged by King John.

The Pictures:
1 Holkham Beach, Norfolk;
2 Globe Inn, Linslade,
   Bedfordshire;
3 Thorpeness, Suffolk;
4 Nene Valley Railway,
   Stibbington, Cambridgeshire;
5 Punting on the River Cam,
   Cambridge.

Holkham Hall

Wells-next-the-Sea, Norfolk NR23 1AB
Tel: (01328) 710227
A classic 18thC Palladian-style mansion. Part of a great agricultural estate and a living treasure-house of artistic and architectural history. Bygones collection.

Ickworth House, Park and Gardens

Horringer, Bury St Edmunds, Suffolk IP29 5QE
Tel: (01284) 735270
An extraordinary oval house with flanking wings, begun in 1795. Fine paintings, a beautiful collection of Georgian silver, an Italian garden and stunning parkland.

Imperial War Museum

Duxford, Cambridgeshire CB2 4QR
Tel: (01223) 835000
Over 150 aircraft on display with tanks, vehicles and guns. Simulator ride and an adventure playground. Shops and restaurant.

Kentwell Hall

Long Melford, Sudbury, Suffolk CO10 9BA
Tel: (01787) 310207
A mellow redbrick Tudor manor surrounded by a moat. This family home has been interestingly restored with Tudor costume displays, a 16thC house and mosaic Tudor rose maze.

Knebworth House, Gardens and Park

Knebworth, Stevenage, Hertfordshire SG3 6PY
Tel: (01438) 812661
Tudor manor house, re-fashioned in the 19thC, housing a collection of manuscripts. Portraits, Jacobean banquet hall. Formal gardens and adventure playground.

Leighton Buzzard Railway

Page's Park Station, Leighton Buzzard,
Bedfordshire LU7 8TN
Tel: (01525) 373888
An authentic narrow-gauge light railway, built in 1919, offering a 65-minute return journey into the Bedfordshire countryside.

Marsh Farm Country Park

South Woodham, Ferrers, Chelmsford, Essex CM3 5WP
Tel: (01245) 321552
Farm centre with sheep, a pig unit, free-range chickens, milking demonstrations, indoor and outdoor adventure play areas, nature reserve, walks, picnic area and pets' corner.

Melford Hall

Long Melford, Sudbury, Suffolk CO10 9AA
Tel: (01787) 880286
Turreted brick Tudor mansion with 18thC and Regency interiors. Collection of Chinese porcelain, gardens and a walk in the grounds.

Minsmere Nature Reserve

Westleton, Saxmundham, Suffolk IP17 3BY
Tel: (01728) 648281
Purpose-built visitor centre situated on the Suffolk coast. Information areas, nature trails, bird-watching and wildlife. Shop and tearoom.

National Horseracing Museum and Tours

Newmarket, Suffolk CB8 8JL
Tel: (01638) 667333
A museum displaying the development of horse-racing. A display of sporting art includes loans from the Tate gallery. Also a hands-on gallery.

National Stud

Newmarket, Suffolk CB8 0XE
Tel: (01638) 663464
A visit to the National Stud consists of a conducted tour which includes top thoroughbred stallions, mares and foals.

Norfolk Lavender

Caley Mill, Heacham, King's Lynn, Norfolk PE31 7JE
Tel: (01485) 570384
Lavender is distilled from the flowers and the oil made into a wide range of gifts. There is a slide show when the distillery is not working.

Norwich Cathedral

The Close, Norwich, Norfolk NR1 4EH
Tel: (01603) 764385
A Norman cathedral from 1096 with 14thC roof bosses depicting bible scenes from Adam and Eve to the Day of Judgement. Cloisters, cathedral close, shop and restaurant.

Oliver Cromwell's House

St Marys Street, Ely, Cambridgeshire CB7 4HF
Tel: (01353) 662062
The family home of Oliver Cromwell with a 17thC kitchen, parlour and haunted bedroom. Tourist Information Centre, souvenirs and a craft shop.

Peter Beales Roses

Attleborough, Norfolk NR17 1AY
Tel: (01953) 454707
A large display garden featuring a world famous collection of classic roses. Mainly old-fashioned roses plus rare and those of historic value.

Pleasure Beach

Great Yarmouth, Norfolk NR30 3EH
Tel: (01493) 844585
Rollercoaster, Terminator, log flume, Twister, monorail, breakdance, galloping horses, caterpillar, go-karts, ghost train, fun house and sheer terror show.

Pleasurewood Hills Family Leisure Park

Corton, Lowestoft, Suffolk NR32 5DZ
Tel: (01502) 586000
Log flume, chairlift, Horror Dome, two railways, pirate ship, fort, Aladdin's cave, parrot, sealion shows, rollercoaster, waveswinger.

The Pictures:
1 St Alban's Cathedral;
2 South of Ipswich, Suffolk;
3 The Norfolk Broads;
4 'A day at the races', Newmarket;
5 Thurne, Norfolk Broads;
6 Cromer, Norfolk;
7 Imperial War Museum, Duxford.

Sainsbury Centre for Visual Arts

University of East Anglia, Norwich, Norfolk NR4 7TJ

Tel: (01603) 456060

Housing the Sainsbury collection of works by Picasso, Bacon and Henry Moore alongside many objects of pottery and art. Cafe and art bookshop with monthly activities.

Sandringham

Sandringham, King's Lynn, Norfolk PE35 6EN

Tel: (01553) 772675

The country retreat of HM The Queen. A delightful house and 60 acres of grounds and lakes, plus museum of royal vehicles and royal memorabilia.

Shuttleworth Collection

Old Warden Aerodrome, Biggleswade, Bedfordshire SG18 9EP

Tel: (01767) 627288

A unique historical collection of aircraft from a 1909 Bleriot to a 1942 Spitfire in flying condition. Cars dating from an 1898 Panhard in running order.

Somerleyton Hall and Gardens

Somerleyton, Lowestoft, Suffolk NR32 5QQ

Tel: (01502) 730224

Anglo Italian-style mansion with state rooms, a maze, 12-acre garden with azaleas and rhododendrons. Miniature railway, shop and tearooms.

Stondon Museum

Lower Stondon, Henlow Camp, Bedfordshire SG16 6JN

Tel: (01462) 850339

The largest private collection in England of bygone vehicles from the beginning of the century. Transport exhibits from the early 1900s to the 1980s.

Thursford Collection

Thursford Green, Fakenham, Norfolk NR21 0AS

Tel: (01328) 878477

Musical evenings some Tuesdays from mid-July to the end of September. A live musical show with nine mechanical organs and a Wurlitzer show starring Robert Wolfe daily April to October.

Whipsnade Wild Animal Park

Dunstable, Bedfordshire LU6 2LF

Tel: (01582) 872171

Over 2,500 animals set in 600 acres of beautiful parkland. Free animal demonstrations, plus the Great Whipsnade Railway.

Wimpole Hall and Home Farm

Arrington, Royston, Hertfordshire SG8 0BW

Tel: (01223) 207257

An 18thC house in a landscaped park with a folly and Chinese bridge. Plunge bath and yellow drawing room in the house, the work of John Soane. Rare breeds centre at Home Farm.

Woburn Abbey

Woburn, Milton Keynes, Bedfordshire MK43 0TP

Tel: (01525) 290666

An 18thC Palladian mansion, altered by Henry Holland, the Prince Regent's architect. Contains a collection of English silver, French and English furniture and art.

Woburn Safari Park

Woburn, Milton Keynes, Bedfordshire MK17 9QN

Tel: (01525) 290407

Drive through the safari park with 30 species of animals in natural groups just a windscreen's width away. Action-packed Wild World Leisure Area with shows for all.

Find out more about the
EAST OF ENGLAND ooo

Further information about holidays and attractions
in the East of England is available from:

EAST OF ENGLAND TOURIST BOARD
Toppesfield Hall, Hadleigh, Suffolk IP7 5DN.
Tel: (01473) 822922
Fax: (01473) 823063
Email: eastofenglandtouristboard@compuserve.com
Internet: www.visitbritain.com/east-of-england/

The following publications are available free from the East of England Tourist Board:

Bed & Breakfast Touring Map 2001
England's Cycling Country
Travel Trade Directory
Places to Stay

Also available (price includes postage and packaging):

East of England - The Official Guide 2001 - £4.99

The Pictures:
1   South Raynham,
    Norfolk;
2   Ely Cathedral,
    Cambridge;
3   Cromer, Norfolk;
4   Cley next the Sea,
    Norfolk.

Getting to the
EAST OF ENGLAND ...

BY ROAD: The region is easily accessible. From London and the south via the A1, M11,
M25, A10, M1, A46 and A12. From the north via the A17, A1, A15, A5, M1 and A6.
From the west via the A14, A47, A421, A428, A418, A41 and A427.

BY RAIL: Regular fast trains run to all major cities and towns in the region. London
stations which serve the region are Liverpool Street, Kings Cross, Fenchurch Street,
Moorgate, St Pancras, London Marylebone and London Euston. Bedford, Luton and
St Albans are on the Thameslink line which runs to Kings Cross and onto London
Gatwick Airport. There is also a direct link between London Stansted Airport and
Liverpool Street. Through the Channel Tunnel, there are trains direct from Paris and
Brussels to Waterloo Station, London. A short journey on the Underground will bring
passengers to those stations operating services into the East of England. Further
information on rail journeys in the East of England can be obtained on (0845) 748 4950.

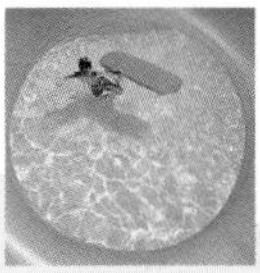

Where to stay in the EAST OF ENGLAND

Accommodation entries in this region are listed in alphabetical order of place name, and then in alphabetical order of establishment.

Map references refer to the colour location maps at the front of this guide. The first number indicates the map to use; the letter and number which follow refer to the grid reference on the map.

At-a-glance symbols at the end of each accommodation entry give useful information about services and facilities. A key to symbols can be found inside the back cover flap. Keep this open for easy reference.

A brief description of the towns and villages offering accommodation in the entries which follow, can be found at the end of this section.

A complete listing of all English Tourism Council assessed hotels appears at the back of this guide.

ALDEBURGH, Suffolk Map ref 3C2

★★★
Ad IFC

THE BRUDENELL HOTEL

The Parade, Aldeburgh, IP15 5BU
T: (01728) 452071
F: (01728) 454082

Situated directly on the seafront of Aldeburgh, a totally unspoilt fishing town of great charm. You can enjoy some fantastic views over the sea and the River Alde. The ideal venue to base yourself whilst you explore the Heritage Coast.

Bedrooms: 7 single, 21 double, 19 twin
Bathrooms: 47 en suite

Lunch available
EM 1830 (LO 2045)
Parking for 26
CC: Amex, Barclaycard, Delta, Eurocard, Mastercard, Solo, Switch, Visa

B&B per night:
S £60.00–£65.00
D £96.00–£106.00

HB per person:
DY £39.00–£60.00

OPEN All year round

CR
Corus & Regal Hotels

CHECK THE MAPS

The colour maps at the front of this guide show all the cities, towns and villages for which you will find accommodation entries. Refer to the town index to find the page on which they are listed.

★★

UPLANDS HOTEL
Victoria Road, Aldeburgh, IP15 5DX
T: (01728) 452420
F: (01728) 454872
I: www.smoothound.co.uk/hotels/
uplands.html

B&B per night:
S £55.00–£55.00
D £75.00–£75.00

HB per person:
DY £42.50–£70.00

OPEN All year round

*This privately-owned Georgian/
Edwardian hotel offers excellent
service in cosy surroundings. Located
only 3 minutes' walk from Aldeburgh
seafront, opposite the parish church.
17 bedrooms, all en suite (7 on
ground floor). Restaurant overlooks
the delightful walled garden and
provides a varied menu featuring
fresh local produce.*

Bedrooms: 1 single,
5 double, 9 twin, 2 triple
Bathrooms: 17 en suite,
1 public

EM 1900 (LO 2030)
Parking for 20
CC: Barclaycard, Delta,
Mastercard, Solo, Switch,
Visa, Visa Electron

★★★

WHITE LION HOTEL
Market Cross Place, Aldeburgh, IP15 5BJ
T: (01728) 452720
F: (01728) 452986
E: whitelionaldeburgh@btinternet.com
I: www.whitelion.co.uk

B&B per night:
S £66.50–£71.50
D £103.00–£130.00

OPEN All year round

Best Western Hotels

*This imposing hotel set directly on
the seafront has the distinction of
being the oldest in Aldeburgh, with
its own beamed restaurant dating
back to 1563. A warm welcome
awaits you in this unspoilt fishing
town which is famous for classical
music concerts. Single room
supplement applies.*

Bedrooms: 4 single,
19 double, 14 twin,
1 triple
Bathrooms: 38 en suite

Lunch available
EM 1900 (LO 2100)
Parking for 15
CC: Amex, Barclaycard,
Delta, Eurocard,
Mastercard, Solo, Switch,
Visa

★★

ROMAN CAMP INN
Holt Road, Aylmerton, Norwich,
NR11 8QD
T: (01263) 838291
F: (01263) 837071

Bedrooms: 1 single,
6 double, 8 twin
Bathrooms: 15 en suite

Lunch available
EM 1800 (LO 2145)
Parking for 50
CC: Barclaycard, Delta,
Eurocard, Mastercard,
Visa

B&B per night:
S £46.00–£50.00
D £76.00–£84.00

OPEN All year round

*An ideal base. Standing close to the highest point in Norfolk, central to all parts of this
beautiful coastline. Landscaped gardens. All rooms en suite.*

COUNTRY CODE Always follow the Country Code ⚘
Enjoy the countryside and respect its life and work ⚘ Guard
against all risk of fire ⚘ Fasten all gates ⚘ Keep your dogs
under close control ⚘ Keep to public paths across farmland
⚘ Use gates and stiles to cross fences, hedges and walls ⚘
Leave livestock, crops and machinery alone ⚘ Take your litter
home ⚘ Help to keep all water clean ⚘ Protect wildlife,
plants and trees ⚘ Take special care on country roads ⚘
Make no unnecessary noise

BASILDON, Essex Map ref 3B3

★★★

THE CHICHESTER HOTEL
Old London Road, Wickford, SS11 8UE
T: (01268) 560555
F: (01268) 560580

B&B per night:
S £64.00–£77.00
D £86.00–£86.00

OPEN All year round

Picturesque family-run hotel surrounded by rural farmland in the Basildon, Chelmsford, Southend triangle. Try our beautiful gallery restaurant (open to non-residents) – fully air conditioned, it overlooks the hotel's charming courtyard garden. Special mini-break packages available at weekends.

Bedrooms: 17 single, 10 double, 8 twin
Bathrooms: 35 en suite

Lunch available
EM 1900 (LO 2130)
Parking for 41
CC: Amex, Barclaycard, Delta, Diners, Mastercard, Switch, Visa

BLAKENEY, Norfolk Map ref 3B1

★★
Gold
Award

MORSTON HALL
Morston, Holt, NR25 7AA
T: (01263) 741041
F: (01263) 740419
E: reception@morstonhall.com.uk
I: www.morstonhall.com.uk

Bedrooms: 5 double, 1 twin; suite available
Bathrooms: 6 en suite

EM 1930 (LO 2100)
Parking for 50
CC: Amex, Barclaycard, Delta, Diners, Mastercard, Switch, Visa

HB per person:
DY £95.00–£100.00

OPEN Feb–Dec

Peaceful 17thC country house hotel with delightful gardens, 2 miles from Blakeney. Fine restaurant, large, attractive bedrooms, caring staff, efficient and friendly.

★★

THE PHEASANT HOTEL
The Coast Road, Kelling, Holt, NR25 7EG
T: (01263) 588382
F: (01263) 588101
E: enquiries@
pheasanthotelnorfolk.co.uk
I: www.pheasanthotelnorfolk.co.uk

Bedrooms: 1 single, 14 double, 14 twin
Bathrooms: 29 en suite

Lunch available
EM 1845 (LO 2100)
Parking for 52
CC: Delta, Maestro, Mastercard, Solo, Switch, Visa, Visa Electron

B&B per night:
S Min £48.00
D Min £76.00

HB per person:
DY £45.00–£65.00

OPEN All year round

North Norfolk's "Top Hotel 1998". Country house with facilities for disabled. Brasserie serving home-made food. Three acres of grounds. Midway between Blakeney and Sheringham.

BRENTWOOD, Essex Map ref 2D2 *Tourist Information Centre Tel: (01277) 200300*

★★★★
Silver
Award

MARYGREEN MANOR HOTEL
London Road, Brentwood, CM14 4NR
T: (01277) 225252
F: (01277) 262809
E: info@marygreenmanor.co.uk
I: www.marygreenmanor.co.uk

Bedrooms: 26 double, 17 twin; suites available
Bathrooms: 43 en suite

Lunch available
EM 1915 (LO 2215)
Parking for 100
CC: Barclaycard, Delta, Mastercard, Switch, Visa

B&B per night:
S £126.50–£140.00
D £138.50–£145.00

OPEN All year round

Original Tudor building dating back to 1512. Hunting lodge visited by Catherine of Aragon. Old world garden. B&B prices are per room.

AT-A-GLANCE SYMBOLS
Symbols at the end of each accommodation entry give useful information about services and facilities. A key to symbols can be found inside the back cover flap. Keep this open for easy reference.

187

★

THE KINGS HEAD HOTEL
Market Place, Bungay, NR35 1AF
T: (01986) 893583 & 893582 (Payphone)
F: (01986) 893583
I: www.admin@vintagealecompany.co.uk

B&B per night:
S £38.00–£42.00
D £45.00–£60.00

HB per person:
DY £48.00–£52.00

OPEN All year round

16thC coaching inn, rebuilt in 1690 after the great fire of Bungay. In the heart of the Waveney Valley on the Suffolk/Norfolk border, Bungay is a central base for touring. You can be sure of a friendly Suffolk welcome. Choice of 2 restaurants serving traditional food and of course local Lowestoft fish.

Bedrooms: 1 single, 9 double, 2 twin, 1 family room
Bathrooms: 13 en suite

Lunch available
EM 1830 (LO 2130)
Parking for 23
CC: Amex, Barclaycard, Delta, Diners, Eurocard, JCB, Maestro, Mastercard, Solo, Switch, Visa, Visa Electron

---

★★★

ANGEL HOTEL
Angel Hill, Bury St Edmunds, IP33 1LT
T: (01284) 753926 (reservations)
F: (01284) 750092
E: sales@theangel.co.uk
I: www.theangel.co.uk

B&B per night:
S £50.00–£69.99
D £70.00–£150.00

HB per person:
DY £57.00–£82.00

OPEN All year round

Dating back to 1452, the Angel stands on one of the prettiest squares in the country, overlooking the historic and award-winning Abbey Gardens. Guests dine either in the magnificent award-winning Abbeygate Restaurant, or the 12thC Vaults undercroft, reputed to be part of the original Abbey, offering brasserie-style food.

Bedrooms: 11 single, 40 double, 14 twin; suites available
Bathrooms: 65 en suite

Lunch available
EM 1900 (LO 2200)
Parking for 54
CC: Amex, Barclaycard, Delta, Diners, Eurocard, Mastercard, Switch, Visa

---

★★★

BUTTERFLY HOTEL
A14 Bury East Exit, Moreton Hall,
Bury St Edmunds, IP32 7BW
T: (01284) 760884
F: (01284) 755476
E: burybutterfly@lineone.net
I: www.butterflyhotels.co.uk

Bedrooms: 32 single, 19 double, 14 twin
Bathrooms: 65 en suite

Lunch available
EM 1800 (LO 2200)
Parking for 70
CC: Amex, Diners

B&B per night:
S £57.45–£75.45
D £65.40–£83.40

HB per person:
DY £72.95–£90.95

OPEN All year round

Modern building with rustic style and decor, around open central courtyard. Special weekend rates available.

★★★

PRIORY HOTEL AND RESTAURANT
Fornham Road, Tollgate,
Bury St Edmunds, IP32 6EH
T: (01284) 766181
F: (01284) 767604
E: reservations@prioryhotel.co.uk
I: www.prioryhotel.co.uk

Bedrooms: 3 single, 18 double, 5 twin, 1 triple
Bathrooms: 27 en suite

Lunch available
EM 1900 (LO 2130)
Parking for 60
CC: Amex, Barclaycard, Delta, Diners, JCB, Maestro, Mastercard, Switch, Visa

B&B per night:
S £50.00–£79.00
D £63.00–£120.00

HB per person:
DY £66.00–£160.00

OPEN All year round

Ⓒ®
Best Western Hotels

Well-known local establishment noted for high standards and cuisine. Set in 2 acres of landscaped gardens yet only minutes from the town.

PRICES
Please check prices and other details at the time of booking.

CAMBRIDGE, Cambridgeshire Map ref 2D1 *Tourist Information Centre Tel: (01223) 322640*

★★
Silver
Award

ARUNDEL HOUSE HOTEL
Chesterton Road, Cambridge, CB4 3AN
T: (01223) 367701
F: (01223) 367721

B&B per night:
S £55.00–£75.00
D £71.00–£99.00

OPEN All year round

Elegant, privately-owned 19thC terraced hotel, beautifully located overlooking the River Cam and open parkland, close to the city centre and famous historic colleges. The hotel has a reputation for providing some of the best food in the area in both its restaurant and all-day conservatory. Small secluded garden.

Bedrooms: 41 single, 35 double, 23 twin, 5 triple, 1 family room
Bathrooms: 102 en suite, 3 public

Lunch available
EM 1830 (LO 2130)
Parking for 70
CC: Amex, Barclaycard, Delta, Diners, Eurocard, Mastercard, Switch, Visa

★

BRIDGE HOTEL (MOTEL)
Clayhythe, Waterbeach, Cambridge, CB5 9NZ
T: (01223) 860252
F: (01223) 440448

B&B per night:
S £40.00–£44.00
D £65.00–£75.00

OPEN All year round

13thC building set on the riverside, with beautiful lawns. On the outskirts of Cambridge, but only 5 minutes from the M11. An ideal location for day trips. A la carte restaurant and a warm and welcoming atmosphere.

Bedrooms: 3 single, 20 double, 5 twin; suites available
Bathrooms: 28 en suite

Lunch available
EM 1830 (LO 2130)
Parking for 50
CC: Amex, Barclaycard, Mastercard, Switch, Visa

★★★
Silver
Award

GONVILLE HOTEL
Gonville Place, Cambridge, CB1 1LY
T: (01223) 366611 &
221111 (Reservations)
F: (01223) 315470
E: enq@gonvillehotel.co.uk
I: www.gonvillehotel.co.uk

Bedrooms: 23 single, 19 double, 21 twin, 1 triple
Bathrooms: 64 en suite

Lunch available
EM 1900 (LO 2045)
Parking for 80
CC: Amex, Barclaycard, Delta, Diners, Eurocard, Mastercard, Switch, Visa

B&B per night:
S £99.00–£114.00
D £125.00–£135.00

HB per person:
DY £62.50–£130.00

OPEN All year round

Ⓒ®
Best Western Hotels

Occupies one of the most favoured positions in Cambridge, overlooking Parkers Piece and close to most of the colleges and shopping areas.

QUALITY ASSURANCE SCHEME
For an explanation of the quality and facilities represented by the Stars please refer to the front of this guide. A more detailed explanation can be found in the information pages at the back.

189

CHATTERIS, Cambridgeshire Map ref 3A2

★
Ad on this page

CROSS KEYS INN HOTEL

12-16 Market Hill, Chatteris, PE16 6BA
T: (01354) 693036 & 692644
F: (01354) 694454

B&B per night:
S £21.00–£40.00
D £32.50–£68.00

HB per person:
DY £44.00–£49.00

OPEN All year round

This delightful Elizabethan coaching inn, built around 1540, Grade II Listed, sits in the town centre opposite the parish church of St Peter and St Paul. A la carte menu and bar meals 7 days a week. Friendly atmosphere, oak-beamed lounge with log fires to welcome the traveller during winter. Ideal base in the heart of the Fens for touring this wonderful area.

Bedrooms: 7 double, 3 twin, 1 triple
Bathrooms: 11 en suite, 1 public

Lunch available
EM 1900 (LO 2200)
Parking for 10
CC: Barclaycard, Delta, Eurocard, JCB, Mastercard, Solo, Switch, Visa

CHELMSFORD, Essex Map ref 3B3 *Tourist Information Centre Tel: (01245) 283400*

★★★

ATLANTIC HOTEL

Brook Street, Off New Street, Chelmsford, CM1 1PP
T: (01245) 268168
F: (01245) 268169
E: info@atlantichotel.co.uk
I: www.atlantichotel.co.uk

B&B per night:
S £55.00–£125.00
D £60.00–£125.00

HB per person:
DY £50.00–£75.00

OPEN All year round

Opened in May 1999, the Atlantic is a contemporary and individual hotel designed with you in mind. Our aim is to provide an efficient and reliable professional service, in smart and stylish surroundings. Ideal for business or pleasure, the hotel is situated close to the town centre and railway station.

Bedrooms: 31 double, 28 twin
Bathrooms: 59 en suite

Lunch available
EM 1900 (LO 2230)
Parking for 60
CC: Amex, Barclaycard, Delta, Diners, Eurocard, JCB, Mastercard, Switch, Visa, Visa Electron

Best Western Hotels

ACCESSIBILITY

Look for the 🔲🔲🔲 symbols which indicate accessibility for wheelchair users. A list of establishments is at the front of this guide.

Cross Keys Inn Hotel

This delightful Elizabethan coaching inn, built around 1540. Grade II listed, sits in the town centre opposite the parish church of St Peter and St Paul. A la carte menu and bar meals 7 days a week. Friendly atmosphere, oak-beamed lounge with log fires to welcome the traveller during winter. Ideal base in the heart of the Fens for touring this wonderful area.

• 12 bedrooms (10 en-suite)
• Parking facilities
• Lunch available
• All major credit cards accepted

OPEN ALL YEAR ROUND

Single	£21.00 - £40.00
Double	£32.50 - £68.00
Half board	£36.00 - £55.00

Prices quoted are subject to change

Cross Keys Inn, 12-16 Market Hill, Chatteris, Cambridgeshire PE16 6BA
Tel: (01354) 693036 or 692644 Fax: (01354) 694454
E-mail: thefens@crosskeyshotel.fsnet.co.uk

★★★
Silver
Award

COUNTY HOTEL
Rainsford Road, Chelmsford, CM1 2PZ
T: (01245) 455700
F: (01245) 492762
E: sales@countyhotel-essex.co.uk
I: www.countyhotel.co.uk

B&B per night:
S £32.00–£75.00
D £64.00–£85.00

HB per person:
DY £37.50–£95.00

OPEN All year round

Friendly welcome and excellent customer care. 10 minutes' walk from parks, rivers and town centre. Families welcome – free cots and extra beds. Artista Brasserie open 10am to 10pm. Light meals, snacks, lunch and dinner menus. Children's menu available. Additional 28 bedrooms planned. Minimum rates are for Friday, Saturday and Sunday nights.

Bedrooms: 18 single, 8 double, 10 twin; suites available
Bathrooms: 36 en suite

Lunch available
EM 1800 (LO 2200)
Parking for 70
CC: Amex, Barclaycard, Delta, Diners, Mastercard, Switch, Visa

---

★★
MIAMI HOTEL
Princes Road, Chelmsford, CM2 9AJ
T: (01245) 264848 & 269603
F: (01245) 259860
E: miamihotel@hotmail.com
I: www.miamihotel.co.uk

Bedrooms: 22 single, 23 double, 10 twin
Bathrooms: 55 en suite

Lunch available
EM 1830 (LO 2130)
Parking for 80
CC: Amex, Barclaycard, Delta, Diners, Mastercard, Switch, Visa

B&B per night:
S £52.00–£66.00
D £62.00–£77.00

OPEN All year round

The Independents

Family-run hotel, 1 mile from town centre. All rooms are twin/double size (let as singles when required). Stay for 7 nights and pay for 6.

★
SNOWS HOTEL
240 Springfield Road, Chelmsford, CM2 6BP
T: (01245) 352004
F: (01245) 356675
E: sales@snowshotel.com
I: www.snowshotel.com

Bedrooms: 2 single, 6 double, 3 twin, 3 triple, 1 family room
Bathrooms: 13 en suite, 2 private

Lunch available
EM 1830 (LO 2100)
Parking for 14
CC: Amex, Barclaycard, Delta, Eurocard, Maestro, Mastercard, Solo, Switch, Visa, Visa Electron

B&B per night:
S £45.00–£55.00
D £55.00–£75.00

HB per person:
DY £55.00–£85.00

OPEN All year round

A neo-Georgian hotel set in its own grounds in the heart of Chelmsford, historic county town of Essex. Special weekend rates available, see our web site.

★

CHUDLEIGH HOTEL
Agate Road, Marine Parade West, Clacton-on-Sea, CO15 1RA
T: (01255) 425407
F: (01255) 470280

B&B per night:
S £32.50–£35.00
D £42.50–£50.00

HB per person:
DY £45.00–£47.50

OPEN All year round

An oasis in a town centre location, 200 metres from the central seafront gardens, near pier and main shops. Ideal for the business visitor, the tourist and for overnight stays. Free parking. Assurance of comfort and efficiency combined with informality. Fluent Italian and French spoken by the proprietor.

Bedrooms: 3 single, 3 double, 1 twin, 3 triple
Bathrooms: 9 en suite, 1 private

EM 1830 (LO 1900)
Parking for 6
CC: Amex, Barclaycard, Delta, Diners, Eurocard, JCB, Mastercard, Solo, Switch, Visa, Visa Electron

---

SYMBOLS The symbols in each entry give information about services and facilities. A key to these symbols appears at the back of this guide.

COGGESHALL, Essex Map ref 3B2

★★ **THE WHITE HART HOTEL**

Market End, Coggeshall, Colchester, CO6 1NH	Bedrooms: 2 single, 12 double, 4 twin	Lunch available EM 1900 (LO 2200)	B&B per night: S £52.50–£61.50
T: (01376) 561654	Bathrooms: 18 en suite	Parking for 41	D £70.00–£97.00
F: (01376) 561789		CC: Amex, Barclaycard,	
E: wharthotel@ndirect.co.uk		Delta, Mastercard, Solo,	HB per person:
I: www.oldenglish.co.uk		Switch, Visa	DY £65.00–£112.00

Historically picturesque coach house with luxuriously appointed en suite bedrooms. The charming restaurant offers fine Italian cuisine and an extensive wine list.

OPEN All year round

COLCHESTER, Essex Map ref 3B2 *Tourist Information Centre Tel: (01206) 282920*

★★★ **BUTTERFLY HOTEL**

A12-A120 Ardleigh Junction,	Bedrooms: 22 single,	Lunch available	B&B per night:
Old Ipswich Road, Colchester,	12 double, 12 twin,	EM 1800 (LO 2200)	S £57.45–£75.45
CO7 7QY	4 family rooms; suites	Parking for 75	D £65.40–£83.40
T: (01206) 230900	available	CC: Amex, Barclaycard,	
F: (01206) 231095	Bathrooms: 50 en suite	Delta, Diners, Eurocard,	HB per person:
E: colbutterfly@lineone.net		Mastercard, Switch, Visa	DY £72.95–£90.95
I: www.butterflyhotels.co.uk			

Purpose-built hotel in traditional style. Modern coaching inn by the water's edge on the outskirts of Colchester at the junction of A12 and A120.

OPEN All year round

★★★

ROSE & CROWN
East Street, Colchester, CO1 2TZ
T: (01206) 866677
F: (01206) 866616
E: info@rose-and-crown.com
I: www.rose-and-crown.com

B&B per night:
S £55.00–£82.00
D £60.00–£135.00

HB per person:
DY £55.00–£90.00

OPEN All year round

Ⓖ
Best Western Hotels

The oldest inn, in England's oldest recorded town. En suite rooms, a beauty salon, Tudor bar with open log fires and noted restaurant. With a friendly, relaxed atmosphere, it is one of Colchester's finest hotels and restaurants. Located on the Ipswich road, 2 miles off the A12 and half a mile from town centre.	Bedrooms: 1 single, 23 double, 2 twin, 3 triple Bathrooms: 29 en suite	Lunch available EM 1900 (LO 2200) Parking for 60 CC: Amex, Barclaycard, Delta, Diners, Eurocard, JCB, Mastercard, Solo, Switch, Visa, Visa Electron

CROMER, Norfolk Map ref 3C1 *Tourist Information Centre Tel: (01263) 512497*

★★ **YE OLDE RED LION HOTEL**

Brook Street, Cromer, NR27 9HD	Bedrooms: 1 single,	Lunch available	B&B per night:
T: (01263) 514964	7 double, 2 twin, 1 triple,	EM 1800 (LO 2200)	S £46.00–£50.00
F: (01263) 512834	1 family room	Parking for 12	D £76.00–£84.00
	Bathrooms: 12 en suite	CC: Barclaycard, Delta,	
		Mastercard, Visa	OPEN All year round

Charming Victorian hotel by the sea, offering quality accommodation. "Scene Changer Breaks", honeymoon/romantic specials, champagne weekends. Ask for brochure.

USE YOUR *i*s
There are more than 550 Tourist Information Centres throughout England offering friendly help with accommodation and holiday ideas as well as suggestions of places to visit and things to do. You'll find TIC addresses in the local Phone Book.

★★★

THE CORNWALLIS COUNTRY HOTEL AND RESTAURANT
Brome, Eye, IP23 8AJ
T: (01379) 870326
F: (01379) 870051
E: info@thecornwallis.com
I: www.thecornwallis.com

B&B per night:
S Min £72.50
D Min £90.00

HB per person:
DY Min £65.00

OPEN All year round

Drive up the lime tree-lined avenue to a former dower house, dating back to 1561, set in 20 acres of gardens with finest yew topiary and a water garden. A perfect setting for an award-winning restaurant, the Tudar Bar and superbly appointed accommodation with fine antique furniture.

Bedrooms: 15 double,
1 twin
Bathrooms: 16 en suite

Lunch available
EM 1900 (LO 2130)
Parking for 150
CC: Barclaycard, Delta,
Mastercard, Switch, Visa

⚼ ⚑ ❄ 80 ♪ ✿ ⚍ ⚲ SP ⊞

★★

BROOK HOTEL AND CARVERY
Orwell Road, Felixstowe, IP11 7PF
T: (01394) 278441
F: (01394) 670422

B&B per night:
S £45.00–£53.00
D £55.00–£75.00

HB per person:
DY £53.95–£61.95

OPEN All year round

This family-owned hotel is centrally placed in the seaside resort of Felixstowe, only a few minutes walk from the shops and seafront. Well appointed with all en suite accommodation offering friendly prepared food, mouth watering carvery, cast ale, fine wines and generally excellent value for money.

Bedrooms: 2 single,
16 double, 5 twin,
2 triple, 2 family rooms;
suite available
Bathrooms: 27 en suite

Lunch available
EM 1900 (LO 2200)
Parking for 20
CC: Amex, Barclaycard,
Delta, Diners, Mastercard,
Solo, Switch, Visa

⚼ ⚑ ❄ 100 ♪ ✿ ⚲ SP T

★★

MARLBOROUGH HOTEL
Sea Front, Felixstowe, IP11 2BJ
T: (01394) 285621
F: (01394) 670724

Bedrooms: 4 single,
19 double, 21 twin,
1 triple
Bathrooms: 45 en suite

Lunch available
EM 1900 (LO 2145)
Parking for 20
CC: Amex, Barclaycard,
Delta, Diners, Mastercard,
Solo, Switch, Visa, Visa
Electron

B&B per night:
S £37.00–£47.00
D £52.00–£62.00

HB per person:
DY £37.00–£62.00

OPEN All year round

Fine Edwardian seafront hotel offering comfort and attentive service to the holidaymaker and business person. Many rooms face the sea. Five executive rooms.

⚼2 ⚑ ❄ 100 ♪ SC ⚲ SP T ⊚

TOWN INDEX
This can be found at the back of the guide. If you know where you want to stay, the index will give you the page number listing accommodation in your chosen town, city or village.

★★

FURZEDOWN PRIVATE HOTEL

19-20 North Drive, Great Yarmouth, NR30 4EW
T: (01493) 844138
F: (01493) 844138

B&B per night:
S £36.50–£46.50
D £53.00–£73.00

HB per person:
DY £39.00–£49.00

OPEN All year round

Open all year and occupying the finest position on the seafront, we are famous for the quality of our food which is served in our spacious dining room. All rooms have TV and tea-making facilities and majority are fully en suite. Private car park.

Bedrooms: 2 single, 9 double, 6 twin, 6 triple
Bathrooms: 19 en suite, 4 private

Lunch available
EM 1800 (LO 2100)
Parking for 25
CC: Barclaycard, Delta, Eurocard, JCB, Maestro, Mastercard, Solo, Switch, Visa, Visa Electron

🐾☐♿🛈⑤⌇🅟📺◗🏛🍴100▶❄SC♨SP🆃

★★

HORSE & GROOM MOTEL

Rollesby, Great Yarmouth, NR29 5ER
T: (01493) 740624
F: (01493) 740022
E: chris@groommotel.freeserve.co.uk

Bedrooms: 13 double, 3 twin, 2 triple, 2 family rooms
Bathrooms: 20 en suite

Lunch available
EM 1800 (LO 2115)
Parking for 50
CC: Barclaycard, Delta, Mastercard, Switch, Visa

B&B per night:
S £43.00–£47.00
D £46.00–£54.00

HB per person:
DY £40.00–£42.50

OPEN All year round

The Independents

Recently built motel on A149 in Norfolk Broads area. All rooms en suite with satellite TV and tea/coffee facilities. Prices are per room.

🏍🐾♿℡🖲☐♿🛈⑤🅟🏛🍴30❄🐴SC SP🆃

★★★

REGENCY DOLPHIN HOTEL

Albert Square, Great Yarmouth, NR30 3JH
T: (01493) 855070
F: (01493) 853798
E: regency@meridianleisure.com
I: www.meridianleisure.com

B&B per night:
S £37.50–£65.00
D £55.00–£75.00

HB per person:
DY £50.00–£77.50

OPEN All year round

Great Yarmouth's premier and unique venue, ideally located within walking distance of Central Beach. En suite bedrooms with satellite channels and all modern amenities. Weddings, conferences and special occasion dining successfully catered for. Licensed to perform marriages. Heated swimming pool, landscaped garden and complimentary parking.

Bedrooms: 6 single, 32 double, 6 twin, 4 triple
Bathrooms: 48 en suite

Lunch available
EM 1830 (LO 2130)
Parking for 28
CC: Amex, Barclaycard, Delta, Diners, Eurocard, Mastercard, Solo, Switch, Visa

🏍🐾♿℡🖲☐♿🦑🛈⑤⌇🅟📺◗🏛🍴120🏊∪▶❄♨SP🎠🆃⊛

CHECK THE MAPS

The colour maps at the front of this guide show all the cities, towns and villages for which you will find accommodation entries. Refer to the town index to find the page on which they are listed.

HARWICH, Essex Map ref 3C2 *Tourist Information Centre Tel: (01255) 506139*

★★

Hotel overlooking quiet sandy beaches and ever-changing seacape, busy with shipping activity, minutes from Harwich port. All rooms different. Quality food with organically grown ingredients extensively used. We cater for all tastes and diets. Well stocked bar, restaurant and pavement cafe open to the public. Value for money.

THE HOTEL CONTINENTAL

28-29 Marine Parade, Dovercourt, Harwich, CO12 3RG
T: (01255) 551298 &
07770 308976 (mobile)
F: (01255) 551698
E: hotconti@aol.com
I: www.hotelcontinental-harwich.co.uk

Bedrooms: 5 single,
4 double, 2 twin,
2 family rooms
Bathrooms: 13 en suite,
1 public

Lunch available
EM 1700 (LO 2330)
Parking for 6
CC: Amex, Barclaycard,
Delta, Diners, Mastercard,
Solo, Switch, Visa, Visa
Electron

B&B per night:
S £30.00–£50.00
D £60.00–£75.00

HB per person:
DY Min £40.00

OPEN All year round

The Independents

[icons] 15 ⊙ ☂ ✳ 🚲 ☏ SP T

HITCHIN, Hertfordshire Map ref 2D1

Rating
Applied For
Ad p15

THISTLE STEVENAGE
Blakemore End Road,
Little Wymondley, Hitchin, SG4 7JJ
T: (01438) 355821
F: (01438) 742114
E: stevenage@thistle.co.uk
I: www.thistlehotels.com

Bedrooms: 5 single,
60 double, 13 twin,
3 triple; suites available
Bathrooms: 81 en suite

Lunch available
EM 1900 (LO 2130)
Parking for 250
CC: Amex, Barclaycard,
Delta, Diners, Mastercard,
Solo, Switch, Visa

B&B per night:
S £123.00–£126.00
D £138.00–£162.00

OPEN All year round

Thistle Hotels/Utell
International

A secluded Georgian-style hotel, midway between Hitchin and Stevenage. Luton Airport 9 miles. Attractive gardens, with outdoor pool heated in summer months.

[icons] 150 ⟵ ☂ ✳ ☏ SP T

HORNING, Norfolk Map ref 3C1

★★★

Set slightly back from the banks of the River Bure, the hotel occupies one of the choicest positions on the Norfolk Broads. We offer midweek and weekend breaks. There is a dinner dance most Saturdays throughout the year. Children welcome. Call for a brochure or visit our web site.

PETERSFIELD HOUSE HOTEL

Lower Street, Horning, Norwich, NR12 8PF
T: (01692) 630741
F: (01692) 630745
E: reception@petersfield.co.uk
I: www.petersfieldhotel.co.uk

Bedrooms: 3 single,
9 double, 5 twin,
1 family room
Bathrooms: 18 en suite

Lunch available
EM 1930 (LO 2130)
Parking for 25
CC: Amex, Barclaycard,
Diners, Mastercard, Visa

B&B per night:
S £59.00–£65.00
D £79.00–£89.00

HB per person:
DY £50.00–£55.00

OPEN All year round

[icons] 60 ♪ ✳ 🚲 SP T

HUNTINGDON, Cambridgeshire Map ref 3A2 *Tourist Information Centre Tel: (01480) 388588*

★★★
Silver
Award

OLD BRIDGE HOTEL
1 High Street, Huntingdon,
PE18 6TQ
T: (01480) 452681
F: (01480) 411017

Bedrooms: 5 single,
15 double, 4 twin
Bathrooms: 24 en suite

Lunch available
EM 1830 (LO 2230)
Parking for 70
CC: Amex, Barclaycard,
Delta, Diners, Eurocard,
Mastercard, Switch, Visa

B&B per night:
S £79.50–£110.00
D £89.50–£149.50

HB per person:
DY £67.50–£89.50

OPEN All year round

Beautifully decorated Georgian town hotel by River Ouse. Oak-panelled dining room, terrace brasserie with award-winning wine list, real ales and log fires. All rooms air-conditioned, most with CD stereo systems.

[icons] 50 ♪ ✳ SP T

REGIONAL TOURIST BOARD The ⋀ symbol in an
establishment entry indicates that it is a Regional Tourist Board member.

IPSWICH, Suffolk Map ref 3B2 *Tourist Information Centre Tel: (01473) 258070*

★★★
Silver
Award

THE MARLBOROUGH AT IPSWICH
Henley Road, Ipswich, IP1 3SP
T: (01473) 257677
F: (01473) 226927
E: reception@themarlborough.co.uk
I: www.themarlborough.co.uk

Bedrooms: 4 single,
13 double, 5 twin; suite
available
Bathrooms: 22 en suite

Lunch available
EM 1930 (LO 2130)
Parking for 60
CC: Amex, Barclaycard,
Delta, Diners, JCB,
Mastercard, Switch, Visa

B&B per night:
S £59.00–£80.00
D £84.00–£111.00

HB per person:
DY £59.50–£69.50

OPEN All year round

Small family-owned hotel close to town centre and Christchurch Park. Tastefully furnished en suite bedrooms. Comfortable restaurant (rosettes for food) overlooking the floodlit garden.

ⒸⓇ

Best Western Hotels

🅰🔆🍴🍷📠💻🖙🐕📵Ⓢ⅄📶🌐🖥🍽🚪🍴60 ✂🥾 🆂🅿 🆃

KING'S LYNN, Norfolk Map ref 3B1 *Tourist Information Centre Tel: (01553) 763044*

★★★
BUTTERFLY HOTEL
A10-A47 Roundabout,
Hardwick Narrows, King's Lynn,
PE30 4NB
T: (01553) 771707
F: (01553) 768027
E: kingsbutterfly@lineone.net
I: www.butterflyhotels.co.uk

Bedrooms: 23 single,
15 double, 12 twin
Bathrooms: 50 en suite

Lunch available
EM 1800 (LO 2200)
Parking for 70
CC: Amex, Diners

B&B per night:
S £57.45–£75.45
D £65.40–£83.40

HB per person:
DY £72.95–£90.95

OPEN All year round

Modern building with rustic style and decor, set around an open central courtyard. Special weekend rates available.

🅰🔆🍴🍷📠💻🖙🍽Ⓢ⅄📶📺🌐🖥🚪🍴50 ✂ 🆂🅿 🆃

★★★
KNIGHTS HILL HOTEL
South Wootton, King's Lynn,
PE30 3HQ
T: (01553) 675566
F: (01553) 675568
E: reception@knightshill.co.uk
I: www.abacushotels.co.uk

Bedrooms: 4 single,
42 double, 15 twin
Bathrooms: 61 en suite

Lunch available
EM 1900 (LO 2200)
Parking for 350
CC: Amex, Barclaycard,
Delta, Diners, Eurocard,
JCB, Mastercard, Solo,
Switch, Visa, Visa Electron

B&B per night:
S £93.25–£118.25

OPEN All year round

ⒸⓇ

Best Western Hotels

Sympathetically restored farm complex offering a choice of accommodation styles, 2 restaurants, a country pub and an extensive health club. Special breaks available.

🅰🔆🍴🍷🛎📠💻🖙🍷🍽Ⓢ⅄📶🌐🖥🚪🍴299 🚶🗡🎣🕳✂🥾 🆂🅿 🏨🆃⚽

★★

THE TUDOR ROSE HOTEL
St Nicholas Street,
Off Tuesday Market Place, King's Lynn,
PE30 1LR
T: (01553) 762824
F: (01553) 764894
E: kltudorrose@aol.com
I: www.tudorrose-hotel.co.uk

B&B per night:
S £37.50–£45.00
D £50.00–£60.00

OPEN All year round

ⒸⓇ

The Independents

Built around 1500 by a local merchant and extended in 1640, the hotel offers comfortable accommodation, traditional British cooking and a choice of 4 real ales in 2 bars. The only family owned and run hotel in King's Lynn, it is located in the heart of the Old Town opposite the magnificent St Nicholas Chapel.

Bedrooms: 5 single,
5 double, 3 twin
Bathrooms: 11 en suite,
2 private

Lunch available
EM 1900 (LO 2100)
CC: Amex, Barclaycard,
Delta, Diners, Eurocard,
JCB, Mastercard, Solo,
Switch, Visa, Visa Electron

🅰🔆🍴🍷📠💻🖙🍷🍽⅄📺🌐🖥🚪🌸 🆂🅿 🏨🆃

COUNTRY CODE Always follow the Country Code 🌳 Enjoy the countryside and respect its life and work 🌳 Guard against all risk of fire 🌳 Fasten all gates 🌳 Keep your dogs under close control 🌳 Keep to public paths across farmland 🌳 Use gates and stiles to cross fences, hedges and walls 🌳 Leave livestock, crops and machinery alone 🌳 Take your litter home 🌳 Help to keep all water clean 🌳 Protect wildlife, plants and trees 🌳 Take special care on country roads 🌳 Make no unnecessary noise

LEAVENHEATH, Suffolk Map ref 3B2

Rating
Applied For

THE STOKE BY NAYLAND CLUB HOTEL

Keepers Lane, Leavenheath, Colchester, Essex CO6 4PZ
T: (01206) 262836 (24 hours)
F: (01206) 263356
E: info@golf-club.co.uk
I: www.stokebynaylandclub.co.uk

B&B per night:
S £60.00–£78.50
D £79.00–£108.00

HB per person:
DY £70.00–£95.00

OPEN All year round

Set in 300 acres of rolling Constable Country, this beautifully appointed hotel offers superb facilities. All rooms, including suites/family rooms, are en suite with stunning views of lake and golf courses; tea and coffee, satellite TV, telephone with ISDN and hairdryer. Facilities include 36-hole golf, driving range, indoor pool, gym, beauty treatments, restaurants and bars.

Bedrooms: 13 double, 13 twin, 4 triple; suites available
Bathrooms: 30 en suite

Parking for 280
CC: Barclaycard, Delta, Mastercard, Switch, Visa

LEISTON, Suffolk Map ref 3C2

★

WHITE HORSE HOTEL
Station Road, Leiston, IP16 4HD
T: (01728) 830694
F: (01728) 833105
E: whihorse@globalnet.co.uk
I: www.whitehorsehotel.co.uk

Bedrooms: 3 single, 5 double, 3 twin, 2 family rooms
Bathrooms: 13 en suite, 1 public

Lunch available
EM 1930 (LO 2200)
Parking for 16
CC: Amex, Barclaycard, Delta, Diners, Mastercard, Switch, Visa

B&B per night:
S Min £35.00
D Min £55.00

OPEN All year round

18thC Georgian hotel with a relaxed and informal atmosphere, only 2 miles from the sea, in the heart of bird-watching country.

LUTON, Bedfordshire Map ref 2D1 *Tourist Information Centre Tel: (01582) 401579*

Rating
Applied For
Ad p15

THISTLE LUTON
Arndale Centre, Luton, Bedfordshire LU1 2TR
T: (01582) 734199
F: (01582) 402528
E: luton@thistle.co.uk
I: www.thistlehotels.com

Bedrooms: 33 single, 41 double, 73 twin, 3 triple; suites available
Bathrooms: 150 en suite

Lunch available
EM 1800 (LO 2200)
Parking for 44
CC: Amex, Barclaycard, Delta, Diners, Eurocard, JCB, Maestro, Mastercard, Solo, Switch, Visa, Visa Electron

B&B per night:
S £108.00–£111.00
D £140.00–£164.00

OPEN All year round

CR
Thistle Hotels/Utell International

Modern city centre hotel overlooking the trees and gardens of George Square. Luton Airport 1.5 miles. Convenient for Woburn, Whipsnade and Hatfield House.

MALDON, Essex Map ref 3B3 *Tourist Information Centre Tel: (01621) 856503*

★★★★
Silver
Award

FIVE LAKES HOTEL, GOLF AND COUNTRY CLUB AND SPA
Colchester Road, Tolleshunt Knights, Maldon, CM9 8HX
T: (01621) 868888
F: (01621) 869696
E: enquiries@fivelakes.co.uk
I: www.fivelakes.co.uk

Bedrooms: 2 single, 69 double, 43 twin; suites available
Bathrooms: 114 en suite, 9 public

Lunch available
EM 1900 (LO 2200)
Parking for 520
CC: Amex, Barclaycard, Delta, Diners, Mastercard, Switch, Visa, Visa Electron

B&B per night:
S Max £108.50
D Max £161.00

HB per person:
DY Max £79.00

OPEN All year round

CR
Best Western Hotels

Set in 320 acres. Unparalleled sporting and leisure activities including two 18-hole golf courses, indoor/outdoor tennis and health spa complemented by quality accommodation, bars and 2 restaurants.

QUALITY ASSURANCE SCHEME
Star ratings and awards were correct at the time of going to press but are subject to change. Please check at the time of booking.

★★★

THE SMOKE HOUSE
Beck Row, Bury St Edmunds,
IP28 8DH
T: (01638) 713223
F: (01638) 712202
E: enquiries@smoke-house.co.uk
I: www.smoke-house.co.uk

Bedrooms: 20 double,
74 twin; suites available
Bathrooms: 94 en suite

Lunch available
EM 1700 (LO 2200)
Parking for 200
CC: Amex, Barclaycard,
Delta, Diners, Mastercard,
Switch, Visa

B&B per night:
S £90.00–£130.00
D £110.00–£155.00

OPEN All year round

Ⓒ®
Best Western Hotels

Listed Tudor/Georgian manor house with inglenook fireplaces and comfortable, well-equipped rooms. Two bars, licensed restaurant, barbecue in season. Conference centre.

▨⅍⌂🅗✆🖃▯♨🖲🛈Ⓢ✂🄼⟨TV⟩◑📶🖥🛢🍽120🅫↻✿✈🐾SP⌂T

★★★

HEATH COURT HOTEL
Moulton Road, Newmarket,
CB8 8DY
T: (01638) 667171
F: (01638) 666533
E: quality@heathcourt-hotel.co.uk
I: www.heathcourt-hotel.co.uk

Bedrooms: 20 single,
14 double, 5 twin;
2 triple; suites available
Bathrooms: 41 en suite

Lunch available
EM 1900 (LO 2145)
Parking for 60
CC: Amex, Barclaycard,
Delta, Diners, Eurocard,
Mastercard, Switch, Visa

B&B per night:
S £75.00–£105.00
D £90.00–£150.00

HB per person:
DY £55.00–£90.00

OPEN All year round

Ⓒ®
Best Western Hotels

Hotel of high standards in a quiet central position. Ideal location for touring, horseracing and local countryside.

▨⅍✆🖃▯♨🛈Ⓢ✂🄼⟨TV⟩◑📶🖥🛢🍽120▶🐾SP T◉

★★★

Swynford Paddocks is an elegant 18thC country house hotel nestling in idyllic countryside with racehorses grazing its pastures. It's the ideal base for exploring both Newmarket and Cambridge. Individually decorated bedrooms, all with Sky TV and mini-bar. First-class restaurant, spacious lounge and bar area.

SWYNFORD PADDOCKS HOTEL
Six Mile Bottom, Newmarket, CB8 0UE
T: (01638) 570234 (24 hours)
F: (01638) 570283
E: sales@swynfordpaddocks.com
I: www.swynfordpaddocks.com

Bedrooms: 1 single,
11 double, 3 twin
Bathrooms: 15 en suite

Lunch available
EM 1900 (LO 2130)
Parking for 120
CC: Amex, Barclaycard,
Delta, Diners, Eurocard,
JCB, Mastercard, Switch,
Visa, Visa Electron

B&B per night:
D £135.00–£215.00

OPEN All year round

▨⅍⌂🅗✆🖃▯♨🛈Ⓢ✂◑🖥🛢🍽40🅫↻✿🐾SP⌂T◉

See under Bungay, Great Yarmouth, Horning, North Walsham, Norwich, Wroxham

★★
Silver
Award

Chosen by Agatha Christie as her Norfolk hideaway, the award-winning Beechwood Hotel is an ivyclad Georgian house with a warm and friendly atmosphere where a brigade of four chefs prepare a nightly changing menu. Winner of a 1999 award for the "Most Excellent value for Money" hotel in the UK.

BEECHWOOD HOTEL
20 Cromer Road, North Walsham,
NR28 0HD
T: (01692) 403231
F: (01692) 407284

Bedrooms: 9 double,
1 twin
Bathrooms: 10 en suite

Lunch available
EM 1900 (LO 2100)
Parking for 15
CC: Barclaycard, Delta,
Maestro, Mastercard,
Solo, Switch, Visa, Visa
Electron

B&B per night:
S £50.00–£60.00
D £68.00–£90.00

HB per person:
DY £40.00–£65.00

OPEN All year round

▨🛢⌂✆🖃▯♨🛈Ⓢ✂🄼🖥🛢🍽20↻▶✿🐾SP⌂T◉

QUALITY ASSURANCE SCHEME
Star ratings and awards are explained at the back of this guide.

★★★

BARNHAM BROOM HOTEL, GOLF, CONFERENCE & LEISURE CENTRE

Honingham Road, Barnham Broom, Norwich, NR9 4DD
T: (01603) 759393 (Main switchboard) &
759552 (Golf Shop)
F: (01603) 758224
E: enquiry@barnhambroomhotel.co.uk
I: www.barnham-broom.co.uk

Set in 250 acres of Norfolk countryside, Barnham has 52 en suite bedrroms (fully refurbished April 2000), two 18-hole golf courses, leisure complex with indoor pool, sports bar and cafe, restaurant, indoor golf simulator and conference centre. The Peter Ballingall Golf School offers residential golf courses and individual tuition.

Bedrooms: 8 double,
36 twin, 1 triple, 7 family
rooms; suites available
Bathrooms: 52 en suite

Lunch available
EM 1900 (LO 2130)
Parking for 200
CC: Amex, Barclaycard,
Delta, Diners, Mastercard,
Switch, Visa

B&B per night:
S Min £75.00
D Min £99.00

HB per person:
DY Min £66.50

OPEN All year round

Best Western Hotels

 ★★
Silver
Award

BEECHES HOTEL

2-6 Earlham Road, Norwich, NR2 3DB
T: (01603) 621167 & 667357 (Direct
Line-Mr Hill)
F: (01603) 620151
E: reception@beeches.co.uk
I: www.beeches.co.uk

"An oasis in the heart of Norwich". Three separate Grade II Listed Victorian houses and modern extension create a welcoming and individual hotel, complemented by a tranquil English Heritage Victorian garden, yet only a 10-minute stroll to city centre. Tastefully refurbished, comfortable accommodation in a relaxed, informal atmosphere. HB prices are for single room.

Bedrooms: 8 single,
24 double, 4 twin
Bathrooms: 36 en suite

EM 1830 (LO 2100)
Parking for 36
CC: Amex, Barclaycard,
Delta, Diners, Eurocard,
Mastercard, Solo, Switch,
Visa

B&B per night:
S £54.00-£64.00
D £70.00-£88.00

HB per person:
DY £68.00-£78.00

OPEN All year round

The Independents

★★

THE GEORGIAN HOUSE HOTEL

32-34 Unthank Road, Norwich, NR2 2RB
T: (01603) 615655
F: (01603) 765689
E: reception@georgian-hotel.co.uk
I: georgian-hotel.co.uk

The Georgian House Hotel is set in beautiful gardens and just a short stroll away from the heart of the historic city of Norwich. A great base for both business and pleasure. Goodwins restaurant offers a choice of table d'hote or a la carte dining. Ample free parking for guests.

Bedrooms: 3 single,
17 double, 3 twin,
3 triple, 1 family room
Bathrooms: 27 en suite

Lunch available
EM 1830 (LO 2200)
Parking for 30
CC: Amex, Barclaycard,
Delta, Diners, JCB,
Mastercard, Switch, Visa,
Visa Electron

B&B per night:
S £55.00-£60.00
D £75.00-£85.00

OPEN All year round

The Independents/
Minotel

MAP REFERENCES
Map references apply to the colour maps at the front of this guide.

★★

OLD RECTORY

North Walsham Road, Crostwick,
Norwich, NR12 7BG
T: (01603) 738513
F: (01603) 738712
I: www.accomodata.co.uk/020896.
htm

Bedrooms: 5 double,
6 twin, 2 family rooms;
suites available
Bathrooms: 13 en suite

EM 1830 (LO 1930)
Parking for 100
CC: Amex, Barclaycard,
Delta, Eurocard, JCB,
Mastercard, Solo, Switch,
Visa

B&B per night:
S £40.00–£42.00
D £55.00–£57.50

HB per person:
DY £37.00–£51.50

OPEN All year round

Old Victorian rectory with bedroom extension, set amidst 3.5 acres of mature trees. Well placed for the Broads and 5 miles from Norwich. Homely accommodation.

150

★★★

PARK FARM COUNTRY HOTEL & LEISURE

Hethersett, Norwich, NR9 3DL
T: (01603) 810264
F: (01603) 812104
E: enq@parkfarm-hotel.co.uk

B&B per night:
S £79.00–£99.00
D £105.00–£139.00

HB per person:
DY £99.50–£119.50

OPEN All year round

Set in beautiful landscaped gardens, this exclusive country hotel, with its award-winning Georgian restaurant, has been tastefully extended to include a superb health and beauty complex. There are 47 individually designed bedrooms, the executive rooms being furnished with 4-poster beds and whirlpool baths.

Bedrooms: 4 single,
22 double, 10 twin,
12 family rooms
Bathrooms: 48 en suite

Lunch available
EM 1900 (LO 2130)
Parking for 151
CC: Amex, Barclaycard,
Delta, Diners, Mastercard,
Solo, Switch, Visa

120

★★★

SEA MARGE HOTEL

16 High Street, Overstrand, Cromer,
NR27 0AB
T: (01263) 579579
F: (01263) 579524
E: seamarge.hotel@virgin.net

B&B per night:
S £62.00–£84.00
D £84.00–£106.00

HB per person:
DY £56.95–£67.95

OPEN All year round

Discover Sea Marge, set in an Area of Outstanding Natural Beauty in the quaint unspoilt fishing village of Overstrand. All 17 en suite rooms are luxuriously furnished, some with spectacular sea views across the terraced gardens. Our high standards of food and service have made us one of North Norfolk's finest hotels.

Bedrooms: 12 double,
4 twin, 1 triple
Bathrooms: 17 en suite

Lunch available
EM 1900 (LO 2130)
Parking for 40
CC: Barclaycard, Delta,
Eurocard, JCB,
Mastercard, Solo, Switch,
Visa

60

AT-A-GLANCE SYMBOLS

Symbols at the end of each accommodation entry give useful information about services and facilities. A key to symbols can be found inside the back cover flap. Keep this open for easy reference.

★★★

THE BELL INN HOTEL

Great North Road, Stilton, Peterborough,
Cambridge PE7 3RA
T: (01733) 241066
F: (01733) 245173
E: reception@thebellstilton.co.uk
I: www.thebellstilton.co.uk

B&B per night:
S £69.50–£89.50
D £89.50–£109.50

OPEN All year round

The Bell Inn, "Birthplace of Stilton Cheese", offers today's demanding traveller modern first class accommodation and conference facilities in the unique setting of this ancient inn. Sited just off the A1 on the Great Old North Road, with easy access to all main transport routes and the thriving city of Peterborough.

Bedrooms: 2 single, 15 double, 1 twin, 1 triple Bathrooms: 19 en suite	Lunch available EM 1900 (LO 2130) Parking for 30 CC: Amex, Barclaycard, Delta, Diners, JCB, Mastercard, Switch, Visa, Visa Electron	

꙰ ♿ 🏠 ☎ ▤ 🖵 ♨ 🍷 🎦 ⑤ ⅄ ⤢ ◑ ▥ ⇩ 🍴100 ∪ ✿ ✈ SP 🎫 ⊤

★★★

BUTTERFLY HOTEL

Thorpe Meadows,
Off Longthorpe Parkway,
Peterborough, PE3 6GA
T: (01733) 564240
F: (01733) 565538
E: peterbutterfly@lineone.net
I: www.butterflyhotels.co.uk

Bedrooms: 33 single, 18 double, 15 twin, 4 triple; suites available Bathrooms: 70 en suite	Lunch available EM 1800 (LO 2200) Parking for 80 CC: Amex, Barclaycard, Delta, Diners, Eurocard, Mastercard, Switch, Visa

B&B per night:
S £57.45–£77.45
D £65.40–£85.40

HB per person:
DY £72.95–£92.95

OPEN All year round

By the water's edge at Thorpe Meadows, this modern hotel maintains all the traditional values of design and comfort. Special weekend rates available.

꙰ ♿ ♨ 🏠 ☎ 🖵 ♨ 🍷 ⑤ ⅄ TV ◑ ▥ ⇩ 🍴80 ✿ SP ⊤

★★★

ORTON HALL HOTEL

The Village, Orton Longueville,
Peterborough, Cambridgeshire PE2 7DN
T: (01733) 391111
F: (01733) 231912
E: reception@ortonhall.co.uk
I: www.ortonhall.co.uk

B&B per night:
S Min £96.85

HB per person:
DY Min £59.50

OPEN All year round

Ⓒⓡ

Best Western Hotels

17thC manor house in 20 acres of mature parkland 2.5 miles from city centre. Fully equipped en suite bedrooms, some with 4-posters. Choice of dining in either the Huntly Restaurant or Ramblewood Inn traditional country pub. Adjacent to Nene Park and two 18-hole golf courses. Picturesque Stamford is nearby. Half board price shown is special break rate.

Bedrooms: 9 single, 47 double, 7 twin, 2 triple Bathrooms: 65 en suite	Lunch available EM 1830 (LO 2130) Parking for 200 CC: Amex, Barclaycard, Delta, Diners, Eurocard, JCB, Mastercard, Switch, Visa

꙰ ♿ ♨ 🏠 ☎ 🖵 ♨ 🍷 ⑤ ⅄ ▥ ◑ ▥ ⇩ 🍴120 ∪ ▶ ✿ SC ✎ SP 🎫 ⊤

★★

THOMAS COOK BLUEBELL LODGE LEISURE CENTRE

P O Box 36, Thorpe Wood,
Peterborough, PE3 6SB
T: (01733) 502555 & 503008
F: (01733) 502020

Bedrooms: 2 double, 9 twin, 2 triple Bathrooms: 13 en suite	Lunch available EM 1830 (LO 2200) Parking for 250 CC: Barclaycard, Mastercard, Switch, Visa

B&B per night:
S £30.00–£55.00
D £40.00–£70.50

OPEN All year round

Friendly, efficient service is provided at this modern hotel. All rooms en suite. Complimentary use of extensive leisure facilities during stay. Bar and restaurant.

♿ ☎ ▤ 🖵 ♨ ⅄ ⤢ TV ☰ ▥ ⇩ 🍴50 ⚽ ☀ ✎ ♨ ▶ ✿ ✈ ⛴ SP

COLOUR MAPS Colour maps at the front of this guide pinpoint all places under which you will find accommodation listed.

PETTISTREE, Suffolk Map ref 3C2

Rating
Applied For

THE THREE TUNS COACHING INN

Main Road, Pettistree, Woodbridge,
IP13 0HW
T: (01728) 747979 & 746244
F: (01728) 746244
E: jon@threetuns-coachinginn.co.uk
I: www.threetuns-coachinginn.co.uk

John and Brenda invite you to visit their enchanting coaching inn, ideally situated for visiting the Suffolk Heritage Coast. All rooms are en suite and fully equipped. After experiencing local ales at the bar and fine food in the restaurant, just relax in the comfortable lounge with its open log fires.

Bedrooms: 1 single,
8 double, 2 twin
Bathrooms: 11 en suite

Lunch available
EM (LO 2100)
Parking for 40
CC: Barclaycard, Delta,
JCB, Mastercard, Solo,
Switch, Visa, Visa Electron

B&B per night:
S £40.00–£45.00
D £60.00–£65.00

HB per person:
DY £39.95–£54.95

OPEN All year round

ST ALBANS, Hertfordshire Map ref 2D1 *Tourist Information Centre Tel: (01727) 864511*

★★

THE APPLES HOTEL

133 London Road, St Albans,
AL1 1TA
T: (01727) 844111
F: (01727) 861100

Bedrooms: 1 single,
4 double, 3 twin, 1 triple
Bathrooms: 9 en suite

Lunch available
EM 1930 (LO 2100)
Parking for 10
CC: Amex, Barclaycard,
Delta, Eurocard,
Mastercard, Switch, Visa

B&B per night:
S £43.00–£50.00
D £60.00–£70.50

HB per person:
DY £45.00–£55.00

OPEN All year round

Family-run hotel in beautiful gardens within easy reach of city centre, station and major motorways. Heated swimming pool. Facilities for disabled.

⒞Ⓡ
The Independents

★★★★

Ad p15

THISTLE ST ALBANS

Watford Road, St Albans, AL2 3DS
T: (01727) 854252
F: (01727) 841906
E: st.albans@thistle.co.uk
I: www.thistlehotels.com

Bedrooms: 64 double,
43 twin, 4 triple
Bathrooms: 111 en suite

Lunch available
EM 1900 (LO 2200)
Parking for 150
CC: Amex, Barclaycard,
Delta, Diners, JCB,
Mastercard, Switch, Visa

B&B per night:
S £145.00–£165.00
D £145.00–£165.00

OPEN All year round

⒞Ⓡ
Thistle Hotels/Utell
International

Delightful country house style hotel. Close to M1, M10 and M25. Otium health and leisure club. Convenient for Woburn and Hatfield House.

ST IVES, Cambridgeshire Map ref 3A2

★

THE GOLDEN LION HOTEL

Market Hill, St Ives, Huntingdon,
PE27 5AL
T: (01480) 492100
F: (01480) 497109

Bedrooms: 5 single,
9 double, 3 twin, 2 triple,
1 family room
Bathrooms: 20 en suite

Lunch available
EM 1900 (LO 2200)
Parking for 4
CC: Amex, Barclaycard,
Delta, Diners, Eurocard,
Maestro, Mastercard,
Solo, Switch, Visa, Visa
Electron

B&B per night:
S £38.00–£44.00
D £48.00–£54.00

OPEN All year round

16thC coaching inn of great historic interest in the town centre. Good facilities for business people and tourists, full a la carte menu. Weekend rates available.

TOWN INDEX

This can be found at the back of this guide. If you know where you want to stay, the index will give you the page number listing accommodation in your chosen town, city or village.

★★★

OLIVERS LODGE HOTEL
Needingworth Road, St Ives, Huntingdon, PE27 5JP

T: (01480) 463252
F: (01480) 461150
E: reception@oliverslodge.co.uk
I: www.oliverslodge.co.uk

B&B per night:
S £65.00–£85.00
D £70.00–£90.00

HB per person:
DY £46.00–£58.00

OPEN All year round

Victorian house of character with attractive patio garden. Real ale bar, conservatory restaurant, extensive a la carte and bar snacks. Fresh fish and game specialities. Independently owned and operated. Just 20 minutes' drive from centre of Cambridge in the picturesque riverside town of St Ives. Half board price includes half bottle wine pp, on Sunday nights.

Bedrooms: 1 single, 6 double, 7 twin, 3 family rooms
Bathrooms: 17 en suite

Lunch available
EM 1900 (LO 2130)
Parking for 30
CC: Amex, Barclaycard, Delta, Eurocard, JCB, Mastercard, Switch, Visa, Visa Electron

75 ♪ ▸ ✲ SC ⚲ SP 🎯 T

★★★ **SLEPE HALL HOTEL**

Ramsey Road, St Ives, Huntingdon, PE27 5RB
T: (01480) 463122
F: (01480) 300706
E: mail@slepehall.co.uk
I: www.slepehall.co.uk

Bedrooms: 2 single, 10 double, 4 twin
Bathrooms: 16 en suite

Lunch available
EM 1900 (LO 2130)
Parking for 70
CC: Amex, Barclaycard, Delta, Diners, Mastercard, Switch, Visa

B&B per night:
S £50.00–£80.00
D £65.00–£110.00

OPEN All year round

Former private Victorian girls' school converted in 1966. Now a Grade II Listed building, 5 minutes' walk from the River Great Ouse and historic town centre. Extensive bar and restaurant menus.

200 ✲ ✕ 🚲 SP 🎯 T

ST NEOTS, Cambridgeshire Map ref 2D1 *Tourist Information Centre Tel: (01480) 388788*

★★ **ABBOTSLEY GOLF HOTEL & COUNTRY CLUB**

Eynesbury Hardwicke, St Neots, Huntingdon, PE19 4XN
T: (01480) 474000
F: (01480) 471018

Bedrooms: 2 single, 2 double, 13 twin
Bathrooms: 17 en suite, 2 public

Lunch available
EM 1930 (LO 2130)
Parking for 140
CC: Barclaycard, Delta, Diners, Eurocard, Mastercard, Switch, Visa

B&B per night:
S £47.00–£57.00
D £79.00–£89.00

HB per person:
DY £55.00–£63.00

OPEN All year round

Charming country hotel amidst its own 2 excellent 18-hole golf-courses. Golf Monthly: "The design is a revelation, the presentation superb". Non-golfers just as welcome!

40 ✲ ✕ ⚲ ⚓ ∪ ▸ ✲ SC ⚲ SP 🎯 T

ST NEOTS, continued

SHERINGHAM, Norfolk Map ref 3B1

★★ **BEAUMARIS HOTEL**

15 South Street, Sheringham, NR26 8LL
T: (01263) 822370
F: (01263) 821421
E: beauhotel@aol.com.
I: www.ecn.co.uk/beaumaris/

Bedrooms: 5 single, 10 double, 6 twin
Bathrooms: 21 en suite

Lunch available
EM 1900 (LO 2030)
Parking for 20
CC: Amex, Barclaycard, Delta, Diners, Eurocard, Mastercard, Solo, Switch, Visa, Visa Electron

B&B per night:
S £40.00–£45.00
D £80.00–£90.00

HB per person:
DY £55.00–£60.00

OPEN Mar–Dec

Family-run hotel established in 1947, with a reputation for personal service and English cuisine. Quietly located close to beach, shops and golf club.

50 ✲ ⚓ SP T

★★ **SOUTHLANDS HOTEL**

South Street, Sheringham, NR26 8LL
T: (01263) 822679
F: (01263) 822679

Bedrooms: 2 single, 9 double, 6 twin
Bathrooms: 17 en suite

Lunch available
EM 1845 (LO 2000)
Parking for 20
CC: Barclaycard, Mastercard, Visa

B&B per night:
S £33.00–£35.00
D £66.00–£70.00

HB per person:
DY £43.00–£45.00

OPEN Apr–Oct

Privately owned hotel ideally situated close to town, seafront and golf-courses.

120 ∪ ✲

★★

BALMORAL HOTEL
32-36 Valkyrie Road, Southend-on-Sea, Essex SS0 8BU
T: (01702) 342947
F: (01702) 337828
E: balmoralhotel@netscapeonline.co.uk

Bedrooms: 10 single, 13 double, 6 twin; suite available
Bathrooms: 29 en suite

Lunch available
EM 1830 (LO 2130)
Parking for 28
CC: Amex, Maestro, Mastercard, Solo, Switch, Visa, Visa Electron

B&B per night:
S £41.00–£49.00
D £65.00–£70.00

HB per person:
DY £51.00–£69.00

OPEN All year round

Highly appealing hotel, designer furnished. En suite rooms, excellent bar, restaurant, 24-hour service. Near station, buses, shops and sea. Secure parking.

🛂♿♨🛎📧📺♦🎣ⓘⓈ🐾📺◐🛏🚃🍽12 ❋ ♿ SP T

★★
Silver
Award

CAMELIA HOTEL AND RESTAURANT
178 Eastern Esplanade, Thorpe Bay, Southend-on-Sea, SS1 3AA
T: (01702) 587917
F: (01702) 585704
E: cameliahotel@fsbdial.co.uk
I: www.cameliahotel.com

B&B per night:
S £39.50–£65.00
D £60.00–£90.00

HB per person:
DY £42.50–£57.50

OPEN All year round

Well-appointed, family-run hotel in a quiet residential area on the seafront, with superb views of the Thames Estuary. All rooms are fully en suite. Our air conditioned restaurant offers an excellent variety of fine cuisine: table d'hote, extensive a la carte menus and specials of the day.

Bedrooms: 6 single, 12 double, 1 triple
Bathrooms: 19 en suite

Lunch available
EM 1830 (LO 2200)
Parking for 100
CC: Amex, Barclaycard, Delta, Diners, Eurocard, Mastercard, Solo, Switch, Visa, Visa Electron

🛂♿♨🛎📧📺♦🎣ⓘⓈ🍴♦🛏🚃🍽🐾 SP T ⊛

★★★

ROSLIN HOTEL
Thorpe Esplanade, Thorpe Bay, Southend-on-Sea, Essex SS1 3BG
T: (01702) 586375
F: (01702) 586663
I: www.roslinhotel.com

B&B per night:
S £36.00–£62.00
D £65.00–£80.00

HB per person:
DY £51.00–£68.00

OPEN All year round

On seafront in residential Thorpe Bay within easy reach of main town centre. Terrace, public rooms and many bedrooms overlook Estuary. First class restaurant open to non-residents. All rooms have full facilities, including tea/coffee-making, hairdryers, telephone, Sky TV.

Bedrooms: 14 single, 11 double, 9 twin, 4 triple, 1 family room
Bathrooms: 39 en suite

Lunch available
EM 1830 (LO 2200)
Parking for 34
CC: Amex, Barclaycard, Delta, Diners, Eurocard, Maestro, Mastercard, Solo, Switch, Visa, Visa Electron

🏧🛂♿♨🛎📧📺♦🎣ⓘⓈ🍴♦📺◐🛏🚃🍽30 ❋ SC 🐾 SP T

QUALITY ASSURANCE SCHEME

For an explanation of the quality and facilities represented by the Stars please refer to the front of this guide. A more detailed explanation can be found in the information pages at the back.

TIVETSHALL ST MARY, Norfolk Map ref 3B2

★★ Silver Award

THE OLD RAM COACHING INN

Ipswich Road, Tivetshall St Mary, Norwich, NR15 2DE
T: (01379) 676794
F: (01379) 608399
E: theoldram@btinternet.com
I: www.theoldram.com

B&B per night:
S £51.95–£51.95
D £70.90–£70.90

OPEN All year round

A warm welcome awaits you at this delightful 17thC coaching inn (15 miles south of Norwich). Recent refurbishments give the inn superb bedrooms, many with oak beams. Well known for its quality food. The public rooms are full of character with exposed beams and open log fires. A sheltered, flower-filled terrace restaurant is open for al fresco dining in summer.

Bedrooms: 10 double, 1 family room
Bathrooms: 11 en suite

Lunch available
EM 1700 (LO 2200)
Parking for 150
CC: Barclaycard, Delta, JCB, Mastercard, Solo, Switch, Visa, Visa Electron

WHITTLESFORD, Cambridgeshire Map ref 2D1

★

RED LION HOTEL

Station Road East, Whittlesford, Cambridge, CB2 4NL
T: (01223) 832047 & 832115
F: (01223) 837576

Bedrooms: 7 single, 6 double, 1 twin, 2 triple, 2 family rooms
Bathrooms: 18 en suite

Lunch available
EM 1900 (LO 2130)
Parking for 75
CC: Amex, Barclaycard, Delta, Mastercard, Solo, Switch, Visa

B&B per night:
S £37.00–£39.00
D £50.00–£54.00

OPEN All year round

Traditional 13thC English inn with modern facilities. Well situated for Cambridge with excellent road and rail connections. One mile from Duxford Imperial War Museum.

WOODBRIDGE, Suffolk Map ref 3C2 *Tourist Information Centre Tel: (01394) 382240*

★★★ Silver Award

SECKFORD HALL HOTEL

Woodbridge, IP13 6NU
T: (01394) 385678
F: (01394) 380610
E: reception@seckford.co.uk
I: www.seckford.co.uk

Bedrooms: 3 single, 14 double, 10 twin, 1 triple, 4 family rooms; suites available
Bathrooms: 32 en suite

Lunch available
EM 1915 (LO 2130)
Parking for 102
CC: Amex, Barclaycard, Delta, Diners, Eurocard, JCB, Mastercard, Switch, Visa

B&B per night:
S £79.00–£130.00
D £110.00–£165.00

OPEN All year round

Elizabethan country house hotel with 4-poster beds, spa baths, indoor heated swimming pool and 18-hole golf-course. Excellent cuisine in 2 restaurants.

WROXHAM, Norfolk Map ref 3C1

★★

HOTEL WROXHAM

The Bridge, Wroxham, Norwich, NR12 8AJ
T: (01603) 782061
F: (01603) 784279
I: www.smoothhound.co.uk/hotels/hotelwro.html

B&B per night:
D £65.00–£85.00

OPEN All year round

Minotel

On the banks of the River Bure in the capital of Broadland, only 7 miles from Norwich, this is a riverside oasis catering for both leisure and business visitors. Unique waterside terrace bar and restaurant, excellent wedding and conference facilities, riverside suites with balconies, private boat moorings, car parking.

Bedrooms: 1 single, 15 double, 2 twin
Bathrooms: 18 en suite

Lunch available
EM 1900 (LO 2130)
Parking for 60
CC: Amex, Barclaycard, Delta, Diners, Eurocard, JCB, Maestro, Mastercard, Solo, Switch, Visa, Visa Electron

CONFIRM YOUR BOOKING

You are advised to confirm your booking in writing.

★★

WYMONDHAM CONSORT HOTEL

28 Market Street, Wymondham,	Bedrooms: 5 single,	Lunch available	B&B per night:
NR18 0BB	9 double, 5 twin, 1 triple	EM 1900 (LO 2130)	S £55.00–£60.00
T: (01953) 606721	Bathrooms: 20 en suite	Parking for 16	D £60.00–£75.00
F: (01953) 601361		CC: Amex, Barclaycard,	
E: wymondham@bestwestern.co.		Delta, Diners, Eurocard,	HB per person:
uk		Mastercard, Switch, Visa,	DY Min £44.00
I: www.hotelnet.co.uk/wymondham		Visa Electron	

Award-winning hotel and restaurant in centre of historic market town, close to Norwich. Fully refurbished en suite rooms offering superb comfort. Private car park.

OPEN All year round

Best Western Hotels

COUNTRY CODE

Always follow the Country Code

Enjoy the countryside and respect its life and work

Guard against all risk of fire

Fasten all gates

Keep your dogs under close control

Keep to public paths across farmland

Use gates and stiles to cross fences, hedges and walls

Leave livestock, crops and machinery alone

Take your litter home

Help to keep all water clean

Protect wildlife, plants and trees

Take special care on country roads

Make no unnecessary noise

A brief guide to the main Towns and Villages offering accommodation in the EAST OF ENGLAND

A **ALDEBURGH, SUFFOLK** - A prosperous port in the 16th C, now famous for the Aldeburgh Music Festival held annually in June. The 16th C Moot Hall, now a museum, is a timber-framed building once used as an open market.

B **BASILDON, ESSEX** - One of the New Towns planned after World War II. It overlooks the estuary of the River Thames and is set in undulating countryside. The main feature is the town square with a traffic-free pedestrian concourse.

● **BLAKENEY, NORFOLK** - Picturesque village on the north coast of Norfolk and a former port and fishing village. Marshy creeks extend towards Blakeney Point (National Trust) and are a paradise for naturalists, with trips to the reserve and to see the seals from Blakeney Quay.

● **BRENTWOOD, ESSEX** - The town grew up in the late 12th C and then developed as a staging post, being strategically placed close to the London to Chelmsford road. Deer roam by the lakes in the 428 acre park at South Weald, part of Brentwood's attractive Green Belt.

● **BUNGAY, SUFFOLK** - Market town and yachting centre on the River Waveney with the remains of a great 12th C castle. In the market-place stands the Butter Cross, rebuilt in 1689 after being largely destroyed by fire. Nearby at Earsham the Otter Trust.

● **BURY ST EDMUNDS, SUFFOLK** - Ancient market and cathedral town which takes its name from the martyred Saxon King, St Edmund. Bury St Edmunds has many fine buildings including the Athenaeum and Moyses Hall, reputed to be the oldest Norman house in the county.

C **CAMBRIDGE, CAMBRIDGESHIRE** - A most important and beautiful city on the River Cam with 31 colleges forming one of the oldest universities in the world. Numerous museums, good shopping centre, restaurants, theatres, cinema and fine bookshops.

● **CHATTERIS, CAMBRIDGESHIRE** - A small market town in the heart of the Fens.

● **CHELMSFORD, ESSEX** - The county town of Essex, originally a Roman settlement, Caesaromagus, thought to have been destroyed by Boudicca. Growth of the town's industry can be traced in the excellent museum in Oaklands Park. 15th C parish church has been Chelmsford Cathedral since 1914.

● **CLACTON-ON-SEA, ESSEX** - Developed in the 1870s into a popular holiday resort with pier, pavilion, funfair, theatres and traditional amusements. The Martello Towers on the seafront were built like many others in the early 19th C to defend Britain against Napoleon.

● **COGGESHALL, ESSEX** - The National Trust property "Paycocke's" is at Coggeshall. It is a 16th century half-timbered merchant's house featuring a richly-carved interior.

● **COLCHESTER, ESSEX** - Britain's oldest recorded town standing on the River Colne and famous for its oysters. Numerous historic buildings, ancient remains and museums. Plenty of parks and gardens, extensive shopping centre, theatre and zoo.

● **CROMER, NORFOLK** - Once a small fishing village and now famous for its fishing boats that still work off the beach and offer freshly caught crabs. Excellent bathing on sandy beaches fringed by cliffs. The town boasts a fine pier, theatre, museum and a lifeboat station.

E **EYE, SUFFOLK** - "Eye" means island and this town was once surrounded by marsh. The fine church of SS Peter and Paul has a tower over 100ft high and a carving of the Archangel Gabriel can be seen on the 16th C Guildhall.

F **FELIXSTOWE, SUFFOLK** - Seaside resort that developed at the end of the 19th C. Lying in a gently curving bay with a 2-mile-long beach and backed by a wide promenade of lawns and floral gardens.

G **GREAT YARMOUTH, NORFOLK** - One of Britain's major seaside resorts with 5 miles of seafront and every possible amenity including an award winning leisure complex offering a huge variety of all-weather facilities. Busy harbour and fishing centre.

H **HARWICH, ESSEX** - Port where the Rivers Orwell and Stour converge and enter the North Sea. The old town still has a medieval atmosphere with its narrow streets. To the south is the seaside resort of Dovercourt with long sandy beaches.

● **HITCHIN, HERTFORDSHIRE** - Once a flourishing wool town. Full of interest, with many fine old buildings around the market square. These include the 17th C almshouses, old inns and the Victorian Corn Exchange.

● **HORNING, NORFOLK** - Riverside village and well-known Broadland centre. Occasional glimpses of the river can be caught between picturesque thatched cottages.

● **HUNTINGDON, CAMBRIDGESHIRE** - Attractive, interesting town which abounds in associations with the Cromwell family. The town is connected to Godmanchester by a beautiful 14th C bridge over the River Great Ouse.

I **IPSWICH, SUFFOLK** - Interesting county town and major port on the River Orwell. Birthplace of Cardinal Wolsey. Christchurch Mansion, set in a fine park, contains a good collection of furniture and pictures, with works by Gainsborough, Constable and Munnings.

K **KING'S LYNN, NORFOLK** - A busy town with many outstanding buildings. The Guildhall and Town Hall are both built of flint in a striking chequer design. Behind the Guildhall in the Old Gaol House the sounds and smells of prison life 2 centuries ago are recreated.

L **LEISTON, SUFFOLK** - Centrally placed for visiting the Suffolk Heritage Coast, Leiston is a bustling, working town in a rural setting famous for Leiston Abbey and the award winning Long Shop Museum.

● **LUTON, BEDFORDSHIRE** - Bedfordshire's largest town with its own airports several. industries and an excellent shopping centre. The town's history is depicted in the museum and art gallery in Wardown Park. Luton Hoo has a magnificent collection of treasures.

M **MALDON, ESSEX** - The Blackwater Estuary has made Maldon a natural base for yachtsmen. Boat-building is also an important industry. Numerous buildings of interest. The 13th C church of All Saints has the only triangular church tower in Britain. Also a museum and maritime centre.

● **MILDENHALL, SUFFOLK** - Town that has grown considerably in size in the last 20 years but still manages to retain a pleasant small country town centre. Mildenhall and District Museum deals with local history, particularly RAF Mildenhall and the Mildenhall Treasure.

N **NEWMARKET, SUFFOLK** - Centre of the English horse-racing world and the headquarters of the Jockey Club and National Stud. Racecourse and horse sales. The National Horse Racing Museum traces the history and development of the Sport of Kings.

● **NORTH WALSHAM, NORFOLK** - Weekly market has been held here for 700 years. 1 mile south of town is a cross commemorating the Peasants' Revolt of 1381. Nelson attended the local Paston Grammar School, founded in 1606 and still flourishing.

● **NORWICH, NORFOLK** - Beautiful cathedral city and county town on the River Wensum with many fine museums and medieval churches. Norman castle, Guildhall and interesting medieval streets. Good shopping centre and market.

P **PETERBOROUGH, CAMBRIDGESHIRE** - Prosperous and rapidly expanding cathedral city on the edge of the Fens on the River Nene. Catherine of Aragon is buried in the cathedral. City Museum and Art Gallery. Ferry Meadows Country Park has numerous leisure facilities.

S **ST ALBANS, HERTFORDSHIRE** - As Verulamium this was one of the largest towns in Roman Britain and its remains can be seen in the museum. The Norman cathedral was built from Roman materials to commemorate Alban, the first British Christian martyr.

- **ST IVES, CAMBRIDGESHIRE** - Picturesque market town with a narrow 6-arched bridge spanning the River Ouse on which stands a bridge chapel. There are numerous Georgian and Victorian buildings and the Norris Museum has a good local collection.

- **ST NEOTS, CAMBRIDGESHIRE** – Pleasant market town on the River Ouse with a large sqaure which grew up around a 10th C priory. There are many interesting buildings and St Mary's is one of the largest medieval churches in the country.

- **SHERINGHAM, NORFOLK** - Holiday resort with Victorian and Edwardian hotels and a sand and shingle beach where the fishing boats are hauled up. The North Norfolk Railway operates from Sheringham station during the summer. Other attractions include museums, theatre and Splash Fun Pool.

- **SOUTHEND-ON-SEA, ESSEX** - On the Thames Estuary and the nearest seaside resort to London. Famous for its pier and unique pier trains. Other attractions include Peter Pan's Playground, indoor swimming pools, indoor rollerskating and ten pin bowling.

- **TIVETSHALL ST MARY, NORFOLK** - Conveniently located on the A140 for access to Norwich.

- **WHITTLESFORD, CAMBRIDGESHIRE** - Pleasant village with a 15th C church with interesting carvings. Restored 16th C half-timbered guildhall. Close to the world famous Imperial War Museum at Duxford.

- **WOODBRIDGE, SUFFOLK** - Once a busy seaport, the town is now a sailing centre on the River Deben. There are many buildings of architectural merit including the Bell and Angel Inns. The 18th C Tide Mill is now restored and open to the public.

- **WROXHAM, NORFOLK** - Yachting centre on the River Bure which houses the headquarters of the Norfolk Broads Yacht Club. The church of St Mary has a famous doorway and the manor house nearby dates back to 1623.

- **WYMONDHAM, NORFOLK** - Thriving historic market town of charm and architectural interest. The octagonal market cross, 12th C abbey and 15th C Green Dragon inn blend with streetscapes spanning three centuries. An excellent touring base.

www.travelengland.org.uk

Log on to travelengland.org.uk and discover something different around every corner. Meander through pages for ideas of places to visit and things to do. Spend time in each region and discover the diversity – from busy vibrant cities to rural village greens; rugged peaks to gentle rolling hills; dramatic coastline to idyllic sandy beaches. England might be a small country but it is brimming with choice and opportunity. Visit www.travelengland.org.uk and see for yourself.

England

SOUTH WEST

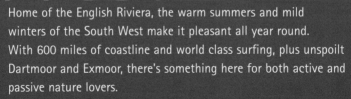

Home of the English Riviera, the warm summers and mild winters of the South West make it pleasant all year round. With 600 miles of coastline and world class surfing, plus unspoilt Dartmoor and Exmoor, there's something here for both active and passive nature lovers.

Step back 2000 year's in Bath's Roman Baths. Other great cities include Bristol, Plymouth and Wells. Clovelly, with its cobbled, car-free streets, and the little fishing village of Mousehole (which really is the cat's whiskers!) are just two of the many quaint places to visit.

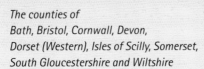

The two-week Bath International Music Festival is on from mid May with something for everyone — from contemporary to classical, including jazz and more.

The counties of
Bath, Bristol, Cornwall, Devon,
Dorset (Western), Isles of Scilly, Somerset,
South Gloucestershire and Wiltshire

FOR MORE INFORMATION CONTACT:
South West Tourism
Admail 3186, Exeter EX2 7WH
Tel: (0870) 442 0880
Fax: (0870) 442 0881
Email: info@westcountryholidays.com
Internet: www.westcountryholidays.com

The Pictures:
1   Isles of Scilly;
2   Fingle Bridge, Dartmoor, Devon;
3   Cotehele, Cornwall.

Where to Go in the South West - see pages 210-214
Where to Stay in the South West - see pages 215-248

Whilst in the
SOUTH WEST ...

You will find hundreds of interesting places to visit during your stay, just some of which are listed in these pages.

Contact any Tourist Information Centre in the region for more ideas on days out in the South West.

At Bristol Harbourside

Bristol BS1 5DB

A new international, waterfront, leisure, education and entertainment complex. Including two visitor attractions — Wildscreen@Bristol, featuring wildlife and the environment, and Explore@Bristol, focusing on science and technology.

Atwell-Wilson Motor Museum Trust

Calne, Wiltshire SN11 0NF
Tel: (01249) 813119

Motor museum with vintage, post-vintage and classic cars, including American models. Classic motorbikes. A 17thC water meadow walk and play area.

Babbacombe Model Village

Babbacombe, Devon TQ1 3LA
Tel: (01803) 315315

Over 400 models many with sound and animation in four acres of award-winning gardens. See modern towns, villages and rural areas. Stunning illuminations.

Bristol City Museum & Art Gallery

Queen's Road, Bristol BS8 1RL
Tel: (0117) 922 3571

Collection representing applied, oriental and fine art, archaeology, geology, natural history, ethnography and Egyptology.

Bristol Zoo Gardens

Clifton, Bristol BS8 3HA
Tel: (0117) 973 8951

Enjoy an exciting real life experience and see over 300 species of wildlife in beautiful gardens.

Buckland Abbey

Yelverton, Devon PL20 6EY
Tel: (01822) 853607

Originally a Cistercian monastery, then home of Sir Francis Drake. Ancient buildings, exhibitions, herb garden, craft workshops and estate walks.

Cheddar Caves and Gorge

Cheddar, Somerset BS27 3QF
Tel: (01934) 742343

Beautiful caves located in Cheddar Gorge. Gough's Cave with cathedral-like caverns and Cox's Cave with stalagmites and stalactites. Also 'The Crystal Quest' fantasy adventure.

The Combe Martin Motor Cycle Collection

Combe Martin, Ilfracombe, Devon EX34 0DH
Tel: (01271) 882346

Collection of British motorcycles displayed against a background of old petrol pumps, signs and garage equipment. Motoring nostalgia in an old world atmosphere.

Combe Martin Wildlife and Dinosaur Park

Combe Martin, Ilfracombe, Devon EX34 0NG
Tel: (01271) 882486

Wildlife park and life-size models of dinosaurs.

International Animal Rescue Animal Tracks

Ash Mill, South Molton, Devon EX36 4QW
Tel: (01769) 550277
A 60-acre animal sanctuary with a wide range of rescued animals from monkeys to chinchillas. Shire horses and ponies. Also rare plant nursery.

Crealy Park

Clyst St Mary, Exeter, Devon EX5 1DR
Tel: (01395) 233200
One of Devon's largest animal farms. Milk a cow, feed a lamb and pick up a piglet. Adventure playgrounds. Dragonfly Lake and farm trails.

Dairyland Farm World

Tresillian, Barton, Newquay, Cornwall TR8 5AA
Tel: (01872) 510246
One hundred and seventy cows milked in a rotary parlour. Heritage centre. Farm nature trail. Farm park with animals, pets and wildfowl. Daily events.

Exmoor Falconry & Animal Farm

West Lynch Farm, Allerford, Somerset TA24 8HJ
Tel: (01643) 862816
Farm animals, rare breeds, pets' corner, birds of prey and owls. Flying displays daily. Historic farm buildings.

Flambards Village

Culdrose Manor, Helston, Cornwall TR13 0QA
Tel: (01326) 573404
Life-size Victorian village with fully stocked shops, carriages and fashions. 'Britain in the Blitz' life-size wartime street, historic aircraft. Exploratorium.

Heale Garden & Plant Centre

Middle Woodford, Salisbury, Wiltshire SP4 6NT
Tel: (01722) 782504
Mature, traditional garden with shrubs, musk and other roses, plus kitchen garden. Authentic Japanese teahouse in water garden. Magnolias. Snowdrops and aconites in winter.

Jamaica Inn Museums (Potters Museum of Curiosity)

Bolventor, Launceston, Cornwall PL15 7TS
Tel: (01566) 86838
Museums contain lifetime work of Walter Potter, a Victorian taxidermist. Exhibits include Kittens' Wedding, Death of Cock Robin and The Story of Smuggling.

Longleat

Warminster, Wiltshire BA12 7NW
Tel: (01985) 844400
Great Elizabethan house with lived-in atmosphere. Important libraries and Italian ceilings. 'Capability' Brown designed parkland. Safari Park.

The Lost Gardens of Heligan

Heligan, Pentewan, St Austell, Cornwall PL26 6EN
Tel: (01726) 845100
The largest garden restoration project undertaken since the war. New for 2000: The Lost Valley, covering 35 acres.

Lyme Regis Philpot Museum

Lyme Regis, Dorset DT7 3QA
Tel: (01297) 443370
Fossils, geology, local history and lace exhibitions. Museum shop.

The Pictures:
1 Selworthy, Somerset;
2 The interior of Salisbury Cathedral;
3 Land's End, Cornwall;
4 Wells Cathedral, Somerset;
5 Clifton Suspension Bridge, Bristol.

National Marine Aquarium

Plymouth, Devon PL4 0LF
Tel: (01752) 600301
The UK's only world-class aquarium. Visitor experiences include a mountain stream and Caribbean reef complete with sharks.

Paignton Zoo Environmental Park

Paignton, Devon TQ4 7EU
Tel: (01803) 557479
One of England's largest zoos with over 1200 animals in the beautiful setting of 75 acres of botanical gardens. A popular family day out.

Plant World

Newton Abbot, Devon TQ12 4SE
Tel: (01803) 872939
Four acres of gardens including the unique 'map of the world' gardens. Cottage garden. Panoramic views. Comprehensive nursery of rare and more unusual plants.

Plymouth Dome

The Hoe, Plymouth, Devon PL1 2NZ
Tel: (01752) 603300
Purpose-built visitor interpretation centre showing the history of Plymouth and its people from Stone Age beginnings to satellite technology.

Powderham Castle

Kenton, Exeter, Devon EX6 8JQ
Tel: (01626) 890243
Built in 1390 and restored in 18thC. Georgian interiors, china, furnishings and paintings. Family home of the Courtenays for over 600 years. Fine views across the deer park and River Exe.

Quaywest

Goodrington Sands, Paignton, Devon TQ4 6LN
Tel: (01803) 555550
Wettest and wildest fun at this outdoor waterpark. Eight flumes. Adult and children's swimming pool with water heated to 26°C. Grand-Prix go karts, amusement rides, bumper boats and crazy golf.

Railway Village Museum

Swindon, Wiltshire SN1 5BJ
Tel: (01793) 466555
Foreman's house in original Great Western Railway village. Furnished to re-create a Victorian working-class home.

Roman Baths Museum

Abbey Church Yard, Bath BA1 1LZ
Tel: (01225) 477785
Roman baths, hot springs and Roman temple. Jewellery, coins, curses and votive offerings from the sacred spring.

St Michael's Mount

Marazion, Cornwall TR17 0HT
Tel: (01736) 710507
Originally the site of a Benedictine chapel, the castle on its rock dates from 14thC. Fine views towards Land's End and the Lizard. Reached by foot, or ferry at high tide in the summer.

Steam – Museum of the Great Western Railway

Swindon, Wiltshire
Tel: (01793) 466646
Historic Great Western Railway locomotives, wide range of nameplates, models, illustrations, posters and tickets.

Stourhead House and Garden

Stourton, Warminster, Wiltshire BA12 6QH
Tel: (01747) 841152
Landscaped garden laid out in 1741-1780, with lakes, temples, rare trees and plants. The house, begun in 1721 by Colen Campbell, contains fine paintings and Chippendale furniture.

Tate Gallery St Ives

Porthmeor Beach, St Ives, Cornwall TR26 1TG
Tel: (01736) 796226
Opened in 1993 and offering a unique introduction to modern art. Changing displays focus on the modern movement St Ives is famous for.

Teignmouth Museum

French Street, Teignmouth, Devon TQ14 8ST

Tel: (01626) 777041

Exhibits include 16thC cannon and artefacts from Armada wreck and local history, 1920s pier machines and 1877 cannon.

The Time Machine

Weston-super-Mare, North Somerset BS23 1PR

Tel: (01934) 621028

Edwardian gaslight company building with central glazed courtyard. Seaside gallery, costume, Victorian cottage. Doll collection, local archaeology and natural history. Art gallery, people's collection.

Tintagel Castle

Tintagel, Cornwall PL34 0HE

Tel: (01840) 770328

Medieval ruined castle on wild, wind-swept coast. Famous for associations with Arthurian legend. Built largely in 13thC by Richard, Earl of Cornwall. Used as a prison in 14thC.

Tithe Barn Children's Farm

New Barn Road, Abbotsbury, Dorset DT3 4JF

Tel: (01305) 871817

Extensive children's farm for children under 11 years. Activities include hand-feeding milk to lambs and kids by bottle. Replicas of Terracotta Warriors on display in barn.

Totnes Costume Museum – Devonshire Collection of Period Costume

High Street, Totnes, Devon TQ9 5NP

Tel: (01803) 863821

New exhibition of costumes and accessories each season, displayed in one of the historic merchant's houses of Totnes.

Underground Passages

Exeter, Devon EX4 3PZ

Tel: (01392) 265887

Remarkable city passageways built during medieval times to carry water into the city centre. Now the only one's in Britain open to the public. Exhibition, video and guided tour.

West Somerset Railway

Minehead, Somerset TA24 5BG

Tel: (01643) 704996

Preserved steam railway operating between Minehead and Bishops Lydeard, near Taunton. Model railway and museums enroute. Longest independent railway in Britain, 32 km (20 miles).

Woodlands Leisure Park

Blackawton, Totnes, Devon TQ9 7DQ

Tel: (01803) 712598

A full day of variety set in 60 acres of countryside. Twelve venture playzones including 500-metre (1,640 ft) toboggan run, commando course, large indoor play area, toddlers' area and animals.

Wookey Hole Caves and Papermill

Wookey Hole, Wells, Somerset BA5 1BB

Tel: (01749) 672243

Spectacular caves and legendary home of the Witch of Wookey. Working Victorian papermill including Old Penny Arcade, Magical Mirror Maze and Cave Diving Museum.

The Pictures:
1 Dartmoor Ponies;
2 Torquay, Devon;
3 Bath;
4 Tarr Steps, Exmoor
   National Park;
5 Sunset at Stonehenge;
6 Shaftesbury Hill,
   Dorset;
7 Salisbury Cathedral,
   Wiltshire.

Find out more about the
SOUTH WEST ...

Further information about holidays and attractions
in the South West is available from:

SOUTH WEST TOURISM
Admail 3186, Exeter EX2 7WH.

Tel: (0870) 442 0880

Fax: (0870) 442 0881

Email: info@westcountryholidays.com

Internet: www.westcountryholidays.com

The following publications are available free from South West Tourism:

Bed & Breakfast Touring Map

West Country Holiday Homes & Apartments

West Country Hotels and Guesthouses

Glorious Gardens of the West Country

Camping and Caravan Touring Map

Tourist Attractions Touring Map

Trencherman's West Country, Restaurant Guide

The Pictures:
1 Stonehenge;
2 Newquay, Cornwall.

Getting to the
SOUTH WEST ...

BY ROAD: Somerset, Devon and Cornwall are well served from the North and Midlands by the M6/M5 which extends just beyond Exeter, where it links in with the dual carriageways of the A38 to Plymouth, A380 to Torbay and the A30 into Cornwall. The North Devon Link Road A361 joins Junction 37 with the coast of north Devon and A39, which then becomes the Atlantic Highway into Cornwall.

BY RAIL: The main towns in the South West are served throughout the year by fast, direct and frequent rail services from all over the country. InterCity 125 trains operate from London (Paddington) to Chippenham, Swindon, Bath, Bristol, Weston-super-Mare, Taunton, Exeter, Plymouth and Penzance, and also from Scotland, the North East and the Midlands to the South West. A service runs from London (Waterloo) to Exeter, via Salisbury, Yeovil and Crewkerne. Sleeper services operate between Devon and Cornwall and London as well as between Bristol and Glasgow and Edinburgh. Motorail services operate from strategic points to key South West locations.

Where to stay in the
SOUTH WEST

Accommodation entries in this region are listed in alphabetical order of place name, and then in alphabetical order of establishment.

Map references refer to the colour location maps at the front of this guide. The first number indicates the map to use; the letter and number which follow refer to the grid reference on the map.

At-a-glance symbols at the end of each accommodation entry give useful information about services and facilities. A key to symbols can be found inside the back cover flap. Keep this open for easy reference.

A brief description of the towns and villages offering accommodation in the entries which follow, can be found at the end of this section.

A complete listing of all English Tourism Council assessed hotels appears at the back of this guide.

BADMINTON, South Gloucestershire Map ref 2B2

★★★ **PETTY FRANCE HOTEL**

A46, Dunkirk, Badminton, GL9 1AF	Bedrooms: 2 single,	Lunch available	B&B per night:
T: (01454) 238361	12 double, 5 twin,	EM 1900 (LO 2130)	S £69.00–£99.00
F: (01454) 238768	1 triple	Parking for 91	D £89.00–£125.00
E: hotel@pettyfrance.telme.com	Bathrooms: 20 en suite	CC: Amex, Barclaycard,	
I: ds.dial.pipex.com/pettyfrance/		Diners, Mastercard,	HB per person:
		Switch, Visa	DY £59.00–£79.00

Informal country house atmosphere on the edge of the Cotswolds. Good walking, many sights to visit, convenient for Bath and Bristol.

OPEN All year round

❶❷❸❹❺❻❼❽❾❿50 ⟳ ✶ SC ⬚ SP ⌂ T ❖

TOWN INDEX

This can be found at the back of the guide. If you know where you want to stay, the index will give you the page number listing accommodation in your chosen town, city or village.

★★
Silver
Award

HARINGTONS HOTEL

8-10 Queen Street, Bath, BA1 1HE
T: (01225) 461728
F: (01225) 444804
E: post@haringtonshotel.co.uk
I: www.haringtonshotel.co.uk

B&B per night:
S £65.00–£88.00
D £88.00–£108.00

OPEN All year round

Charming hotel set in a picturesque cobbled street in the heart of Bath, just minutes from all major attractions, theatre and premier shopping. The coffee lounge and bar are open throughout the day and evening and you can enjoy a leisurely, delicious breakfast until 10am. Delightful bedrooms with cable TV.

Bedrooms: 1 single,
9 double, 1 twin, 2 triple
Bathrooms: 13 en suite

Lunch available
EM 1800 (LO 2000)
CC: Amex, Barclaycard,
Delta, Diners, Eurocard,
JCB, Maestro, Mastercard,
Solo, Switch, Visa, Visa
Electron

★★★★
Gold
Award

LUCKNAM PARK
Colerne, Chippenham, Wiltshire
SN14 8AZ
T: (01225) 742777
F: (01225) 743536
E: reservations@lucknampark.co.uk
I: www.lucknampark.co.uk

Bedrooms: 1 single,
18 double, 22 twin;
suites available
Bathrooms: 41 en suite

Lunch available
EM 1900 (LO 2200)
Parking for 70
CC: Amex, Barclaycard,
Delta, Diners, Mastercard,
Switch, Visa

B&B per night:
S Min £150.00
D £190.00–£670.00

HB per person:
DY £135.00–£375.00

OPEN All year round

Magnificent Georgian country house with extensive leisure, spa and equestrian facilities, in 500 acres of parkland 7 miles from Bath. Prices per room. (HB minimum 2 nights).

★★

OLD MALT HOUSE HOTEL

Radford, Timsbury, Bath, BA3 1QF
T: (01761) 470106
F: (01761) 472726
E: hotel@oldmalthouse.co.uk
I: www.oldmalthouse.co.uk

B&B per night:
S £30.00–£39.00
D £60.00–£78.00

HB per person:
DY £54.50–£56.00

OPEN All year round

Minotel

Between Bath and Wells in beautiful countryside. Ideally situated for exploring Bath, Wells, Bristol, Mendips, Somerset. Built in 1835 as a malt house, now a hotel with comfort and character. Owned and run by same family for over 25 years. Log fires, extensive menus, bar. Well appointed bedrooms (ground floor rooms available).

Bedrooms: 1 single,
4 double, 5 twin, 2 triple
Bathrooms: 12 en suite

EM 1900 (LO 2030)
Parking for 40
CC: Amex, Barclaycard,
Diners, Mastercard,
Switch, Visa

CHECK THE MAPS

The colour maps at the front of this guide show all the cities, towns and villages for which you will find accommodation entries. Refer to the town index to find the page on which they are listed.

★★
Silver
Award

THE OLD MILL HOTEL
Tollbridge Road, Batheaston, Bath,
BA1 7DE
T: (01225) 858576
F: (01225) 852600
E: oldmill@batheaston1.freeserve.co.uk
I: www.pr-inns.freeserve.co.uk

B&B per night:
S £49.00–£69.00
D £65.00–£95.00

HB per person:
DY £55.00–£59.00

OPEN All year round

*Riverside hotel with breathtaking
views, 1.5 miles from centre of Bath.
Unique water wheel restaurant. Most
rooms have river views and all were
recently delightfully refurbished.
Specialises in short breaks
throughout the year. Own fishing
rights, local golfing arrangements.
Free car parking.*

Bedrooms: 1 single,
19 double, 4 twin,
1 triple, 2 family rooms
Bathrooms: 26 private,
1 private shower

EM 1800 (LO 2200)
Parking for 40
CC: Amex, Delta,
Mastercard, Switch, Visa

Rating
Applied For

RUDLOE HALL HOTEL
Leafy Lane, Box, Corsham, Wiltshire
SN13 0PA
T: (01225) 810555
F: (01225) 811412
E: mail@rudloehall.co.uk
I: www.rudloehall.co.uk

B&B per night:
S £72.00–£102.00
D £92.00–£212.00

HB per person:
DY £92.00–£122.00

OPEN All year round

*Unlike an hotel, a delightful period
Victorian mansion, so cosy to come
home to. Many rooms with 4-poster
beds, real open fires and Victorian
bathing alcoves. Dine by candle and
fire light. Fresh home-cooked foods,
lovely wines. Tranquil beauty spot
with stunning views to Bath. Acres of
Victorian gardens and woodland.*

Bedrooms: 11 double
Bathrooms: 11 en suite

Lunch available
EM 1900 (LO 2130)
Parking for 70
CC: Amex, Barclaycard,
Delta, Diners, Eurocard,
Mastercard, Switch, Visa

★★
Silver
Award

THE HENLEY HOTEL
Folly Hill, Bigbury-on-Sea,
Kingsbridge, TQ7 4AR
T: (01548) 810240
F: (01548) 810240

Bedrooms: 3 double,
2 twin, 1 triple
Bathrooms: 6 en suite

Lunch available
EM 1900 (LO 2000)
Parking for 10
CC: Amex, Barclaycard,
Eurocard, Mastercard,
Visa

B&B per night:
S £33.00–£50.00
D £66.00–£80.00

HB per person:
DY £53.00–£55.00

OPEN Apr–Nov

*Small, comfortable hotel on the edge of the sea. Spectacular views with private steps
through garden down to lovely beach. A non-smoking establishment.*

★★★
Silver
Award

EDGEMOOR HOTEL
Haytor Road, Lowerdown Cross,
Bovey Tracey, TQ13 9LE
T: (01626) 832466
F: (01626) 834760
E: edgemoor@btinternet.com
I: www.edgemoor.co.uk

B&B per night:
S £54.50–£60.00
D £80.00–£110.00

OPEN All year round

*Situated in a wonderful position for
touring the area, being literally
adjacent to Dartmoor National Park,
yet only 2 miles from the A38. Many
National Trust properties and places
of interest are within easy driving
distance. All rooms en suite. Good
Food. Elegance without pretension.*

Bedrooms: 3 single,
9 double, 3 twin, 1 triple,
1 family room
Bathrooms: 17 en suite

Lunch available
EM 1900 (LO 2100)
Parking for 50
CC: Amex, Barclaycard,
Delta, Eurocard, JCB,
Mastercard, Switch, Visa,
Visa Electron

★★

FRIARN COURT HOTEL

37 St Mary Street, Bridgwater,	Bedrooms: 2 single,	Lunch available	B&B per night:
TA6 3LX	7 double, 6 twin	EM 1900 (LO 2100)	S £39.90–£59.90
T: (01278) 452859	Bathrooms: 15 en suite	Parking for 14	D £50.00–£69.90
F: (01278) 452988		CC: Amex, Barclaycard,	
		Diners, Eurocard, JCB,	OPEN All year round
		Mastercard, Solo, Switch,	
		Visa, Visa Electron	

Comfortable, friendly hotel with restaurant and cosy bar, ideal base for business or pleasure. Double price is for special weekend breaks. Colour brochure.

ⓐⓑⓒⓓⓔⓕⓖⓗⓘ80 SP ⓩ T

★★★

HADDON HOUSE HOTEL
West Bay, Bridport, DT6 4EL
T: (01308) 423626 & 425323
F: (01308) 427348

B&B per night:
D £60.00–£90.00

OPEN All year round

Country hotel 300 yards from picturesque harbour, coast and golf course. Breathtaking views of Lyme Bay and Chesil Beach. All bedrooms refurbished to a very high standard and of good size. Restaurant renowned for cuisine. Well situated for touring Dorset, Devon and Somerset.

Bedrooms: 6 double,	Lunch available	
4 twin, 2 triple	EM 1900 (LO 2100)	
Bathrooms: 12 en suite	Parking for 44	
	CC: Amex, Barclaycard,	
	Diners, Mastercard,	
	Switch, Visa	

ⓐⓑⓒⓓⓔⓕⓖⓗ40 ⓤⓥⓦ SP ⓩ T

★★
Silver
Award

ROUNDHAM HOUSE HOTEL
Roundham Gardens, West Bay Road,
Bridport, DT6 4BD
T: (01308) 422753
F: (01308) 421500

B&B per night:
S £30.00–£40.00
D £60.00–£80.00

HB per person:
DY Min £48.50

OPEN Mar–Dec

An Edwardian country-house hotel set in an acre of cultivated gardens on elevated ground overlooking the rolling West Dorset hills, the majestic coastline and the sea. Many awards for quality and cuisine. Spacious en suite bedrooms with glorious views, 10 minutes' walk to the sea.

Bedrooms: 1 single,	EM 1900 (LO 2030)
3 double, 2 twin,	Parking for 12
2 family rooms	CC: Barclaycard, JCB,
Bathrooms: 7 en suite,	Mastercard, Visa
1 private	

ⓐⓑⓒⓓⓔⓕⓖⓗ SP T ⓩ

COUNTRY CODE Always follow the Country Code 🌳 Enjoy the countryside and respect its life and work 🌳 Guard against all risk of fire 🌳 Fasten all gates 🌳 Keep your dogs under close control 🌳 Keep to public paths across farmland 🌳 Use gates and stiles to cross fences, hedges and walls 🌳 Leave livestock, crops and machinery alone 🌳 Take your litter home 🌳 Help to keep all water clean 🌳 Protect wildlife, plants and trees 🌳 Take special care on country roads 🌳 Make no unnecessary noise

BRISTOL, Map ref 2A2 *Tourist Information Centre Tel: (0117) 926 0767 or (01275) 474444 (airport)*

★★

COURTLANDS HOTEL
1 Redland Court Road, Redland, Bristol, BS6 7EE
T: (0117) 9424432
F: (0117) 9232432

B&B per night:
S Min £52.00
D Min £62.00

OPEN All year round

This very comfortable family-run hotel is centrally located in a quiet residential area, overlooking tree-lined Victorian gardens. All bedrooms are well appointed and are decorated to a high standard. Our private restaurant offers freshly prepared dishes in a friendly atmosphere and has won a 'Food Hygiene Award' every year since 1985.

Bedrooms: 5 single,
11 double, 4 twin,
3 triple, 2 family rooms
Bathrooms: 25 en suite

Lunch available
EM 1900 (LO 2000)
Parking for 15
CC: Amex, Barclaycard,
Delta, Eurocard,
Mastercard, Switch, Visa

★★★

HENBURY LODGE HOTEL
Station Road, Henbury, Bristol,
BS10 7QQ
T: (0117) 950 2615
F: (0117) 950 9532

Bedrooms: 1 single,
14 double, 2 twin,
4 triple
Bathrooms: 21 en suite,
1 public

Lunch available
EM 1900 (LO 2130)
Parking for 24
CC: Amex, Barclaycard,
Delta, Diners, Mastercard,
Solo, Switch, Visa

B&B per night:
S £46.00–£89.50
D £72.00–£99.50

HB per person:
DY £60.00–£102.00

One mile from junction 17 off M5, 15 minutes' drive from city centre. Local interest includes Blaise Castle and Blaise Hamlet. Various special diets catered for.

OPEN All year round

★★★

JARVIS GRANGE HOTEL AND COUNTRY CLUB
Northwoods, Winterbourne, Bristol,
BS36 1RP
T: (01454) 777333
F: (01454) 777447
I: www.jarvis.co.uk

Bedrooms: 2 single,
56 double, 10 twin
Bathrooms: 68 en suite

Lunch available
EM 1900 (LO 2145)
Parking for 100
CC: Amex, Barclaycard,
Delta, Diners, Eurocard,
Mastercard, Switch, Visa

B&B per night:
S £45.00–£125.00
D £70.00–£140.00

HB per person:
DY £57.50–£82.50

Recently refurbished hotel in a peaceful rural setting. 10 miles north of Bristol and 20 minutes from Bath. All bedrooms en suite. Facilities include health and leisure club.

OPEN All year round

Ⓒ
Jarvis Hotels/Utell
International

★★

THE OLD BOWL INN AND LILIES RESTAURANT
16 Church Road, Lower Almondsbury,
Almondsbury, Bristol, BS32 4DT
T: (01454) 612757
F: (01454) 619910
E: thebowl@3wa.co.uk

B&B per night:
S £35.00–£79.50
D £58.00–£99.50

OPEN All year round

We invite you to enjoy the best of the past and the present in this historic and well established village inn. Whether travelling on business or just taking a leisurely break, you will find all the comforts of modern life housed in 16thC surroundings. Five minutes from M4/M5 interchange.

Bedrooms: 10 double,
3 twin
Bathrooms: 13 en suite

Lunch available
EM 1830 (LO 2200)
Parking for 40
CC: Amex, Barclaycard,
Delta, Diners, Eurocard,
Maestro, Mastercard,
Solo, Switch, Visa, Visa
Electron

RATING All accommodation in this guide has been rated, or is awaiting a rating, by a trained English Tourism Council assessor.

BRISTOL continued

Rating Applied For	THISTLE BRISTOL			
Ad p15	Broad Street, Bristol, BS1 2EL T: (0117) 929 1645 F: (0117) 922 7619 E: bristol@thistle.co.uk	Bedrooms: 37 single, 54 double, 91 twin Bathrooms: 182 en suite	Lunch available EM 1800 (LO 2200) Parking for 380 CC: Amex, Barclaycard, Delta, Diners, Eurocard, JCB, Mastercard, Switch, Visa	B&B per night: S £128.00–£132.00 D £141.00–£165.00 OPEN All year round ⓒⓡ Thistle Hotels

Situated in the heart of Bristol, the Thistle Bristol is a superb Victorian hotel with modern facilities. Within two minutes of "@ Bristol", the city's largest convention centre.

⅏🏱✆🗐☐♨♟🛈⑤⊬🅜◑⊞⪒⚑⌖600 ⚓ SP 🆃⊛

★★★

THE TOWN AND COUNTRY LODGE
A38 Bridgwater Road, Bristol, BS13 8AG
T: (01275) 392441
F: (01275) 393362
E: reservations@tclodge.co.uk
I: www.tclodge.co.uk

B&B per night:
S £44.00–£57.50
D £54.00–£74.50

HB per person:
DY £55.00–£64.50

OPEN All year round

ⓒⓡ
The Independents

Highly comfortable hotel offering genuine value for money. Splendid rural location on the A38 but only 3 miles central Bristol and handy for airport, Bath, Weston and all major local attractions. Excellent restaurant offering international cuisine with a la carte and set menus. Ideal for functions, wedding receptions and conferences.

| | Bedrooms: 10 single,
12 double, 10 twin,
4 triple; suites available
Bathrooms: 36 en suite | Lunch available
EM 1800 (LO 2230)
Parking for 300
CC: Amex, Barclaycard,
Delta, Diners, Mastercard,
JCB, Maestro, Solo, Switch, Visa, Visa Electron | |

Ⓜ⅏♿🏱✆🗐☐♨♟🛈⑤⊬🅜🆃🅥◑⊞🖶⊜⪒⌖100🏱✵⚓SP🆃

BRIXHAM, Devon Map ref 1D2 *Tourist Information Centre Tel: 0906 680 1268 (calls cost 25p per minute)*

★★★ | **THE BERRY HEAD HOTEL** | | | |
|---|---|---|---|
| | Berry Head Road, Brixham, Devon
TQ5 9AJ
T: (01803) 853225
F: (01803) 882084
E: berryhd@aol.com
I: www.scoot.co.uk/
berry-head-hotel | Bedrooms: 3 single,
13 double, 9 twin,
7 family rooms
Bathrooms: 32 en suite | Lunch available
EM 1900 (LO 2130)
Parking for 202
CC: Amex, Barclaycard,
Delta, Eurocard,
Mastercard, Switch, Visa | B&B per night:
S £40.00–£62.00
D £80.00–£124.00

HB per person:
DY £50.00–£75.00

OPEN All year round |

Steeped in history, nestling on water's edge in 6 acres of grounds and in an Area of Outstanding Natural Beauty. Heated indoor swimming pool.

Ⓜ⅏🏱✆🗐☐♨♟🛈⑤⊬🅜🆃🅥◑⪒⌖250♟⟲🏱✵⚓SP🆃

BUDE, Cornwall Map ref 1C2 *Tourist Information Centre Tel: (01288) 354240*

★★★

THE FALCON HOTEL
Breakwater Road, Bude, EX23 8SD
T: (01288) 352005
F: (01288) 356359

B&B per night:
S £40.00–£42.00
D £80.00–£84.00

HB per person:
DY £54.00–£56.00

OPEN All year round

Elegant Georgian hotel in a beautiful position overlooking the historic Bude Canal. Surrounded by many lovely scenic walks and 2 minutes away from the shops and sandy beaches. Well-appointed bedrooms with luxurious bathrooms, TVs with Teletext and Sky. Superb restaurant and bar meals. Private walled gardens, mini gymnasium.

| | Bedrooms: 6 single,
15 double, 5 twin; suites
available
Bathrooms: 26 en suite | Lunch available
EM 1900 (LO 2100)
Parking for 40
CC: Amex, Barclaycard,
Delta, Diners, Eurocard,
Mastercard, Solo, Switch,
Visa | |

Ⓜ⅏🏱✆🗐☐♨♟🛈⑤⊬🅜⠇⊜⪒⌖250⌖⟲🏱✵🚚⚓SP♿🆃

WHERE TO STAY
Please mention this guide when making your booking.

★★★

LORDLEAZE HOTEL

Henderson Drive, Off Forton Road, Chard, TA20 2HW

T: (01460) 61066
F: (01460) 66468
E: lordleaze@fsbdial.co.uk

B&B per night:
S £52.50–£57.50
D £75.00–£85.00

OPEN All year round

Delightfully converted 18thC farmhouse with 16 en suite bedrooms. 3-star accommodation with fine food and friendly, efficient service. Ideal for Dorset/Devon coastline and splendid houses and gardens. Family-owned and run. Surrounded by fields but just 3 minutes from centre of Chard.

Bedrooms: 1 single, 11 double, 3 twin, 1 triple
Bathrooms: 16 en suite

Lunch available
EM 1830 (LO 2130)
Parking for 60
CC: Amex, Barclaycard, Delta, Eurocard, Mastercard, Solo, Switch, Visa, Visa Electron

🅰🐾🔔📧🖵↓🍵🛈⌖🅿📺🛏🖨🍽100▶✳🚬SC♦SP🏥Ⓣ

★★

HENSLEIGH HOTEL

Lower Sea Lane, Charmouth, Bridport, DT6 6LW
T: (01297) 560830
F: (01297) 560830

Bedrooms: 2 single, 3 double, 4 twin, 1 family room
Bathrooms: 10 en suite

EM 1830 (LO 1930)
Parking for 15
CC: Amex, Barclaycard, Delta, Eurocard, Mastercard, Switch, Visa

B&B per night:
S £25.00–£35.00
D £50.00–£70.00

HB per person:
DY £39.00–£51.00

OPEN Mar–Oct

Family-run hotel with a reputation for friendly service, comfort, hospitality and delicious food. Situated just 300 metres from beach and spectacular cliff walks.

🅰🐾3🖨↓🛈🍵🛏🖨♦✳🚬SP Ⓣ

★★

THE NEW INN

High Street, Clovelly, Bideford, EX39 5TQ
T: (01237) 431303
F: (01237) 431636
E: newinnatclovelly.co.uk

B&B per night:
S £34.25–£57.25
D £68.50–£84.50

HB per person:
DY £36.50–£61.75

OPEN All year round

Fascinating 17thC inn nestling amongst the flower-strewn cottages which line the cobbled street as it tumbles down the hill to the little harbour. The street is traffic-free, so your luggage is portered by sledge or donkey. Recently refurbished bedrooms with sea or village views. Restaurant serves regional dishes.

Bedrooms: 1 single, 6 double, 1 triple
Bathrooms: 8 en suite

Lunch available
EM 1900 (LO 2100)
CC: Amex, Barclaycard, Delta, Eurocard, Maestro, Mastercard, Switch, Visa, Visa Electron

🅰🐾🔔📧🖵↓🍵🛛🛏🖨♦✳🐎🚬♦SP🏥Ⓣ

AT-A-GLANCE SYMBOLS

Symbols at the end of each accommodation entry give useful information about services and facilities. A key to symbols can be found inside the back cover flap. Keep this open for easy reference.

★★

RED LION HOTEL

The Quay, Clovelly, Bideford, EX39 5TF
T: (01237) 431237
F: (01237) 431044
E: redliionatclovelly.co.uk

B&B per night:
S £40.50–£66.25
D £81.00–£102.50

HB per person:
DY £43.00–£73.75

OPEN All year round

Ancient inn enjoying a dramatic quayside setting in unique heritage village. Beautifully comfortable bedrooms all with wonderful sea views and the sound of the sea to lull you to sleep. Characterful bars and an intimate lounge. The restaurant specialises in seafood and has rosette awards. Staying here is a special experience.

Bedrooms: 7 double, 2 twin, 2 triple
Bathrooms: 11 en suite

Lunch available
EM 1900 (LO 2030)
Parking for 11
CC: Amex, Barclaycard, Delta, Eurocard, Maestro, Mastercard, Switch, Visa, Visa Electron

DARTMOOR

See under Bovey Tracey, Ilsington, Moretonhampstead, Okehampton

DARTMOUTH, Devon Map ref 1D3 *Tourist Information Centre Tel: (01803) 834224*

★★★
Silver
Award
Ad on this page

ROYAL CASTLE HOTEL

11 The Quay, Dartmouth, TQ6 9PS
T: (01803) 833033
F: (01803) 835445
E: enquiry@royalcastle.co.uk
I: www.royalcastle.co.uk

B&B per night:
S £54.45–£68.95
D £107.90–£143.90

HB per person:
DY £67.95–£85.95

OPEN All year round

Historic 17thC quayside inn, with two beamed bars with open fires on cooler days, cask beers, welcoming staff. Fine restaurant overlooking the river. Individually decorated rooms, many with spa baths, 4-poster beds and brass beds. Fine river views and a warm welcoming atmosphere. "Eco-Hotel" of the year 1999.

Bedrooms: 4 single, 10 double, 8 twin, 3 triple
Bathrooms: 25 en suite

Lunch available
EM 1845 (LO 2200)
Parking for 17
CC: Amex, Barclaycard, Delta, Mastercard, Solo, Switch, Visa, Visa Electron

CHECK THE MAPS

The colour maps at the front of this guide show all the cities, towns and villages for which you will find accommodation entries. Refer to the town index to find the page on which they are listed.

THE ROYAL CASTLE HOTEL

★★★

Unique 17th Century Inn overlooking the River Dart
Privately owned award winning hotel.
25 en-suite rooms, many with 4-poster beds and fine antiques.
First floor restaurant with a magnificent view.
Excellent local meat and seafood.
Busy Inn with cask conditioned ales and bar meals.
Friendly and efficient staff.

★★★

THE ROYAL CASTLE HOTEL, THE QUAY, DARTMOUTH,
DEVON, TQ6 9PS.
Tel: 01803 833033 Fax: 01803 835445 Website: www.royalcastle.co.uk

DARTMOUTH continued

★★★

STOKE LODGE HOTEL
Stoke Fleming, Dartmouth, TQ6 0RA
T: (01803) 770523
F: (01803) 770851
E: mail@stokelodge.co.uk
I: www.stokelodge.co.uk

B&B per night:
S £48.00–£55.00
D £78.00–£105.00

HB per person:
DY £52.00–£68.00

OPEN All year round

Family-run country-house hotel set in 3 acres of attractive gardens overlooking the sea. En suite bedrooms, indoor and outdoor swimming pools, sauna, jacuzzi, tennis court and full-size snooker table. Reduced green fees at Dartmouth Golf Club. Excellent food and fine wines. Open all year.

Bedrooms: 2 single, 8 double, 8 twin, 7 triple
Bathrooms: 25 en suite

Lunch available
EM 1900 (LO 2100)
Parking for 50
CC: Amex, Barclaycard, Delta, Mastercard, Switch, Visa

Ⓜ🅿️🏧♿✆☎☐♨♟⚓Ⓢ⌨🅟🖥💷⚲🍽100 ⏢🔍🎾🏹♜🌳✿🚲♿🆂🅿️🏛Ⓣ

★★

TOWNSTAL FARMHOUSE
Townstal Road, Dartmouth, TQ6 9HY
T: (01803) 832300
F: (01803) 835428

Bedrooms: 1 single, 9 double, 1 twin, 4 triple, 1 family room
Bathrooms: 16 en suite

EM 1900 (LO 2030)
Parking for 17
CC: Amex, Barclaycard, Delta, Eurocard, Mastercard, Switch, Visa

B&B per night:
D £50.00–£140.00

HB per person:
DY £40.00–£45.00

Charming 16thC Listed building within a 10-minute walk of town centre. Home-cooked meals in friendly atmosphere. Pets welcome. Rooms suitable for disabled available. Special breaks.

OPEN All year round

🅿️♿✆☎☐♨🍴Ⓢ🏛Ⓣ🖥💷⚓►✿🚲♿🆂🅿️🏛Ⓣ

DUNSTER, Somerset Map ref 1D1

★★★

YARN MARKET HOTEL (EXMOOR)
25 High Street, Dunster, Minehead, TA24 6SF
T: (01643) 821425
F: (01643) 821475
E: yarnmarket.hotel@virgin.net
I: www.s-h-systems.co.uk/hotels/yarnmkt

B&B per night:
S £30.00–£40.00
D £50.00–£85.00

HB per person:
DY £40.00–£58.00

OPEN All year round

Central and accessible hotel, an ideal location for walking and exploring Exmoor National Park. Family-run with a friendly, relaxed atmosphere. En suite rooms with colour TV and tea-making facilities. Non-smoking. Pets by arrangement. Special 2 and 3-night breaks – please enquire for details. Please quote WTS01 for restaurant discount during your visit (cash only).

Bedrooms: 11 double, 1 twin, 2 family rooms
Bathrooms: 14 en suite

EM 1730 (LO 2100)
Parking for 3
CC: Barclaycard, Delta, Eurocard, JCB, Mastercard, Solo, Switch, Visa, Visa Electron

Ⓜ🅿️🏧✆☎☐♨🍴Ⓢ⌨🅟🖥💷⚓🍽35 Ʊ►🆂🅂🅿️🏛Ⓣ

EXETER, Devon Map ref 1D2 *Tourist Information Centre Tel: (01392) 265700*

★★★

EBFORD HOUSE HOTEL
Exmouth Road, Ebford, Exeter, EX3 0QH
T: (01392) 877658
F: (01392) 874424
E: ebford@eclipse.co.uk
I: www.eclipse.co.uk/ebford

Bedrooms: 3 single, 11 double, 2 twin
Bathrooms: 16 en suite

Lunch available
EM 1830 (LO 2130)
Parking for 45
CC: Amex, Barclaycard, Delta, Eurocard, Mastercard, Solo, Switch, Visa

B&B per night:
S £60.00–£68.00
D £80.00–£95.00

HB per person:
DY £63.00–£68.50

OPEN All year round

Beautiful Georgian country house surrounded by lovely gardens, fine views. Noted restaurant where superb food and service are paramount. Convenient for 8 golf courses, sea, moors.

Ⓜ🅿️🏧♿✆☎☐♨🍴Ⓢ⌨🅟Ⓞ💷⚓🍽45 ⏢✳Ʊ►✏✿🏛Ⓣ◉

HALF BOARD PRICES Half board prices are given per person, but in some cases these may be based on double/twin occupancy.

EXETER continued

★★ FAIRWINDS HOTEL

Kennford, Exeter, EX6 7UD
T: (01392) 832911

Bedrooms: 3 double,
2 twin, 1 triple
Bathrooms: 6 en suite

EM 1830 (LO 1930)
Parking for 9
CC: Barclaycard, Eurocard,
Mastercard, Visa

B&B per night:
S £35.00–£39.00
D £45.00–£52.00

HB per person:
DY £34.00–£49.00

Friendly little hotel, south of Exeter, exclusively for non -smokers. Beautiful rural surroundings. Delightful en suite bedrooms, (same on ground floor). Delicious home-made food. Car park. Bargain breaks.

OPEN Jan–Nov

★★★★ THISTLE EXETER
Ad p15

Queen Street, Exeter, EX4 3SP
T: (01392) 254982
F: (01392) 420928
E: exeter@thistle.co.uk

Bedrooms: 25 single,
15 double, 46 twin,
4 triple; suites available
Bathrooms: 90 en suite

Lunch available
EM 1900 (LO 2200)
Parking for 40
CC: Amex, Barclaycard,
Delta, Diners, Mastercard,
Switch, Visa

B&B per night:
S £109.00–£132.00
D £119.00–£143.00

OPEN All year round

Ⓒ®
Thistle Hotels/Utell
International

This hotel offers friendly, old fashioned service in a charming city centre location. Easy reach of the cathedral and the beautiful Dartmoor countryside.

EXMOOR

See under Dunster, Lynmouth, Lynton, Martinhoe, Minehead, Porlock, Wheddon Cross

---

EXMOUTH, Devon Map ref 1D2 Tourist Information Centre Tel: (01395) 222299

★ THE KERANS HOTEL

Esplanade, Exmouth, EX8 1DS
T: (01395) 275275
E: kerans@eclipse.co.uk
I: www.exmouth-guide.co.uk/
kerans.htm

Bedrooms: 1 single,
3 double, 1 twin, 1 triple;
suite available
Bathrooms: 6 en suite,
1 public

EM 1830 (LO 1200)
Parking for 5
CC: Barclaycard,
Mastercard, Visa

B&B per night:
S £30.00–£37.00
D £43.00–£70.00

HB per person:
DY £30.00–£47.00

OPEN All year round

For those who enjoy the quieter side of life! A seafront hotel (totally non-smoking) with superior rooms, personal service and easily accessible by train or coach.

★★★

THE ROYAL BEACON HOTEL

The Beacon, Exmouth, EX8 2AF
T: (01395) 264886
F: (01395) 268890
E: reception@royalbeaconhotel.co.uk
I: www.royalbeaconhotel.co.uk

B&B per night:
S £35.00–£45.00
D £70.00–£85.00

HB per person:
DY £50.00–£60.00

OPEN All year round

An elegant Georgian former posting house. All rooms have been recently refurbished, most overlooking the River Exe estuary and the sea. The restaurant offers charming ambience and superb cuisine. The hotel is conveniently located, a short walk to the beach and is within easy reach of the city centre.

Bedrooms: 3 single,
12 double, 8 twin
Bathrooms: 23 en suite

Lunch available
EM 1900 (LO 2130)
Parking for 30
CC: Amex, Barclaycard,
Delta, Diners, Eurocard,
JCB, Mastercard, Switch,
Visa

FALMOUTH, Cornwall Map ref 1B3 Tourist Information Centre Tel: (01326) 312300

★★★
Silver
Award

GREEN LAWNS HOTEL

Western Terrace, Falmouth,
TR11 4QJ
T: (01326) 312734 & 312007
F: (01326) 211427
E: info@green-lawns-hotel.co.uk
I: www.green-lawns-hotel.co.uk

Bedrooms: 6 single,
16 double, 9 twin,
2 triple, 6 family rooms
Bathrooms: 39 en suite

Lunch available
EM 1845 (LO 2145)
Parking for 60
CC: Amex, Barclaycard,
Delta, Diners, Eurocard,
Mastercard, Solo, Switch,
Visa, Visa Electron

B&B per night:
S £50.00–£95.00
D £80.00–£150.00

HB per person:
DY £60.00–£115.00

OPEN All year round

Ⓒ®
The Independents

Elegant chateau-style hotel situated between the main beaches and town, with indoor leisure complex. Honeymoon and executive suites.

★★
Silver
Award

MARINA HOTEL

Esplanade, Fowey, PL23 1HY
T: (01726) 833315
F: (01726) 832779
E: marina.hotel@dial.pipex.com
I: www.cornwall-online.co.uk/
marina_hotel/

B&B per night:
D £76.00–£108.00

OPEN Feb–Dec

Beautifully located hotel (centre of picture), on the water's edge. Privately run. Rooms include the new Forecastle family suite, balcony, sea view and inland rooms. Waterside restaurant, sun terrace and garden. Excellent cuisine. Guests can take advantage of the hotel's Boston whaler and ride in style on the estuary.

Bedrooms: 7 double,
4 twin
Bathrooms: 11 en suite

EM 1900 (LO 2030)
CC: Amex, Barclaycard,
Delta, Eurocard,
Mastercard, Solo, Switch,
Visa, Visa Electron

HINDON, Wiltshire Map ref 2B2

★★

GROSVENOR ARMS
High Street, Hindon, Salisbury,
SP3 6DJ
T: (01747) 820696
F: (01747) 820869

Bedrooms: 4 double,
1 twin, 2 triple
Bathrooms: 7 en suite

Lunch available
EM 1900 (LO 2200)
Parking for 20
CC: Amex, Barclaycard,
Delta, Eurocard, JCB,
Mastercard, Switch, Visa

B&B per night:
S £45.00–£65.00
D £75.00–£95.00

OPEN All year round

Grade II Georgian stabling/coaching inn. Recently refurbished in the Georgian character, offering a unique glass-fronted, theatre-style kitchen.

HOLFORD, Somerset Map ref 1D1

★★
Silver
Award

COMBE HOUSE HOTEL
Holford, Bridgwater, TA5 1RZ
T: (01278) 741382
F: (01278) 741322
E: John@combehouse.co.uk

Bedrooms: 4 single,
5 double, 7 twin
Bathrooms: 16 en suite,
1 public

Lunch available
EM 1930 (LO 2030)
Parking for 20
CC: Amex, Barclaycard,
Delta, Maestro,
Mastercard, Solo, Switch,
Visa, Visa Electron

B&B per night:
S £30.00–£40.00
D £60.00–£90.00

HB per person:
DY £49.00–£83.00

OPEN Feb–Dec

17thC country hotel in beautiful Butterfly Combe in the heart of the Quantock Hills. Traditional hospitality in rural peace and quiet.

HONITON, Devon Map ref 1D2 *Tourist Information Centre Tel: (01404) 43716*

★★
Silver
Award

HOME FARM HOTEL AND RESTAURANT
Wilmington, Honiton, EX14 9JR
T: (01404) 831278 & 831246
F: (01404) 831411

Bedrooms: 3 single,
4 double, 2 twin, 4 triple;
suite available
Bathrooms: 13 en suite,
1 public

Lunch available
EM 1900 (LO 2130)
Parking for 20
CC: Delta, Mastercard,
Switch, Visa

B&B per night:
S £36.50–£45.00
D £65.00–£75.00

HB per person:
DY £49.00–£61.50

OPEN All year round

Thatched 16thC farmhouse hotel in lovely countryside. Restaurant uses local produce to serve food of high standard. Bar with light meals. Log fires. Six miles from sea.

QUALITY ASSURANCE SCHEME

For an explanation of the quality and facilities represented by the Stars please refer to the front of this guide. A more detailed explanation can be found in the information pages at the back.

★★

BEECHWOOD HOTEL

Torrs Park, Ilfracombe, EX34 8AZ

T: (01271) 863800

F: (01271) 863800

E: info@beechwoodhotel.co.uk

I: www.beechwoodhotel.co.uk

B&B per night:
S £22.00–£25.00
D £44.00–£50.00

HB per person:
DY £30.00–£34.00

OPEN All year round

Beautifully situated Victorian mansion with fine views over the town to the sea, wooded grounds bordering spectacular National Trust Land and splendid coastal walks starting from our own woodland path. The Beechwood offers a relaxed informal atmosphere, good food and wine and an exceptionally peaceful environment. A non-smoking hotel.

Bedrooms: 5 double,
2 twin
Bathrooms: 7 en suite,
1 public

EM 1900 (LO 1900)
Parking for 8
CC: Barclaycard, Delta,
Diners, Eurocard,
Mastercard, Solo, Switch,
Visa

★★

ELMFIELD HOTEL

Torrs Park, Ilfracombe, EX34 8AZ

T: (01271) 863377

F: (01271) 866828

B&B per night:
S £35.00–£40.00
D £70.00–£80.00

HB per person:
DY £45.00–£50.00

OPEN Apr–Oct
& Christmas

The hotel stands in its own acre of gardens, with heated indoor swimming pool, jacuzzi, sauna, solarium. For that special occasion two rooms have 4-poster beds. We have achieved an excellent reputation for our cuisine, using fresh local produce. Book from any day and for any number of days.

Bedrooms: 2 single,
8 double, 3 twin
Bathrooms: 13 en suite

Lunch available
EM 1900 (LO 1930)
Parking for 15
CC: Barclaycard, Delta,
Mastercard, Switch, Visa

★★

THE ILFRACOMBE CARLTON HOTEL

Runnacleave Road, Ilfracombe, EX34 8AR

T: (01271) 862446 & 863711

F: (01271) 865379

E: downrew@globalnet.co.uk

I: www.downrew.co.uk

B&B per night:
S £27.50–£29.50
D £45.00–£50.00

HB per person:
DY £30.00–£42.00

OPEN All year round

Premier resort hotel in central location adjacent to beach, seafront and Tarka Trail. Comfortable rooms with good facilities. Buttery, dancing. One non-smoking lounge, non-smoking bedrooms. Special breaks all year. A warm welcome from the "Hotel with a Smile".

Bedrooms: 9 single,
18 double, 13 twin,
7 triple, 1 family room
Bathrooms: 48 en suite,
2 public

EM 1900 (LO 2030)
Parking for 20
CC: Amex, Barclaycard,
Delta, Diners, Eurocard,
Mastercard, Switch, Visa

MAP REFERENCES
The map references refer to the colour maps at the front of this guide. The first figure is the map number; the letter and figure which follow indicate the grid reference on the map.

★

WESTWELL HALL HOTEL
Torrs Park, Ilfracombe, EX34 8AZ
T: (01271) 862792
F: (01271) 862792

B&B per night:
S £22.00–£26.00
D £44.00–£52.00

HB per person:
DY £34.00–£38.00

OPEN All year round

Elegant early Victorian house set in 2
acres of mature gardens, adjacent to
National Trust walks. Overlooking the
sea and town in quiet location. An
ideal base for exploring the beautiful,
rugged coastline of North Devon.

Bedrooms: 1 single,
7 double, 2 triple
Bathrooms: 10 en suite

EM 1930 (LO 1830)
Parking for 12
CC: Amex, Barclaycard,
Delta, Diners, Eurocard,
JCB, Maestro, Mastercard,
Solo, Switch, Visa, Visa
Electron

ILLOGAN, Cornwall Map ref 1B3

★★
Silver
Award

AVIARY COURT HOTEL
Marys Well, Illogan, Redruth, TR16 4QZ
T: (01209) 842256
F: (01209) 843744
E: aviarycourt@connexions.uk

B&B per night:
S £40.00–£44.00
D £60.00–£62.00

HB per person:
DY £43.00–£45.00

OPEN All year round

Charming country house in 2 acres
of secluded, well-kept gardens with
tennis court. Family-run, personal
service, good food. Superior en suite
bedrooms with TV, telephone, tea/
coffee, fresh fruit. Ideal touring
location (coast 5 minutes). St Ives,
Tate, Heligan, Eden Project all within
easy reach.

Bedrooms: 4 double,
1 twin, 1 triple
Bathrooms: 6 en suite

EM 1900 (LO 2030)
Parking for 25
CC: Barclaycard,
Mastercard, Solo, Switch,
Visa

ILSINGTON, Devon Map ref 1D2

ILSINGTON HOTEL
Ilsington, Newton Abbot, TQ13 9RR
T: (01364) 661452
F: (01364) 661307
E: hotel@ilsington.co.uk
I: www.ilsington.co.uk

B&B per night:
S £62.50–£71.00
D £100.00–£105.00

HB per person:
DY £52.50–£140.00

OPEN All year round

Set in 10 acres of private land within
Dartmoor National Park, providing
unspoilt vistas over rolling
landscapes. A family-run and owned
hotel. We pride ourselves on a
friendly welcome and relaxed
atmosphere. Excellent food and
on-site leisure facilities. Within easy
driving distance of many of Devon's
finest attractions.

Bedrooms: 2 single,
16 double, 7 twin; suites
available
Bathrooms: 25 en suite

Lunch available
EM 1830 (LO 2100)
Parking for 100
CC: Amex, Barclaycard,
Delta, Eurocard, JCB,
Mastercard, Solo, Switch,
Visa, Visa Electron

Best Western Hotels

NB

IMPORTANT NOTE Information on accommodation listed
in this guide has been supplied by the proprietors. As changes may occur
you are advised to check details at the time of booking.

★★
Silver
Award

ERMEWOOD HOUSE HOTEL

Totnes Road, Ermington, Ivybridge,
PL21 9NS
T: (01548) 830741
F: (01548) 830741
E: info@ermewood-house.co.uk
I: www.ermewood-house.co.uk

B&B per night:
S £40.00–£45.00
D £67.00–£79.00

HB per person:
DY £51.00–£62.50

OPEN All year round

*Award-winning country hotel. Fresh
food policy – utilising local produce
whenever possible. Excellent touring
and walking base. Unspoilt coastline
4 miles south and Dartmoor National
Park 4 miles north. Special mini-
break offers throughout the year.
Local activities: sea bathing, fly
fishing, riding, sailing, sports
complex and golf.*

Bedrooms: 2 single,	EM 1830 (LO 2030)
6 double, 2 twin	Parking for 20
Bathrooms: 10 en suite	CC: Barclaycard, Delta,
	Eurocard, Maestro,
	Mastercard, Solo, Switch,
	Visa

★★
Silver
Award
Ad on this page

FIELDHEAD HOTEL

Portuan Road, Hannafore, West Looe, Looe,
PL13 2DR
T: (01503) 262689
F: (01503) 264114
E: field.head@virgin.net
I: www.chycor.co.uk/fieldhead

B&B per night:
S £26.00–£84.00
D £52.00–£94.00

HB per person:
DY £42.00–£63.00

OPEN All year round

Minotel

*Built as a private house in the grand
style in 1896 and now a true country
house hotel by the sea. Most
bedrooms and all public rooms have
wonderful panoramic views over
Looe Bay. Lovely tropical gardens
with heated pool and patios.
Restaurant with daily changing
menus and seafood specialities.*

Bedrooms: 1 single,	EM 1830 (LO 2045)
8 double, 3 twin, 1 triple,	Parking for 15
2 family rooms	CC: Amex, Barclaycard,
Bathrooms: 15 en suite	Delta, Mastercard, Solo,
	Switch, Visa

CENTRAL RESERVATIONS OFFICES

The symbol ⒸⓇ and a group name in an entry indicate that bookings
can be made through a central reservations office. These are listed in
a separate section towards the back of this guide.

FIELDHEAD HOTEL

Open all
year round

SILVER AWARD

Portuan Road, Hannafore, West Looe, Looe PL13 2DR
Tel: (01503) 262689 • Fax: (01503) 264114
Email: field.head@virgin.net • Web: www.fieldheadhotel.co.uk

Built as a private house in the grand style in 1896 and now a true
country house hotel by the sea. Most bedrooms and all public
rooms have wonderful panoramic views over Looe Bay. Lovely
tropical gardens with heated pool and patios. Restaurant with
daily changing menus and seafood specialities.

Single	*£35 - £50*
Double	*£56 - £94*
Half board	*£45 - £67*

LOSTWITHIEL, Cornwall Map ref 1B2

★★★ **LOSTWITHIEL HOTEL GOLF & COUNTRY CLUB**

Lower Polscoe, Lostwithiel,	Bedrooms: 2 single,	Lunch available	B&B per night:
PL22 0HQ	3 double, 13 twin,	EM 1900 (LO 2130)	**S £30.00–£56.00**
T: (01208) 873550	1 family room	Parking for 150	**D £60.00–£92.00**
F: (01208) 873479	Bathrooms: 19 en suite	CC: Amex, Barclaycard,	
E: reception@golf-hotel.co.uk		Delta, Diners, Eurocard,	HB per person:
I: www.golf-hotel.co.uk		Mastercard, Switch, Visa	**DY £37.00–£61.00**

Overlooking the beautiful River Fowey valley in idyllic setting. Charm, character and high levels of comfort and service. Bedrooms are converted from Cornish stone farm buildings.

OPEN All year round

LYME REGIS, Dorset Map ref 1D2 *Tourist Information Centre Tel: (01297) 442138*

★★

ORCHARD COUNTRY HOTEL

Rousdon, Lyme Regis, DT7 3XW

T: (01297) 442972

F: (01297) 443670

E: the.orchard@btinternet.com

B&B per night:
S £39.00–£42.00
D £58.00–£76.00

HB per person:
DY £46.00–£53.00

OPEN Mar–Nov

Superb food (including vegetarian), quality en suite accommodation (ground floor available) and a friendly atmosphere. Totally non-smoking. Bar, sun terrace, gardens and ample parking. Good location for visiting National Trust properties and gardens, walking, fossil hunting, bird-watching, golf – and relaxing. Short breaks. Groups welcome. Brochure available.

Bedrooms: 2 single,	EM 1915 (LO 1945)	
6 double, 4 twin	Parking for 15	
Bathrooms: 9 en suite,	CC: Barclaycard, Delta,	
3 private	Mastercard, Switch, Visa	

LYNMOUTH, Devon Map ref 1C1

★★ **BATH HOTEL**

Lynmouth, EX35 6EL	Bedrooms: 1 single,	Lunch available	B&B per night:
T: (01598) 752238	12 double, 8 twin,	EM 1900 (LO 2030)	**S £35.00–£45.00**
F: (01598) 752544	3 triple	Parking for 17	**D £58.00–£80.00**
E: bathhotel@torslynmouth.co.uk	Bathrooms: 24 en suite	CC: Amex, Barclaycard,	
I: www.torslynmouth.co.uk		Delta, Diners, Mastercard,	HB per person:
		Switch, Visa	**DY £38.00–£49.00**

Friendly, family-run hotel by picturesque Lynmouth harbour. Ideal centre for exploring Exmoor National Park. Special offers and discounts available throughout the year.

OPEN Feb–Nov

LYNTON, Devon Map ref 1C1 *Tourist Information Centre Tel: (01598) 752225*

★★

SANDROCK HOTEL

Longmead, Lynton, EX35 6DH

T: (01598) 753307

F: (01598) 752665

B&B per night:
S £22.50–£25.00
D £47.00–£55.00

OPEN Mar–Oct

Relaxing Edwardian hotel with modern comforts, in delightful sunny spot amid Exmoor's superb coastal scenery and beauty spots. En suite double rooms, own car park.

Bedrooms: 1 single,	EM 1900 (LO 2000)	
4 double, 3 twin	Parking for 9	
Bathrooms: 7 en suite,	CC: Amex, Barclaycard,	
1 private	Delta, Mastercard, Switch,	
	Visa	

CREDIT CARD BOOKINGS
If you book by telephone and are asked for your credit card number it is advisable to check the proprietor's policy should you cancel your reservation.

LYNTON continued

★
Silver
Award

SEAWOOD HOTEL
North Walk Drive, Lynton, EX35 6HJ
T: (01598) 752272
F: (01598) 752272

Bedrooms: 1 single,
9 double, 2 twin
Bathrooms: 12 en suite,
2 public

EM 1900 (LO 1930)
Parking for 10

B&B per night:
S £29.00
D £58.00–£62.00

Family-run country house hotel nestling on wooded cliffs overlooking Lynmouth Bay and headland. Varied menu and friendly service.

HB per person:
DY £44.50–£46.50

OPEN Apr–Oct

🐎12 🎠 🖃 ❑ ♦ ⚑ 🛈 🖪 ⊬ 🖳 🖫 🖼 ✿ 🚲 SP 🎎 T

MALMESBURY, Wiltshire Map ref 2B2 *Tourist Information Centre Tel: (01666) 823748*

★★

MAYFIELD HOUSE HOTEL
Crudwell, Malmesbury, SN16 9EW
T: (01666) 577409 & 577198
F: (01666) 577977
E: mayfield@callnetuk.com

B&B per night:
S £54.00–£56.00
D £76.00–£78.00

HB per person:
DY £29.00–£46.00

OPEN All year round

Delightful country house hotel set in 2 acres of walled garden. Privately owned and operated. The hotel and staff offer a warm and friendly welcome. With comfortable lounges and award-winning restaurant, we are an ideal base for touring the Cotswolds and Bath. Speciality short breaks throughout the year.

Bedrooms: 3 single,
11 double, 7 twin,
3 triple
Bathrooms: 24 en suite

Lunch available
EM 1900 (LO 2100)
Parking for 40
CC: Amex, Barclaycard,
Delta, Diners, Eurocard,
JCB, Mastercard, Switch,
Visa, Visa Electron

®
Best Western Hotels

🅰 🐎 ♨ ❑ ♦ ⚑ 🛈 🖪 ⊬ 🖳 🖫 🖼 🍽 30 ✿ ✕ 🚲 SP 🎎 T ⊛

MANACCAN, Cornwall Map ref 1B3

★★
Silver
Award

TREGILDRY HOTEL
Gillan, Manaccan, Helston,
TR12 6HG
T: (01326) 231378
F: (01326) 231561
E: trgildry@globalnet.co.uk
I: www.tregildryhotel.co.uk

Bedrooms: 1 single,
6 double, 3 twin
Bathrooms: 10 en suite

EM 1900 (LO 2030)
Parking for 15
CC: Barclaycard, Delta,
JCB, Mastercard, Switch,
Visa

HB per person:
DY £70.00–£75.00

OPEN Mar–Oct

Elegant, small, beautifully appointed hotel in unspoilt area, with stunning sea views. Welcoming, relaxed atmosphere. Award-winning modern British cuisine. Peaceful coastal walks. No children.

🅰 ✆ 🖃 ❑ ♦ ⚑ 🛈 🖪 ⊬ 🖳 🖫 🖼 ▶ ✿ 🚲 SP T

MARTINHOE, Devon Map ref 1C1

★★

OLD RECTORY HOTEL
Martinhoe, Barnstaple, EX31 4QT
T: (01598) 763368
F: (01598) 763567
E: reception@oldrectoryhotel.co.uk
I: www.oldrectoryhotel.co.uk

B&B per night:
S £49.00–£56.00
D £78.00–£92.00

HB per person:
DY £55.00–£79.00

OPEN Mar–Nov

Welcoming country house hotel idyllically situated in Exmoor National Park near picturesque coastal path and Lynmouth. Set in 3 acres of delightful gardens with a cascading brook and duck pond. Elegantly furnished, with attractive bedrooms, spacious dining room and vinery. Fine food using traditionally reared meat and free-range poultry.

Bedrooms: 5 double,
4 twin
Bathrooms: 9 en suite

EM 1915 (LO 1945)
Parking for 14
CC: Barclaycard, Delta,
Eurocard, JCB,
Mastercard, Solo, Switch,
Visa, Visa Electron

♨ ❑ ♦ ⚑ 🛈 🖪 ⊬ 🖳 🖫 🖼 ↺ ✿ ✕ 🚲 SP 🎎 T

IDEAS For ideas on places to visit refer to the introduction at the beginning of this section.

MAWGAN PORTH, Cornwall Map ref 1B2

★★

TREDRAGON HOTEL

Mawgan Porth, Newquay, TR8 4DQ
T: (01637) 860213
F: (01637) 860269
E: tredragon@btinternet.com
I: www.cornwallonline.com

B&B per night:
S £31.50–£45.50
D £55.00–£95.00

HB per person:
DY £45.00–£65.00

OPEN All year round

Grounds lead directly to sandy cove. Magnificent coastal walks and views. Relax in our indoor pool complex. Excellent food and wine. Family owned and personally run for 35 years. Open all year. Ideal for short breaks. Special interest breaks brochure available.

Bedrooms: 2 single, 9 double, 5 twin, 13 family rooms
Bathrooms: 29 en suite

Lunch available
EM 1900 (LO 2000)
Parking for 32
CC: Eurocard, Mastercard, Visa

MEVAGISSEY, Cornwall Map ref 1B3

★★

TREMARNE HOTEL

Mevagissey, St Austell, PL26 6UY
T: (01726) 842213
F: (01726) 843420
E: tremarne@talk21.com
I: www.tremarne-hotel.co.uk

B&B per night:
S £30.00–£35.00
D £52.00–£68.00

HB per person:
DY £42.00–£50.00

OPEN All year round

Guestaccom

Charming, licensed hotel and restaurant. Quiet elevated position in Area of Outstanding Natural Beauty. Views over sea and countryside, near harbour and beach. On Cornish Coastal Path, close to Lost Gardens of Heligan and Eden Project. Excellent reputation for service, hospitality and cuisine. Vegetarians catered for. Outdoor heated pool and gardens.

Bedrooms: 2 single, 7 double, 3 twin, 1 triple, 1 family room
Bathrooms: 14 en suite

Lunch available
EM 1830 (LO 2100)
Parking for 13
CC: Barclaycard, Delta, Eurocard, JCB, Mastercard, Solo, Switch, Visa, Visa Electron

MINEHEAD, Somerset Map ref 1D1 *Tourist Information Centre Tel: (01643) 702624*

★★
Gold
Award

CHANNEL HOUSE HOTEL

Church Path, Off Northfield Road, Minehead, TA24 5QG
T: (01643) 703229
F: (01643) 708925
E: channel.house@virgin.net
I: www.channelhouse.co.uk

B&B per night:
D £88.00–£114.00

HB per person:
DY £54.00–£67.00

OPEN Mar–Nov
& Christmas

First class award-winning hotel specialising in superb cuisine and comfort. Nestling on the lower slopes of Exmoor's picturesque North Hill, it sits within 2 acres of peaceful award-winning gardens. All well-appointed bedrooms enjoy lovely views. The hotel will best suit those who appreciate quality and the delights of Exmoor.

Bedrooms: 2 double, 5 twin, 1 triple
Bathrooms: 8 en suite

EM 1900 (LO 2030)
Parking for 10
CC: Amex, Barclaycard, Delta, Diners, Eurocard, JCB, Maestro, Mastercard, Solo, Switch, Visa, Visa Electron

WELCOME HOST This is a nationally recognised customer care programme which aims to promote the highest standards of service and a warm welcome. Establishments taking part in this initiative are indicated by the ⬡ symbol.

MORETONHAMPSTEAD, Devon Map ref 1C2

★★★★
Silver
Award

MANOR HOUSE HOTEL AND GOLF COURSE

Moretonhampstead, Newton Abbot,
TQ13 8RE
T: (01647) 440355
F: (01647) 440961
I: www.principalhotels.co.uk

Bedrooms: 16 single,
33 double, 33 twin,
3 triple; suites available
Bathrooms: 85 en suite

Lunch available
EM 1900 (LO 2130)
Parking for 70
CC: Amex, Barclaycard,
Delta, Diners, Mastercard,
Switch, Visa

B&B per night:
S Min £75.00
D Min £98.00

OPEN All year round

Principal Hotels/Utell
International

Set in majestic rolling countryside, this stunning Jacobean hotel with an exceptional level of style and comfort offers championship golf and various outdoor pursuits.

120

NEWQUAY, Cornwall Map ref 1B2 *Tourist Information Centre Tel: (01637) 854020*

★★★

THE ESPLANADE HOTEL

9 Esplanade Road, Pentire,
Newquay, TR7 1PS
T: (01637) 873333
F: (01637) 851413
E: info@newquay-hotels.co.uk
I: www.newquay-hotels.co.uk

Bedrooms: 4 single,
21 double, 10 twin,
17 triple, 31 family
rooms
Bathrooms: 83 en suite

Lunch available
EM 1900 (LO 2030)
Parking for 32
CC: Amex, Barclaycard,
Delta, Maestro,
Mastercard, Switch, Visa,
Visa Electron

B&B per night:
S £25.00–£45.00
D £50.00–£90.00

HB per person:
DY £25.00–£45.00

OPEN All year round

Modern hotel overlooking beautiful Fistral Bay. Excellent food, friendly service and excellent facilities for a happy, relaxing holiday.

250

★★

PHILEMA HOTEL

1 Esplanade Road, Pentire,
Newquay, TR7 1PY
T: (01637) 872571
F: (01637) 873188
E: info@philema.demon.co.uk
I: www.smoothhound.co.uk/hotels/
philema.html

Bedrooms: 6 double,
3 twin, 6 triple, 18 family
rooms; suites available
Bathrooms: 33 en suite,
2 public

Lunch available
EM 1830 (LO 1930)
Parking for 38
CC: Barclaycard, Delta,
Eurocard, Mastercard,
Solo, Switch, Visa

B&B per night:
S £20.00–£35.00
D £40.00–£70.00

HB per person:
DY £25.00–£40.00

OPEN Mar–Oct

Furnished to a high standard with magnificent views overlooking Fistral Beach and golf-course. Friendly informal hotel with good facilities, including indoor pool, leisure complex and apartments.

★★★

TREBARWITH HOTEL

Newquay, TR7 1BZ
T: (01637) 872288
F: (01637) 875431
E: enquiry@trebarwith-hotel.co.uk
I: www.trebarwith-hotel.co.uk

B&B per night:
S £20.00–£50.00
D £40.00–£100.00

HB per person:
DY £26.00–£60.00

OPEN Mar–Oct

"Probably the best views in Newquay". There's more too! Gardens, sun terraces, private beach entrance, large indoor pool. All complemented by relaxing, comfortable, friendly atmosphere, high standards of housekeeping, excellent food and caring hospitality. Extensive indoor leisure facilities, entertainment, secure parking. Quiet, central location, an oasis in the heart of Newquay.

Bedrooms: 3 single,
20 double, 12 twin,
6 family rooms
Bathrooms: 41 en suite

Lunch available
EM 1915 (LO 2030)
Parking for 40
CC: Barclaycard, Delta,
Mastercard, Switch, Visa

ACCESSIBILITY

Look for the symbols which indicate accessibility for wheelchair users. A list of establishments is at the front of this guide.

OKEHAMPTON, Devon Map ref 1C2

★★

OXENHAM ARMS
South Zeal, Okehampton, EX20 2JT
T: (01837) 840244
F: (01837) 840791
E: jhenry1928@aol.com

Bedrooms: 3 double,
3 twin, 2 triple
Bathrooms: 7 en suite,
1 private

Lunch available
EM 1930 (LO 2100)
Parking for 8
CC: Amex, Barclaycard,
Delta, Diners, JCB,
Maestro, Mastercard,
Solo, Switch, Visa, Visa
Electron

B&B per night:
S £40.00–£50.00
D £60.00–£70.00

HB per person:
DY £45.00–£50.00

OPEN All year round

In the centre of Dartmoor village, originally built in the 12thC. Wealth of granite fireplaces, oak beams, mullion windows. Various diets available on request.

★★

WHITE HART HOTEL
Fore Street, Okehampton, EX20 1HD
T: (01837) 52730 & 54514
F: (01837) 53979
E: graham@whitehart hotel.telme.com

Bedrooms: 2 single,
11 double, 5 twin
Bathrooms: 18 en suite

Lunch available
EM 1900 (LO 2100)
Parking for 22
CC: Barclaycard, Delta,
Eurocard, JCB,
Mastercard, Solo, Switch,
Visa, Visa Electron

B&B per night:
S £35.00–£45.00
D £50.00–£60.00

OPEN All year round

Town centre 17thC coaching inn. Fully licensed freehouse with bars, restaurant, function suites and car parking. Under recent new management.

OTTERY ST MARY, Devon Map ref 1D2

★★★

SALSTON MANOR HOTEL

Fluxton Road, Ottery St Mary, Exeter, EX11 1RQ
T: (01404) 815581
F: (01404) 811245
E: smh@cosmic.org.uk
I: www.salstonhotel.co.uk

B&B per night:
S £45.00–£60.00
D £72.00–£85.00

HB per person:
DY £37.50–£55.00

OPEN All year round

Welcoming early Victorian country house hotel in the heart of East Devon. Amenities include indoor pool, squash courts and sauna. Ideal for business or pleasure. Special interest breaks include golf, walking, painting, antiques, houses and gardens. Conferences and groups catered for. Check us out on our website.

Bedrooms: 3 single,
7 double, 4 twin,
12 triple, 1 family room
Bathrooms: 27 en suite

EM 1900 (LO 2100)
Parking for 80
CC: Barclaycard, Delta,
Mastercard, Solo, Switch,
Visa, Visa Electron

PAIGNTON, Devon Map ref 1D2 *Tourist Information Centre Tel: 0906 680 1268 (calls cost 25p per minute)*

★★

GOODRINGTON LODGE HOTEL

23 Alta Vista Road, Paignton, Devon TQ4 6DA
T: (01803) 558382
F: (01803) 550066

B&B per night:
S £22.00–£26.00
D £44.00–£52.00

HB per person:
DY £32.00–£36.00

OPEN Mar–Oct

Standing in 1 acre of grounds overlooking Goodrington Park and beach. Family-run hotel for 30 years. Outdoor heated pool, all rooms en suite, choice menu, pool-side services.

Bedrooms: 3 single,
11 double, 1 twin,
4 triple, 1 family room
Bathrooms: 20 en suite

EM 1800 (LO 1900)
Parking for 19
CC: Barclaycard, Delta,
Mastercard, Switch, Visa

PRICES

Please check prices and other details at the time of booking.

★★★

REDCLIFFE HOTEL
Marine Drive, Paignton, Devon TQ3 2NL
T: (01803) 526397
F: (01803) 528030
E: Redclfe@aol.com
I: www.redcliffehotel.co.uk

B&B per night:
S £45.00–£50.00
D £90.00–£100.00

HB per person:
DY £55.00–£60.00

OPEN All year round

Superbly situated in 3 acres of grounds on the very water's edge in the centre of beautiful Torbay. Panoramic sea views from the restaurant, lounges and majority of bedrooms. Indoor leisure complex plus heated outdoor pool. Ample car parking.

Bedrooms: 13 single, 25 double, 20 twin, 2 triple, 5 family rooms
Bathrooms: 65 en suite, 1 public

EM 1900 (LO 2030)
Parking for 100
CC: Amex, Barclaycard, Delta, Mastercard, Switch, Visa

CR
The Independents

160

★

ESTORIL HOTEL
46 Morrab Road, Penzance, TR18 4EX
T: (01736) 362468 & 367471
F: (01736) 367471
E: estorilhotel@aol.com
I: www.chycor.co.uk/tourism/hotels/penzance-hotel-assoc

Bedrooms: 1 single, 4 double, 2 twin, 1 triple, 1 family room
Bathrooms: 9 en suite

EM 1845 (LO 1930)
Parking for 4
CC: Barclaycard, Mastercard, Visa

B&B per night:
S £27.00–£30.00
D £54.00–£60.00

HB per person:
DY £47.00–£55.00

OPEN All year round

Elegant Victorian house with the highest standards of cleanliness, providing comprehensive smoke-free en suite accommodation and warm, efficient, personal service.

★★★

THE QUEENS HOTEL
The Promenade, Penzance, TR18 4HG
T: (01736) 362371
F: (01736) 350033
E: enquiries@queens-hotel.com
I: www.queens-hotel.com

B&B per night:
S £40.00–£55.00
D £76.00–£120.00

HB per person:
DY £45.00–£67.00

OPEN All year round

Elegant Victorian hotel enjoying pride of place on the seafront promenade of Penzance with majestic views across Mounts Bay from Mousehole Point to Lizard Peninsula and St Michael's Mount. Our award-winning dining room which overlooks the bay offers a table d'hote menu including local fresh fish and produce.

Bedrooms: 15 single, 22 double, 23 twin, 9 triple, 1 family room
Bathrooms: 70 en suite, 2 public

Lunch available
EM 1900 (LO 2045)
Parking for 40
CC: Amex, Barclaycard, Delta, Diners, Mastercard, Solo, Switch, Visa

150

★

GROSVENOR PARK HOTEL
114-116 North Road East, Plymouth, PL4 6AH
T: (01752) 229312
F: (01752) 252777
I: www.smoothhound.co.uk/hotels/grosvpk.html

Bedrooms: 6 single, 5 double, 4 twin, 1 family room
Bathrooms: 11 en suite, 2 public, 5 private showers

Lunch available
EM 1900 (LO 2000)
Parking for 6
CC: Amex, Barclaycard, Delta, Eurocard, JCB, Mastercard, Switch, Visa, Visa Electron

B&B per night:
S £22.00–£33.00
D £44.00–£44.00

OPEN All year round

Popular, comfortable hotel offering good food and drink and great value. Nearest hotel to station and city centre. Look no further! Golf, bowls and diving package breaks a speciality.

SYMBOLS The symbols in each entry give information about services and facilities. A key to these symbols appears at the back of this guide.

PLYMOUTH continued

★★ **INVICTA HOTEL**
11/12 Osborne Place,
Lockyer Street, The Hoe, Plymouth,
PL1 2PU
T: (01752) 664997
F: (01752) 664994
I: www.invictahotel.co.uk

Bedrooms: 5 single,
5 double, 7 twin, 6 triple
Bathrooms: 23 en suite

Lunch available
EM 1900 (LO 2100)
Parking for 10
CC: Amex, Barclaycard,
Delta, Eurocard,
Mastercard, Switch, Visa

B&B per night:
S £45.00–£52.00
D £55.00–£62.00

HB per person:
DY £39.00–£40.00

OPEN All year round

Elegant Victorian hotel opposite the famous Plymouth Hoe, close to all amenities. Well-appointed bedrooms, warm and personal service. Lock-up car park.

ΛΛ⅖12⚹ℭ⌂⚱⚑🅘🆂⚄🅜📺🌓𝄞.⚓🍴55🏹 🆂🅲 🆂🅿 🏠 🆃

★★★

KITLEY HOUSE HOTEL AND RESTAURANT
Kitley Estate, Yealmpton, Plymouth,
PL8 2NW
T: (01752) 881555
F: (01752) 881667
E: sales@kitleyhousehotel.com
I: www.kitleyhousehotel.com

B&B per night:
S £45.00–£115.00
D £60.00–£145.00

HB per person:
DY £39.50–£79.50

OPEN All year round

Unique country house hotel, set in own valley and overlooking a trout lake. Luxury suites and standard bedrooms feature contemporary facilities with magnificent views. Restaurant is popular with local residents and is open for lunch and dinner. Grade I Listed building, originally a Tudor Revival house and remodelled by George Repton in 1820s.

Bedrooms: 4 single,
2 double, 14 twin; suites
available
Bathrooms: 20 en suite

Lunch available
EM 1900 (LO 2130)
Parking for 60
CC: Amex, Barclaycard,
Delta, Diners, Eurocard,
Mastercard, Switch, Visa,
Visa Electron

ΛΛ⅖♿🕮ℭ🖥⌂⚱⚑🅘🆂⚄🅜🌓𝄞.⚓🍴100 ☆♻♪↑✓❋🏹♻ 🆂🅿 🏠 🆃 ◉

★★★

NEW CONTINENTAL HOTEL
Millbay Road, Plymouth, Devon PL1 3LD
T: (01752) 220782
F: (01752) 227013
E: newconti@aol.com
I: www.newcontinental.co.uk

B&B per night:
S £58.00–£83.00
D £73.00–£160.00

HB per person:
DY Max £49.00

OPEN All year round

Victorian Grade II Listed building, Plymouth's largest independent hotel, in the city centre adjacent to conference and leisure centre and close to Theatre Royal, Barbican and Plymouth Hoe. Beautifully appointed bedrooms offering some of the finest accommodation available in Plymouth today. Half board prices for minimum 2-night break.

Bedrooms: 22 single,
35 double, 14 twin,
25 triple, 3 family
rooms; suites available
Bathrooms: 99 en suite

Lunch available
EM 1800 (LO 2200)
Parking for 100
CC: Amex, Barclaycard,
Delta, Eurocard,
Mastercard, Switch, Visa

ΛΛ⅖🕮ℭ🖥⌂⚱⚑🅘🆂🅜📺🌓⊞📖.⚓🍴400♨☆♻↑►♻ 🆂🅲♻ 🆂🅿 🏠 🆃

USE YOUR *i*s
There are more than 550 Tourist Information Centres throughout England offering friendly help with accommodation and holiday ideas as well as suggestions of places to visit and things to do. You'll find TIC addresses in the local Phone Book.

235

★★★

Attractive, quiet, comfortable hotel at water's edge. Picturesque harbour – amidst Exmoor's magnificent scenery and coastline. Wildlife everywhere – red deer, buzzards with 5ft wing spans. Ancient villages, medieval castles, smugglers' caves. The hotel concentrates on excellent food and attentive service.

ANCHOR AND SHIP HOTEL

Porlock Harbour, Porlock, Minehead, TA24 8PB
T: (01643) 862753
F: (01643) 862843
E: anchorhotel@clara.net

Bedrooms: 1 single, 13 double, 4 twin, 2 triple
Bathrooms: 20 en suite

Lunch available
EM 1900 (LO 2115)
Parking for 30
CC: Amex, Barclaycard, Delta, Eurocard, Mastercard, Switch, Visa, Visa Electron

B&B per night:
S £49.00–£69.00
D £88.00–£131.50

HB per person:
DY £68.75–£92.75

OPEN Feb–Dec

★★
Silver Award

Formerly a hunting lodge, now a small, friendly hotel where you can enjoy good food and wines and roaring log fires – perfect for a short break at any time of year. Its situation could hardly be bettered, nestling where Exmoor meets the sea, with spectacular views across Porlock Bay.

PORLOCK VALE HOUSE

Porlock Weir, Minehead, TA24 8NY
T: (01643) 862338
F: (01643) 863338
E: info@porlockvale.co.uk
I: www.porlockvale.co.uk

Bedrooms: 10 double, 5 twin
Bathrooms: 15 en suite, 2 public

Lunch available
EM (LO 1930)
Parking for 20
CC: Amex, Barclaycard, Delta, Eurocard, JCB, Mastercard, Switch, Visa

B&B per night:
S £47.00–£70.00
D £65.00–£110.00

HB per person:
DY £55.00–£70.00

OPEN All year round

★★★

LUGGER HOTEL AND RESTAURANT

Portloe, Truro, TR2 5RD
T: (01872) 501322
F: (01872) 501691

Bedrooms: 3 single, 9 double, 7 twin; suites available
Bathrooms: 19 en suite

Lunch available
EM 1900 (LO 2130)
Parking for 25
CC: Amex, Barclaycard, Delta, Diners, JCB, Mastercard, Solo, Switch, Visa

B&B per night:
S £60.00–£60.00
D £120.00–£120.00

HB per person:
DY £80.00–£90.00

OPEN Mar–Oct

17thC smugglers' inn, at the water's edge in a quiet, picturesque cove, where fishing boats moor alongside. Hotel does not cater for children under 12 years of age.

★★

THE MARINERS HOTEL

The Slipway, Rock, Wadebridge, PL27 6LD
T: (01208) 862312
F: (01208) 863827
E: amiller767@aol.com
I: www.chycor.co.uk/mariners/

Bedrooms: 1 single, 12 double, 7 twin, 2 family rooms
Bathrooms: 22 en suite

Lunch available
EM 1900 (LO 2100)
Parking for 25
CC: Amex, Barclaycard, Delta, Mastercard, Switch, Visa

B&B per night:
S £35.00–£40.00
D £55.00–£60.00

OPEN Mar–Oct

Situated in a popular water sports area with panoramic views over the Camel Estuary to Padstow. Wrecker's Bar and Samantha's Restaurant.

REGIONAL TOURIST BOARD The ⋀ symbol in an establishment entry indicates that it is a Regional Tourist Board member.

★★
Silver
Award

THE HUNDRED HOUSE HOTEL

Ruan High Lanes, Truro, TR2 5JR
T: (01872) 501336
F: (01872) 501151

B&B per night:
S £45.00–£48.00
D £90.00–£106.00

HB per person:
DY £65.00–£75.00

OPEN Mar–Oct

Peaceful 19thC Cornish country house in 3-acre garden, near St Mawes, Fal Estuary and 12 miles from Truro. Beautifully furnished with antiques, pictures and fresh flowers. Pretty en suite bedrooms. Log fire, delicious candlelit dinners using fresh West Country produce. Ideal for walking coastal path, exploring Cornish gardens and National Trust properties.

Bedrooms: 2 single, 4 double, 4 twin
Bathrooms: 10 en suite

EM 1930 (LO 2000)
Parking for 15
CC: Amex, Barclaycard, Delta, Mastercard, Switch, Visa

★★★

ROSE-IN-VALE COUNTRY HOUSE HOTEL

Mithian, St Agnes, TR5 0QD
T: (01872) 552202
F: (01872) 552700
E: reception@rose-in-vale-hotel.co.uk
I: www.rose-in-vale-hotel.co.uk

B&B per night:
S £50.50–£50.50
D £89.00–£109.00

HB per person:
DY £59.50–£69.50

OPEN Mar–Dec

Minotel

Secluded 18thC Georgian country residence in peaceful 11-acre wooded valley grounds with waterfowl ponds and stream, close to magnificent North Cornwall coast. High standards of comfort, service and cuisine. Glorious coastal and country scenery, pretty coves, lovely sandy beaches, historic houses and gardens close by. Excellent walking and touring base.

Bedrooms: 2 single, 8 double, 8 twin; suites available
Bathrooms: 18 en suite

Lunch available
EM 1900 (LO 2030)
Parking for 40
CC: Barclaycard, Delta, Mastercard, Switch, Visa

★★

CHY-AN-DOUR HOTEL

Trelyon Avenue, St Ives, TR26 2AD
T: (01736) 796436
F: (01736) 795772
E: chyndour@aol.com
I: www.connexions.co.uk/chyandourhotel

B&B per night:
D £70.00–£96.00

HB per person:
DY £50.00–£65.00

OPEN All year round

Built in the 1890s, the home of a local sea-going Captain. The lounge, bar, dining room and most bedrooms have superb breathtaking views overlooking St Ives harbour, bay and beaches. Terraced gardens lead on to the coastal footpath. The chef/ proprietor ensures excellent cuisine. Picture shows view from hotel.

Bedrooms: 13 double, 7 twin, 1 triple, 2 family rooms; suite available
Bathrooms: 23 en suite

EM 1900 (LO 2030)
Parking for 23
CC: Barclaycard, Delta, Eurocard, JCB, Maestro, Mastercard, Solo, Switch, Visa, Visa Electron

QUALITY ASSURANCE SCHEME

Star ratings and awards are explained at the back of this guide.

ST KEYNE, Cornwall Map ref 1C2

THE OLD RECTORY COUNTRY HOUSE HOTEL

St Keyne, Liskeard, PL14 4RL
T: (01579) 342617 (Ansaphone)
F: (01579) 342293
I: www.theoldrectorystkeyne.com

B&B per night:
D £85.00–£120.00

OPEN All year round

Peacefully secluded, old Georgian rectory hotel in 4 acres of grounds, known for its award-winning food and personal service. Recently totally refurbished. All bedrooms are en suite, with colour TV, direct-dial telephone and trouser press. No children under 15, please.

Bedrooms: 4 double, 2 twin
Bathrooms: 6 en suite

EM 1900 (LO 2100)
Parking for 30
CC: Amex, Barclaycard, Delta, Eurocard, Maestro, Mastercard, Switch, Visa, Visa Electron

SALCOMBE, Devon Map ref 1C3 *Tourist Information Centre Tel: (01548) 843927*

★★★★
Gold
Award

THURLESTONE HOTEL

Thurlestone, Kingsbridge, TQ7 3NN
T: (01548) 560382
F: (01548) 561069
E: enquiries@thurlestone.co.uk
I: www.thurlestone.co.uk

B&B per night:
S £40.00–£122.00
D £80.00–£244.00

HB per person:
DY £48.00–£137.00

OPEN All year round

Set in a peaceful old Devon village, with glorious views of Bigbury Bay. In the same family ownership for 100 years, offering intenational cusine, outstanding leisure and sporting facilities, first class service from friendly and efficient staff, luxury and elegance in a relaxing and comfortable atmosphere.

Bedrooms: 5 single, 18 double, 24 twin, 13 triple, 4 family rooms; suites available
Bathrooms: 64 en suite

Lunch available
EM 1930 (LO 2100)
Parking for 119
CC: Amex, Barclaycard, Eurocard, JCB, Mastercard, Switch, Visa

SALISBURY, Wiltshire Map ref 2B3 *Tourist Information Centre Tel: (01722) 334956*

★★

THE INN AT HIGH POST

High Post, Salisbury, SP4 6AT
T: (01722) 782592
F: (01722) 782630

Bedrooms: 1 single, 13 double, 15 twin, 1 family room
Bathrooms: 30 en suite

Lunch available
EM 1900 (LO 2130)
Parking for 100
CC: Amex, Barclaycard, Delta, Diners, Eurocard, Maestro, Mastercard, Solo, Switch, Visa Electron

B&B per night:
S £59.00–£69.00
D £78.00–£88.00

HB per person:
DY Min £50.00

OPEN All year round

Country location, opposite 18-hole golf course. Good value quality restaurant. Leisure centre with indoor pool, gym, sauna and spa. Four miles north of Salisbury.

SALISBURY PLAIN

See under Hindon, Salisbury

SHALDON, Devon Map ref 1D2

★★

NESS HOUSE HOTEL

Marine Parade, Shaldon, Teignmouth, TQ14 0HP
T: (01626) 873480
F: (01626) 873486
E: nesshtl@dialntart.net

Bedrooms: 2 single, 7 double, 2 family rooms
Bathrooms: 11 en suite

Lunch available
EM 1900 (LO 2215)
Parking for 20
CC: Amex, Barclaycard, Eurocard, Mastercard, Switch, Visa

B&B per night:
S £45.00–£69.00
D £79.00–£99.00

HB per person:
DY £60.00–£84.00

OPEN All year round

Overlooking Teign Estuary. Elegant restaurant and comfortable bars. Most rooms have balconies overlooking the sea. En suite facilities. Easy access to Torquay, Exeter and Dartmoor.

SHEPTON MALLET, Somerset Map ref 2A2 *Tourist Information Centre Tel: (01749) 345258*

★★

THE SHRUBBERY HOTEL
Commercial Road, Shepton Mallet,
BA4 5BU
T: (01749) 346671
F: (01749) 346581

Bedrooms: 7 double,
3 family rooms
Bathrooms: 10 en suite

Lunch available
EM 1900 (LO 2100)
Parking for 100
CC: Amex, Barclaycard,
Delta, Diners, Eurocard,
Mastercard, Switch, Visa

B&B per night:
S Max £52.50
D Max £75.00

OPEN All year round

A small in-town oasis. Privately owned hotel set in delightful gardens, offering customer comfort, a quality restaurant and lounge with light eating facilities. Ideal stopping-off point for the West Country.

〽️ 🐎 🏠 📞 🖥 💻 ⬇️ 🍷 ℹ️ ⑤ ✂️ ♨️ 📺 🛏 🔌 🍽30 ▶ ✳️ 🚲 🚭 SP T

SIDMOUTH, Devon Map ref 1D2 *Tourist Information Centre Tel: (01395) 516441*

★★
Silver
Award

DEVORAN HOTEL
The Esplanade, Sidmouth, EX10 8AU
T: (01395) 513151 & 0800 317171
F: (01395) 579929
E: devoran@cosmic.org.uk
I: www.devoran.com

Bedrooms: 5 single,
7 double, 7 twin, 4 triple
Bathrooms: 23 en suite,
2 public

EM 1845 (LO 1930)
Parking for 4
CC: Delta, Mastercard,
Switch, Visa

B&B per night:
S £32.00–£48.00
D £64.00–£90.00

OPEN Mar–Nov

Family-run hotel overlooking beach, very close to town centre and amenities. Relaxed, happy atmosphere, with traditional home-cooked food using local produce.

〽️ 🐎 ℹ️ ⑤ ✂️ ♨️ 📺 🛏 🔌 💻 ⬇️ ▶ ✳️ 🚭 SC SP T ◎

★★★★
Gold
Award

HOTEL RIVIERA
The Esplanade, Sidmouth, EX10 8AY
T: (01395) 515201
F: (01395) 577775
E: enquiries@hotelriviera.co.uk
I: www.hotelriviera.co.uk

B&B per night:
S £77.00–£103.00
D £134.00–£186.00

HB per person:
DY £77.00–£113.00

OPEN All year round

The hotel has a long tradition of hospitality and is perfect for unforgettable holidays, long weekends, unwinding breaks and all the spirit of the glorious festive season... you will be treated to the kind of friendly personal attention that can only be found in a private hotel of this quality.

Bedrooms: 7 single,
6 double, 14 twin; suites
available
Bathrooms: 27 en suite,
1 public

Lunch available
EM 1900 (LO 2100)
Parking for 26
CC: Amex, Barclaycard,
Diners, Mastercard, Visa

〽️ 🐎 📞 🖥 📳 🍷 ℹ️ ⑤ ✂️ ♨️ ◐ 🛏 💻 🫖 💺 🍽85 ∪ ▶ ✓ ✳️ 🚭 SP ♿ T

★★
Silver
Award

ROYAL YORK AND FAULKNER HOTEL
Esplanade, Sidmouth, EX10 8AZ
T: 0800 220714 (freefone) &
(01395) 513043
F: (01395) 577472
E: yorkhotel@eclipse.co.uk
I: www.royal-york-hotel.co.uk

B&B per night:
S £28.50–£50.50
D £57.00–£101.00

HB per person:
DY £36.50–£58.50

OPEN Feb–Dec

Charming Regency hotel on centre of Sidmouth's delightful Esplanade and adjacent to picturesque town centre. Long established, family-run hotel with emphasis on personal and efficient service, coupled with all amenities and extensive indoor leisure facilities. Superb refurbished de luxe balcony bedrooms. Ideally based for touring the whole of glorious Devon.

Bedrooms: 22 single,
9 double, 29 twin,
8 triple
Bathrooms: 66 en suite,
2 private, 4 public

EM 1915 (LO 2030)
Parking for 20
CC: Barclaycard, Delta,
Eurocard, Mastercard,
Solo, Switch, Visa, Visa
Electron

〽️ 🐎 🛗 📞 🖥 📳 🍷 ℹ️ ⑤ ✂️ ♨️ 📺 🫖 💻 💺 🍽50 🔔 ⚡ ♣ ▶ ✳️ 🚭 SP ♿ T ◎

MAP REFERENCES
Map references apply to the colour maps at the front of this guide.

SIDMOUTH continued

★★ **WOODLANDS HOTEL**

Cotmaton Cross, Station Road,	Bedrooms: 7 single,	EM 1900 (LO 2000)
Sidmouth, EX10 8HG	6 double, 6 twin, 1 triple;	Parking for 28
T: (01395) 513120 &	suite available	CC: Barclaycard, Delta,
513166 (Payphone for guests)	Bathrooms: 20 en suite	Diners, Eurocard, JCB,
F: (01395) 513348		Mastercard, Switch, Visa,
E: info@woodlands-hotel.com		Visa Electron
I: www.woodlands-hotel.com		

B&B per night:
S £24.00–£42.00
D £48.00–£88.00

HB per person:
DY £34.00–£54.00

OPEN All year round

Family-owned and run Regency hotel in tranquil garden. Excellent home-cooked food using fresh local produce. Some ground floor rooms. Near sea and shops.

ⁿⁿ icons

STANTON ST QUINTIN, Wiltshire Map ref 2B2

★★★

STANTON MANOR HOTEL & BURGHLEYS RESTAURANT

Stanton St Quintin, Chippenham,
SN14 6DQ
T: (01666) 837552
F: (01666) 837022
E: reception@stantonmanor.co.uk
I: www.stantonmanor.co.uk

B&B per night:
S £75.00–£95.00
D £95.00–£125.00

HB per person:
DY £65.00–£75.00

OPEN All year round

Just 1 mile from junction 17 of M4, set in 7 tranquil acres, the hotel offers graciously appointed accommodation in the traditional style of a fine English country home. Spacious en suite bedrooms. Burghley's Restaurant enjoys a very high reputation for the quality of its cuisine and wine cellar. Ideal for exploring Cotswolds, Bath, Swindon and Bristol.

Bedrooms: 9 double,	Lunch available
4 twin	EM 1845 (LO 2130)
Bathrooms: 13 en suite,	Parking for 50
1 public	CC: Amex, Barclaycard,
	Delta, Eurocard,
	Mastercard, Switch, Visa

icons 60

STREET, Somerset Map ref 2A2

★★★ **WESSEX HOTEL**

High Street, Street, BA16 0EF	Bedrooms: 7 double,	Lunch available
T: (01458) 443383	39 twin, 4 triple	EM 1900 (LO 2130)
F: (01458) 446589	Bathrooms: 50 en suite	Parking for 90
E: wessex@hotel-street.freeserve.		CC: Amex, Barclaycard,
co.uk		Delta, Diners, Eurocard,
I: www.travel-uk.net/wessexhotel		Mastercard, Solo, Switch,
		Visa

B&B per night:
S £47.00–£57.00
D £64.00–£74.00

HB per person:
DY £47.00–£57.00

OPEN All year round

In the heart of Somerset, legendary country of King Arthur. Nearby attractions include Bath, Glastonbury Abbey, Cheddar Gorge, Wookey Hole Caves and Wells Cathedral.

icons 250

SWINDON, Wiltshire Map ref 2B2 *Tourist Information Centre Tel: (01793) 530328 or 466454*

Rating
Applied For
Ad p15

THISTLE SWINDON

Fleming Way, Swindon, SN1 1TN	Bedrooms: 40 double,	Lunch available
T: (01793) 528282	53 twin, 2 triple	EM 1900 (LO 2145)
F: (01793) 541283	Bathrooms: 95 en suite	CC: Amex, Barclaycard,
		Delta, Diners, JCB,
		Mastercard, Solo, Switch,
		Visa

B&B per night:
S £123.00–£146.00
D £123.00–£146.00

OPEN All year round

℗

Thistle Hotels/Utell
International

A modern hotel situated in the centre of Swindon. The hotel provides the perfect base for business executives or holiday makers. Car parking available.

icons 200

Rating
Applied For

VILLIERS INN

Moormead Road, Wroughton,	Bedrooms: 6 single,	Lunch available
Swindon, Wiltshire SN4 9BY	16 double, 11 twin	EM 1900 (LO 2130)
T: (01793) 814744	Bathrooms: 33 en suite	Parking for 60
F: (01793) 814119		CC: Amex, Barclaycard,
E: info@villiersinn.co.uk		Delta, Diners, Maestro,
I: www.villiersinn.co.uk		Mastercard, Switch, Visa,
		Visa Electron

B&B per night:
S £55.00–£77.00
D £77.00–£100.00

OPEN All year round

Warm-hearted, full-service hotel with personality! An 18thC farmhouse with first class en suite bedrooms and two popular restaurants.

icons 90

TAUNTON, Somerset Map ref 1D1 *Tourist Information Centre Tel: (01823) 336344*

TRAVEL ACCOMMODATION

EXPRESS BY HOLIDAY INN TAUNTON

Blackbrook Business Park,
Blackbrook Park Avenue, Taunton,
TA1 2RW
T: (01823) 624000
F: (01823) 624024
I: www.hiexpress.com/taunton

Bedrooms: 61 double,
31 twin
Bathrooms: 86 en suite

Parking for 100
CC: Amex, Barclaycard,
Delta, Diners, Eurocard,
JCB, Maestro, Mastercard,
Solo, Switch, Visa, Visa
Electron

B&B per night:
S £43.00–£49.50
D £43.00–£49.50

OPEN All year round

Excellent value for money for business and leisure travellers. Conveniently located at junction 25 of the M5 providing easy access to Britain's motorway network and local attractions.

TINTAGEL, Cornwall Map ref 1B2

★★

ATLANTIC VIEW HOTEL

Treknow, Tintagel, PL34 0EJ
T: (01840) 770221
F: (01840) 770995
E: atlantic-view@eclipse.co.uk
I: www.holidayscornwall.com

B&B per night:
S £28.00–£32.00
D £56.00–£64.00

HB per person:
DY £42.00–£48.00

OPEN Feb–Oct

Homely Victorian country hotel built around 1850. Situated in an elevated position, set 300 yards from cliff top, on path to beautiful beach, in the heart of King Arthur's country. Family run, all en suite, sea or country views, some 4-poster beds, excellent cuisine, licensed bar, indoor pool (heated April to October).

Bedrooms: 6 double,
2 twin, 1 triple
Bathrooms: 9 en suite

Lunch available
EM 1900 (LO 2030)
Parking for 10
CC: Amex, Barclaycard,
Delta, Mastercard, Solo,
Switch, Visa

★★

BOSSINEY HOUSE HOTEL

Bossiney Road, Tintagel, PL34 0AX
T: (01840) 770240 & 07770 951411
F: (01840) 770501
E: bossineyhh@eclipse.co.uk
I: www.cornwall-online.co.uk/bossiney

B&B per night:
S £24.00–£34.00
D £48.00–£66.00

HB per person:
DY £38.00–£48.00

OPEN Feb–Oct

Family-run hotel overlooking Cornish countryside and Atlantic coastline. 18 en suite bedrooms, 2 bedrooms with own private facilities. All with colour TV, hairdryer, tea/coffee-making facilities. Heated indoor pool, sauna and solarium, 9-hole putting course. Licensed bar and restaurant. Ideal base for touring south west. Large car park.

Bedrooms: 11 double,
7 twin, 1 triple, 1 family
room
Bathrooms: 18 en suite,
2 private

EM 1900 (LO 2100)
Parking for 30
CC: Amex, Barclaycard,
Delta, Diners, Eurocard,
JCB, Mastercard, Solo,
Switch, Visa, Visa Electron

TOWN INDEX

This can be found at the back of the guide. If you know where you want to stay, the index will give you the page number listing accommodation in your chosen town, city or village.

★★

WILLAPARK MANOR HOTEL

Bossiney, Tintagel, PL34 0BA

T: (01840) 770782

B&B per night:
S £29.00–£35.00
D £59.00–£70.00

HB per person:
DY £43.00–£49.00

OPEN All year round

"One of the most beautifully situated hotels in Cornwall". Set in 14 acres of garden and woodland overlooking picturesque bay and with direct access to coastal path and beach. Our unique situation, well appointed rooms, excellent cuisine and friendly, informal atmosphere bring our guests back year after year.

Bedrooms: 2 single,
7 double, 2 twin, 1 triple,
1 family room
Bathrooms: 13 en suite

Lunch available
EM 1900 (LO 2000)
Parking for 20

★★

THE WOOTONS COUNTRY HOTEL

Fore Street, Tintagel, PL34 0DD
T: (01840) 770170
F: (01840) 770170

Bedrooms: 1 single,
7 double, 3 twin
Bathrooms: 11 en suite

Lunch available
EM 1900 (LO 2130)
Parking for 30
CC: Amex, Barclaycard,
Delta, Diners, Eurocard,
Mastercard, Switch, Visa

B&B per night:
S Min £25.00
D Min £50.00

HB per person:
DY Min £32.50

OPEN All year round

Family-managed hotel offering highest standard en suite accommodation, excellent cuisine and homely atmosphere. Five golf courses within easy reach and numerous local recreational activities.

★★

WHITSAND BAY HOTEL

Portwrinkle, Torpoint, PL11 3BU
T: (01503) 230276
F: (01503) 230329

Bedrooms: 2 single,
10 double, 18 twin,
2 triple, 11 family
rooms; suites available
Bathrooms: 43 en suite,
2 public

Lunch available
EM 1930 (LO 2030)
Parking for 60
CC: Barclaycard, Delta,
Diners, Eurocard,
Mastercard, Switch, Visa

B&B per night:
S £25.00–£50.00
D £70.00–£90.00

HB per person:
DY £45.00–£75.00

OPEN All year round

Spectacularly sited elegant country mansion with sea views. Own 18-hole golf-course. Indoor heated pools and leisure complex. Self-catering units also available.

★★
Silver
Award

BARN HAYES COUNTRY HOTEL

Brim Hill, Maidencombe, Torquay, Devon
TQ1 4TR
T: (01803) 327980
F: (01803) 327980
E: info@barnhayescountryhotel.co.uk
I: www.barnhayescountryhotel.co.uk

B&B per night:
S £32.00–£36.00
D £64.00–£72.00

HB per person:
DY £45.00–£49.00

OPEN mid Feb– end Nov

Warm, friendly, family-run, non-smoking hotel with beautiful gardens overlooking countryside and sea, in a lovely walking Area of Outstanding Natural Beauty. Relaxation is guaranteed in these lovely surroundings with genuine hospitality and excellent home cooking. Ideally placed to discover the delights of Devon, whatever the season. Prestigious dining award.

Bedrooms: 4 double,
1 twin, 3 triple, 2 family
rooms
Bathrooms: 10 en suite,
1 public

EM 1900
Parking for 16
CC: Barclaycard, Delta,
Mastercard, Solo, Switch,
Visa, Visa Electron

COLOUR MAPS
Colour maps at the front of this guide pinpoint all places under which you will find accommodation listed.

★★

BUTE COURT HOTEL
Belgrave Road, Torquay, Devon TQ2 5HQ
T: (01803) 213055
F: (01803) 213429
I: www.bute-court-hotel.co.uk

B&B per night:
S £23.00–£35.00
D £46.00–£70.00

HB per person:
DY £28.00–£40.00

OPEN All year round

Run by the same family for 50 years, the hotel is situated in its own grounds with garden, swimming pool and car park, overlooking Torbay. All 45 bedrooms are en suite. Lift, bar, spacious lounges and games rooms. Off-season mini-breaks. Entertainment in season. Pets welcome.	Bedrooms: 10 single, 15 double, 10 twin, 8 triple, 2 family rooms Bathrooms: 45 en suite, 1 public	Lunch available EM 1830 (LO 2000) Parking for 38 CC: Amex, Barclaycard, Delta, Diners, Eurocard, Mastercard, Solo, Switch, Visa, Visa Electron

⚅🏇♿📞🖥✆🛏⑤📺📺🌙⬆🏢📠✆40🔍🗡✂🌸🔌 SP 🏨 T

★

EXMOUTH VIEW HOTEL
St Albans Road, Babbacombe, Torquay,
Devon TQ1 3LG
T: (01803) 327307
F: (01803) 326697
E: relax@exmouth-view.co.uk
I: www.exmouth-view.co.uk

B&B per night:
S £18.00–£30.00
D £36.00–£60.00

HB per person:
DY £25.00–£38.00

OPEN All year round

A warm welcome awaits guests from the resident family owners. Only a few metres from Babbacombe Downs and close to all local attractions. Luxury en suite rooms, colour TV, tea/coffee facilities, central heating. Coastal facing restaurant with freshly prepared home-cooked food. Licensed bar, TV lounge, private car park.	Bedrooms: 2 single, 8 double, 5 twin, 7 family rooms Bathrooms: 22 en suite	EM 1830 (LO 1915) Parking for 25 CC: Amex, Delta, Eurocard, JCB, Mastercard, Solo, Switch, Visa, Visa Electron

⚅🏇♿📞✆🛏⑤✂🌙📺📺🏢📠✆40🐴 SC 🔌 SP T

★★

FROGNEL HALL
Higher Woodfield Road, Torquay, Devon
TQ1 2LD
T: (01803) 298339
F: (01803) 215115
E: frognel@btinternet.com
I: www.frognelhall.co.uk

B&B per night:
S £23.00–£30.00
D £46.00–£60.00

HB per person:
DY £31.00–£39.00

OPEN All year round

Beautiful Victorian mansion set in large, peaceful gardens near harbour, beaches and Torquay centre. With a wide choice of freshly prepared food and good wine, fine views, parking and lift, this is the ideal base from which to explore Devon, Cornwall, Dartmoor National Park and the South Coastal path.	Bedrooms: 4 single, 8 double, 7 twin, 7 triple, 2 family rooms Bathrooms: 27 en suite, 1 private	Lunch available EM 1830 (LO 2000) Parking for 20 CC: Amex, Barclaycard, Delta, Diners, Eurocard, JCB, Maestro, Mastercard, Solo, Switch, Visa, Visa Electron

⚅🏇♿📞✆🛏⑤✂🌙📺⑤🏢📠✆60🌱🗡🔍🌸🔌 SP 🏨 T

QUALITY ASSURANCE SCHEME
Star ratings and awards were correct at the time of going to press but are subject to change. Please check at the time of booking.

★★★★

PALACE HOTEL
Babbacombe Road, Torquay, Devon
TQ1 3TG
T: (01803) 200200
F: (01803) 299899
E: mail1@palacetorquay.co.uk
I: www.palacetorquay.co.uk

B&B per night:
S £61.00–£71.00
D £142.00–£162.00

HB per person:
DY £71.00–£81.00

OPEN All year round

A fine independent hotel, beautifully set in 25 acres of magnificent grounds, overlooking the charming Anstey's Cove. The unrivalled leisure facilities include a 9-hole short golf course, indoor and outdoor swimming pools and tennis courts. The hotel offers exceptionally high standards of service and excellent cuisine.

Bedrooms: 45 single, 40 double, 36 twin, 6 triple, 14 family rooms; suites available
Bathrooms: 141 en suite

Lunch available
EM 1930 (LO 2115)
Parking for 150
CC: Barclaycard, Delta, Diners, Eurocard, Mastercard, Switch, Visa

1000

★★

RED HOUSE HOTEL
Rousdown Road, Chelston, Torquay, TQ2 6PB
T: (01803) 607811
F: (01803) 200592
E: stay@redhouse-hotel.co.uk
I: www.redhouse-hotel.co.uk

Bedrooms: 1 single, 3 double, 1 twin, 3 triple, 2 family rooms
Bathrooms: 10 en suite

EM 1830 (LO 2000)
Parking for 12
CC: Barclaycard, Delta, Mastercard, Solo, Switch, Visa

B&B per night:
S £20.00–£31.00
D £40.00–£62.00

HB per person:
DY £26.00–£37.00

OPEN All year round

Small friendly hotel offering indoor/outdoor pools, spa, sauna, gym and beauty salon. Adjoining self-catering or serviced apartments. Convenient for seafront and other amenities.

20

★★

SHEDDEN HALL HOTEL
Shedden Hill, Torquay, TQ2 5TX
T: (01803) 292964
F: (01803) 295306
E: sheddenhtl@aol.com
I: www.sheddenhallhotel.co.uk

B&B per night:
S £27.00–£35.00
D £54.00–£70.00

HB per person:
DY £32.00–£40.00

OPEN Mar–Dec

Situated in one of the most enviable postions in Torquay with magnificent panoramic sea views, this quality family-run hotel is within easy walking distance of Torre Abbey sands, the town, theatre and leisure centre. Heated outdoor swimming pool set in own gardens, entertainment, superb cuisine, car park.

Bedrooms: 1 single, 12 double, 7 twin, 5 family rooms
Bathrooms: 25 en suite

EM 1830 (LO 2000)
Parking for 30
CC: Amex, Barclaycard, Delta, Diners, Eurocard, JCB, Maestro, Mastercard, Solo, Switch, Visa, Visa Electron

4

★★

SYDORE HOTEL
Meadfoot Road, Torquay, TQ1 2JP
T: (01803) 294758
F: (01803) 294489
E: john@sydore.co.uk
I: www.sydore.co.uk

Bedrooms: 6 double, 3 twin, 3 triple, 1 family room
Bathrooms: 13 en suite

Lunch available
EM 1830 (LO 2000)
Parking for 20
CC: Amex, Barclaycard, Delta, Diners, JCB, Maestro, Mastercard, Solo, Switch, Visa, Visa Electron

B&B per night:
S £25.00–£35.00
D £45.00–£65.00

HB per person:
DY £30.00–£40.00

OPEN All year round

Detached Georgian villa in secluded garden, within walking distance of harbour and central shopping. High proportion of rooms with 4-poster beds. English-style cooking including puddings selection.

TOTNES, Devon Map ref 1D2 *Tourist Information Centre Tel: (01803) 863168*

★★ **ROYAL SEVEN STARS HOTEL**

The Plains, Totnes, TQ9 5DD
T: (01803) 862125 & 863241
F: (01803) 867925
I: www.smoothhound.co.uk/hotels/
royal7.html

Bedrooms: 1 single,
10 double, 3 twin,
1 triple, 1 family room
Bathrooms: 14 en suite
2 private, 1 public

Lunch available
EM 1900 (LO 2115)
Parking for 20
CC: Amex, Barclaycard,
Delta, Diners, Eurocard,
JCB, Maestro, Mastercard,
Switch, Visa, Visa Electron

B&B per night:
S £49.00–£59.00
D £62.00–£69.00

HB per person:
DY £46.00–£74.00

OPEN All year round

Old coaching inn in the centre of Totnes, near River Dart. Short drive to coast and Dartmoor. Brochures available on request. Weekend breaks available.

TRURO, Cornwall Map ref 1B3 *Tourist Information Centre Tel: (01872) 274555*

★★★

ALVERTON MANOR
Tregolls Road, Truro, TR1 1ZQ
T: (01872) 276633
F: (01872) 222989
E: alverton@connexions.co.uk

B&B per night:
S £67.00–£110.00

OPEN All year round

The Alverton Manor is an impressive sight on its hillside setting, providing luxurious and relaxing accommodation, superb award-winning cuisine and the highest standard of service. Alverton also boasts its own 18-hole golf course located in over 400 acres of rolling parkland within the historic Killiow Estate.

Bedrooms: 6 single,
23 double, 5 twin; suites
available
Bathrooms: 34 en suite

Lunch available
EM 1900 (LO 2130)
Parking for 120
CC: Amex, Barclaycard,
Delta, Diners, JCB,
Mastercard, Switch, Visa

WATCHET, Somerset Map ref 1D1

★★
Silver
Award

DOWNFIELD HOUSE HOTEL

16 St Decuman's Road, Watchet,
TA23 0HR
T: (01984) 631267
F: (01984) 634369

Bedrooms: 5 double,
2 twin
Bathrooms: 7 en suite

EM 1900 (LO 2030)
Parking for 15
CC: Amex, Barclaycard,
Delta, Eurocard, JCB,
Mastercard, Solo, Switch,
Visa

B&B per night:
S £34.00–£43.00
D £44.00–£62.00

HB per person:
DY £44.00–£51.00

OPEN All year round

Attractive Victorian country house, set in secluded grounds with views over harbour and town. Comfortable lounge, chandeliered dining room. Close to Quantocks and Exmoor.

WELLS, Somerset Map ref 2A2 *Tourist Information Centre Tel: (01749) 672552*

THE MARKET PLACE HOTEL AND RESTAURANT

Wells, BA5 2RW
T: (01749) 672616
F: (01749) 679670
E: marketplace@bhere.co.uk
I: www.bhere.co.uk

Bedrooms: 1 single,
14 double, 17 twin,
2 triple
Bathrooms: 34 en suite

Lunch available
EM 1900 (LO 2200)
Parking for 25
CC: Amex, Barclaycard,
Delta, Eurocard, Maestro,
Mastercard, Switch, Visa

B&B per night:
S £75.00–£79.50
D £85.00–£119.50

HB per person:
DY £52.50–£77.50

OPEN All year round

CR
Best Western Hotels

A 15thC hotel situated in the lee of Wells Cathedral. Recent extensive refurbishment, original features. Master bedrooms.

★★★
Silver
Award

SWAN HOTEL

Sadler Street, Wells, BA5 2RX
T: (01749) 678877
F: (01749) 677647
E: swan@bhere.co.uk
I: www.bhere.co.uk

Bedrooms: 9 single,
19 double, 10 twin
Bathrooms: 38 en suite

Lunch available
EM 1900 (LO 2130)
Parking for 35
CC: Amex, Barclaycard,
Delta, Eurocard, Maestro,
Mastercard, Switch, Visa

B&B per night:
S £75.00–£79.50
D £85.00–£119.50

HB per person:
DY £52.50–£77.50

OPEN All year round

CR
Best Western Hotels

Privately-owned 15thC hotel with views of the cathedral's west front. Restaurant, saddle bar, log fires. Four-poster beds available.

WELLS continued

★★

THE WHITE HART HOTEL
Sadler Street, Wells, BA5 2RR
T: (01749) 672056
F: (01749) 672056
E: whitehart@wells.demon.co.uk
I: www.wells.demon.co.uk

B&B per night:
S £50.00–£55.00
D £70.00–£80.00

HB per person:
DY £40.00–£50.00

OPEN All year round

A 14thC coaching inn offering en
suite bedrooms, conference facilities
for up to 80, extensive brasserie
menu and separate restaurant. The
hotel's refurbishment was completed
in 1997, resulting in what many have
stated is now a classic example of a
traditional coaching inn.

Bedrooms: 1 single,
10 double, 2 twin
Bathrooms: 13 en suite

Lunch available
EM 1800 (LO 2130)
Parking for 17
CC: Amex, Barclaycard,
Delta, Mastercard, Solo,
Switch, Visa, Visa Electron

Ⓜ︎ ➤ ✆ 🖥 ➡️ ♨ ✇ 🛈 Ⓢ ⦂ 🖨 🛏 ⟱ ➡️ 🍴60 ▶ ✎ 🆂🅿️ 🎦 Ⓣ

WEST BEXINGTON, Dorset Map ref 2A3

★★

THE MANOR HOTEL
West Bexington, Dorchester,
DT2 9DF
T: (01308) 897616 & 897785
F: (01308) 897035
E: themanorhotel@btconnect.com
I: www.dorset-info.co.uk/
manor_hotel_bexington.htm

Bedrooms: 1 single,
8 double, 3 twin, 1 triple
Bathrooms: 13 en suite

Lunch available
EM 1900 (LO 2200)
Parking for 20
CC: Amex, Barclaycard,
Mastercard, Switch, Visa

B&B per night:
S £57.00–£60.00
D £95.00–£100.00

HB per person:
DY £69.00–£73.50

OPEN All year round

16thC manor house, 500 yards from Chesil Beach. Panoramic views from most bedrooms.
3 real ales and character cellar bar.

Ⓜ︎ ➤ ✆ 🖥 ➡️ ♨ ✇ 🛈 Ⓢ ⦂ 🖨 🛏 ⟱ ➡️ 🍴60 ▶ ❋ ✗ 🆂🅿️ 🎦 Ⓣ

WESTON-SUPER-MARE, North Somerset Map ref 1D1 *Tourist Information Centre Tel: (01934) 888800*

★★

AROSFA HOTEL
Lower Church Road, Weston-super-
Mare, BS23 2AG
T: (01934) 419523
F: (01934) 636084
E: info@arosfahotel.co.uk
I: www.arosfahotel.co.uk

Bedrooms: 14 single,
12 double, 15 twin,
3 triple, 2 family rooms
Bathrooms: 46 en suite

Lunch available
EM 1830 (LO 2030)
Parking for 6
CC: Amex, Barclaycard,
Delta, Diners, Eurocard,
Maestro, Mastercard,
Solo, Switch, Visa, Visa
Electron

B&B per night:
S £40.00–£50.00
D £60.00–£65.00

HB per person:
DY £45.00–£55.00

OPEN All year round

Refurbished hotel with 3 lounges, bars, dining room and comfortable bedrooms. Situated
on level ground 100 yards from the town centre and seafront.

➤ ✆ 🖥 ➡️ ♨ ✇ 🛈 Ⓢ ⦂ 🖨 📺 🌓 ✉ 🛏 ⟱ ➡️ 🍴120 ☎ ∪ ▶ 🆂🅲 🆂🅿️ Ⓣ

WEYMOUTH, Dorset Map ref 2B3 *Tourist Information Centre Tel: (01305) 785747*

★★

THE GLENBURN HOTEL
42 Preston Road, Weymouth,
DT3 6PZ
T: (01305) 832353
F: (01305) 835610

Bedrooms: 3 single,
6 double, 2 twin,
2 family rooms
Bathrooms: 13 en suite

EM 1830 (LO 2100)
Parking for 16
CC: Barclaycard, Delta,
Mastercard, Solo, Switch,
Visa, Visa Electron

B&B per night:
S £30.00–£43.00
D £50.00–£70.00

HB per person:
DY £35.00–£53.00

OPEN All year round

Home from home. Very comfortable, family-run small hotel, refurbished, large garden.
Quieter side of Weymouth. Excellent home-cooked fresh food, all diets catered for.

➤ 🔥 🖥 ➡️ ♨ ✇ 🛈 Ⓢ ⦂ 🖨 🛏 ⟱ ➡️ ❋ ✗ Ⓣ

CHECK THE MAPS
The colour maps at the front of this guide show
all the cities, towns and villages for which you will
find accommodation entries. Refer to the town
index to find the page on which they are listed.

★★★

HOTEL REMBRANDT

12-18 Dorchester Road, Weymouth, DT4 7JU

T: (01305) 764000
F: (01305) 764022
E: reception@hotelrembrandt.co.uk
I: www.hotelrembrandt.co.uk

Weymouth's premier hotel, within easy walking distance of the seafront and town centre. Carvery restaurant and bar, coffee shop leading to secluded garden. Large car park. Hotel leisure club has a large heated indoor pool, sauna, steam room, jacuzzi and gymnasium.

Bedrooms: 6 single, 27 double, 12 twin, 31 triple, 6 family rooms; suites available	Lunch available
	EM 1830 (LO 2115)
Bathrooms: 82 en suite, 2 public	Parking for 90
	CC: Amex, Barclaycard, Delta, Diners, Mastercard, Solo, Switch, Visa

B&B per night:
S £45.00–£70.00
D £70.00–£90.00

HB per person:
DY £39.50–£49.50

OPEN All year round

⋔ 👥 ⚒ 🛏 📞 ▤ ▢ ♦ 🔍 🛈 🔑 Ⅺ ● ⬆ 🏛 🍽 ⚓ 🍴200 👥 🏸 🎿 🚵 🐟 🕸 SP Ⓣ

★★★

HOTEL REX

29 The Esplanade, Weymouth, DT4 8DN

T: (01305) 760400
F: (01305) 760500
E: rex@kingshotels.f9.co.uk

Georgian townhouse situated on the Esplanade overlooking Weymouth Bay, adjacent to the harbour and town centre and close to the Pavilion. Easy access to beautiful Thomas Hardy Country. Portland and Chesil Beach with its Jurassic coastline is close by.

Bedrooms: 11 single, 8 double, 7 twin, 5 triple	Lunch available
	EM 1800 (LO 2200)
Bathrooms: 31 en suite	Parking for 6
	CC: Amex, Barclaycard, Delta, Diners, Eurocard, Mastercard, Solo, Switch, Visa

B&B per night:
S £45.00–£55.00
D £72.00–£99.00

HB per person:
DY £56.00–£118.00

OPEN All year round

⋔ 👥 🛏 📞 ▤ ▢ ♦ 🔍 🛈 Ⅺ TV ● ⬆ 🏛 ⚓ 🍴45 SC 🕸 SP 🛗 Ⓣ

WHEDDON CROSS, Somerset Map ref 1D1

★★

RALEIGH MANOR COUNTRY HOUSE HOTEL
Wheddon Cross, Minehead, TA24 7BB
T: (01643) 841484
E: raleighmanor@easynet.co.uk
I: www.raleighmanorhotel.co.uk

Bedrooms: 1 single, 3 double, 2 twin	EM 1930 (LO 2030)
	Parking for 10
Bathrooms: 6 en suite	CC: Barclaycard, Delta, Mastercard, Switch, Visa, Visa Electron

B&B per night:
S £31.00–£35.00
D £62.00–£70.00

HB per person:
DY £46.50–£56.50

OPEN Mar–Dec

Enchanting 19thC manor in idyllic Exmoor setting with outstanding views. Secluded and peaceful, offering log fires, good food and fine wines.

👥5 🏛 ▤ ▢ ♦ 🔍 🛈 🔑 Ⅺ ▥ ⚓ ✳ 🐕 🐎 🛗

WOOLACOMBE, Devon Map ref 1C1 *Tourist Information Centre Tel: (01271) 870553*

★
Silver
Award

CROSSWAYS HOTEL

The Esplanade, Woolacombe, EX34 7DJ

T: (01271) 870395
F: (01271) 870395
I: www.smoothhound.co.uk/hotels/crossway.html

Friendly, award-winning family-run hotel in quiet seafront position with superb views of Combesgate beach, Morte Point and Lundy Island. Surfing and swimming from the hotel which is surrounded by National Trust land. Personal service, menu choice, children and pets welcome. Why not find out why guests return year after year?

Bedrooms: 1 single, 3 double, 2 twin, 3 family rooms	Lunch available
	EM 1830 (LO 1830)
Bathrooms: 6 en suite, 1 private, 1 public	Parking for 10

B&B per night:
S £24.00–£31.00
D £48.00–£62.00

HB per person:
DY £29.00–£36.00

OPEN Mar–Oct

⋔ 👥 ⚒ ▢ ♦ 🔍 Ⅺ ▥ ⚓ 🐕 SP Ⓣ

WOOLACOMBE continued

★★★
Silver
Award

WATERSMEET HOTEL
Mortehoe, Woolacombe, EX34 7EB
T: (01271) 870333
F: (01271) 870890
E: watersmeethotel@compuserve.com
I: www:watersmeethotel.co.uk

B&B per night:
S £73.00–£112.00
D £116.00–£197.00

HB per person:
DY £81.00–£120.00

OPEN Feb–Nov

Watersmeet personifies the comfortable luxury of a country-house hotel. Gardens reach down to the sea and coast path, with nearby steps leading directly to the beach. The main bedrooms have sea views towards Hartland Point and Lundy Island. Tempting English and international dishes are served in the award-winning restaurant.

Bedrooms: 1 single, 12 double, 8 twin, 2 triple; suite available
Bathrooms: 22 en suite

Lunch available
EM 1900 (LO 2030)
Parking for 50
CC: Amex, Barclaycard, Delta, Diners, Mastercard, Switch, Visa

🛇 🚿 🎬 📞 🖥 🖵 🥤 ⓘ Ⓢ ✂ 🎦 🛏 ☕ 🍴 40 ⚹ ⚹ ⚲ ∪ ♪ ✸ ✈ 🚲 SP Ⓣ

YEOVIL, Somerset Map ref 2A3 *Tourist Information Centre Tel: (01935) 471279*

★

PRESTON HOTEL AND MOTEL
64 Preston Road, Yeovil, BA20 2DL
T: (01935) 474400
F: (01935) 410142
E: prestonhotel.freeserve.co.uk

Bedrooms: 1 single, 3 double, 9 triple, 1 family room
Bathrooms: 14 en suite

Lunch available
EM 1900 (LO 2100)
Parking for 20
CC: Amex, Barclaycard, Delta, Diners, Eurocard, JCB, Mastercard, Solo, Switch, Visa

B&B per night:
S £42.00–£55.00
D £55.00–£68.00

OPEN All year round

Friendly, comfortable hotel, bar and restaurant. All 14 spacious rooms have private bath, TV and telephone. Facilities for disabled.

🛇 🚿 📞 🖵 🤵 ⓘ Ⓢ ✂ 🎦 📺 🛏 ☕ ✿ SP Ⓣ

USE YOUR *i*s
There are more than 550 Tourist Information Centres throughout England offering friendly help with accommodation and holiday ideas as well as suggestions of places to visit and things to do. You'll find TIC addresses in the local Phone Book.

A brief guide to the main Towns and Villages
offering accommodation in the SOUTH WEST

BADMINTON, GLOUCESTERSHIRE - Small village close to Badminton House, a 17th to 18th C Palladian mansion which has been the seat of the Dukes of Beaufort for centuries. The 3-day Badminton Horse Trials are held in the Great Park every May.

● **BATH, BATH & NORTH EAST SOMERSET** - Georgian spa city beside the River Avon. Important Roman site with impressive reconstructed baths, uncovered in the 19th C. Bath Abbey built on the site of the monastery where the first king of England was crowned (AD 973). Fine architecture in mellow local stone. Pump Room and museums.

● **BIGBURY-ON-SEA, DEVON** - Small resort on Bigbury Bay at the mouth of the River Avon. Wide sands, rugged cliffs. Burgh Island can be reached on foot at low tide.

● **BOVEY TRACEY, DEVON** - Standing by the river just east of Dartmoor National Park, this old town has good moorland views. Its church, with a 14th C tower, holds one of Devon's finest medieval rood screens.

● **BRIDGWATER, SOMERSET** - Former medieval port on the River Parrett, now small industrial town with mostly 19th C or modern architecture. Georgian Castle Street leads to West Quay and site of 13th C castle razed to the ground by Cromwell. Birthplace of Cromwellian Admiral Robert Blake is now museum. Arts centre.

● **BRIDPORT, DORSET** - Market town and chief producer of nets and ropes just inland of dramatic Dorset coast. Old, broad streets built for drying and twisting and long gardens for rope-walks. Grand arcaded Town Hall and Georgian buildings. Local history museum has Roman relics.

● **BRISTOL** - Famous for maritime links, historic harbour, Georgian terraces and Brunel's Clifton suspension bridge. Many attractions including SS Great Britain, Bristol Zoo, museums and art galleries and top name entertainments. Events include Balloon Fiesta and Regatta.

● **BRIXHAM, DEVON** - Famous for its trawling fleet in the 19th C, a steeply-built fishing port overlooking the harbour and fish market. A statue of William of Orange recalls his landing here before deposing James II. There is an aquarium and museum. Good cliff views and walks.

● **BUDE, CORNWALL** - Resort on dramatic Atlantic coast. High cliffs give spectacular sea and inland views. Golf-course, cricket pitch, folly, surfing, coarse-fishing and boating. Mother-town Stratton was base of Royalist Sir Bevil Grenville.

CHARD, SOMERSET - Market town in hilly countryside. The wide main street has some handsome buildings, among them the Guildhall, court house and almshouses. Modern light industry and dairy produce have replaced 19th C lace making which came at decline of cloth trade.

● **CHARMOUTH, DORSET** - Set back from the fossil-rich cliffs, a small coastal town where Charles II came to the Queen's Armes when seeking escape to France. Just south at low tide, the sandy beach rewards fossil-hunters; at Black Ven an ichthyosaurus (now in London's Natural History Museum) was found.

● **CLOVELLY, DEVON** - Clinging to wooded cliffs, fishing village with steep cobbled street zigzagging, or cut in steps, to harbour. Carrying sledges stand beside whitewashed flower-decked cottages. Charles Kingsley's father was rector of the church set high up near the Hamlyn family's Clovelly Court.

DARTMOUTH, DEVON - Ancient port at mouth of Dart. Has fine period buildings, notably town houses near Quay and Butterwalk of 1635. Harbour castle ruin. In 12th C Crusader fleets assembled here. Royal Naval College dominates from Hill. Carnival, June; Regatta, August.

● **DUNSTER, SOMERSET** - Ancient town with views of Exmoor. The hilltop castle has been continuously occupied since 1070. Medieval prosperity from cloth built 16th C octagonal Yarn Market and the church. A riverside mill, packhorse bridge and 18th C hilltop folly occupy other interesting corners in the town.

EXETER, DEVON - University city rebuilt after the 1940s around its cathedral. Attractions include 13th C cathedral with fine west front; notable waterfront buildings; Guildhall; Royal Albert Memorial Museum; underground passages; Northcott Theatre.

● **EXMOUTH, DEVON** - Developed as a seaside resort in George III's reign, set against the woods of the Exe Estuary and red cliffs of Orcombe Point. Extensive sands, small harbour, chapel and almshouses, a model railway and A la Ronde, a 16-sided house.

FALMOUTH, CORNWALL - Busy port and fishing harbour, popular resort on the balmy Cornish Riviera. Henry VIII's Pendennis Castle faces St Mawes Castle across the broad natural harbour and yacht basin Carrick Roads, which receives 7 rivers.

● **FOWEY, CORNWALL** - Set on steep slopes at the mouth of the Fowey River, important clayport and fishing town. Ruined forts guarding the shore recall days of "Fowey Gallants" who ruled local seas. The lofty church rises above the town. Ferries to Polruan and Bodinnick; August Regatta.

HOLFORD, SOMERSET - Sheltered in a wooded combe on the edge of the Quantocks, small village near Alfoxden House where William Wordsworth and his sister Dorothy lived in the late 1790s. Samuel Coleridge occupied a cottage at Nether Stowey during the same period. Nearby Quantock Forest has nature trails.

● **HONITON, DEVON** - Old coaching town in undulating farmland. Formerly famous for lace-making, it is now an antiques trade centre and market town. Small museum.

ILFRACOMBE, DEVON - Resort of Victorian grandeur set on hillside between cliffs with sandy coves. At the mouth of the harbour stands an 18th C lighthouse, built over a medieval chapel. There are fine formal gardens and a museum. Chambercombe Manor, an interesting old house, is nearby.

● **ILLOGAN, CORNWALL** - Former mining village 2 miles north-west of Redruth and close to the coast. The Victorian engineer and benefactor, Sir Richard Tangye, was born here in 1833.

● **ILSINGTON, DEVON** - Village 4 miles north-east of Ashburton, and within the Dartmoor National Park. Yarner Wood National Nature Reserve to the north.

● **IVYBRIDGE, DEVON** - Town set in delightful woodlands on the River Erme. Brunel designed the local railway viaduct. South Dartmoor Leisure Centre.

LOOE, CORNWALL - Small resort developed around former fishing and smuggling ports occupying the deep estuary of the East and West Looe Rivers. Narrow winding streets, with old inns; museum and art gallery are housed in interesting old buildings. Shark fishing centre, boat trips; busy harbour.

● **LOSTWITHIEL, CORNWALL** - Cornwall's ancient capital which gained its Royal Charter in 1189. Tin from the mines around the town was smelted and coined in the Duchy Palace. Norman Restormel Castle, with its circular keep and deep moat, overlooks the town.

ACCESSIBILITY
Look for the 🦽🦽🧑 symbols which indicate accessibility for wheelchair users. A list of establishments is at the front of this guide.

- **LYME REGIS, DORSET** - Pretty, historic fishing town and resort set against the fossil-rich cliffs of Lyme Bay. In medieval times it was an important port and cloth centre. The Cobb, a massive stone breakwater, shelters the ancient harbour which is still lively with boats.

- **LYNMOUTH, DEVON** - Resort set beneath bracken-covered cliffs and pinewood gorges where 2 rivers meet, and cascade between boulders to the town. Lynton, set on cliffs above, can be reached by water-operated cliff railway from the Victorian esplanade. Valley of the Rocks, to the west, gives dramatic walks.

- **LYNTON, DEVON** - Hilltop resort on Exmoor coast linked to its seaside twin, Lynmouth, by a water-operated cliff railway which descends from the town hall. Spectacular surroundings of moorland cliffs with steep chasms of conifer and rocks through which rivers cascade.

- **MALMESBURY, WILTSHIRE** - Overlooking the River Avon, an old town dominated by its great church, once a Benedictine abbey. The surviving Norman nave and porch are noted for fine sculptures, 12th C arches and musicians' gallery.

- **MAWGAN PORTH, CORNWALL** - Holiday village occupying a steep valley on the popular coastal route to Newquay. Golden sands, rugged cliffs and coves. Nearby Bedruthan Steps offers exhilarating cliff walks and views. The chapel of a Carmelite nunnery, once the home of the Arundells, may be visited.

- **MEVAGISSEY, CORNWALL** - Small fishing town, a favourite with holidaymakers. Earlier prosperity came from pilchard fisheries, boat-building and smuggling. By the harbour are fish cellars, some converted, and a local history museum is housed in an old boat-building shed. Handsome Methodist chapel; shark fishing, sailing.

- **MINEHEAD, SOMERSET** - Victorian resort with spreading sands developed around old fishing port on the coast below Exmoor. Former fishermen's cottages stand beside the 17th C harbour; cobbled streets climb the hill in steps to the church. Boat trips, steam railway. Hobby Horse festival 1 May.

- **MORETONHAMPSTEAD, DEVON** - Small market town with a row of 17th C almshouses standing on the Exeter road. Surrounding moorland is scattered with ancient farmhouses, prehistoric sites.

- **NEWQUAY, CORNWALL** - Popular resort spread over dramatic cliffs around its old fishing port. Many beaches with abundant sands, caves and rock pools; excellent surf. Pilots' gigs are still raced from the harbour and on the headland stands the stone Huer's House from the pilchard-fishing days.

- **OKEHAMPTON, DEVON** - Busy market town near the high tors of northern Dartmoor. The Victorian church, with William Morris windows and a 15th C tower, stands on the site of a Saxon church. A Norman castle ruin overlooks the river to the west of the town. Museum of Dartmoor Life in a restored mill.

- **OTTERY ST MARY, DEVON** - Former wool town with modern light industry set in countryside on the River Otter. The Cromwellian commander, Fairfax, made his headquarters here briefly during the Civil War. The interesting church, dating from the 14th C, is built to cathedral plan.

- **PAIGNTON, DEVON** - Lively seaside resort with a pretty harbour on Torbay. Bronze Age and Saxon sites are occupied by the 15th C church, which has a Norman door and font. The beautiful Chantry Chapel was built by local landowners, the Kirkhams.

- **PENZANCE, CORNWALL** - Resort and fishing port on Mount's Bay with mainly Victorian promenade and some fine Regency terraces. Former prosperity came from tin trade and pilchard fishing. Grand Georgian style church by harbour. Georgian Egyptian building at head of Chapel Street and Morrab Gardens.

- **PLYMOUTH, DEVON** - Devon's largest city, major port and naval base. Old houses on the Barbican and ambitious architecture in modern centre, with new National Marine Aquarium, museum and art gallery, the Dome - a heritage centre on the Hoe. Superb coastal views over Plymouth Sound from the Hoe.

- **PORLOCK, SOMERSET** - Village set between steep Exmoor hills and the sea at the head of beautiful Porlock Vale. The narrow street shows a medley of building styles. South westward is Porlock Weir with its old houses and tiny harbour and further along the shore at Culbone is England's smallest church.

- **PORTLOE, CORNWALL** - Old fishing village and small resort where majestic cliffs rise from Veryan Bay. Unspoilt National Trust coast stretches south-westward to Nare Head.

- **ROCK, CORNWALL** - Small resort and boating centre beside the abundant sands of the Camel Estuary. A fine golf-course stretches northward along the shore to Brea Hill, thought to be the site of a Roman settlement. Passenger ferry service from Padstow.

- **RUAN HIGH LANES, CORNWALL** - Village at the northern end of the Roseland Peninsula.

- **ST AGNES, CORNWALL** - Small town in a once-rich mining area on the north coast. Terraced cottages and granite houses slope to the church. Some old mine workings remain, but the attraction must be the magnificent coastal scenery and superb walks. St Agnes Beacon offers one of Cornwall's most extensive views.

- **ST IVES, CORNWALL** - Old fishing port, artists' colony and holiday town with good surfing beach. Fishermen's cottages, granite fish cellars, a sandy harbour and magnificent headlands typify a charm that has survived since the 19th C pilchard boom. Tate Gallery opened in 1993.

- **SALCOMBE, DEVON** - Sheltered yachting resort of whitewashed houses and narrow streets in a balmy setting on the Salcombe Estuary. Palm, myrtle and other Mediterranean plants flourish. There are sandy bays and creeks for boating.

- **SALISBURY, WILTSHIRE** - Beautiful city and ancient regional capital set amid water meadows. Buildings of all periods are dominated by the cathedral whose spire is the tallest in England. Built between 1220 and 1258, it is one of the purest examples of Early English architecture.

- **SHALDON, DEVON** - Pretty resort facing Teignmouth from the south bank of the Teign Estuary. Regency houses harmonise with others of later periods; there are old cottages and narrow lanes. On the Ness, a sandstone promontory nearby, a tunnel built in the 19th C leads to a beach revealed at low tide.

- **SHEPTON MALLET, SOMERSET** - Historic town in the Mendip foothills, important in Roman times and site of many significant archaeological finds. Cloth industry reached its peak in the 17th C, and many fine examples of cloth merchants' houses remain. Beautiful parish church, market cross, local history museum, Collett Park.

- **SIDMOUTH, DEVON** - Charming resort set amid lofty red cliffs where the River Sid meets the sea. The wealth of ornate Regency and Victorian villas recalls the time when this was one of the south coast's most exclusive resorts. Museum; August International Festival of Folk Arts.

NB **IMPORTANT NOTE** Information on accommodation listed in this guide has been supplied by the proprietors. As changes may occur you are advised to check details at the time of booking.

• **STREET, SOMERSET** - Busy shoe-making town set beneath the Polden Hills. A museum at the factory, which was developed with the rest of the town in the 19th C, can be visited. Just south, the National Trust has care of woodland on Ivythorn Hill which gives wide views northward. Factory shopping village.

• **SWINDON, WILTSHIRE** - Wiltshire's industrial and commercial centre, an important railway town in the 19th C, situated just north of the Marlborough Downs. The railway village created in the mid-19th C has been preserved. Railway museum, art gallery, theatre and leisure centre. Designer shopping village.

TAUNTON, SOMERSET - County town, well-known for its public schools, sheltered by gentle hill-ranges on the River Tone. Medieval prosperity from wool has continued in marketing and manufacturing and the town retains many fine period buildings. Museum.

• **TINTAGEL, CORNWALL** - Coastal village near the legendary home of King Arthur. There is a lofty headland with the ruin of a Norman castle and traces of a Celtic monastery are still visible in the turf.

• **TORPOINT, CORNWALL** – Town beside the part of the Tamar Estuary known as the Hamoaze, linked by car ferry to Devonport. The fine 18th C Anthony House (National Trust) is noted for its 19th C portico.

• **TORQUAY, TORBAY** - Devon's grandest resort, developed from a fishing village. Smart apartments and terraces rise from the seafront and Marine Drive, along the headland, gives views of beaches and colourful cliffs.

• **TOTNES, DEVON** - Old market town steeply built near the head of the Dart Estuary. Remains of motte and bailey castle, medieval gateways, a noble church, 16th C Guildhall and medley of period houses recall former wealth from cloth and shipping, continued in rural and water industries.

• **TRURO, CORNWALL** - Cornwall's administrative centre and cathedral city, set at the head of Truro River on the Fal Estuary. A medieval stannary town, it handled mineral ore from west Cornwall; fine Georgian buildings recall its heyday as a society haunt in the second mining boom.

WATCHET, SOMERSET - Small port on Bridgwater Bay, sheltered by the Quantocks and the Brendon Hills. A thriving paper industry keeps the harbour busy; in the 19th C it handled iron from the Brendon Hills. Cleeve Abbey, a ruined Cistercian monastery, is 3 miles to the south-west.

• **WELLS, SOMERSET** - Small city set beneath the southern slopes of the Mendips. Built between 1180 and 1424, the magnificent cathedral is preserved in much of its original glory and with its ancient precincts forms one of our loveliest and most unified groups of medieval buildings.

• **WEST BEXINGTON, DORSET** - Village on the stretch of Dorset coast known as Chesil Beach. Close to the famous Abbotsbury Sub-tropical Gardens and Swannery.

• **WESTON-SUPER-MARE, NORTH SOMERSET** - Large, friendly resort developed in the 19th C. Traditional seaside attractions include theatres and a dance hall. The museum has a Victorian seaside gallery and Iron Age finds from a hill fort on Worlebury Hill in Weston Woods.

• **WEYMOUTH, DORSET** - Ancient port and one of the south's earliest resorts. Curving beside a long, sandy beach, the elegant Georgian esplanade is graced with a statue of George III and a cheerful Victorian Jubilee clock tower. Museum, Sea-Life Centre.

• **WHEDDON CROSS, SOMERSET** - Crossroads hamlet in the heart of Exmoor National Park.

• **WOOLACOMBE, DEVON** - Between Morte Point and Baggy Point, Woolacombe and Mortehoe offer 3 miles of the finest sand and surf on this outstanding coastline. Much of the area is owned by the National Trust.

YEOVIL, SOMERSET – Lively market town, famous for glove making, set in dairying country beside the River Yeo. Interesting parish church. Museam of South Somerset at Hendford Manor.

USE YOUR *i*'s

There are more than 550 Tourist Information Centres throughout England offering friendly help with accommodation and holiday ideas as well as suggestions of places to visit and things to do.

You'll find TIC addresses in the local Phone Book.

FINDING ACCOMMODATION
IS AS EASY AS *1 2 3*

Where to Stay makes it quick and easy to find a place to stay.
There are several ways to use this guide.

1 Town Index
The town index, starting on page 381, lists all the places with
accommodation featured in the regional sections. The index
gives a page number where you can find full accommodation
and contact details.

2 Colour Maps
All the place names in black on the colour maps at the front
have an entry in the regional sections. Refer to the town index
for the page number where you will find one or more
establishments offering accommodation in your chosen
town or village.

3 Accommodation listing
Contact details for **all** English Tourism Council assessed
accommodation throughout England, together with their
national Star rating is given in the listing section of this guide.
Establishments with a full entry in the regional sections are
shown in blue. Look in the town index for the page number on
which their full entry appears.

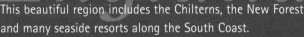

SOUTH OF ENGLAND

This beautiful region includes the Chilterns, the New Forest and many seaside resorts along the South Coast.

For cream teas and sightseeing, Windsor is an olde worlde delight. And nearby Runnymede, where the Magna Carta was signed, is a beautiful spot for a picnic. Oxford, Winchester and Salisbury offer shopping, nightlife and culture. While Southampton and Portsmouth are awash with maritime museums. But if you're mainly interested in sun, sea and sand, hire a deckchair in the seaside resorts of Bournemouth, Poole, Swanage or Weymouth.

The annual regatta at Cowes on the Isle of Wight, starting at the end of July, is something even land lubbers will enjoy.

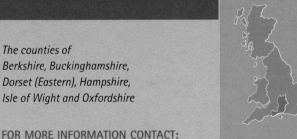

The counties of
Berkshire, Buckinghamshire,
Dorset (Eastern), Hampshire,
Isle of Wight and Oxfordshire

FOR MORE INFORMATION CONTACT:
Southern Tourist Board
40 Chamberlayne Road, Eastleigh,
Hampshire SO50 5JH
Tel: (023) 8062 0555
Fax: (023) 8062 0010
Email: stbinfo@bta.org.uk
Internet: www.visitbritain.com

The Pictures:
1 HMS Victory, Portsmouth;
2 Deer at Bolderwood, New Forest;
3 Blenheim Palace, Oxfordshire.

Where to Go in the South of England - see pages 254-257
Where to Stay in the South of England - see pages 258-277

Whilst in the
SOUTH OF ENGLAND ₀₀₀

You will find hundreds of interesting places to visit during your stay, just some of which are listed in these pages.

Contact any Tourist Information Centre in the region for more ideas on days out in the South of England.

Beale Park

Lower Basildon, Reading, Berkshire RG8 9NH
Tel: (0118) 9845172
An extraordinary collection of rare birds and animals. Narrow gauge railway, adventure playground, splash pools. Also nature trails and fishing on day tickets.

Beaulieu National Motor Museum

Beaulieu, Brockenhurst, Hampshire SO42 7ZN
Tel: (01590) 612345
Motor museum with over 250 exhibits showing the history of motoring from 1896. Also Palace House, Wheels Experience, Beaulieu Abbey ruins and a display of monastic life.

Bekonscot Model Village

Beaconsfield, Buckinghamshire HP9 2PL
Tel: (01494) 672919
The oldest model village in the world, Bekonscot depicts rural England in the 1930s where time has stood still for 70 years.

Blenheim Palace

Woodstock, Oxfordshire OX20 1PX
Tel: (01993) 811325
Home of the 11th Duke of Marlborough. Birthplace of Sir Winston Churchill. Designed by Vanbrugh in the English baroque style. Landscaped by 'Capability' Brown.

Breamore House

Breamore, Fordingbridge, Hampshire SP6 2DF
Tel: (01725) 512233
Elizabethan manor house of 1583 with fine collection of works of art. Furniture, tapestries, needlework, paintings mainly 17th and 18thC Dutch School.

Buckinghamshire County Museum

Aylesbury, Buckinghamshire HP20 2QP
Tel: (01296) 331441
Lively, hands-on, innovative museum complex consisting of county heritage displays, regional art gallery and Roald Dahl Children's Gallery in lovely garden setting.

Carisbrooke Castle

Newport, Isle of Wight PO30 1X
Tel: (01983) 522107
A splendid Norman castle where Charles I was imprisoned. The governor's lodge houses the county museum. Wheelhouse with wheel operated by donkeys.

Compton Acres

Canford Cliffs, Poole, Dorset BH13 7ES
Tel: (01202) 700778
Ten separate and distinct gardens of the world including Italian, Japanese, subtropical glen, rock and water gardens. Country crafts and 'Off the Beaten Track Trail'.

Cotswold Wild Life Park

Burford, Oxford, Oxfordshire OX18 4JW
Tel: (01993) 823006
Wildlife park in 200 acres of gardens and woodland. Includes a variety of animals from all over the world.

The D Day Museum and Overlord Embroidery

Clarence Esplanade, Portsmouth, Hampshire PO5 3NT
Tel: (023) 9282 7261
The magnificent 83 metre long 'Overlord Embroidery' depicts the allied invasion of Normandy on 6 June 1944. Soundguides available in three languages.

Didcot Railway Centre

Didcot, Oxfordshire OX11 7NJ
Tel: (01235) 817200
Living museum re-creating the golden age of the Great Western Railway. Steam locomotives and trains, engine shed and small relics museum.

2

Exbury Gardens

Exbury, Southampton SO45 1AZ
Tel: (023) 8089 1203
Over 200 acres of woodland garden, including the Rothschild collection of rhododendrons, azaleas, camellias and magnolias.

Flagship Portsmouth

HM Naval Base, Portsmouth, Hampshire PO1 3LJ
Tel: (023) 9283 9766
The world's greatest historic ships - Mary Rose, HMS Victory, HMS Warrior 1860, plus Royal Naval Museum, 'Warships by Water' tours, and Dockyard Apprentice exhibition.

Gilbert White's House and Garden and The Oates Museum

Selborne, Alton, Hampshire GU34 3JH
Tel: (01420) 511275
Historic house and garden, home of Gilbert White, author of 'The Natural History of Selborne'. Exhibition on Frank Oates, explorer and Captain Lawrence Oates of Antarctic fame.

The Hawk Conservancy

Andover, Hampshire SP11 8DY
Tel: (01264) 772252
Unique to Great Britain - 'Valley of the Eagles' held here daily at 1400.

Jane Austen's House

Chawton, Alton, Hampshire GU34 1SD
Tel: (01420) 83262
The 17thC house where Jane Austen lived from 1809-1817, and wrote or revised her six great novels. Letters, pictures, memorabilia, garden with old-fashioned flowers.

Legoland Windsor

Windsor, Berkshire SL4 4AY
Tel: 0870 5040404
A family park with hands-on activities, rides, themed playscapes and more Lego bricks than you ever dreamed possible.

Manor Farm

Manor Farm Country Park, Bursledon, Hampshire SO30 2ER
Tel: (01489) 787055
Traditional Hampshire farmstead - buildings, farm animals, machinery and equipment, pre-1950's farmhouse and 13thC church set for 1900.

Newport Roman Villa

Newport, Isle of Wight PO36 1EY
Tel: (01983) 529720
Underfloor heated bath system, tessellated floors displayed in reconstructed rooms, corn-drying kiln plus small site museum of objects recovered.

Osborne House

East Cowes, Isle of Wight PO32 6JY
Tel: (01983) 200022
Queen Victoria and Prince Albert's seaside holiday home. Swiss Cottage where royal children learnt cooking and gardening. Victorian carriage service to Swiss Cottage.

The Oxford Story

Broad Street, Oxford, Oxfordshire OX1 3AJ
Tel: (01865) 728822
An excellent introduction to Oxford - experience 800 years of University history in one hour. From scientists to poets, astronomers to comedians.

River and Rowing Museum

Mill Meadows, Henley-on-Thames, Oxfordshire RG9 1BF
Tel: (01491) 415600
A spectacular journey through over 250,000 years of life on the river. Discover the river's role in feeding the nation, its navigation and wildlife.

The Pictures:
1 Poole, Dorset;
2 Swan Green, New Forest;
3 Oxford;
4 Lulworth Cove, Dorset;
5 Windsor, Berkshire;
6 Winchester Cathedral, Hampshire;
7 Hertford and New College, Oxford.

Royal Marines Museum

Southsea, Hampshire PO4 9PX
Tel: (023) 9281 9385
History of the Royal Marines from 1664 to present day. Jungle and trench warfare sight and sound exhibitions. Supporting exhibitions and memorial gardens.

Royal Navy Submarine Museum

Jetty Road, Gosport PO12 2AS
Tel: (023) 9252 9217
HM Submarine Alliance, HM Submarine No 1 (Holland 1) under restoration. Midget submarines and models of every type from earliest days to present nuclear age submarines.

The Sir Harold Hillier Gardens and Arboretum

Ampfield, Romsey, Hampshire SO51 0QA
Tel: (01794) 368787
Established in 1953, The Sir Harold Hillier Gardens and Arboretum comprises the greatest collection of wild and cultivated woody plants in the world.

Staunton Country Park

Havant, Hampshire PO9 5HB
Tel: (023) 9245 3405
Restored Victorian glasshouses with displays of exotic plants in the charming setting of the historic walled gardens. Ornamental farm with a wide range of animals.

Swanage Railway

Swanage, Dorset BH19 1HB
Tel: (01929) 425800
Enjoy a nostalgic steam-train ride on the Purbeck line. Steam trains run every weekend throughout the year, and daily at peak times.

The Tank Museum

Bovington, Wareham, Dorset BH20 6JG
Tel: (01929) 405096
The world's finest display of armoured fighting vehicles. Experimental vehicles, interactive displays, disabled access and facilities.

Tudor House Museum

Bugle Street, Southampton SO14 2AD
Tel: (023) 8033 2513
Large half-timbered Tudor house with exhibitions on Tudor, Georgian and Victorian domestic and local history. Unique Tudor garden.

The Vyne

Sherborne St John, Hampshire RG24 9HL
Tel: (01256) 881337
Original house dating back to Henry VIII's time. Extensively altered in the mid 17thC. Tudor chapel, beautiful gardens and lake.

Waterperry Gardens

Waterperry, Oxford, Oxfordshire OX33 1JZ
Tel: (01844) 339254
Ornamental gardens covering six acres of the 83-acre estate. Saxon village church, garden shop, teashop, art and craft gallery.

Whitchurch Silk Mill

Whitchurch, Hampshire RG28 7AL
Tel: (01256) 892065
A unique Georgian silk-weaving watermill still producing fine silk fabrics on Victorian machinery. Riverside garden, tearoom for light meals, silk gift shop.

Winchester Cathedral

Winchester, Hampshire SO23 9LS
Tel: (01962) 857200
Originally Norman, with nave converted to perpendicular. 16thC additions. Old Saxon site adjacent. Tombs, library, medieval wall paintings and Close.

Windsor Castle

Windsor, Berkshire SL4 1NJ
Tel: (01753) 869898
Official residence of HM The Queen and royal residence for nine centuries. State apartments, Queen Mary's Doll's House.

Find out more about the
SOUTH OF ENGLAND ...

Further information about holidays and attractions in the South of England is available from:

SOUTHERN TOURIST BOARD
40 Chamberlayne Road, Eastleigh, Hampshire SO50 5JH.
Tel: (023) 8062 0555
Fax: (023) 8062 0010
Email: stbinfo@bta.org.uk
Internet: www.visitbritain.com

The Pictures:
1 Alum Bay,
   Isle of Wight;
2 Beaulieu, Hampshire;
3 Bucklers Hard,
   New Forest;
4 Broughton Castle,
   Oxfordshire;
5 Corfe, Dorset;
6 Cheyney Court,
   Winchester;
7 Radcliffe Camera, Oxford;
8 Chawton Church,
   Hampshire;
9 New Forest, Hampshire.

Getting to the
SOUTH OF ENGLAND ...

BY ROAD: A good road network links London and the rest of the UK with major Southern destinations. The M27 provides a near continuous motorway route along the south coast and the M25/M3/A33 provides a direct route from London to Winchester and Southampton. The scenic A31 stretches from London, through Hampshire and to mid Dorset, whilst the M40/A34 have considerably cut travelling times from the West Midlands to the South. The M25 has speeded up access to Berkshire on the M4, Buckinghamshire and Oxfordshire on the M40.

BY RAIL: From London's Waterloo, trains travel to Portsmouth, Southampton and Bournemouth approximately three times an hour. From these stations, frequent trains go to Poole, Salisbury and Winchester. Further information on rail journeys in the South of England can be obtained from 08457 484950.

Where to stay in the
SOUTH OF ENGLAND

Accommodation entries in this region are listed in alphabetical order of place name, and then in alphabetical order of establishment.

Map references refer to the colour location maps at the front of this guide. The first number indicates the map to use; the letter and number which follow refer to the grid reference on the map.

At-a-glance symbols at the end of each accommodation entry give useful information about services and facilities. A key to symbols can be found inside the back cover flap. Keep this open for easy reference.

A brief description of the towns and villages offering accommodation in the entries which follow, can be found at the end of this section.

A complete listing of all English Tourism Council assessed hotels appears at the back of this guide.

ALRESFORD, Hampshire Map ref 2C2

★★ **THE SWAN HOTEL**

11 West Street, Alresford, SO24 9AD	Bedrooms: 1 single, 14 double, 5 twin,	Lunch available EM 1830 (LO 2130)
T: (01962) 732302 & 734427	3 family rooms	Parking for 70
F: (01962) 735274	Bathrooms: 23 en suite,	CC: Barclaycard, Delta,
E: swanhotel@btinternet.com	1 public	Mastercard, Switch, Visa

B&B per night:
S £37.50–£42.50
D £50.00–£60.00

HB per person:
DY £52.50–£57.50

OPEN All year round

Warm and friendly, 18thC coaching inn, 15 minutes from Winchester.

🅰️ 🏠 ♿ 🏨 📞 🖥️ ♨️ 🅿️ Ⓢ ⟋ 🔟 ▦ 🍴 100 ∪ ► ❄️ SC ☜ SP 🏛️ Ⓣ

ALTON, Hampshire Map ref 2C2 *Tourist Information Centre Tel: (01420) 88448*

★★★ **ALTON GRANGE HOTEL & RESTAURANT**

London Road, Alton, GU34 4EG	Bedrooms: 10 single,	Lunch available
T: (01420) 86565	9 double, 8 twin, 1 triple,	EM 1900 (LO 2130)
F: (01420) 541346	1 family room; suite	Parking for 60
E: Info@AltonGrange.co.uk	available	CC: Amex, Barclaycard,
I: www.AltonGrange.co.uk	Bathrooms: 29 en suite	Delta, Diners, Eurocard,
		JCB, Mastercard, Solo,
		Switch, Visa, Visa Electron

B&B per night:
S £75.00–£92.50
D £92.50–£105.00

HB per person:
DY £71.00–£100.00

OPEN All year round

Privately-run country house style hotel, set in 2 acres, with "Truffles" restaurant for award-winning cuisine and fine wines. Executive rooms to the highest luxury standard.

🅰️ 🏠 4 ♿ 🏨 📞 🖥️ 📠 ♨️ 🅿️ Ⓢ ⟋ 🔟 ▦ 🍴 80 ∪ ✎ ❄️ SP 🏛️ Ⓣ

CHECK THE MAPS

The colour maps at the front of this guide show all the cities, towns and villages for which you will find accommodation entries. Refer to the town index to find the page on which they are listed.

ANDOVER, Hampshire Map ref 2C2 *Tourist Information Centre Tel: (01264) 324320*

THE BOURNE VALLEY INN
St Mary Bourne, Andover, SP11 6BT
T: (01264) 738361
F: (01264) 738126
E: bourneinn@aol.com
I: www.townpages.com

Bedrooms: 1 single,
4 double, 4 twin
Bathrooms: 9 en suite

Lunch available
EM 1900 (LO 2130)
Parking for 54
CC: Amex, Barclaycard,
Delta, Eurocard, Maestro,
Mastercard, Solo, Switch,
Visa, Visa Electron

B&B per night:
S £40.00–£50.00
D £53.00–£60.00

HB per person:
DY £40.00–£55.00

OPEN All year round

Country inn. Green Oak restaurant, conference facilities. Summer barbecues, riverside garden. Popular with locals and travellers for our charming and friendly service and excellent food.

Ⓒ The Independents

Ⓜ ☆ ⚲ 🍴 ☎ 🖥 ❑ ↓ ☜ 🛈 Ⓢ ✂ 🅿 📺 ▥ ♨ 🍴 100 Ⓤ ➤ ✺ 🚲 SP T

AYLESBURY, Buckinghamshire Map ref 2C1 *Tourist Information Centre Tel: (01296) 330559*

★★

WEST LODGE HOTEL
45 London Road, Aston Clinton,
Aylesbury, HP22 5HL
T: (01296) 630331 & 630362
F: (01296) 630151
E: jib.@westlodge.co.uk
I: www.westlodge.co.uk

Bedrooms: 2 single,
3 double, 1 twin
Bathrooms: 6 en suite

EM 1900 (LO 2000)
Parking for 11
CC: Amex, Barclaycard,
Delta, Eurocard, JCB,
Maestro, Mastercard,
Solo, Switch, Visa, Visa
Electron

B&B per night:
S £50.00–£60.00
D £70.00–£75.00

HB per person:
DY £65.00–£75.00

OPEN All year round

Victorian elegance in individually styled bedrooms with all modern comforts. Picturesque water garden, indoor pool, sauna, hot-air balloon trips. Fifty minutes London/Gatwick.

Ⓜ ☆ 8 ⚲ 🍴 ☎ ❑ ↓ ☜ 🛈 Ⓢ ✂ 🅿 ◐ ▥ 🍴 12 ☕ ⬡ ➤ ✺ 🚶 🚲 SP 🏠 T

BASINGSTOKE, Hampshire Map ref 2C2 *Tourist Information Centre Tel: (01256) 817618*

★★★★
Ad p15

AUDLEYS WOOD (A THISTLE COUNTRY HOUSE HOTEL)
Alton Road, Basingstoke, RG25 2JT
T: (01256) 817555
F: (01256) 817500
E: audleys.wood@thistle.co.uk
I: www.hotelbook.com/live/
welcome/13059

Bedrooms: 42 double,
27 twin, 2 triple; suites
available
Bathrooms: 71 en suite

Lunch available
EM 1900 (LO 2145)
Parking for 100
CC: Amex, Barclaycard,
Delta, Diners, Eurocard,
JCB, Mastercard, Switch,
Visa

B&B per night:
S £153.00–£178.00
D £153.00–£178.00

OPEN All year round

Ⓒ Thistle Hotels/Utell International

Audleys Wood is a 19thC mansion house, set in 9 acres of attractive landscaped and wooded grounds on the edge of Basingstoke on the Hampshire Downs.

Ⓜ ☆ ⚲ 🍴 ☎ ❑ ↓ ☜ 🛈 Ⓢ ✂ 🅿 ◐ ▥ 🍴 50 Ⓤ ✺ 🚲 SP 🏠 T ◉

★★★

RED LION HOTEL
24 London Street, Basingstoke, RG21 7NY
T: (01256) 328525
F: (01256) 844056
E: redlion@msihotels.co.uk
I: www.msihotels.co.uk

B&B per night:
S £45.00–£99.50
D £65.00–£120.00

HB per person:
DY £40.00–£70.00

OPEN All year round

The Red Lion Hotel is in the heart of Basingstoke town centre. The hotel offers high levels of service and comfort in settings full of character and charm, making it the ideal venue for a relaxing stay, either for business or leisure guests. With friendly staff and a first class service, who could ask for more?

Bedrooms: 18 single,
31 double, 8 twin,
2 triple
Bathrooms: 59 en suite

EM 1900 (LO 2130)
Parking for 66
CC: Amex, Barclaycard,
Delta, Diners, Eurocard,
Mastercard, Switch, Visa

Ⓜ ☆ 🍴 ☎ ❑ ↓ ☜ 🛈 Ⓢ ✂ 🅿 📺 ◐ 🍴 ▥ ☕ 🍴 30 🔌 Ⓤ SC 🚲 SP 🏠 T

BEACONSFIELD, Buckinghamshire Map ref 2C2

★★

CHEQUERS INN HOTEL & RESTAURANT
Kiln Lane, Wooburn Common,
High Wycombe, HP10 0JQ
T: (01628) 529575
F: (01628) 850124
E: info@chequers-inn.com
I: www.chequers-inn.com

Bedrooms: 15 double,
2 twin
Bathrooms: 17 en suite

Lunch available
EM 1900 (LO 2130)
Parking for 60
CC: Barclaycard, Delta,
Diners, Eurocard,
Mastercard, Switch, Visa

B&B per night:
S £97.50–£97.50
D £102.50–£102.50

OPEN All year round

A delightful blend of old world charm and modern comfort. In the Chilterns, about 2 miles from Beaconsfield and convenient for Windsor, Cookham and Heathrow.

Ⓜ ☆ ⚲ 🍴 ☎ ❑ ↓ ☜ 🛈 Ⓢ ▥ 🍴 50 Ⓤ ➤ ✺ 🚶 🚲 SP 🏠 T

BLANDFORD FORUM, Dorset Map ref 2B3 *Tourist Information Centre Tel: (01258) 454770*

★★ **ANVIL HOTEL & RESTAURANT**

Salisbury Road, Pimperne,
Blandford Forum, DT11 8UQ
T: (01258) 453431 & 480182
F: (01258) 480182

Bedrooms: 1 single,
7 double, 2 twin, 1 triple
Bathrooms: 11 en suite

Lunch available
EM 1900 (LO 2145)
Parking for 25
CC: Amex, Barclaycard,
Delta, Diners, Eurocard,
Mastercard, Solo, Switch,
Visa

B&B per night:
S £50.00–£55.00
D £75.00–£90.00

OPEN All year round

Picturesque 16thC thatched hotel. Separate beamed a la carte restaurant with log fire. Mouth-watering menu with delicious desserts. Comprehensive tasty bar meals and specials board.

★★★ **CROWN HOTEL**
Silver
Award

8 West Street, Blandford Forum,
DT11 7AJ
T: (01258) 456626
F: (01258) 451084

Bedrooms: 12 single,
8 double, 10 twin,
2 family rooms
Bathrooms: 32 en suite

Lunch available
EM 1915 (LO 2115)
Parking for 105
CC: Amex, Barclaycard,
Diners, Mastercard,
Switch, Visa

B&B per night:
S £65.00–£70.00
D £78.00–£90.00

HB per person:
DY £45.00–£50.00

OPEN All year round

Original Georgian coaching hotel built in 1750, overlooking watermeadows on the southern edge of town.

BOURNEMOUTH, Dorset Map ref 2B3 *Tourist Information Centre Tel: 0906 802 0234 (premium rate)*

★★★ **BELVEDERE HOTEL**

Bath Road, Bournemouth, Dorset
BH1 2EU
T: (01202) 297556 & 293336
F: (01202) 294699
E: Belvedere_Hotel@msn.com
I: www.belvedere-hotel.co.uk

Bedrooms: 11 single,
25 double, 13 twin,
11 triple, 1 family room
Bathrooms: 61 en suite

Lunch available
EM 1800 (LO 2100)
Parking for 55
CC: Amex, Barclaycard,
Delta, Diners, Eurocard,
JCB, Mastercard, Switch,
Visa, Visa Electron

B&B per night:
S £39.00–£55.00
D £56.00–£98.00

HB per person:
DY £39.50–£69.50

OPEN All year round

Centrally located with a large car park. Superb food and friendly service. Ideal for both business and holidays, offering high standards all round. Group rates available on request.

★★ **BONNINGTON HOTEL**

44 Tregonwell Road, Bournemouth,
Dorset BH2 5NT
T: (01202) 553621
F: (01202) 317797
E: bonnington.bournemouth@
btinternet.com
I: www.bonnington.co.uk

Bedrooms: 9 double,
8 twin, 1 triple, 2 family
rooms
Bathrooms: 20 en suite

EM 1815 (LO 1845)
Parking for 16
CC: Barclaycard, Delta,
Mastercard, Solo, Switch,
Visa, Visa Electron

B&B per night:
S £22.00–£35.00
D £44.00–£70.00

HB per person:
DY £30.00–£43.00

OPEN All year round

Friendly hotel a short stroll from beach, conference centre and shops. Excellent choice of menu. Cocktail bar. Own car park.

★★

THE COTTAGE PRIVATE HOTEL

12 Southern Road, Southbourne,
Bournemouth, Dorset BH6 3SR
T: (01202) 422764
F: (01202) 381442
E: ron+val@rjvhalliwell.force9.co.uk
I: www.SmoothHound.co.uk/hotels/
cottage3.html

B&B per night:
S £21.50–£32.50
D £43.00–£57.00

HB per person:
DY £29.50–£40.50

OPEN Mar–Oct

Charming, character, family-run licensed private hotel in restful location near Blue Flag beach yet convenient for the New Forest and Dorset countryside. Noted for home-prepared fresh cooking, cleanliness and tastefully furnished accommodation. Totally non-smoking. Minimum age children 8 years. Acclaimed for award-winning floral displays.

Bedrooms: 1 double,
2 twin, 3 triple
Bathrooms: 4 en suite,
2 private, 1 public

EM 1800 (LO 1800)
Parking for 7

BOURNEMOUTH continued

★★★

CUMBERLAND HOTEL

East Overcliff Drive, Bournemouth,
Dorset BH1 3AF
T: (01202) 290722
F: (01202) 311394
E: hotels@arthuryoung.co.uk
I: www.arthuryoung.co.uk

Bedrooms: 12 single,
34 double, 44 twin,
12 triple; suite available
Bathrooms: 102 en suite

Lunch available
EM 1900 (LO 2030)
Parking for 50
CC: Amex, Barclaycard,
Delta, Mastercard, Switch,
Visa

B&B per night:
S Max £56.70
D Max £113.40

HB per person:
DY Max £67.75

Family hotel on East Cliff overlooking the bay and offering a high standard of service and cuisine for all ages. Complimentary use of nearby indoor leisure facility.

OPEN All year round

120 ⚙ ⊘ ⏰

★★★

This elegant hotel is situated on the exclusive East Cliff. Convenient for town centre, shops, beach and Bournemouth International Centre. Good base for touring. Groups and conferences welcome. Our new head chef is gaining a reputation for delicious food. Category 1 disability accessible bedroom on ground floor. Spacious car park.

DURLSTON COURT HOTEL

47 Gervis Road, East Cliff, Bournemouth,
Dorset BH1 3DD
T: (01202) 316316
F: (01202) 316999
E: dch@seaviews.co.uk
I: www.seaviews.co.uk

Bedrooms: 8 single,
21 double, 16 twin,
11 triple
Bathrooms: 56 en suite

Lunch available
EM 1830 (LO 2100)
Parking for 40
CC: Barclaycard, Delta,
Eurocard, JCB, Maestro,
Mastercard, Solo, Switch,
Visa, Visa Electron

B&B per night:
S £26.50–£46.00
D £53.00–£92.00

HB per person:
DY £37.00–£56.50

OPEN All year round

120

★★★
Silver
Award

Award-winning hotel with en-suite bedrooms. Superb indoor leisure facilities with gym and heated indoor pool, snooker, pool. Ample car parking. Mouth watering home-cooked food and friendly service in the elegant restaurant. Set in a quiet, tree-lined avenue only 5 minutes from town centre and seafront.

ELSTEAD HOTEL

Knyveton Road, Bournemouth, Dorset
BH1 3QP
T: (01202) 293071
F: (01202) 293827
E: info@the-elstead.co.uk
I: www.the-elstead.co.uk

Bedrooms: 8 single,
20 double, 7 twin,
15 triple
Bathrooms: 50 en suite

Lunch available
EM 1900 (LO 2030)
Parking for 50
CC: Amex, Barclaycard,
Delta, Mastercard, Solo,
Switch, Visa

B&B per night:
S £55.00–£65.00
D £90.00–£100.00

HB per person:
DY £59.00–£65.00

OPEN All year round

70

★★

FIRCROFT HOTEL

Owls Road, Bournemouth, Dorset
BH5 1AE
T: (01202) 309771
F: (01202) 395644
I: www.fircrofthotel.co.uk

Bedrooms: 6 single,
16 double, 11 twin,
8 triple, 11 family rooms
Bathrooms: 52 en suite

Lunch available
EM 1830 (LO 2000)
Parking for 50
CC: Amex, Barclaycard,
Delta, Diners, Eurocard,
JCB, Maestro, Mastercard,
Solo, Switch, Visa, Visa
Electron

B&B per night:
S £24.00–£30.00
D £48.00–£60.00

HB per person:
DY £35.00–£40.00

OPEN All year round

Long-established family hotel, close to sea and comprehensive shopping. Free entry to hotel-owned sports and leisure club 9am – 6pm. Licensed, entertainment in season.

200

CONFIRM YOUR BOOKING

You are advised to confirm your booking in writing.

BOURNEMOUTH continued

★★★

MARSHAM COURT HOTEL
Russell-Cotes Road, East Cliff,
Bournemouth, Dorset BH1 3AB
T: (01202) 552111
F: (01202) 294744
E: reservations@marshamcourt.co.uk
I: www.marshamcourt.co.uk

Bedrooms: 8 single,
28 double, 35 twin,
15 triple; suite available
Bathrooms: 86 en suite

Lunch available
EM 1900 (LO 2100)
Parking for 100
CC: Amex, Barclaycard,
Delta, Diners, Mastercard,
Solo, Switch, Visa

B&B per night:
S £53.00–£60.00
D £86.00–£100.00

HB per person:
DY £55.00–£62.00

OPEN All year round

Overlooking bay in a quiet, central situation. Sun terraces, outdoor swimming pool, Edwardian bar, pool room and summer entertainment. Free parking. Telephone for special offers.

★★★★

NORFOLK ROYALE HOTEL
Richmond Hill, Bournemouth, Dorset
BH2 6EN
T: (01202) 551521
F: (01202) 299729
E: norfolkroyale@englishrosehotels.co.uk
I: www.englishrosehotels.co.uk

B&B per night:
S £105.00–£215.00
D £145.00–£350.00

HB per person:
DY £59.50–£77.50

OPEN All year round

The Independents

A quality country-house style hotel in the heart of this cosmopolitan and vibrant resort. Leisure club and secure parking add to the hotel's comfortable and relaxed style. Beautifully appointed bedrooms with all the amenities you would expect together with friendly and efficient staff.

Bedrooms: 9 single,
55 double, 27 twin,
3 triple, 1 family room;
suites available
Bathrooms: 95 en suite

Lunch available
EM 1900 (LO 2200)
Parking for 98
CC: Amex, Barclaycard,
Delta, Diners, Eurocard,
JCB, Mastercard, Switch,
Visa

★★★

QUEEN'S HOTEL
Meyrick Road, East Cliff,
Bournemouth, Dorset BH1 3DL
T: (01202) 554415
F: (01202) 294810
E: hotels@arthuryoung.co.uk
I: www.arthuryoung.co.uk

Bedrooms: 12 single,
43 double, 46 twin,
8 triple
Bathrooms: 109 en suite

Lunch available
EM 1900 (LO 2030)
Parking for 80
CC: Amex, Barclaycard,
Diners, Mastercard,
Switch, Visa

B&B per night:
S £42.50–£65.00
D £82.50–£125.00

HB per person:
DY £49.50–£69.50

OPEN All year round

Modern, family-run hotel near the beach, ideal for family holidays and with facilities for business conventions. Leisure club. Award-winning cuisine.

★★

ULLSWATER HOTEL
Westcliff Gardens, Bournemouth, Dorset
BH2 5HW
T: (01202) 555181
F: (01202) 317896
E: enq@ullswater.uk.com
I: www.ullswater.uk.com

B&B per night:
S £25.00–£32.00
D £50.00–£64.00

HB per person:
DY £32.00–£39.00

OPEN All year round

The Ullswater is situated within sight of the sea in the most favoured position on the West Cliff and within a few minutes' walking distance of the beach, town centre and Bournemouth International Centre. The Ullswater offers a high degree of comfort in tasteful surroundings, with good food and personal service.

Bedrooms: 9 single,
13 double, 13 twin,
7 triple
Bathrooms: 42 en suite

Lunch available
EM 1900 (LO 2000)
Parking for 10
CC: Amex, Barclaycard,
Mastercard, Switch, Visa

MAP REFERENCES
The map references refer to the colour maps at the front of this guide. The first figure is the map number; the letter and figure which follow indicate the grid reference on the map.

BOURNEMOUTH continued

★★★

WINTERBOURNE HOTEL
Priory Road, Bournemouth, Dorset BH2 5DJ
T: (01202) 296366
F: (01202) 780073
E: reservations@winterbourne.co.uk
I: www.winterbourne.co.uk

B&B per night:
S £33.00–£47.00
D £58.00–£86.00

HB per person:
DY £36.00–£53.00

OPEN All year round

Ⓒℝ
The Independents

Enjoying a prime position with magnificent sea views, this award-winning hotel is within 400 metres of the pier, beaches and town centre shops and theatres. Delightful garden with 30ft heated pool. Free winter swimming at adjacent BIC leisure pool and free golf at Queens Park. Car parking and lift.	Bedrooms: 6 single, 15 double, 9 twin, 7 triple, 4 family rooms Bathrooms: 41 en suite	Lunch available EM 1830 (LO 2000) Parking for 34 CC: Amex, Barclaycard, Delta, Mastercard, Solo, Switch, Visa

♠ ⅋ ♿ & 📞 ▤ ❑ ↻ ℚ ⓘ Ⓢ ⊁ 🄼 📺 ➕ 🔲 ⌨ ⛱ 80 ⌖ ⅃ ▸ ⚘ 🐴 ⚲ ⓈⓅ Ⓣ ⊛

BUCKINGHAM, Buckinghamshire Map ref 2C1 *Tourist Information Centre Tel: (01280) 823020*

★★★
Silver
Award

VILLIERS HOTEL
3 Castle Street, Buckingham,
MK18 1BS
T: (01280) 822444
F: (01280) 822113
E: villiers@villiers-hotels.demon.co.uk

	Bedrooms: 3 single, 27 double, 16 twin; suites available Bathrooms: 46 en suite	Lunch available EM 1900 (LO 2230) Parking for 46 CC: Amex, Barclaycard, Delta, Diners, Eurocard, Mastercard, Switch, Visa

B&B per night:
S £82.00–£105.00
D £99.00–£160.00

OPEN All year round

Individually designed bedrooms and suites are set around an old coaching inn cobbled courtyard, incorporating English restaurant and Jacobean pub.

♠ ⅋ 🚗 📞 ▤ ❑ ↻ ℚ ⓘ Ⓢ 🄼 ◐ ➕ 🔲 ⌨ ⛱ 300 ⚘ ✳ ⚲ ↻ ▸ 🐴 ⚲ ⓈⓅ 🏨 Ⓣ

BURFORD, Oxfordshire Map ref 2B1 *Tourist Information Centre Tel: (01993) 823558*

★★★

THE BAY TREE
Sheep Street, Burford, OX18 4LW
T: (01993) 822791
F: (01993) 823008
E: bookings@cotswold-inns-hotels.co.uk
I: www.cotswold-inns-hotels.co.uk

	Bedrooms: 14 double, 7 twin Bathrooms: 21 en suite	Lunch available EM 1900 (LO 2130) Parking for 42 CC: Amex, Barclaycard, Delta, Diners, JCB, Mastercard, Solo, Switch, Visa

B&B per night:
S Min £90.00
D £135.00–£210.00

OPEN All year round

Ⓒℝ
Cotswolds Inns &
Hotels

16thC Cotswold-stone building with exposed beams, flagstone floors and open log fires. Decorated throughout with antique furniture.

⅋ 🚗 📞 ▤ ❑ ↻ ℚ ⓘ Ⓢ 🄼 ⌨ ⛱ 50 ↻ ▸ ✳ ⚲ ⓈⓅ 🏨 Ⓣ

BURLEY, Hampshire Map ref 2B3

★★

THE BURLEY INN
The Cross, Burley, Ringwood,
BH24 4AB
T: (01425) 403448
F: (01425) 402058

	Bedrooms: 1 single, 6 double, 2 triple Bathrooms: 9 en suite	Lunch available EM 1900 (LO 2230) Parking for 18 CC: Barclaycard, Delta, Eurocard, Mastercard, Switch, Visa

B&B per night:
S £45.00–£60.00
D £60.00–£90.00

HB per person:
DY £55.00–£65.00

OPEN Feb–Dec

Welcoming country inn, in the heart of the New Forest, with wonderful food and all facilities to ensure comfort.

⅋ 🚗 📞 ▤ ❑ ↻ ℚ ⓘ Ⓢ ⊁ 🄼 📺 ⌨ ⌨ ↻ ▸ 🐴 🐴 Ⓢ🄲 ⚲ ⓈⓅ Ⓣ ⊛

★★★

MOORHILL HOUSE HOTEL
Burley, Ringwood, BH24 4AG
T: (01425) 403285
F: (01425) 403715
E: information@carehotels.co.uk
I: www.carehotels.co.uk

	Bedrooms: 2 single, 13 double, 2 twin, 7 triple Bathrooms: 24 en suite	Lunch available EM 1900 (LO 2045) Parking for 40 CC: Amex, Barclaycard, Diners, Mastercard, Switch, Visa

B&B per night:
S £55.00–£65.00
D £110.00–£130.00

HB per person:
DY £76.50–£90.00

OPEN All year round

Ⓒℝ
Care Hotels

Quiet country house hotel in secluded two and a half acres, in picturesque village of Burley. All bedrooms en suite, indoor leisure facilities.

♠ ⅋ ♿ & 📞 ▤ ❑ ↻ ℚ ⓘ Ⓢ ⊁ 🄼 📺 ⌨ ⌨ ⛱ 40 ⚘ ⅃ ↻ ✳ 🐴 ⚲ ⓈⓅ 🏨 Ⓣ ⊛

CHESTERTON, Oxfordshire Map ref 2C1

★★
Silver
Award

BIGNELL PARK HOTEL
Chesterton, Bicester, OX6 8UE
T: (01869) 241444 & 241192
F: (01869) 241444

Bedrooms: 1 single,
20 double, 2 twin
Bathrooms: 23 en suite

Lunch available
EM 1900 (LO 2130)
Parking for 18
CC: Amex, Barclaycard,
Diners, Eurocard,
Mastercard, Switch, Visa

B&B per night:
S £70.00–£80.00
D £90.00–£100.00

OPEN All year round

Cotswold period house, circa 1740, with mature gardens, set in 2.5 acres in rural Oxfordshire.

🅰🐕6♿🏠☎🖥☐♨🍷🛈⛓🏧🌙🕐⊙🖩🖨🍽30🏃☸ SC SP 🏤

CORFE CASTLE, Dorset Map ref 2B3

★★★
Silver
Award

MORTONS HOUSE HOTEL
East Street, Corfe Castle, Wareham,
BH20 5EE
T: (01929) 480988
F: (01929) 480820
E: stay@mortonshouse.co.uk
I: www.mortonshouse.co.uk

Bedrooms: 13 double,
3 twin, 1 family room;
suite available
Bathrooms: 17 en suite

Lunch available
EM 1900 (LO 2030)
Parking for 35
CC: Amex, Barclaycard,
Delta, Diners, Mastercard,
Switch, Visa

B&B per night:
D £106.00–£116.00

HB per person:
DY £130.00–£140.00

OPEN All year round

Attractive Elizabethan manor house with castle views. Walled gardens, coastal and country pursuits. Suites and 4-poster bed. Licensed gourmet restaurant.

🅰🐕♿🏠☎🖥☐♨🍷🛈⛓🏧🖩🖨🍽40☸ 🐎 🏤 SP 🏤 T

COTSWOLDS

See under Burford, Chesterton, Deddington, Steeple Aston, Witney
See also Cotswolds in Heart of England region

DEDDINGTON, Oxfordshire Map ref 2C1

★★★
Silver
Award

Delightful, 17thC family-run, award-winning hotel in lovely Cotswold village near Woodstock and Oxford. Character rooms, all en suite with every comfort. Family rooms available. Restaurant renowned for most outstanding food. Elegantly refurbished country house, relaxed old world charm, genuine hospitality and personal attention. Private free car park.

HOLCOMBE HOTEL & RESTAURANT
High Street, Deddington, Banbury,
OX15 0SL
T: (01869) 338274
F: (01869) 337167
E: reception@holcombehotel.freeserve.co.uk
I: www.bestwestern.co.uk

Bedrooms: 2 single,
8 double, 6 twin, 1 triple
Bathrooms: 17 en suite

Lunch available
EM 1900 (LO 2200)
Parking for 40
CC: Amex, Barclaycard,
Delta, Eurocard, JCB,
Mastercard, Switch, Visa,
Visa Electron

B&B per night:
S £68.00–£78.00
D £93.00–£115.00

HB per person:
DY £65.00–£72.50

OPEN All year round

©®

Best Western Hotels/
The Independents

🐕♿🏠☎🖥☐♨🍷🛈⛓🏧TV🖩🖨🍽28⊙🏃☸ SC 🌂 SP 🏤 T

DROXFORD, Hampshire Map ref 2C3

★★

Family-run hotel set in 10 acres of landscaped gardens in the Meon Valley, with a private lake adjoining the Meon River. Well situated for touring Southern England – only 6 miles from the M27 and at the foot of South Downs Way. Welcoming staff and award-winning restaurant.

UPLAND PARK HOTEL
Garrison Hill (A32), Droxford,
Southampton, SO32 3QL
T: (01489) 878507
F: (01489) 877853
E: clarelay@globalnet.co.uk

Bedrooms: 3 single,
9 double, 3 twin,
2 family rooms
Bathrooms: 17 en suite

Lunch available
EM 1900 (LO 2130)
Parking for 100
CC: Amex, Barclaycard,
Delta, Diners, Mastercard,
Switch, Visa

B&B per night:
S £42.00–£44.00
D £58.00–£64.00

HB per person:
DY Min £65.00

OPEN All year round

🅰🐕♿🏠☎🖥☐♨🍷🛈⛓TV🖩🖨🍽150⚓⊙♪🏃☸ SC 🌂 SP T

FARINGDON, Oxfordshire Map ref 2B2

★★

FARINGDON HOTEL
Market Place, Faringdon, SN7 7HL
T: (01367) 240536
F: (01367) 243250

B&B per night:
S £50.00–£60.00
D £65.00–£75.00

HB per person:
DY £65.00–£75.00

OPEN All year round

Situated near the 12thC parish church, the Faringdon Hotel stands on the site of what is believed to have been the royal palace of Alfred the Great. Its tradition of hospitality dates from before the coaching age. An inn stood on this site in the time of King John.

Bedrooms: 3 single, 13 double, 1 twin, 3 triple
Bathrooms: 20 en suite

Lunch available
EM 1800 (LO 2200)
Parking for 5
CC: Amex, Barclaycard, Delta, Diners, Eurocard, Mastercard, Switch, Visa

GOSPORT, Hampshire Map ref 2C3 *Tourist Information Centre Tel: (023) 9252 2944*

★★

THE MANOR HOTEL
Brewers Lane, Gosport, PO13 0JY
T: (01329) 232946
F: (01329) 220392
E: tony_lid@msn.com
I: www.smoothhound.co.uk/hotels/manorhtml

Bedrooms: 1 single, 7 double, 1 twin, 3 triple
Bathrooms: 12 en suite

Lunch available
EM 1800 (LO 2130)
Parking for 46
CC: Amex, Barclaycard, Delta, Eurocard, Mastercard, Solo, Switch, Visa, Visa Electron

B&B per night:
S £37.50–£45.00
D £55.00–£65.00

OPEN All year round

Very popular private hotel and public house. Close to Portsmouth's naval history. Midway between Fareham and Gosport.

ISLE OF WIGHT

See under Sandown, Shanklin, Totland Bay, Ventnor

LIPHOOK, Hampshire Map ref 2C3

★★★

OLD THORNS HOTEL, GOLF & COUNTRY CLUB
Griggs Green, Liphook, GU30 7PE
T: (01428) 724555
F: (01428) 725036
E: reservations@oldthornsfreeserve.co.uk
I: www.oldthorns.co.uk

Bedrooms: 3 double, 28 twin, 1 triple; suite available
Bathrooms: 32 en suite, 5 public

Lunch available
EM 1930 (LO 2130)
Parking for 200
CC: Amex, Barclaycard, Delta, Diners, Eurocard, JCB, Mastercard, Switch, Visa

B&B per night:
S £100.00–£125.00
D £130.00–£145.00

HB per person:
DY £85.00–£92.50

OPEN All year round

Set in 400 acres of Hampshire parkland with an 18-hole golf course, hotel, Japanese and European restaurants and leisure complex. 1 hour's drive from London, Heathrow and Gatwick airports.

LYMINGTON, Hampshire Map ref 2C3

★★★
Silver
Award

SOUTH LAWN HOTEL
Lymington Road, Milford-on-Sea, Lymington, SO41 0RF
T: (01590) 643911
F: (01590) 644820
E: enquiries@southlawn.co.uk
I: www.southlawn.co.uk

B&B per night:
S £65.00–£65.00
D £110.00–£130.00

HB per person:
DY £65.00–£77.50

OPEN All year round except Christmas and New Year

A beautiful former dower house, set in own grounds. The chef/proprietor's award-winning restaurant is well supported locally, offering homely elegance with professional, friendly staff. Individually furnished rooms decorated to a high standard with all facilities for the discerning traveller. Special breaks and golf concessions.

Bedrooms: 6 double, 18 twin
Bathrooms: 24 en suite

Lunch available
EM 1900 (LO 2030)
Parking for 50
CC: Barclaycard, Delta, Eurocard, Mastercard, Switch, Visa

★★★

STANWELL HOUSE HOTEL

15 High Street, Lymington, SO41 9AA
T: (01590) 677123
F: (01590) 677756
I: www.scoot.uk/stanwell_house_hotel/.

B&B per night:
D £105.00–£155.00

HB per person:
DY £75.00–£100.00

OPEN All year round

Stanwell House is a superb example of Georgian architecture, sympathetically restored to combine luxury, style and informal comfort. Dining facilities are excellent. The bar and bistro are truly Georgian, stunningly simple. Lovely flower-filled patio, charming walled garden, 50ft yacht. Ideally located for the New Forest and Lymington Marinas.

Bedrooms: 2 single, 19 double, 8 twin, 1 family room; suites available
Bathrooms: 30 en suite, 1 public

Lunch available
EM 1900 (LO 2200)
CC: Amex, Barclaycard, Delta, Diners, Mastercard, Switch, Visa

---

★

KNIGHTWOOD LODGE

Southampton Road, Lyndhurst, SO43 7BU
T: (023) 8028 2502
F: (023) 8028 3730

Bedrooms: 2 single, 12 double, 2 twin, 1 triple, 1 family room
Bathrooms: 18 en suite, 1 public

Lunch available
EM 1830 (LO 2000)
Parking for 15
CC: Amex, Barclaycard, Delta, Diners, Eurocard, JCB, Mastercard, Solo, Switch, Visa

B&B per night:
S £36.00–£50.00
D £70.00–£90.00

HB per person:
DY £45.00–£60.00

OPEN All year round

Minotel/The Independents

On the edge of Lyndhurst overlooking the New Forest. Facilities include an indoor health centre with spa, sauna, swimming pool, steam room and gym. Cosy bar. Parking.

★★★

WOODLANDS LODGE HOTEL

Bartley Road, Woodlands, Southampton, SO40 7GN
T: (023) 8029 2257
F: (023) 8029 3090
E: woodlands@nortels.ltd.uk
I: www.nortels.ltd.uk

B&B per night:
S £70.00–£80.00
D £118.00–£178.00

HB per person:
DY £84.00–£114.00

OPEN All year round

Georgian country house hotel set in 3 acres of gardens, within the beautiful New Forest. Well-equipped en suite rooms with whirlpool baths and king size beds. The restaurant has an award for excellent cuisine, making use of fresh local produce. Many local attractions to visit or just enjoy the peace and tranquillity.

Bedrooms: 12 double, 1 twin, 1 triple, 2 family rooms; suites available
Bathrooms: 16 en suite

Lunch available
EM 1900 (LO 2100)
Parking for 40
CC: Barclaycard, Delta, Eurocard, Mastercard, Switch, Visa

★

ELVA LODGE HOTEL

Castle Hill, Maidenhead, Berkshire SL6 4AD
T: (01628) 622948 & 634883
F: (01628) 778954
E: reservations@elvalodgehotel.demon.co.uk
I: www.elvalodgehotel.demon.co.uk

Bedrooms: 10 single, 13 double, 1 twin, 1 triple, 1 family room
Bathrooms: 18 en suite, 3 private, 2 public

EM 1830 (LO 2130)
Parking for 31
CC: Amex, Barclaycard, Delta, Diners, Mastercard, Solo, Switch, Visa

B&B per night:
S £55.00–£90.00
D £65.00–£100.00

OPEN All year round

Family-run hotel in central Maidenhead. Friendly atmosphere and personal attention. Ideal for Heathrow, Windsor, Henley and Ascot. M4 5 minutes, M40 and M25 10 minutes.

RATING All accommodation in this guide has been rated, or is awaiting a rating, by a trained English Tourism Council assessor.

MARLOW, Buckinghamshire Map ref 2C2

★★★★
Silver
Award

DANESFIELD HOUSE

Henley Road, Marlow-on-Thames,
Marlow, SL7 2EY
T: (01628) 891010
F: (01628) 890408
E: sales@danesfieldhouse.co.uk
I: www.danesfieldhouse.co.uk

Bedrooms: 9 single,
59 double, 16 twin,
3 family rooms; suites
available
Bathrooms: 87 en suite

Lunch available
EM 1830 (LO 2200)
Parking for 130
CC: Amex, Barclaycard,
Delta, Diners, JCB,
Mastercard, Switch, Visa

B&B per night:
S £145.00–£210.00
D £185.00–£300.00

OPEN All year round

CR
Small Luxury Hotels

Country house hotel set within 65 acres of outstanding gardens, overlooking the River Thames between Marlow and Henley. Luxurious spa scheduled to open early 2001.

⛰🐾♿🚗📞☎🖥🔌📶ⓢ♿♪🕐⊙🔲⌨🛏🍽100 ⚡🔍⛱🅿🚶🚴🎿🎯🌟🍴🛫⛷SP🏛Ⓣ

MILFORD-ON-SEA, Hampshire Map ref 2C3

★★★
Gold
Award

WESTOVER HALL HOTEL

Park Lane, Milford-on-Sea, Lymington,
SO41 0PT
T: (01590) 643044
F: (01590) 644490
E: westoverhallhotel@barclays.net
I: www.westoverhallhotel.com

B&B per night:
S £70.00–£90.00
D £120.00–£160.00

HB per person:
DY £80.00–£110.00

OPEN All year round

Victorian mansion in the New Forest with uninterrupted sea views. Magnificent oak panelling and dramatic stained glass windows are complemented by family antiques and contemporary art. Luxury bathrooms and stylish bedrooms complete a relaxed "home from home" atmosphere. Award-winning restaurant, candlelit and with sea views. Unique!

Bedrooms: 1 single,
5 double, 6 twin,
1 family room
Bathrooms: 13 en suite

Lunch available
EM 1900 (LO 2100)
Parking for 40
CC: Amex, Barclaycard,
Delta, Diners, JCB,
Mastercard, Switch, Visa

⛰🐾♿📞☎🚗🖥ⓢ♿📺🛏🍽50 🅿🚶🌟🚗⛷SP🏛

MILTON COMMON, Oxfordshire Map ref 2C1

★★★

THE OXFORD BELFRY

Milton Common, Thame, OX9 2JW
T: (01844) 279381
F: (01844) 279624
E: oxfordbelfry@marstonhotels.co.uk
I: www.marstonhotels.co.uk

B&B per night:
S £108.00–£128.00
D £137.00–£177.00

HB per person:
DY £77.50–£97.50

OPEN All year round

CR
Best Western Hotels

Delightful hotel with stunning views of the Cotswold countryside, yet convenient M40. Minutes from centre of Oxford. Wide range of rooms available including executive rooms and spacious suites. Award-winning restaurant. Leisure facilities including heated indoor pool. Within easy reach of Blenheim Palace, Woburn Abbey, Chilterns and Cotswolds.

Bedrooms: 34 double,
31 twin; suites available
Bathrooms: 65 en suite

Lunch available
EM 1900 (LO 2130)
Parking for 200
CC: Amex, Barclaycard,
Delta, Diners, Eurocard,
Mastercard, Switch, Visa

⛰🐾♿📞☎🚗🔌ⓢ♿⊙🛏🍽370 🚗🌟🅿🎿🌟⛷SPⓉ

MILTON KEYNES, Buckinghamshire Map ref 2C1 *Tourist Information Centre Tel: (01908) 558300*

★★

SWAN REVIVED HOTEL

High Street, Newport Pagnell,
Milton Keynes, Buckinghamshire
MK16 8AR
T: (01908) 610565
F: (01908) 210995
E: swanrevived@btinternet.com
I: www.swanrevived.co.uk

Bedrooms: 17 single,
19 double, 4 twin,
1 triple, 1 family room;
suites available
Bathrooms: 42 en suite

Lunch available
EM 1915 (LO 2200)
Parking for 18
CC: Amex, Barclaycard,
Delta, Diners, Mastercard,
Solo, Switch, Visa

B&B per night:
S £42.50–£76.00
D £60.00–£95.00

HB per person:
DY £44.00–£99.00

OPEN All year round

CR
The Independents

Extensively modernised coaching inn boasting comfortable guest rooms, 2 bars, a la carte restaurant, conference and banqueting facilities. Close to Silverstone, Woburn and 50 miles from London.

⛰🐾♿📞☎🚗🔌☎ⓢ♿♪⊙📺⌨🛏🍽75 SCSP🏛Ⓣ

NEW FOREST

See under Burley, Lymington, Lyndhurst, Milford-on-Sea, Sway

NEWBURY, Berkshire Map ref 2C2 *Tourist Information Centre Tel: (01635) 30267*

★★★★
Silver
Award

DONNINGTON VALLEY HOTEL & GOLF COURSE

Old Oxford Road, Donnington,
Newbury, Berkshire RG14 3AG
T: (01635) 551199
F: (01635) 551123
E: general@donningtonvalley.co.uk
I: www.donningtonvalley.co.uk

Bedrooms: 43 double,
15 twin; suites available
Bathrooms: 58 en suite,
2 public

Lunch available
EM 1900 (LO 2200)
Parking for 150
CC: Amex, Barclaycard,
Delta, Diners, Mastercard,
Switch, Visa, Visa Electron

B&B per night:
S £80.00–£145.00
D £105.00–£125.00

HB per person:
DY £87.00–£184.00

OPEN All year round

Stylish country house hotel set in Berkshire countryside. 18-hole golf-course, award-winning restaurant. Excellent touring base for southern England.

ⓜ ♿ ⚑ & 📞 🖥 🗄 ♦ 🔍 🐕 🔕 ⊘ ⬆ 🛗 🚗 🍴 140 ♻ ∪ ► ❄ 🚭 🐾 SP T

★★★★
Silver
Award

REGENCY PARK HOTEL

Bowling Green Road, Thatcham, Berkshire
RG18 3RP
T: (01635) 871555
F: (01635) 871571
E: regencypark@bestwestern.co.uk
I: www.regencyparkhotel.co.uk

B&B per night:
S £115.00–£260.00
D £145.00–£290.00

HB per person:
DY £82.50–£102.50

OPEN All year round

Set in 5 acres of Berkshire countryside, 7 minutes from junction 13, M4 this recently refurbished luxury hotel is renowned for its high standards of service. Extensive indoor leisure facilities with pool, gymnasium and health & beauty treatment rooms. Executive standard bedrooms and award-winning restaurant, The Watermark.

Bedrooms: 3 single,
29 double, 14 twin,
2 triple; suite available
Bathrooms: 48 en suite

Lunch available
EM 1900 (LO 2200)
Parking for 125
CC: Amex, Barclaycard,
Delta, Diners, Mastercard,
Solo, Switch, Visa, Visa
Electron

ⓜ ♿ & 📞 🖥 🗄 ♦ 🔍 🐕 🔕 ✂ 🔗 ◑ ⬆ 🛗 🚗 🍴 160 ♻ ∪ ► ❄ 🐾 SP T

ODIHAM, Hampshire Map ref 2C2

★★

GEORGE HOTEL

High Street, Odiham, Hook, RG29 1LP
T: (01256) 702081
F: (01256) 704213

B&B per night:
S £65.00–£85.00
D £80.00–£95.00

OPEN All year round

15thC coaching inn with many fine beams and original wattle and daub visible. Oak-panelled restaurant with flagstone floor and fireplace said to have come from Basing House. Traditionally restored bedrooms in the old building, some with 4-poster beds, and newer rooms designed with every modern comfort in mind for today's traveller.

Bedrooms: 8 single,
18 double, 2 twin
Bathrooms: 28 en suite

Lunch available
EM 1930 (LO 2200)
Parking for 30
CC: Amex, Barclaycard,
Delta, Diners, Eurocard,
Mastercard, Solo, Switch,
Visa, Visa Electron

ⓜ ♿ ⚑ & 🏨 📞 🖥 🗄 ♦ 🔍 🐕 🔗 ◑ 🛗 🚗 🍴 30 ❄ 🚭 SP ♿ T

OXFORD, Oxfordshire Map ref 2C1 *Tourist Information Centre Tel: (01865) 726871*

★★

THE BALKAN LODGE HOTEL

315 Iffley Road, Oxford, OX4 4AG
T: (01865) 244524
F: (01865) 251090
I: www.oxfordcity.co.uk/hotels/balkan

Bedrooms: 2 single,
10 double, 1 twin
Bathrooms: 13 en suite

EM 1900 (LO 2100)
Parking for 13
CC: Barclaycard, Delta,
Eurocard, Mastercard,
Switch, Visa

B&B per night:
S £55.50–£62.50
D £68.50–£72.50

OPEN All year round

Delightful small hotel, recently refurbished. En suite bedrooms with Sky TV, hairdryer, trouser press, direct-dial telephone, tea/coffee facilities. Four-poster bed, jacuzzi. Car park at rear.

& 🏨 📞 🖥 🗄 ♦ 🔍 🐕 🔗 TV 🛗 🚗 ∪ ❄ SC SP T

★★

MOUNT PLEASANT
76 London Road, Headington,
Oxford, OX3 9AJ
T: (01865) 762749
F: (01865) 762749

Bedrooms: 2 double,
5 twin, 1 triple
Bathrooms: 8 en suite

Lunch available
EM 1800 (LO 2130)
Parking for 6
CC: Amex, Barclaycard,
Diners, Eurocard, JCB,
Mastercard, Visa

B&B per night:
S £45.00–£65.00
D £65.00–£75.00

HB per person:
DY £40.00–£45.00

OPEN All year round

Small, no smoking, family-run hotel offering full facilities. On the A40 and convenient for Oxford shopping, hospitals, colleges, visiting the Chilterns and the Cotswolds.

★★★★
Gold
Award

OLD BANK HOTEL
92-94 High Street, Oxford, OX1 4BN
T: (01865) 799599
F: (01865) 799598
E: info@oldbank-hotel.co.uk

B&B per night:
S Min £140.00
D £165.00–£310.00

OPEN All year round

These beautiful old buildings, formerly a bank, have been superbly converted into a contemporary 44-bedroom luxury hotel. Central location with stunning views of Oxford skyline. All rooms are air conditioned, CD players, satellite TV and 24-hour room service. Restaurant and bar serving Italian-style food. Conference facilities. Private parking.

Bedrooms: 24 double,
13 twin, 7 triple; suites
available
Bathrooms: 44 en suite

Lunch available
EM 1800 (LO 2300)
Parking for 45
CC: Amex, Barclaycard,
Delta, Diners, JCB,
Mastercard, Switch, Visa

★★★
Silver
Award

THE OLD PARSONAGE HOTEL
1 Banbury Road, Oxford, OX2 6NN
T: (01865) 310210
F: (01865) 311262
E: info@oldparsonage-hotel.co.uk
I: www.oxford-hotels-restaurants.co.uk

B&B per night:
S Min £130.00
D £150.00–£200.00

OPEN All year round

17thC wisteria-clad building in central Oxford. 30 beautiful en suite bedrooms with marble bathrooms. Informal restaurant and bar serving excellent food. Meals taken on the front terrace in summer. Private car park, 24-hour room service, roof terrace. A warm welcome from efficient, friendly young staff.

Bedrooms: 1 single,
17 double, 8 twin,
4 triple; suites available
Bathrooms: 30 en suite

Lunch available
EM 1800 (LO 2300)
Parking for 16
CC: Amex, Barclaycard,
Delta, Diners, JCB,
Mastercard, Switch, Visa

★★

OTMOOR LODGE HOTEL
Horton Hill, Horton cum Studley,
Oxford, OX33 1AY
T: (01865) 351235
F: (01865) 351721
E: otmoorlodge@btinternet.com
I: www.otmoorlodge.co.uk

Bedrooms: 3 single,
11 double, 3 twin,
1 triple
Bathrooms: 18 en suite

Lunch available
EM 1800 (LO 2100)
Parking for 30
CC: Amex, Barclaycard,
Delta, Eurocard, JCB,
Mastercard, Solo, Switch,
Visa, Visa Electron

B&B per night:
S £49.00–£59.00
D £69.00–£99.00

HB per person:
DY £49.00–£69.00

OPEN All year round

Charming hotel with a unique atmosphere, in a village close to Oxford. Easy access to M40. Excellent restaurant. Themed bedrooms, some with balcony or patio.

WHERE TO STAY
Please mention this guide when making your booking.

OXFORD continued

★★ **VICTORIA HOTEL**

180 Abingdon Road, Oxford,	Bedrooms: 5 single,	Lunch available	B&B per night:
OX1 4RA	12 double, 1 twin,	EM 1900 (LO 2100)	**S £58.50–£62.50**
T: (01865) 724536	2 triple	Parking for 20	**D £68.50–£78.50**
F: (01865) 794909	Bathrooms: 20 en suite	CC: Barclaycard, Delta,	
I: www.oxfordcity.co.uk/hotels/		Eurocard, Mastercard,	OPEN All year round
victoria		Switch, Visa	

Completely modernised Victorian hotel. All rooms en suite with direct-dial telephone, colour TV, radio, hairdryer, tea/coffee facilities. Walking distance city centre. Competitive prices. Car park at rear.

PANGBOURNE, Berkshire Map ref 2C2

★★★
Silver
Award

THE COPPER INN HOTEL & RESTAURANT

Church Road, Pangbourne, Reading,	Bedrooms: 2 single,	Lunch available	B&B per night:
Berkshire RG8 7AR	14 double, 5 twin,	EM 1900 (LO 2200)	**S £50.00–£105.00**
T: (0118) 984 2244	1 triple	Parking for 20	**D £100.00–£150.00**
F: (0118) 984 5542	Bathrooms: 22 en suite	CC: Amex, Barclaycard,	
E: reservations@copper-inn.co.uk		Diners, Mastercard,	HB per person:
I: www.copper-inn.co.uk		Switch, Visa	**DY £70.00–£135.00**

Lovingly restored 19thC coaching inn next to parish church. Award-winning restaurant overlooks tranquil hotel garden. Convenient for exploring Thames Valley, Oxford, Windsor. Special weekend rates.

OPEN All year round

Best Western Hotels

POOLE, Dorset Map ref 2B3 *Tourist Information Centre Tel: (01202) 253253*

Rating
Applied For
Ad p15

THISTLE POOLE

The Quay, Poole, Dorset BH15 1HD	Bedrooms: 20 single,	Lunch available	B&B per night:
T: (01202) 666800	38 double, 10 twin	EM 1900 (LO 2200)	**S £126.00–£129.00**
F: (01202) 684470	Bathrooms: 68 en suite	Parking for 120	**D £136.00–£160.00**
E: poole@thistle.co.uk		CC: Amex, Barclaycard,	
I: www.thistlehotels.com		Delta, Diners, Eurocard,	OPEN All year round
		JCB, Mastercard, Solo,	
		Switch, Visa	

Modern hotel on the Old Quay with panoramic views. Near town centre, ferry terminal, Poole Pottery and museums. Harbour view restaurant seafood our speciality.

Thistle Hotels/Utell
International

PORTSMOUTH & SOUTHSEA, Hampshire Map ref 2C3 Tourism Information Centre Tel (023) 9282 6722

★★ **OCEAN HOTEL & APARTMENTS**

8-10 St Helens Parade, Southsea,	Bedrooms: 1 single,	EM 1830 (LO 1930)	B&B per night:
Hampshire PO4 0RW	6 double, 1 twin, 3 triple,	Parking for 37	**S £25.00–£35.00**
T: (023) 9273 4233 & 9273 4342	5 family rooms; suites	CC: Barclaycard, Eurocard,	**D £48.00–£56.00**
F: (023) 9229 7046	available	Mastercard, Visa	
E: feris@oceanhotel.freeserve.co.uk	Bathrooms: 13 en suite,		HB per person:
I: www.oceanhotel.freeserve.co.uk	2 private, 4 public		**DY £35.00–£46.00**

Imposing building in foremost seafront position between South Parade Pier and Canoe Lake with magnificent sea views. Choice of hotel rooms, suites, or self-contained apartments.

OPEN All year round

★ **SALISBURY HOTEL**

57-59 Festing Road, Southsea,	Bedrooms: 5 single,	EM 1900 (LO 2000)	B&B per night:
Hampshire PO4 0NQ	6 double, 1 twin, 4 triple,	Parking for 14	**S £25.00–£35.00**
T: (023) 9282 3606 & 07775	2 family rooms; suites	CC: Barclaycard, Eurocard,	**D £40.00–£60.00**
660034 (mobile)	available	Mastercard, Visa	
F: (023) 9282 0955	Bathrooms: 13 en suite,		HB per person:
E: feris@oceanhotel.freeserve.co.uk	1 private, 2 public,		**DY £35.00–£45.00**
I: www.oceanhotel.freeserve.co.uk	4 private showers		

Friendly hotel with character. Two minutes' walk from sea and other attractions. En suite rooms. Private car park. The hotel you will confidently come back to.

OPEN All year round

IMPORTANT NOTE Information on accommodation listed in this guide has been supplied by the proprietors. As changes may occur you are advised to check details at the time of booking.

PORTSMOUTH & SOUTHSEA continued

★★ **THE SANDRINGHAM HOTEL**
7 Osborne Road, Southsea,
Hampshire PO5 3LR
T: (023) 9282 6969 & 9282 2914
F: (023) 9282 2330

Bedrooms: 6 single,
20 double, 9 twin,
5 triple, 1 family room
Bathrooms: 41 en suite

EM 1900 (LO 2030)
CC: Amex, Barclaycard,
Delta, Mastercard, Switch,
Visa

B&B per night:
S £45.00–£55.00
D £56.00–£66.00

HB per person:
DY £30.00–£40.00

OPEN All year round

Seafront hotel with sea views from most bedrooms and pleasantly decorated, spacious public areas. Restaurant, function/conference room, ballroom. Car park opposite. Two minutes' walk to shopping.

★★ **READING, Berkshire Map ref 2C2** *Tourist Information Centre Tel: (0118) 956 6226*

★★ **COMFORT INN READING**
119 Kendrick Road, Reading, Berkshire
RG1 5EB

T: (0118) 931 1311
F: (0118) 931 4136
I: www.hotelchoice.com/travelweb

B&B per night:
S £45.00–£80.00
D £60.00–£95.00

HB per person:
DY £60.00–£75.00

OPEN All year round

Ⓒ®
Choice Hotels Europe

Privately owned hotel, built in the 1890s. Situated in a select conservation area, close to the university, within walking distance of Reading's lively town centre and 1.5 miles from Reading station. All bedrooms en suite, family rooms are available and we welcome children. On-site restaurant overlooking delightful gardens.

Bedrooms: 13 single,
15 double, 7 twin
Bathrooms: 35 en suite

Lunch available
EM 1900 (LO 2130)
Parking for 40
CC: Amex, Barclaycard,
Delta, Diners, Maestro,
Mastercard, Solo, Switch,
Visa, Visa Electron

★★★

★★★ **UPCROSS HOTEL**
68 Berkeley Avenue, Reading, Berkshire
RG1 6HY

T: (0118) 959 0796
F: (0118) 957 6517
E: reservations@upcrosshotel.co.uk

B&B per night:
S £32.50–£75.00
D £51.00–£85.00

HB per person:
DY £50.00–£90.00

OPEN All year round

Privately-owned country house hotel of character and warmth, reputed to have one of the best restaurants in Berkshire. Our conference facilities overlook beautifully kept gardens. Large car park. Town centre/railway station 10 minutes away. Convenient for London, Oxford, Bath, Bristol. Easy access from the M4, junctions 11 and 12.

Bedrooms: 7 single,
8 double, 6 twin, 2 triple
Bathrooms: 23 en suite

Lunch available
EM 1900 (LO 2230)
Parking for 40
CC: Amex, Barclaycard,
Delta, Diners, Eurocard,
JCB, Maestro, Mastercard,
Solo, Switch, Visa, Visa
Electron

COUNTRY CODE Always follow the Country Code ✤ Enjoy the countryside and respect its life and work ✤ Guard against all risk of fire ✤ Fasten all gates ✤ Keep your dogs under close control ✤ Keep to public paths across farmland ✤ Use gates and stiles to cross fences, hedges and walls ✤ Leave livestock, crops and machinery alone ✤ Take your litter home ✤ Help to keep all water clean ✤ Protect wildlife, plants and trees ✤ Take special care on country roads ✤ Make no unnecessary noise

★★★

THE PARKBURY HOTEL

29/31 The Broadway, Sandown,
Isle of Wight PO36 9BB
T: (01983) 402508
F: (01983) 404471
E: sean@parkbury.freeserve.co.uk
I: www.smoothhound.co.uk/hotels/
parkbury.html

B&B per night:
S £25.00–£31.00
D £50.00–£62.00

HB per person:
DY £34.00–£41.00

OPEN All year round

Homely, family-run hotel located only minutes from Sandown's busy centre and seafront. Now completely refurbished, the hotel is themed around the old ocean liners and incorporates unique wood panelling from Cunard's "RMS Aquitania". Centrally heated throughout. Large gardens and large heated outdoor pool. Entertainment most nights.

Bedrooms: 8 single,
20 double, 12 twin,
2 triple, 2 family rooms
Bathrooms: 44 en suite,
1 public

Lunch available
EM 2000 (LO 1930)
Parking for 12
CC: Barclaycard,
Mastercard, Visa

★★

CHINE COURT HOTEL
Popham Road, Shanklin,
Isle of Wight PO37 6RG
T: (01983) 862732
F: (01983) 862732

Bedrooms: 2 single,
8 double, 5 twin, 5 triple,
4 family rooms
Bathrooms: 24 en suite

EM 1830 (LO 1915)
Parking for 24
CC: Barclaycard, Delta,
Eurocard, Mastercard,
Switch, Visa

B&B per night:
S £27.00–£30.00
D £54.00–£64.00

HB per person:
DY £36.00–£42.00

OPEN Apr–Oct

Elegant, lavishly decorated Victorian residence in large grounds, enjoying magnificent sea views from its elevated clifftop position.

★★

HAMBLEDON HOTEL
11 Queens Road, Shanklin,
Isle of Wight PO37 6AW
T: (01983) 862403
F: (01983) 867894
E: hambledon@netguides.co.uk
I: www.netguides.co.uk/wight/
standard/hambledon.html

Bedrooms: 1 single,
5 double, 1 triple,
3 family rooms
Bathrooms: 10 en suite,
1 public

EM 1830 (LO 1830)
Parking for 9
CC: Barclaycard, Delta,
Eurocard, JCB,
Mastercard, Switch, Visa

B&B per night:
S £22.00–£25.00
D £44.00–£50.00

HB per person:
DY £32.00–£39.00

OPEN All year round

Small, family-run hotel close to beach and shops, providing varied food, comfort and friendly service. All rooms en suite, central position. Open all year.

See under Portsmouth & Southsea

THE HOLT HOTEL

Oxford Road, Steeple Aston, Oxford,
OX6 3QQ
T: (01869) 340259
F: (01869) 340865
E: info@holthotel-oxford.co.uk
I: www.holthotel.co.uk

B&B per night:
S £92.82–£99.87
D £116.33–£123.33

HB per person:
DY £59.50–£124.87

OPEN All year round

Unwind, relax and get away from it all! Escape to the 15thC Holt Hotel, situated on the edge of the Cotswolds in 9 acres of Oxfordshire countryside. Award-winning restaurant and bar. Local attractions include Blenheim Palace, Bicester International Outlet Village, Warwick Castle, Stratford and Oxford. Only 10 minutes from junction 10, M40.

Bedrooms: 9 single,
48 double, 25 twin,
2 triple; suites available
Bathrooms: 84 en suite

Lunch available
EM 1900 (LO 2145)
Parking for 200
CC: Amex, Barclaycard,
Delta, Diners, Eurocard,
JCB, Maestro, Mastercard,
Solo, Switch, Visa, Visa
Electron

STONOR, Oxfordshire Map ref 2C2

★★★
Silver
Award

THE STONOR ARMS HOTEL
Stonor, Henley-on-Thames,
RG9 6HE
T: (01491) 638866
F: (01491) 638863
E: stonorarms.hotel@virgin.net
I: www.stonor.arms.co.uk

Bedrooms: 4 double,
6 twin
Bathrooms: 10 en suite

Lunch available
EM 1900 (LO 2130)
Parking for 26
CC: Amex, Barclaycard,
Delta, Mastercard, Solo,
Switch, Visa, Visa Electron

B&B per night:
S £99.00–£115.00
D £125.00–£155.00

OPEN All year round

Situated in the Stonor Valley, 4 miles from Henley-on-Thames on the B480 and 4 miles from M40 junction 6. A charming English country house hotel and award-winning restaurant.

STRATFIELD TURGIS, Hampshire Map ref 2C2

★★★

THE WELLINGTON ARMS
Stratfield Turgis, Hook, RG27 0AS
T: (01256) 882214
F: (01256) 882934

Bedrooms: 7 single,
18 double, 4 twin,
2 family rooms
Bathrooms: 31 en suite

Lunch available
EM 1830 (LO 2130)
Parking for 75
CC: Amex, Barclaycard,
Delta, Diners, Mastercard,
Solo, Switch, Visa, Visa
Electron

B&B per night:
S £60.00–£110.00
D £70.00–£125.00

HB per person:
DY £60.00–£95.00

OPEN All year round

Traditional coaching inn on the Duke of Wellington's estate, midway between Basingstoke and Reading on the A33. Motorway access from junction 6 of M3, junction 11 of M4.

STREATLEY, Berkshire Map ref 2C2

★★★★
Silver
Award

THE SWAN DIPLOMAT HOTEL
Streatley on Thames, Streatley,
Reading, Berkshire RG8 9HR
T: (01491) 878800
F: (01491) 872554
E: sales@swan-diplomat.co.uk
I: www.diplomat-hotel.se

Bedrooms: 9 single,
27 double, 10 twin; suite
available
Bathrooms: 46 en suite

Lunch available
EM 1900 (LO 2200)
Parking for 145
CC: Amex, Barclaycard,
Delta, Diners, Eurocard,
Mastercard, Switch, Visa

B&B per night:
S £68.50–£137.50
D £105.00–£157.00

HB per person:
DY £84.50–£110.50

OPEN All year round

Beautifully situated on the banks of the River Thames. Oxford, Windsor, London and Heathrow Airport are all within one hour's drive of this peaceful and tranquil location.

SWANAGE, Dorset Map ref 2B3 *Tourist Information Centre Tel: (01929) 422885*

★★★

THE PINES HOTEL
Burlington Road, Swanage, BH19 1LT
T: (01929) 425211
F: (01929) 422075
E: reservations@pineshotel.co.uk
I: www.pineshotel.co.uk

B&B per night:
S £45.00–£58.50
D £90.00–£117.00

HB per person:
DY £54.50–£82.00

OPEN All year round

Modern family-run hotel set in the Purbeck countryside at the quiet end of Swanage Bay. The hotel has its own access to the beach and marvellous coastal views. The Pines prides itself on the friendliness of its staff, the comfort of its sea-facing lounges and especially its reputation for cuisine.

Bedrooms: 2 single,
10 double, 11 twin,
24 triple
Bathrooms: 47 en suite,
1 public

Lunch available
EM 1930 (LO 2100)
Parking for 60
CC: Barclaycard, Delta,
Eurocard, JCB,
Mastercard, Solo, Switch,
Visa, Visa Electron

CENTRAL RESERVATIONS OFFICES
The symbol ⓒⓇ and a group name in an entry indicate that bookings can be made through a central reservations office. These are listed in a separate section towards the back of this guide.

★★★

STRING OF HORSES & CARRIAGES RESTAURANT

Mead End Road, Sway, Lymington, SO41 6EH

T: (01590) 682631
F: (01590) 682911
E: relax@stringofhorses.co.uk
I: www.stringofhorses.co.uk

Secluded country lane hotel on edge of the enchanting New Forest. Relaxed atmosphere with service, cuisine and accommodation of the highest standard. Luxurious bedrooms with en suite jacuzzis. Heated pool in peaceful gardens. Perfect for couples in search of comfort and tranquillity – without children. Candlelit award-winning French restaurant. No smoking.

Bedrooms: 7 double, 1 twin
Bathrooms: 8 en suite

Lunch available
EM 1900 (LO 2130)
Parking for 32
CC: Amex, Barclaycard, Delta, Eurocard, JCB, Mastercard, Solo, Switch, Visa

B&B per night:
S £70.00–£75.00
D £98.00–£118.00

HB per person:
DY £72.00–£82.00

OPEN All year round

Ⓜ♨️🏠☎️🖥️💻♿🎱🅂✂️🅗🍴🛏️🚬26 🏌️❄️✈️🚲⚓ ⓈⓅ Ⓣ

★★★   **THE SPREAD EAGLE HOTEL**

Cornmarket, Thame, OX9 2BW
T: (01844) 213661
F: (01844) 261380

Bedrooms: 5 single, 22 double, 5 twin, 1 triple; suites available
Bathrooms: 33 en suite

Lunch available
EM 1900 (LO 2200)
Parking for 80
CC: Amex, Diners, Visa

B&B per night:
S £93.00–£108.00
D £104.00–£127.00

HB per person:
DY £105.95–£118.95

OPEN All year round

Converted 17thC coaching inn, centre of small country market town. Fothergills Restaurant features a choice of menus. Banqueting and conference facilities. Good base for touring Thames Valley.

Ⓜ🏇♨️🏠☎️🖥️♿🅂🍴🛏️Ⓞ🖥️🍴🍹250 ⓊⓅ❄️✈️🚲 ⓈⓅ🏧Ⓣ

★★★

COUNTRY GARDEN HOTEL

Church Hill, Totland Bay, Isle of Wight PO39 1QE

T: (01983) 754521
F: (01983) 754521
E: pat.burton@lineone.net

Delightful, personable, boutique hotel set in beautiful grounds in tranquil West Wight. Lovely strolls/ hikes to the Solent, Needles and Tennyson Downs. Golf and sports centre nearby. En suite garden, sea views and ground floor rooms available. Lounge, bar, locally popular pleasant dining room with great cuisine. Ferry inclusive offer October-April.

Bedrooms: 2 single, 9 double, 5 twin; suite available
Bathrooms: 16 en suite

Lunch available
EM 1900 (LO 2100)
Parking for 30
CC: Barclaycard, Delta, Maestro, Mastercard, Solo, Switch, Visa, Visa Electron

B&B per night:
S £43.00–£63.00
D £78.00–£118.00

HB per person:
DY £48.00–£67.00

OPEN All year round

Ⓜ♨️☎️🖥️💻♿🅂🍴🛏️🍴🛏️🖥️🍴❄️🚲⚓ ⓈⓅ Ⓣ

★★★
Silver
Award

BURLINGTON HOTEL

Bellevue Road, Ventnor, Isle of Wight PO38 1DB
T: (01983) 852113
F: (01983) 853862

Bedrooms: 3 single, 5 double, 9 twin, 6 triple, 1 family room
Bathrooms: 24 en suite

EM 1900 (LO 2030)
Parking for 20
CC: Barclaycard, Delta, Eurocard, Mastercard, Switch, Visa

B&B per night:
S £32.00–£40.00
D £64.00–£80.00

HB per person:
DY £40.00–£48.00

OPEN Mar–Oct

Friendly family-run hotel with heated swimming pool, commanding wonderful sea views. Central, yet affords peace and quiet. Car park.

Ⓜ🏇3♨️🏠☎️🖥️💻♿🅂🍴🛏️🖥️🍴🍹❄️✈️🚲 ⓈⒸ ⓈⓅ Ⓣ

HALF BOARD PRICES Half board prices are given per person, but in some cases these may be based on double/twin occupancy.

★★

KEMPS COUNTRY HOUSE HOTEL

East Stoke, Wareham, BH20 6AL
T: (01929) 462563
F: (01929) 405287

B&B per night:
S £56.00–£78.00
D £84.00–£135.00

OPEN All year round

Personally-run Victorian former rectory, set in its own grounds facing the Purbeck Hills. Lovely views. Daily changing menu plus a la carte. Spacious en suite rooms, 4-poster, whirlpool baths. Real value and bargain breaks all year.

Bedrooms: 8 double,
2 twin, 4 triple
Bathrooms: 14 en suite,
1 public

Lunch available
EM 1900 (LO 2130)
Parking for 36
CC: Amex, Barclaycard,
Delta, Diners, Eurocard,
Mastercard, Solo, Switch,
Visa

♨ ➤ ⚷ 🏨 ✆ 🖂 ⌨ ♨ 🛈 Ⓢ ✂ 🅜 ⊞ 🖨 🍽 70 ▶ ❀ 🚲 ⚲ 🎬 Ⓣ

★★★

SPRINGFIELD COUNTRY HOTEL & LEISURE CLUB

Grange Road, Wareham, BH20 5AL
T: (01929) 552177
F: (01929) 551862

B&B per night:
S £66.00–£80.00
D £100.00–£130.00

HB per person:
DY £60.00–£85.00

OPEN All year round

Family-owned country hotel set in 6 acres of beautifully landscaped gardens at the foot of the Purbeck Hills. 48 en suite rooms, executive rooms with bath, shower and balcony. Luxurious leisure club, choice of restaurants, superb menu, extensive wine list, oak-beamed lounges. Beaches and golf nearby.

Bedrooms: 1 single,
28 double, 14 twin,
3 triple, 2 family rooms
Bathrooms: 48 en suite

Lunch available
EM 1900 (LO 2130)
Parking for 150
CC: Amex, Barclaycard,
Delta, Diners, Eurocard,
JCB, Maestro, Mastercard,
Solo, Switch, Visa, Visa
Electron

♨ ➤ ⚷ ✆ 🖂 ⌨ ♥ ♨ 🛈 Ⓢ ✂ 🅜 ⊤🅥 ◑ 🛅 ⊞ 🖨 🍽 200 ⛳ 🎿 🏹 ⚑ ⚶ ⚸ 🎱 ▶ ❀ 🚲 ⚲ 🆂🅿

★★

CROMWELL HOUSE HOTEL

Lulworth Cove, West Lulworth, Wareham,
BH20 5RJ
T: (01929) 400253 & 400332
F: (01929) 400566
E: catriona@lulworthcove.co.uk
I: www.lulworthcove.co.uk

B&B per night:
S £29.50–£44.50
D £52.00–£71.00

HB per person:
DY £42.50–£48.50

OPEN All year round

Family hotel on the Dorset Heritage Coast footpath. Outstanding sea views over Lulworth Cove. Secluded garden. Good walking country. Swimming pool (May-October). Restaurant, wine list, bar. Fish specialities including local lobsters and scallops. Group bookings welcome. Midweek/weekend breaks available. Private business parties catered for.

Bedrooms: 2 single,
7 double, 5 twin, 3 triple
Bathrooms: 17 en suite

EM 1900 (LO 2030)
Parking for 17
CC: Amex, Barclaycard,
Delta, Diners, Eurocard,
JCB, Maestro, Mastercard,
Solo, Switch, Visa, Visa
Electron

♨ ➤ ⚷ 🏨 ✆ 🖵 ♥ ♨ 🛈 Ⓢ 🅜 ⊤🅥 🛅 ⊞ 🖨 🍽 🏹 ✏ ❀ 🆂🅿 Ⓣ

CREDIT CARD BOOKINGS
If you book by telephone and are asked for your credit card number it is advisable to check the proprietor's policy should you cancel your reservation.

275

WEST LULWORTH continued

SHIRLEY HOTEL

West Lulworth, Wareham, BH20 5RL
T: (01929) 400358
F: (01929) 400167
E: durdle@aol.com

B&B per night:
S £35.00–£44.00
D £70.00–£88.00

HB per person:
DY £40.00–£60.00

OPEN Feb–Nov

In country village, 10 minutes' walk from Lulworth Cove. Small and friendly family-run hotel offering relaxing breaks with good facilities. Fifteen en-suite rooms, including 3 superior for special stays, ensure your comfort. Good food and wine in our relaxed restaurant. Unwind in our indoor heated pool and spa.

Bedrooms: 1 single, 8 double, 4 twin, 2 family rooms
Bathrooms: 15 en suite, 1 public

EM 1845 (LO 2000)
Parking for 22
CC: Amex, Barclaycard, Delta, Eurocard, JCB, Mastercard, Solo, Switch, Visa, Visa Electron

---

WIMBORNE MINSTER, Dorset Map ref 2B3 *Tourist Information Centre Tel: (01202) 886116*

★★
Silver
Award

BEECHLEAS HOTEL & RESTAURANT

17 Poole Road, Wimborne Minster, BH21 1QA
T: (01202) 841684
F: (01202) 849344

B&B per night:
S £69.00–£89.00
D £79.00–£109.00

HB per person:
DY £59.00–£68.00

OPEN All year round

Beautifully restored Grade II Listed Georgian townhouse. Log fires in autumn/winter, delightful conservatory and garden, own car park. Award-winning restaurant. Recognised for hospitality and service. Sailing in Poole Harbour. Visit Wimborne Minster, Kingston Lacey, Corfe Castle, New Forest, Thomas Hardy Country.

Bedrooms: 2 single, 5 double, 2 twin
Bathrooms: 9 en suite

EM 1900 (LO 2100)
Parking for 12
CC: Amex, Barclaycard, Delta, Eurocard, JCB, Mastercard, Switch, Visa

---

WINCHESTER, Hampshire Map ref 2C3 *Tourist Information Centre Tel: (01962) 840500*

★★★

HARESTOCK LODGE HOTEL

Harestock Road, Winchester, SO22 6NX
T: (01962) 881870 & 880038
F: (01962) 886959
I: www.hants.gov.uk/tourist/hotels/harestocklodge

B&B per night:
S £55.00–£60.00
D £75.00–£80.00

HB per person:
DY £50.00–£55.00

OPEN All year round

The Independents

Peacefully situated on the outskirts of Winchester, a short distance from all major road links. A family-run hotel with well-appointed, finely furnished en suite bedrooms. Views over open countryside, large secluded garden and ample parking. Professionally run to a high standard, offering good food and friendly service in a relaxed atmosphere.

Bedrooms: 4 single, 8 double, 4 twin, 1 triple
Bathrooms: 17 en suite

Lunch available
EM 1830 (LO 2245)
Parking for 26
CC: Amex, Barclaycard, Delta, Diners, Eurocard, Mastercard, Solo, Switch, Visa

---

WELCOME HOST
This is a nationally recognised customer care programme which aims to promote the highest standards of service and a warm welcome. Establishments taking part in this initiative are indicated by the ⊛ symbol.

WINCHESTER continued

THE WESSEX

★★★★
Silver
Award

Paternoster Row, Winchester,
SO23 9LQ
T: 0870 400 8126
F: (01962) 841503

Bedrooms: 15 single,
51 double, 28 twin; suite
available
Bathrooms: 94 en suite

Lunch available
EM 1900 (LO 2200)
Parking for 10
CC: Amex, Barclaycard,
Delta, Diners, Eurocard,
JCB, Mastercard, Solo,
Switch, Visa, Visa Electron

B&B per night:
S Min £70.00
D Min £100.00

HB per person:
DY Min £60.00

OPEN All year round

Ⓒ
Utell International

Spacious modern hotel overlooking the magnificent cathedral. Ideal for strolling around this historic city. Former home of Jane Austen, Trollope, Keats and ancient kings of England.

Ⓜ ⅔ 🛏 🍴 ✆ 🖥 ☐ 🔌 ⚑ Ⓢ ✂ ◐ ⊞ ⅲ 🍷 100 ▶ ⚲ SP Ⓣ ◉

WINDSOR, Berkshire Map ref 2D2 *Tourist Information Centre Tel: (01753) 743900*

FAIRLIGHT LODGE ROYAL WINDSOR HOTEL

★★

41 Frances Road, Windsor,
Berkshire SL4 3AQ
T: (01753) 861207
F: (01753) 865963
E: fairlightlodge@hotmail.com
I: www.fairlightlodge.webjump.com

Bedrooms: 2 single,
5 double, 2 twin,
1 family room
Bathrooms: 10 en suite

EM 1900 (LO 2130)
Parking for 10
CC: Amex, Barclaycard,
Delta, Eurocard, JCB,
Mastercard, Solo, Switch,
Visa

B&B per night:
S £57.00–£84.00
D £76.00–£99.00

HB per person:
DY £45.00–£55.00

OPEN All year round

Comfortable Victorian property, once the mayoral residence, quietly situated, but close to River Thames, castle and town centre. Fully licensed bar and restaurant.

Ⓜ ⅔ 🛏 🍴 ✆ 🖥 ☐ 🔌 ⅰ Ⓢ ✂ ⅲ 📺 ⅲ ☎ ⚑ 15 ✿ 🚬 SP 🐾 Ⓣ

SIR CHRISTOPHER WREN'S HOUSE, HOTEL & BUSINESS CENTRE

★★★
Gold
Award

Thames Street, Windsor, Berkshire
SL4 1PX
T: (01753) 861354
F: (01753) 860172
E: hotels@wrensgroup.com
I: www.wrensgroup.com

Bedrooms: 9 single,
48 double, 12 twin,
1 triple; suites available
Bathrooms: 70 en suite

Lunch available
EM 1900 (LO 2200)
Parking for 25
CC: Amex, Barclaycard,
Delta, Diners, Eurocard,
Maestro, Mastercard,
Solo, Switch, Visa, Visa
Electron

B&B per night:
S £102.00–£150.00
D £140.00–£195.00

OPEN All year round

Situated beneath Windsor Castle and on the banks of the River Thames. Historic house, built by Sir Christopher Wren in 1676, with restaurant bar and terraced garden.

Ⓜ ⅔ ⅙ 🛏 🍴 ✆ 🖥 ☐ 🔌 ⅰ Ⓢ ⅲ ◐ ⅲ ☎ 🍷 80 ✿ ✈ 🚬 ⚲ SP 🐾 Ⓣ

STIRRUPS COUNTRY HOUSE HOTEL

★★★
Silver
Award

Maidens Green, Bracknell, Berkshire
RG42 6LD
T: (01344) 882284
F: (01344) 882300
E: reception@stirrupshotel.co.uk
I: www.stirrupshotel.co.uk

Bedrooms: 20 double,
4 twin, 5 triple; suites
available
Bathrooms: 29 en suite

Lunch available
EM 1900 (LO 2200)
Parking for 100
CC: Amex, Barclaycard,
Delta, Diners, Mastercard,
Solo, Switch, Visa, Visa
Electron

B&B per night:
S £100.00–£135.00
D £105.00–£145.00

HB per person:
DY £60.00–£75.00

OPEN All year round

Ⓒ
Best Western Hotels

Privately owned hotel in Berkshire, between Windsor, Ascot and Bracknell and only 3 miles from the Windsor Legoland park. Worth a visit to the award-winning restaurant.

Ⓜ ⅔ ⅙ 🛏 🍴 ✆ 🖥 ☐ 🔌 ⅰ Ⓢ ✂ ◐ ⊞ ⅲ ☎ 🍷 80 ✿ ✈ ⚲ SP Ⓣ ◉

WITNEY, Oxfordshire Map ref 2C1 *Tourist Information Centre Tel: (01993) 775802*

THE MARLBOROUGH HOTEL

★★

28 Market Square, Witney, OX8 7BB
T: (01993) 776353
F: (01993) 702152

Bedrooms: 6 single,
12 double, 2 twin,
2 triple
Bathrooms: 22 en suite

Lunch available
EM 1800 (LO 2130)
Parking for 18
CC: Amex, Barclaycard,
Delta, JCB, Mastercard,
Switch, Visa

B&B per night:
S £51.00–£53.00
D £65.00–£75.00

OPEN All year round

Ⓒ
Minotel

Situated in the town centre. Ideal for touring the Cotswolds, Oxford City and Woodstock (Blenheim Palace). Excellent food along with a warm and friendly welcome.

⅔ ✆ ☐ 🔌 ⅰ Ⓢ ✂ ⅲ ⅲ ☎ 🍷 100 ▶ ⚲ SP 🐾 Ⓣ

ACCESSIBILITY

Look for the 🛆 🛆 🛆 symbols which indicate accessibility for wheelchair users. A list of establishments is at the front of this guide.

A brief guide to the main Towns and Villages offering accommodation in the # SOUTH OF ENGLAND

A **ALRESFORD, HAMPSHIRE** – Between Old and New Alresford lie the remains of Bishop de Lucy's spendid 12th C reservoir. New Alresford is a pleasant market town and Old Alresford a smaller village with a stream running through the green.

● **ALTON, HAMPSHIRE** – Pleasant old market town standing on the Pilgrim's Way, with some attractive Georgian buildings. The parish church still bears the scars of bullet marks, evidence of a bitter struggle between the Roundheads and the Royalists.

● **ANDOVER, HAMPSHIRE** – Town that achieved importance from the wool trade and now has much modern development. A good centre for visiting places of interest.

● **AYLESBURY, BUCKINGHAMSHIRE** – Historic county town in the Vale of Aylesbury. The cobbled market square has a Victorian clock tower and the 15th C King's Head Inn (National Trust). Interesting county museum and 13th C parish church.

B **BASINGSTOKE, HAMPSHIRE** – Rapidly developing commercial and industrial centre. The town is surrounded by charming villages and places to visit.

● **BEACONSFIELD, BUCKINGHAMSHIRE** – Former coaching town with several inns still surviving. The old town has many fine houses and an interesting church. Beautiful countryside and beech woods nearby.

● **BLANDFORD FORUM, DORSET** – Almost completely destroyed by fire in 1731, the town was rebuilt in a handsome Georgian style. The church is large and grand and the town is the hub of a rich farming area.

● **BOURNEMOUTH, DORSET** – Seaside town set among the pines with a mild climate, sandy beaches and fine coastal views. The town has wide streets with excellent shops, a pier, a pavilion, museums and conference centre.

● **BUCKINGHAM, BUCKINGHAMSHIRE** – Interesting old market town surrounded by rich farmland. It has many Georgian buildings, including the Town Hall and Old Jail and many old almshouses and inns. Stowe School nearby has magnificent 18th C landscaped gardens.

● **BURFORD, OXFORDSHIRE** – One of the most beautiful Cotswold wool towns with Georgian and Tudor houses, many antique shops and a picturesque High Street sloping to the River Windrush.

● **BURLEY, HAMPSHIRE** – Attractive centre from which to explore the south-west part of the New Forest. There is an ancient earthwork on Castle Hill nearby, which also offers good views.

C **CHESTERTON, OXFORDSHIRE** - Village close to Bicester noted in the Domesday Book, retaining its character.

● **CORFE CASTLE, DORSET** - One of the most spectacular ruined castles in Britain. Norman in origin, the castle was a Royalist stronghold during the Civil War and held out until 1645. The village had a considerable marble-carving industry in the Middle Ages.

D **DEDDINGTON, OXFORDSHIRE** – On the edge of the Cotswolds and settled since the Stone Age, this is the only village in England to have been granted a full Coat of Arms, displayed on the 16th C Town Hall in the picturesque market square. Many places of interest include the Church of St Peter and St Paul.

● **DROXFORD, HAMPSHIRE** – Village with numerous Georgian buildings. Izaak Walton was a frequent visitor to the 18th C rectory now owned by the National Trust.

F **FARINGDON, OXFORDSHIRE** - Ancient stone-built market town in the Vale of the White Horse. The 17th C market hall stands on pillars and the 13th C church has some fine monuments. A great monastic tithe barn is nearby at Great Coxwell.

G **GOSPORT, HAMPSHIRE** - From a tiny fishing hamlet, Gosport has grown into an important centre with many naval establishments, including HMS Dolphin, the submarine base, with the Naval Submarine Museum which preserves HMS Alliance and Holland I.

L **LIPHOOK, HAMPSHIRE** – Large village astride the A3 and close to the West Sussex border.

● **LYMINGTON, HAMPSHIRE** – Small, pleasant town with bright cottages and attractive Georgian houses, lying on the edge of the New Forest with a ferry service to the Isle of Wight. A sheltered harbour makes it a busy yachting centre.

● **LYNDHURST, HAMPSHIRE** – The "capital" of the New Forest, surrounded by attractive woodland scenery and delightful villages. The town is dominated by the Victorian Gothic-style church where the original Alice in Wonderland is buried.

M **MAIDENHEAD, BERKSHIRE** – Attractive town on the River Thames which is crossed by an elegant 18th C bridge and by Brunel's well-known railway bridge. It is a popular place for boating with delightful riverside walks. The Courage Shire Horse Centre is nearby.

● **MARLOW, BUCKINGHAMSHIRE** – Attractive Georgian town on the River Thames, famous for its 19th C suspension bridge. The High Street contains many old houses and there are connections with writers including Shelley and T S Eliot.

● **MILFORD-ON-SEA, HAMPSHIRE** – Victorian seaside resort with shingle beach and good bathing, set in pleasant countryside and looking out over the Isle of Wight. Nearby is Hurst Castle, built by Henry VIII. The school chapel, former abbey church, can be visited.

● **MILTON KEYNES, BUCKINGHAMSHIRE** – Designated a New Town in 1967, Milton Keynes offers a wide range of housing and is abundantly planted with trees. It has excellent shopping facilities and 3 centres for leisure and sporting activities. The Open University is based here.

N **NEWBURY, BERKSHIRE** – Ancient town surrounded by the Downs and on the Kennet and Avon Canal. It has many buildings of interest, including the 17th C Cloth Hall, which is now a museum. The famous racecourse is nearby.

COUNTRY CODE
Always follow the Country Code ✤ Enjoy the countryside and respect its life and work ✤ Guard against all risk of fire ✤ Fasten all gates ✤ Keep your dogs under close control ✤ Keep to public paths across farmland ✤ Use gates and stiles to cross fences, hedges and walls ✤ Leave livestock, crops and machinery alone ✤ Take your litter home ✤ Help to keep all water clean ✤ Protect wildlife, plants and trees ✤ Take special care on country roads ✤ Make no unnecessary noise

O ODIHAM, HAMPSHIRE - Situated close to the Hampshire/Surrey border. Village retains a sense of historical identity. Convenient for RAF base.

• OXFORD, OXFORDSHIRE - Beautiful university town with many ancient colleges, some dating from the 13th C, and numerous buildings of historic and architectural interest. The Ashmolean Museum has outstanding collections. Lovely gardens and meadows with punting on the Cherwell.

P PANGBOURNE, WEST BERKSHIRE - A pretty stretch of river where the Pang joins the Thames with views of the lock, weir and toll bridge. Once the home of Kenneth Grahame, author of "Wind in the Willows".

• POOLE, DORSET - Tremendous natural harbour makes Poole a superb boating centre. The harbour area is crowded with historic buildings including the 15th C Town Cellars housing a maritime museum.

• PORTSMOUTH & SOUTHSEA, HAMPSHIRE - There have been connections with the Navy since early times and the first dock was built in 1194. HMS Victory, Nelson's flagship, is here and Charles Dickens' former home is open to the public. Neighbouring Southsea has a promenade with magnificent views of Spithead.

R READING, BERKSHIRE - Busy, modern county town with large shopping centre and many leisure and recreation facilities. There are several interesting museums and the Duke of Wellington's Stratfield Saye is nearby.

S SANDOWN, ISLE OF WIGHT - The 6-mile sweep of Sandown Bay is one of the island's finest stretches, with excellent sands. The pier has a pavilion and sun terrace; the esplanade has amusements, bars, eating places and gardens.

• SHANKLIN, ISLE OF WIGHT - Set on a cliff with gentle slopes leading down to the beach, esplanade and marine gardens. The picturesque, old thatched village nestles at the end of the wooded chine.

• STEEPLE ASTON, OXFORDSHIRE - Oxfordshire village whose church has one of the finest examples of church embroidery in the world. Nearby is the Jacobean Rousham House which stands in William Kent's only surviving landscaped garden.

• STONOR, OXFORDSHIRE - The fine manor house of Stonor Park has been a family home for over 800 years and its private chapel has been a centre of Catholicism since Tudor times. The park is one of the most beautiful in southern England.

• STRATFIELD TURGIS, HAMPSHIRE - More a collection of 3 hamlets as opposed to a village. Convenient for Basingstoke.

• STREATLEY, BERKSHIRE - Pretty village on the River Thames, linked to Goring by an attractive bridge. It has Georgian houses and cottages and beautiful views over the countryside and the Goring Gap.

• SWANAGE, DORSET - Began life as an Anglo-Saxon port, then a quarrying centre of Purbeck marble. Now the safe, sandy beach set in a sweeping bay and flanked by downs is good walking country, making it an ideal resort.

• SWAY, HAMPSHIRE - Small village on the south-western edge of the New Forest. It is noted for its 220-ft tower, Peterson's Folly, built in the 1870s by a retired Indian judge to demonstrate the value of concrete as a building material.

T THAME, OXFORDSHIRE - Historic market town on the River Thames. The wide, unspoilt High Street has many styles of architecture with medieval timber-framed cottages, Georgian houses and some famous inns.

• TOTLAND BAY, ISLE OF WIGHT - On the Freshwater Peninsula. It is possible to walk from here around to Alum Bay.

V VENTNOR, ISLE OF WIGHT - Town lies at the bottom of an 800-ft hill and has a reputation as a winter holiday and health resort due to its mild climate. The mile-long esplanade reaches the shore of the delightful village of Bonchurch, and in the other direction are the 22-acre Botanical Gardens.

W WAREHAM, DORSET - This site has been occupied since pre-Roman times and has a turbulent history. In 1762 fire destroyed much of the town, so the buildings now are mostly Georgian.

• WEST LULWORTH, DORSET - Well-known for Lulworth Cove, the almost landlocked circular bay of chalk and limestone cliffs.

• WIMBORNE MINSTER, DORSET - Market town centred on the twin-towered Minster Church of St Cuthberga which gave the town the second part of its name. Good touring base for the surrounding countryside, depicted in the writings of Thomas Hardy.

• WINCHESTER, HAMPSHIRE - King Alfred the Great made Winchester the capital of Saxon England. A magnificent Norman cathedral, with one of the longest naves in Europe, dominates the city. Home of Winchester College founded in 1382.

• WINDSOR, BERKSHIRE - Town dominated by the spectacular castle, home of the Royal Family for over 900 years. Parts are open to the public. There are many attractions including the Great Park, Eton and trips on the river.

• WITNEY, OXFORDSHIRE - Town famous for its blanket-making and mentioned in the Domesday Book. The market place contains the Butter Cross, a medieval meeting place, and there is a green with merchants' houses.

ACCESSIBILITY
Look for the 🚹 symbols which indicate accessibility for wheelchair users. A list of establishments is at the front of this guide.

Where to Stay

2001

The official and best selling guides, offering the reassurance of quality assured accommodation

Hotels, Townhouses and Travel Accommodation in England 2001	Guesthouses, Bed & Breakfast, Farmhouses and Inns in England 2001	Self Catering Holiday Homes in England 2001	Camping & Caravan Parks in Britain 2001
£10.99	£10.99	£9.99	£5.99

THE GUIDES INCLUDE

- Accommodation entries packed with information
- Full colour maps
- Places to visit
- Tourist Information Centres

Look out also for:

SOMEWHERE SPECIAL IN ENGLAND 2001

Accommodation achieving the highest standards in facilities and quality of service - the perfect guide for the discerning traveller

INFORMATIVE   EASY TO USE   GREAT VALUE FOR MONEY

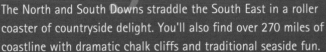

SOUTH EAST ENGLAND

The North and South Downs straddle the South East in a roller coaster of countryside delight. You'll also find over 270 miles of coastline with dramatic chalk cliffs and traditional seaside fun.

Whether you're a shopper or a bopper, Brighton is full of designer stores and nightclubs. While more sedate pleasures such as a Sussex cream tea can be enjoyed in the many picturesque villages.

Kent of course is famous for its hops, but the south east is also a mecca for winegrowers, including Denbies Wine Estate in Surrey, which is the largest in England.

Oyez! Oyez! If you're in Hastings in August, listen out for the National Town Criers Championship.

The counties of
East Sussex, Kent, Surrey
and West Sussex

FOR MORE INFORMATION CONTACT:
South East England Tourist Board,
The Old Brew House, Warwick Park,
Tunbridge Wells, Kent TN2 5TU
Tel: (01892) 540766
Fax: (01892) 511008
Email: enquiries@seetb.org.uk
Internet: www.SouthEastEngland.uk.com

The Pictures:
1 Chiddingfold Village, Surrey;
2 Broadstairs Harbour, Kent;
3 Arundel Castle, West Sussex.

Where to Go in South East England - see pages 282-285
Where to Stay in South East England - see pages 286-296

Whilst in
SOUTH EAST
ENGLAND ...

You will find hundreds of interesting places to visit during your stay, just some of which are listed in these pages.

Contact any Tourist Information Centre in the region for more ideas on days out in South East England.

A Smugglers Adventure at St Clements Caves
West Hill, Hastings, East Sussex TN34 3HY
Tel: (01424) 422964
An extensive exhibition of 18thC smuggling, housed in 2,000 sq m (6,562 sq ft) of caves. Exhibition, museum, video theatre, extensive Adventure Walk incorporating dramatic special effects.

Bateman's
Burwash, East Sussex TN19 7DS
Tel: (01435) 882302
A 17thC Ironmaster's house which was the home of Rudyard Kipling between 1902-1935. His study and Rolls Royce can be seen. Garden with working watermill.

The Bluebell Railway
Sheffield Park, Uckfield, East Sussex TN22 3QL
Tel: (01825) 722370
The Bluebell Railway runs standard-gauge steam trains through 14 km (9 miles) of Sussex countryside and has the largest collection of engines in the South.

Bodiam Castle
Bodiam, East Sussex TN32 5UA
Tel: (01580) 830436
A well-preserved ruin of a castle built in 1385. Exterior walls almost complete. Good views of surrounding area. Wide moat. Museum. Audio visual display on medieval life.

The Body Shop Tour
Watersmead, Littlehampton, West Sussex BN17 6LS
Tel: (01903) 844044
A guided tour of the Body Shop's headquarters. Discover how natural ingredients are used in products and how it campaigns for social and environmental change.

Clandon Park
West Clandon, Guildford, Surrey GU4 7RQ
Tel: (01483) 222482
A Palladian-style house built for Lord Onslow circa 1730. Marble Hall, Gubbay collection of furniture, needlework and porcelain. Royal Surrey Regiment Museum. Parterre in garden.

Claremont Landscape Garden
Esher, Surrey KT10 9JG
Tel: (01372) 467806
One of the earliest surviving English landscape gardens by Vanbourgh and Bridgeman. Lake, island, view points and avenues with pavilion grotto and turf amphitheatre.

Denbies Wine Estate
Dorking, Surrey RH5 6AA
Tel: (01306) 876616
England's largest wine estate, 250 acres in beautiful countryside plus winery and visitor centre featuring 3-D time lapse film of vine growing. Viewing and picture galleries.

Hever Castle and Gardens

Hever, Kent TN8 7NG
Tel: (01732) 865224
Moated castle once the childhood home of Anne Boleyn. Restored by the Astor family, it contains furniture, paintings and panelling. Set in award-winning gardens.

Dover Castle and Secret Wartime Tunnels

Dover, Kent CT16 1HU
Tel: (01304) 201628
One of the most powerful medieval fortresses in Western Europe. St Mary-in-Castro Saxon church. Roman lighthouse, secret wartime tunnels, Henry II Great Keep.

Howletts Wild Animal Park

Bekesbourne, Canterbury, Kent CT4 5EL
Tel: (01303) 264647
Mature parkland containing John Aspinall's animals, famous for its gorilla and tiger collections. Many other animals including elephants, deer and cats.

Fishbourne Roman Palace and Museum

Fishbourne, West Sussex PO19 3QR
Tel: (01243) 785859
The remains of the largest Roman residence in Britain. Many beautiful mosaics, now under cover. Hypocaust and restored formal garden. Museum of finds. Model.

Knockhatch Adventure Park

Hailsham, East Sussex BN27 3PR
Tel: (01323) 442051
Birds of prey centre, laser adventure game, off-road go-karting, paintball, children's farm and crazy golf.

The Gardens of Gaia

Cranbrook, Kent TN17 3NS
Tel: (01580) 715289
Twenty-two acres of gardens and woodland in the spirit of 'Eden'. The historic and magical Lake Chad lies at its heart complimented by enviro-sculptures.

Leonardslee Gardens

Lower Beeding, Horsham, West Sussex RH13 6PP
Tel: (01403) 891212
Rhododendrons and azaleas in a romantic 240-acre valley with seven lakes. Rock garden, bonsai, wallabies and wildfowl. Victorian motorcars and doll's house exhibition.

Great Dixter House and Gardens

Northiam, Kent TN31 6PH
Tel: (01797) 252878
An example of a 15thC manor house with antique furniture and needlework. Home of gardening writer Christopher Lloyd. The house is restored and the gardens were designed by Lutyens.

Marle Place Gardens

Brenchley, Tonbridge, Kent TN12 7HS
Tel: (01892) 722304
Romantic, peaceful gardens with topiary, unusual shrubs and plants, ponds, Edwardian rockery and Victorian gazebo. Walled scented garden and sculptures.

Michelham Priory

Upper Dicker, Hailsham, East Sussex BN27 3QS
Tel: (01323) 844224
An Augustinian priory incorporated into a Tudor mansion. Seven acres of gardens, a working watermill, an Elizabethan Great Barn, smithy and a rope museum.

Guildford Boat House

Millbrook, Guildford, Surrey GU1 3XJ
Tel: (01483) 504494
Regular trips from Guildford to St Catherine's Lock and Godalming along the River Wey. Also 'Alfred Leroy' cruising restaurant. Rowing boats, canoes and holiday narrow boats.

The Pictures:
1 Southover Grange Gardens, Lewes, East Sussex;
2 Leeds Castle, Kent;
3 Chichester Cathedral, West Sussex;
4 Smallhythe Place, Kent;
5 Brighton Marina, East Sussex;
6 Guildford Castle, Surrey;
7 Sheffield Park, East Sussex.

Paddle Steamer Kingswear Castle

The Historic Dockyard, Chatham, Kent ME4 4TQ
Tel: (01634) 827648
A part of Britain's maritime heritage, the award-winning coal-fired paddle steamer, Kingswear Castle, offers morning, afternoon, evening and full day excursions on the Medway.

Penshurst Place and Gardens

Penshurst, Tonbridge, Kent TN11 8DG
Tel: (01892) 870307
A medieval manor house with Baron's Hall, portraits, tapestries, armour, park, lake, venture playground and toy museum. Tudor gardens. Visitor and plant centres.

Petworth House and Park

Petworth, West Sussex GU28 0AE
Tel: (01798) 342207
A late 17thC mansion set in 'Capability' Brown landscaped deer park. The house is noted for its paintings, Gibbons carvings and fine collection of furniture and sculpture.

Polesden Lacey

Great Bookham, Dorking, Surrey RH5 6BD
Tel: (01372) 458203
A Regency villa, re-modelled after 1906 with collections of paintings, porcelain, tapestries and furniture. Walled rose garden and extensive grounds with fine trees and views.

The RHS Garden, Wisley

Wisley, Woking, Surrey GU23 6QB
Tel: (01483) 224234
Stretching over 240 acres of glorious garden, Wisley demonstrates the best in British gardening practices, whatever the season. Plant centre, gift shop and restaurant.

Romney, Hythe and Dymchurch Railway

New Romney, Kent TN28 8PL
Tel: (01797) 362353
The world's only main line in miniature. Fourteen miles (22.5kms) of 15 inch gauge across Romney Marsh. Steam and diesel locomotives, engine sheds and a Toy and Model Museum.

St Mary's House and Gardens

Bramber, Steyning, West Sussex BN44 3WE
Tel: (01903) 816205
A medieval timber-framed Grade I house with rare 16thC wall-leather, fine panelled rooms and a unique painted room. Topiary gardens.

Sheffield Park Garden

Sheffield Park, Uckfield, East Sussex TN22 3QX
Tel: (01825) 790231
One-hundred acres of 'Capability' Brown designed landscaped gardens and woodland with four lakes on different levels. Noted for its rhododendrons, rare trees and azaleas.

Sussex Falconry Centre

Birdham, Chichester, West Sussex PO20 7BS
Tel: (01243) 512472
Aviaries containing birds of prey including hawks, falcons, and owls. Flying displays of birds throughout the day, weather permitting.

Wakehurst Place Gardens

Ardingly, Haywards Heath, West Sussex RH17 6TN
Tel: (01444) 894000
Extensive 202-hectare estate gardens administered by Royal Botanic Gardens, Kew with lakes, ponds and an important collection of exotic trees, plants and shrubs.

The Whitstable Oyster and Fishery Exhibition

The Harbour, Whitstable, Kent CT5 1AB
Tel: (01227) 280753
An exhibition of unique artefacts, memorabilia and photographs depicting oyster fishing. Live fish display and 'hands-on' seashore experience.

Find out more about
SOUTH EAST ENGLAND ○○○

Further information about holidays and attractions in
South East England is available from:

SOUTH EAST ENGLAND TOURIST BOARD
The Old Brew House, Warwick Park,
Tunbridge Wells, Kent TN2 5TU.
Tel: (01892) 540766
Fax: (01892) 511008
Email: enquiries@seetb.org.uk
Internet: www.SouthEastEngland.uk.com

The following publications are available free from the South East England Tourist Board:

Guide to the Guides

Bed and Breakfast Touring Map

Relaxation
*featuring the green, rural areas of the region. For those
seeking rest and relaxation in a rural setting*

Lively
*for those seeking heritage and history combined with
the entertainment possibilities of a city or coastal break*

Walk South East England

Glorious Gardens of South East England

Camping and Caravanning in the South of England

Outstanding Churches and Cathedrals

Golfing in the South East

Eating and Drinking in the South East

The Pictures:
1   Bateman's,
     East Sussex;
2   The Pantiles, Royal
     Tunbridge Wells, Kent;
3   Port Lympne Wild
     Animal Park, Kent;
4   Great Dixter House &
     Gardens, Northiam,
     East Sussex;
5   Bodiam Castle,
     East Sussex;
6   Chichester Cathedral
     Gardens, West Sussex.

Getting to
SOUTH EAST ENGLAND ...

BY ROAD: From the north of England - M1/M25; the west and Wales - M4/M25; the
east of England - M25; the south of England M3/M25; London - M20 or M2.

BY RAIL: Regular services from London's Charing Cross, Victoria and Waterloo East
stations to all parts of South East England.

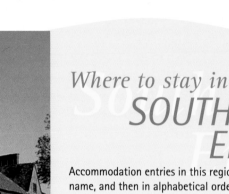

Where to stay in
SOUTH EAST ENGLAND

Accommodation entries in this region are listed in alphabetical order of place name, and then in alphabetical order of establishment.

Map references refer to the colour location maps at the front of this guide. The first number indicates the map to use; the letter and number which follow refer to the grid reference on the map.

At-a-glance symbols at the end of each accommodation entry give useful information about services and facilities. A key to symbols can be found inside the back cover flap. Keep this open for easy reference.

A brief description of the towns and villages offering accommodation in the entries which follow, can be found at the end of this section.

A complete listing of all English Tourism Council assessed hotels appears at the back of this guide.

ASHFORD, Kent Map ref 3B4 *Tourist Information Centre Tel: (01233) 629165*

★★★★
Gold
Award

The finest country house hotel in the South East, boasts 62 bedrooms, restaurant, indoor and outdoor heated 20m swimming pools, tennis court, croquet, petanque, sauna, steam room, solarium, gymnasium, 12 beauty treatment rooms offering therapy from 4 major product houses, hairdressing salon, bar and brasserie.

EASTWELL MANOR HOTEL
Eastwell Park, Boughton Lees, Ashford, TN25 4HR
T: (01233) 219955
F: (01233) 635530
E: eastwell@btinternet.com

Bedrooms: 14 double, 13 twin, 35 family rooms; suites available
Bathrooms: 62 en suite

Lunch available
EM 1930 (LO 2130)
Parking for 112
CC: Amex, Barclaycard, Delta, Diners, Maestro, Mastercard, Solo, Switch, Visa, Visa Electron

B&B per night:
S £150.00–£310.00
D £180.00–£340.00

HB per person:
DY £105.00–£185.00

OPEN All year round

QUALITY ASSURANCE SCHEME
Star ratings and awards were correct at the time of going to press but are subject to change. Please check at the time of booking.

BOGNOR REGIS, West Sussex Map ref 2D3 *Tourist Information Centre Tel: (01243) 823140*

★★

BEACHCROFT HOTEL

Clyde Road, Felpham, Bognor Regis,
West Sussex PO22 7AH

T: (01243) 827142
F: (01243) 827142
E: reservations@beachcroft-hotel.co.uk
I: www.beachcroft-hotel.co.uk

B&B per night:
S £28.00–£40.00
D £48.00–£62.00

HB per person:
DY £33.00–£48.00

OPEN All year round

Family-run, with south-facing beachside garden, adjoining the promenade (1 mile to Bognor Regis town). Indoor heated pool. All bedrooms en suite, many facing the sea, some ground floor. Spacious restaurant offering extensive menu choices, and comprehensive wine list. Lounge bar with hot and cold snacks. Discounted seasonal breaks.

Bedrooms: 9 single,
12 double, 16 twin
Bathrooms: 37 en suite

EM 1900 (LO 2100)
Parking for 40
CC: Amex, Delta, Diners,
Eurocard, JCB,
Mastercard, Solo, Switch,
Visa

BRIGHTON & HOVE, East Sussex Map ref 2D3 Tourist Information Centre 0906 711 2255 (calls cost 50p per minute)

Rating
Applied For
Ad p15

BRIGHTON THISTLE
Kings Road, Brighton, East Sussex
BN1 2GS
T: (01273) 206700
F: (01273) 820692
I: www.thistlehotels.co.uk

Bedrooms: 117 double,
87 twin; suites available
Bathrooms: 204 en suite

Lunch available
EM 1900 (LO 2200)
Parking for 62
CC: Amex, Barclaycard,
Delta, Eurocard,
Mastercard, Switch, Visa

B&B per night:
S £206.00–£232.00
D £206.00–£232.00

OPEN All year round

CR
Thistle Hotels/Utell
International

Modern hotel, fully air-conditioned, overlooking the beach and Palace Pier. Minutes from the Royal Pavilion. Health and leisure club. Car parking.

★★

ST CATHERINES LODGE HOTEL

Kingsway, Hove, East Sussex BN3 2RZ

T: (01273) 778181
F: (01273) 774949

B&B per night:
S £36.00–£55.00
D £60.00–£75.00

HB per person:
DY £45.00–£69.50

OPEN All year round

Well-established seafront hotel. Restaurant specialises in traditional English dishes. Four-poster honeymoon rooms. Attractive cocktail bar, games rooms, garden, and easy parking. Opposite King Alfred sports and leisure centre.

Bedrooms: 8 single,
17 double, 11 twin,
1 triple, 3 family rooms
Bathrooms: 40 en suite,
5 public

Lunch available
EM 1900 (LO 2100)
Parking for 4
CC: Amex, Barclaycard,
Diners, Eurocard,
Mastercard, Switch, Visa

AT-A-GLANCE SYMBOLS

Symbols at the end of each accommodation entry give useful information about services and facilities. A key to symbols can be found inside the back cover flap. Keep this open for easy reference.

★★

BURWOOD HOUSE HOTEL

15 London Road, Camberley, GU15 3UQ
T: (01276) 685686
F: (01276) 62220

B&B per night:
S £40.00–£70.00
D £60.00–£90.00

HB per person:
DY £65.00–£85.00

OPEN All year round

Friendly, family-run hotel set in pleasant gardens. We are one mile from Camberley town centre and close to junctions 3 and 4 of the M3. Ideally situated for business or pleasure – Sandhurst, Ascot, Wentworth and Windsor are all nearby – or just relax in the conservatory bar and enjoy our service!

Bedrooms: 9 single, 6 double, 2 twin, 2 triple
Bathrooms: 19 en suite

EM 1930 (LO 2100)
Parking for 21
CC: Amex, Barclaycard, Delta, Diners, Eurocard, JCB, Mastercard, Solo, Switch, Visa

★★

CANTERBURY HOTEL AND RESTAURANT

71 New Dover Road, Canterbury, CT1 3DZ
T: (01227) 450551
F: (01227) 780145
E: canterbury.hotel@btinternet.com

Bedrooms: 3 single, 14 double, 5 twin, 1 triple
Bathrooms: 23 en suite

Lunch available
EM 1900 (LO 2200)
Parking for 40
CC: Amex, Barclaycard, Delta, Diners, Eurocard, Mastercard, Switch, Visa

B&B per night:
S £55.00–£80.00
D £75.00–£105.00

HB per person:
DY Min £66.00

OPEN All year round

Elegant Georgian-style hotel, 10 minutes from city centre, providing high standards of personal service and comfort. Executive rooms, 4-poster suite. "La Bonne Cuisine" award-winning restaurant.

★★
Silver Award

EBURY HOTEL

65-67 New Dover Road, Canterbury, CT1 3DX
T: (01227) 768433
F: (01227) 459187
E: info@ebury-hotel.co.uk
I: www.ebury-hotel.co.uk

B&B per night:
S £50.00–£65.00
D £65.00–£95.00

HB per person:
DY Min £56.00

OPEN All year round

This family-run hotel is situated within walking distance of the historic city of Canterbury and its renowned shops. The hotel offers a licensed restaurant, spacious public rooms, well-equipped bedrooms and a heated indoor pool and spa. Half board price is based on a minimum 2-night stay.

Bedrooms: 2 single, 7 double, 4 twin, 1 triple, 1 family room
Bathrooms: 15 en suite

EM 1900 (LO 2030)
Parking for 20
CC: Amex, Barclaycard, Delta, Diners, JCB, Maestro, Mastercard, Solo, Switch, Visa, Visa Electron

QUALITY ASSURANCE SCHEME

For an explanation of the quality and facilities represented by the Stars please refer to the front of this guide. A more detailed explanation can be found in the information pages at the back.

CANTERBURY continued

★★

POINTERS HOTEL
1 London Road, Canterbury, CT2 8LR
T: (01227) 456846
F: (01227) 452786
E: pointers.hotel@.dial.pipex.com
I: www.pointers.hotel.dial.pipex.com

B&B per night:
S £45.00–£60.00
D £60.00–£75.00

HB per person:
DY £45.50–£65.00

OPEN All year round

Grade II Listed Georgian townhouse hotel, situated 5 minutes' walk from city centre. University of Kent a short drive away. Pointers is family-run by Christine and Jack O'Brien. An ideal base for touring city, coast and countryside. Overnight gated and locked car parking.

Bedrooms: 1 single, 7 double, 1 twin, 3 triple
Bathrooms: 12 en suite

EM 1930 (LO 2030)
Parking for 10
CC: Amex, Barclaycard, Delta, Diners, Eurocard, JCB, Mastercard, Solo, Switch, Visa, Visa Electron

CLIFTONVILLE, Kent

See under Margate

CUCKFIELD, West Sussex Map ref 2D3

★★★

HILTON PARK HOTEL
Cuckfield, Haywards Heath, West Sussex RH17 5EG
T: (01444) 454555
F: (01444) 457222
E: hiltonpark@janus-systems.com
I: wwwjanus-systems.com/hiltonpark.htm

B&B per night:
S Min £75.00
D Min £100.00

OPEN All year round

Victorian country house in 3 acres of gardens, with magnificent views of South Downs from conservatory bar and bedrooms. An ideal centre for visiting the gardens and stately homes of Sussex.

Bedrooms: 8 double, 2 twin
Bathrooms: 10 en suite, 1 public

Lunch available
EM 1900 (LO 2030)
Parking for 52
CC: Amex, Barclaycard, Delta, Diners, Maestro, Mastercard, Switch, Visa, Visa Electron

DARTFORD, Kent Map ref 2D2

Rating
Applied For
Ad p15

THISTLE BRANDS HATCH HOTEL
Brands Hatch, Dartford, DA3 8PE
T: (01474) 854900
F: (01474) 853220
E: brands.hatch@thistle.co.uk
I: www.thistlehotels.com

Bedrooms: 69 double, 52 twin; suites available
Bathrooms: 121 en suite

Lunch available
EM 1900 (LO 2230)
Parking for 180
CC: Amex, Barclaycard, Delta, Diners, Eurocard, Mastercard, Switch, Visa

B&B per night:
S £125.00–£148.00
D £125.00–£148.00

OPEN All year round

CR
Thistle Hotels/Utell International

Set at the entrance to the world-famous motor racing circuit, the hotel offers elegance and varied cuisine. Easy access, near M20, M25 and M26.

DEAL, Kent Map ref 3C4 Tourist Information Centre Tel: (01304) 369576

★★
Silver
Award

ROYAL HOTEL
Beach Street, Deal, CT14 6JD
T: (01304) 375555
F: (01304) 375555

Bedrooms: 2 single, 9 double, 4 twin, 4 family rooms
Bathrooms: 19 en suite

Lunch available
EM 1830 (LO 2130)
CC: Amex, Barclaycard, Delta, Diners, Mastercard, Switch, Visa, Visa Electron

B&B per night:
S £45.00–£70.00
D £75.00–£150.00

HB per person:
DY £58.50–£83.50

OPEN All year round

A relaxing Georgian townhouse, circa 1720, with amazing sea views. Beautifully decorated rooms, some with 4-poster bed and private balconies. Excellent seafood restaurant.

TOWN INDEX
This can be found at the back of this guide. If you know where you want to stay, the index will give you the page number listing accommodation in your chosen town, city or village.

DORKING, Surrey Map ref 2D2

★★★ **GATTON MANOR HOTEL, GOLF & COUNTRY CLUB**

Standon Lane, Ockley, Dorking,
RH5 5PQ
T: (01306) 627555
F: (01306) 627713
E: gattonmanor@enterprise.net
I: www.smoothhound.co.uk/hotels/
gatton.html

Bedrooms: 2 double,
16 twin
Bathrooms: 18 en suite

Lunch available
EM 1900 (LO 2130)
Parking for 200
CC: Amex, Barclaycard,
Delta, Diners, Mastercard,
Switch, Visa

B&B per night:
S £67.50–£95.00
D £105.00–£120.00

HB per person:
DY £67.50–£82.50

OPEN All year round

18thC manor house on 200-acre estate. Championship length golf-course, hotel, a la carte restaurants, conference suites, bowls, fishing, tennis, gym and health club. Village is 6 miles south of Dorking.

 60 ⚡ SP T

DOVER, Kent Map ref 3C4 *Tourist Information Centre Tel: (01304) 205108*

★★★

THE CHURCHILL

Dover Waterfront, Dover, CT17 9BP

T: (01304) 203633

F: (01304) 216320

E: enquiries@churchill-hotel.com

I: www.churchill-hotel.com

B&B per night:
S £69.00–£69.00
D £98.00–£98.00

OPEN All year round

Best Western Hotels

Dover's only waterfront hotel is a Listed building set in a Regency crescent with panoramic views over the English Channel. We offer excellent standards of cuisine and a very warm and friendly service. Guests have use of the hotel's health club with a choice of activities.

Bedrooms: 6 single,
37 double, 20 twin,
5 family rooms
Bathrooms: 68 en suite,
1 public

Lunch available
EM 1930 (LO 2115)
CC: Amex, Barclaycard,
Delta, Diners, Mastercard,
Switch, Visa, Visa Electron

120 SP T

★★★
Silver
Award

WALLETTS COURT HOTEL & RESTAURANT

West-Cliffe, St-Margarets-at-Cliffe, Dover,
CT15 6EW

T: (01304) 852424

F: (01304) 853430

E: wc@wallettscourt.com

I: www.wallettscourt.com

B&B per night:
S £60.00–£110.00
D £80.00–£150.00

HB per person:
DY £67.50–£110.00

OPEN All year round

Wallett's Court, the 17thC Manor of Westcliffe, is set in 7 acres of beautiful gardens in an Area of Outstanding Natural Beauty. The restaurant is popular with locals. Set in the grounds are an indoor pool, sauna, steam room, jacuzzi and fitness room. Dover is 3 miles away.

Bedrooms: 11 double,
2 twin, 3 triple
Bathrooms: 16 en suite

Lunch available
EM 1900 (LO 2100)
Parking for 20
CC: Amex, Barclaycard,
Delta, Diners, Eurocard,
JCB, Maestro, Mastercard,
Solo, Switch, Visa, Visa
Electron

T

EASTBOURNE, East Sussex Map ref 3B4 *Tourist Information Centre Tel: (01323) 411400*

★★★ **CHATSWORTH HOTEL**

Grand Parade, Eastbourne,
East Sussex BN21 3YR
T: (01323) 411016
F: (01323) 643270
E: peter@chatsworth-hotel.demon.
co.uk
I: www.virtualhotels.com/
chatsworth-hotel

Bedrooms: 10 single,
13 double, 22 twin,
2 family rooms; suites
available
Bathrooms: 47 en suite

Lunch available
EM 1900 (LO 2030)
CC: Amex, Barclaycard,
Delta, Diners, Mastercard,
Switch, Visa

B&B per night:
S £41.00–£56.00
D £82.00–£112.00

HB per person:
DY £51.00–£66.00

OPEN All year round

Elegant Victorian detached hotel in a prominent position on seafront, very close to shops and theatres. Delightful restaurant serving best of British cookery. Sun terrace.

160 U SC SP T

EASTBOURNE continued

★★

CONGRESS HOTEL
31-41 Carlisle Road, Eastbourne,
East Sussex BN21 4JS
T: (01323) 732118 & 644605
F: (01323) 720016

Bedrooms: 13 single,
11 double, 32 twin,
5 triple
Bathrooms: 61 en suite,
1 public

Lunch available
EM 1830 (LO 1945)
CC: Barclaycard, Delta,
Mastercard, Solo, Switch,
Visa

B&B per night:
S £29.00-£38.00
D £58.00-£76.00

HB per person:
DY £32.00-£44.00

OPEN Mar-Nov
& Christmas

Family-run hotel in peaceful location. Close to theatres and seafront. Suitable for wheelchair users. Car parking on site.

★★★
Silver
Award

LANSDOWNE HOTEL
King Edward's Parade, Eastbourne,
East Sussex BN21 4EE
T: (01323) 725174
F: (01323) 739721
E: the.lansdowne@btinternet.com
I: www.btinternet.com/-the.
lansdowne/

Bedrooms: 40 single,
18 double, 53 twin,
4 triple
Bathrooms: 115 en suite

Lunch available
EM 1830 (LO 2030)
Parking for 22
CC: Amex, Barclaycard,
Delta, Diners, JCB,
Maestro, Mastercard,
Solo, Switch, Visa, Visa
Electron

B&B per night:
S £55.00-£63.00
D £87.00-£109.00

HB per person:
DY £43.00-£75.00

OPEN All year round

CR
Best Western Hotels

Premier seafront position, with bar, lounges and elegant public areas. Theatres, shops and sporting facilities nearby. Minimum half-board price is special off-season rate.

★★

YORK HOUSE HOTEL
14-22 Royal Parade, Eastbourne,
East Sussex BN22 7AP
T: (01323) 412918
F: (01323) 646238
E: info@yorkhousehotel.co.uk
I: www.yorkhousehotel.co.uk

Bedrooms: 8 single,
31 double, 40 twin,
6 triple, 1 family room
Bathrooms: 86 en suite

Lunch available
EM 1900 (LO 2030)
CC: Amex, Barclaycard,
Delta, Diners, JCB,
Mastercard, Solo, Switch,
Visa

B&B per night:
S £27.00-£39.00
D £54.00-£78.00

HB per person:
DY £37.00-£56.00

OPEN All year round

Comfortable bedrooms, lounges and bars and an unrivalled seafront position. The day begins with a dip in the heated indoor pool, and finishes with good food and wine in the dining room and dancing in the Crumbles Suite.

EGHAM, Surrey Map ref 2D2

★★★★
Silver
Award

RUNNYMEDE HOTEL AND SPA
Windsor Road, Egham, TW20 0AG
T: (01784) 436171
F: (01784) 436340
E: Info@runnymedehotel.com
I: www.runnymedehotel.com

B&B per night:
S £79.00-£89.00
D £129.00-£158.00

HB per person:
DY £85.00-£95.00

OPEN All year round

Delightfully situated overlooking Thames at Bell-Weir Lock, privately owned modern hotel in 12 acres of landscaped gardens. Extensive state-of-the-art spa and beauty facilities including 18m indoor pool and 5 outdoor tennis courts. Ideally located for the wealth of tourist attractions in the area. On A308, off M25 junction 13. Prices quoted are weekend rates.

Bedrooms: 80 single,
55 double, 35 twin,
7 triple, 3 family rooms
Bathrooms: 180 en suite

Lunch available
EM 1900 (LO 2215)
Parking for 300
CC: Amex, Barclaycard,
Delta, Diners, Mastercard,
Switch, Visa

CHECK THE MAPS
The colour maps at the front of this guide show all the cities, towns and villages for which you will find accommodation entries. Refer to the town index to find the page on which they are listed.

FARNHAM, Surrey Map ref 2C2 *Tourist Information Centre Tel: (01252) 715109*

★★★
Silver
Award

THE BISHOP'S TABLE HOTEL & RESTAURANT

27 West Street, Farnham, GU9 7DR
T: (01252) 710222
F: (01252) 733494
E: bishops.table@btinternet.com

B&B per night:
S £95.00–£105.00
D £110.00–£155.00

HB per person:
DY Min £117.00

OPEN All year round

This award-winning, charming 18thC country town hotel has easy access to motorways M25 and M3. All rooms are individually decorated, en suite and well equipped. The restaurant has an enviable reputation for fine cuisine. A delightful walled garden is at the rear.

Bedrooms: 6 single, 9 double, 2 twin
Bathrooms: 17 en suite

Lunch available
EM 1900 (LO 2145)
CC: Amex, Barclaycard, Diners, Eurocard, Mastercard, Visa

Ⓜ♨✆☐↓🛈✂◑🖥︎▤🅿️🍴26↻⊦❄✗🐾 🆂🅿️ 🏨 Ⓣ

FOREST ROW, East Sussex Map ref 2D2

★★

ASHDOWN FOREST GOLF HOTEL
Chapel Lane, Forest Row,
East Sussex RH18 5BB
T: (01342) 824866
F: (01342) 824869
E: enquiries@ashgolf.co.uk
I: www.ashgolf.co.uk

Bedrooms: 5 double, 14 twin
Bathrooms: 19 en suite

Lunch available
EM 1900 (LO 2130)
Parking for 50
CC: Amex, Barclaycard, Delta, Mastercard, Switch, Visa

B&B per night:
S £65.00–£65.00
D £81.50–£81.50

OPEN All year round

Edwardian country hotel on edge of Ashdown Forest, with an 18-hole golf-course. Adjacent to another golf-course.

Ⓜ⛷✆☐↓🛈🆂▤🅿️🍴70🍷↻⊦🆂🅲✗🆂🅿️Ⓣ

GATWICK AIRPORT, West Sussex

See under Horley

HASTINGS, East Sussex Map ref 3B4 *Tourist Information Centre Tel: (01424) 781111*

★★★

CINQUE PORTS HOTEL

Summerfields, Bohemia Road, Hastings,
East Sussex TN34 1ET
T: (01424) 439222
F: (01424) 437277
E: cphotel@dircon.co.uk
I: www.cinqueports.co.uk

B&B per night:
S £40.00–£59.50
D £55.00–£79.50

HB per person:
DY £37.50–£51.75

OPEN All year round

Modern hotel in woodland setting close to the historic Cinque Port of Hastings. Lounge has open log fire in winter and a cafe bar welcomes you in from the cold. Restaurant renowned for excellent food and sensible wine list. All bedrooms en suite with TV, direct-dial telephone, hairdryer and tea/coffee-making.

Bedrooms: 10 double, 26 twin, 4 triple
Bathrooms: 40 en suite

Lunch available
EM 1900 (LO 2200)
Parking for 90
CC: Amex, Barclaycard, Mastercard, Switch, Visa

Ⓜ⛷♨🏨✆☐↓🛈🆂ⓉⓋ◑▤🅿️🍴300⊦❄✗🆂🅿️🏨Ⓣ

USE YOUR *i*s

There are more than 550 Tourist Information Centres throughout England offering friendly help with accommodation and holiday ideas as well as suggestions of places to visit and things to do. You'll find TIC addresses in the local Phone Book.

★★★

THE BIRCH HOTEL
Lewes Road (A272), Haywards Heath,
West Sussex RH17 7SF
T: (01444) 451565
F: (01444) 440109
E: info@birch-hotel.com
I: www.birch-hotel.com

B&B per night:
S £65.00–£80.00
D £75.00–£90.00

OPEN All year round

*Built in 1874 on the outskirts of
town, this lovely hotel retains many
period features, including an oak
panelled lounge. The hotel boasts a
variety of comfortable bedrooms and
is renowned for its Pavilion
Restaurant. Gatwick Airport is just
19 miles away, whilst Brighton lies
15 miles to the South.*

Bedrooms: 11 single,
28 double, 11 twin
Bathrooms: 50 en suite

Lunch available
EM 1900 (LO 2130)
Parking for 70
CC: Amex, Barclaycard,
Delta, Mastercard, Solo,
Switch, Visa

★★★
Silver
Award

STANHILL COURT HOTEL
Stanhill, Charlwood, Horley, RH6 0EP
T: (01293) 862166
F: (01293) 862773
E: enquiries@stanhillcourthotel.co.uk
I: www.stanhillcourthotel.co.uk

B&B per night:
S Min £110.00
D Min £125.00

OPEN All year round

*The Victorians excelled at building
baronial mansions and this is a fine
example of their skills. In 35 acres of
glorious countryside. Bedrooms are
spacious and comfortable. Spanish
Patio Bar. Eat in restaurant 1881
with fine wine cellar. Gatwick Airport
4 miles. Popular for weddings,
conferences and product launches.
Exclusive use arranged.*

Bedrooms: 13 double
Bathrooms: 13 en suite

Lunch available
EM 1900 (LO 2130)
Parking for 150
CC: Amex, Barclaycard,
Delta, Diners, Eurocard,
JCB, Maestro, Mastercard,
Solo, Switch, Visa, Visa
Electron

Rating
Applied For

THISTLE GATWICK
Brighton Road, Horley, RH6 8PH
T: (01293) 786992
F: (01293) 820625
E: gatwick@thistle.co.uk

Bedrooms: 1 single,
33 double, 44 twin
Bathrooms: 78 en suite

Lunch available
EM 1900 (LO 2130)
Parking for 185
CC: Amex, Diners

B&B per night:
S Min £130.00
D £142.00–£166.00

OPEN All year round

Thistle Hotels/Utell
International

*Modern hotel with some parts of building dating back to early 16thC. Courtesy coach to
Gatwick Airport, which is only 2 miles away. Car parking available.*

See under Brighton & Hove

★★★
STADE COURT HOTEL
West Parade, Hythe, CT21 6DT
T: (01303) 268263
F: (01303) 261803
E: stadecourt@marstonhotels.co.
uk.
I: www.marstonhotels.co.uk

Bedrooms: 11 single,
15 double, 13 twin,
3 triple
Bathrooms: 42 en suite

Lunch available
EM 1830 (LO 2100)
Parking for 12
CC: Amex, Barclaycard,
Delta, Diners, Mastercard,
Switch, Visa

B&B per night:
S £75.00–£85.00
D £105.00–£110.00

HB per person:
DY £62.00–£65.00

OPEN All year round

Best Western Hotels

*Seafront hotel, with well-appointed family suites. Extensive leisure facilities, 600 metres
away at our sister hotel. Daily half board price based on minimum 2-night stay.*

IDEAS For ideas on places to visit refer to the introduction at the
beginning of this section.

LEWES, East Sussex Map ref 2D3 *Tourist Information Centre Tel: (01273) 483448*

★★★
Silver Award

SHELLEYS HOTEL

High Street, Lewes, East Sussex BN7 1XS
T: (01273) 472361
F: (01273) 483152

Once the home of the poet Shelley's aunts, this beautifully appointed country-house style hotel overlooks its own peaceful garden whilst being situated close to the centre of historic Lewes. Convenient for Glyndebourne, South Downs or Brighton. A warm welcome and excellent standards of comfort and cuisine in award-winning restaurant.

Bedrooms: 1 single, 9 double, 9 twin; suite available
Bathrooms: 19 en suite

Lunch available
EM 1900 (LO 2115)
Parking for 25
CC: Amex, Barclaycard, Delta, Diners, Eurocard, JCB, Maestro, Mastercard, Solo, Switch, Visa, Visa Electron

B&B per night:
S £95.00–£145.00
D £112.00–£195.00

HB per person:
DY £80.00–£107.50

OPEN All year round

CR
Utell International

MAIDSTONE, Kent Map ref 3B3 *Tourist Information Centre Tel: (01622) 602169 or 739029 (M20, jct 8)*

★★

GRANGEMOOR HOTEL

St Michael's Road, Maidstone, ME16 8BS
T: (01622) 677623
F: (01622) 678246
E: reservations@grangemoor.co.uk

Bedrooms: 12 single, 15 double, 18 twin, 3 triple, 2 family rooms
Bathrooms: 50 en suite, 2 public

Lunch available
EM 1830 (LO 2200)
Parking for 79
CC: Barclaycard, Delta, Eurocard, Mastercard, Solo, Switch, Visa, Visa Electron

B&B per night:
S £40.00–£48.00
D £50.00–£56.00

OPEN All year round

One hour from London and the Kent coast, in a quiet position on the edge of town. The hotel has rear gardens, restaurant and bar.

MARGATE, Kent Map ref 3C3 *Tourist Information Centre Tel: (01843) 220241*

★★★

PALM COURT HOTEL

Eastern Esplanade, Cliftonville, Margate, CT9
T: (01843) 229980
F: (01843) 299993

Small executive hotel situated on the Cliftonville waterfront and in prime position for all local attractions. Good road links and proximity to Canterbury and Dover make it an ideal base for touring. High quality restaurant, also serving tapas, and a health suite with qualified beautician are on site.

Bedrooms: 2 single, 5 double
Bathrooms: 7 en suite

EM

B&B per night:
S £44.50–£55.00
D £75.00–£83.50

HB per person:
DY £51.00–£68.00

OPEN All year round

NEW ROMNEY, Kent Map ref 3B4

★★

BROADACRE HOTEL

North Street, New Romney, TN28 8DR
T: (01797) 362381
F: (01797) 362381
E: broadacrehotel@newromney1.fsnet.co.uk
I: www.uk-travelguide.co.uk/kent/newromney/broadacrehotel.htm

Bedrooms: 3 single, 4 double, 2 twin, 1 family room
Bathrooms: 10 en suite

Lunch available
EM 1900 (LO 2100)
Parking for 9
CC: Barclaycard, Delta, JCB, Maestro, Mastercard, Solo, Switch, Visa, Visa Electron

B&B per night:
S £35.00–£45.00
D £50.00–£60.00

OPEN All year round

Small 16thC family-run hotel offering a warm, friendly welcome and personal attention. Some ground floor bedrooms in cottage annexe. Weekend breaks.

RAMSGATE, Kent Map ref 3C3 *Tourist Information Centre Tel: (01843) 583333*

★★★

SAN CLU HOTEL

Victoria Parade, East Cliff,
Ramsgate, CT11 8DT
T: (01843) 592345
F: (01843) 580157
E: sancluhotel@lineone.net
I: www.san-clu-hotel.co.uk

Bedrooms: 7 single,
18 double, 5 twin,
12 triple, 2 family
rooms; suites available
Bathrooms: 44 en suite

Lunch available
EM 1900 (LO 2130)
Parking for 20
CC: Amex, Barclaycard,
Delta, Diners, Maestro,
Mastercard, Solo, Switch,
Visa

B&B per night:
S £50.00–£60.00
D £80.00–£120.00

OPEN All year round

Grade II Listed Victorian cliff top hotel, overlooking sea and sands and near cross-Channel ferry terminals and harbour. Quiet location, easy reach of ample parking.

180

ROCHESTER, Kent Map ref 3B3 *Tourist Information Centre Tel: (01634) 843666*

★★★★

BRIDGEWOOD MANOR HOTEL

Bridgewood Roundabout,
Walderslade Woods, Chatham, Kent
ME5 9AX
T: (01634) 201333
F: (01634) 201330
E: bridgewoodmanor@
marstonhotels.co.uk
I: www.marstonhotels.co.uk

Bedrooms: 57 double,
43 twin; suites available
Bathrooms: 100 en suite

Lunch available
EM 1900 (LO 2200)
Parking for 175
CC: Amex, Barclaycard,
Delta, Diners, Mastercard,
Solo, Switch, Visa

B&B per night:
S £108.00–£128.00
D £137.00–£177.00

HB per person:
DY £69.50–£89.50

OPEN All year round

Modern manor built around a classical courtyard. Superb leisure facilities make it an ideal choice for exploring Kent's many attractions.

Best Western Hotels

200

★★

KING CHARLES HOTEL

Brompton Road, Gillingham, Kent
ME7 5QT
T: (01634) 830303
F: (01634) 829430
E: enquiries@kingcharleshotel.co.
uk
I: www.kingcharleshotel.co.uk

Bedrooms: 1 single,
30 double, 24 twin,
21 triple, 10 family
rooms
Bathrooms: 86 en suite

Lunch available
EM 1900 (LO 2230)
Parking for 201
CC: Amex, Barclaycard,
Delta, Diners, Eurocard,
Mastercard, Switch, Visa

B&B per night:
S Min £34.00
D Min £40.00

HB per person:
DY £39.00–£44.00

OPEN All year round

Friendly, modern hotel run by family, catering for all requirements at very reasonable rates in comfortable accommodation. Ideal for groups.

150

RYE, East Sussex Map ref 3B4 *Tourist Information Centre Tel: (01797) 226696*

★★★

FLACKLEY ASH HOTEL & RESTAURANT

London Road, Peasmarsh, Rye,
East Sussex TN31 6YH
T: (01797) 230651
F: (01797) 230510
E: flackleyash@marstonhotels.co.
uk
I: www.marstonhotels.co.uk

Bedrooms: 27 double,
13 twin, 1 triple, 1 family
room; suites available
Bathrooms: 42 en suite

Lunch available
EM 1900 (LO 2130)
Parking for 60
CC: Amex, Barclaycard,
Delta, Diners, Eurocard,
Mastercard, Switch, Visa

B&B per night:
S £79.00–£104.00
D £119.00–£169.00

HB per person:
DY £74.00–£99.00

OPEN All year round

Georgian country house hotel in 5 acres. Swimming pool and leisure centre. Fresh fish, well-stocked cellar. Half board daily rate based on minimum 2-night stay.

Best Western Hotels

100

★★★
Silver
Award

RYE LODGE HOTEL

Hilders Cliff, Rye, East Sussex TN31 7LD
T: (01797) 223838 & 226688
F: (01797) 223585
E: info@ryelodge.co.uk
I: www.ryelodge.co.uk

B&B per night:
S £49.50–£75.00
D £80.00–£150.00

HB per person:
DY £55.00–£87.50

OPEN All year round

Stunning estuary views yet adjacent to town centre. Dine by candlelight in the elegant Terrace Restaurant, delicious food and fine wines. Full room service – enjoy breakfast in bed as late as you like! Indoor swimming pool and sauna. Private car park plus all the delights of the medieval Cinque Port of Rye.

Bedrooms: 2 single,
11 double, 7 twin
Bathrooms: 20 en suite

EM 1900 (LO 2100)
Parking for 20
CC: Amex, Barclaycard,
Delta, Diners, Eurocard,
JCB, Maestro, Mastercard,
Solo, Switch, Visa, Visa
Electron

★★★
Silver
Award

Beautifully appointed hotel at the foot of South Downs, opposite Bramber Castle ruins. Stunning award-winning carvery (booking always advisable). Four-poster bedrooms with jacuzzi available. Ideal touring base with many gardens and places of interest nearby. Set in glorious countryside yet with good road links. In short – a perfect spot.

THE OLD TOLLGATE RESTAURANT & HOTEL

The Street, Bramber, Steyning, West Sussex BN44 3WE
T: (01903) 879494
F: (01903) 813399
E: otr@fastnet.co.uk
I: home.fastnet.co.uk/otr

Bedrooms: 21 double, 10 twin; suites available
Bathrooms: 31 en suite

Lunch available
EM 1900 (LO 2130)
Parking for 60
CC: Amex, Barclaycard, Delta, Diners, Eurocard, JCB, Maestro, Mastercard, Switch, Visa, Visa Electron

B&B per night:
S £79.00–£105.00
D £86.00–£112.00

HB per person:
DY £61.50–£75.00

OPEN All year round

Best Western Hotels

🄴🄿🆂🄸🅃 50 ⛎♿ 🐕 🚲 SP T

★★★
Silver
Award

LITTLE SILVER COUNTRY HOTEL
Ashford Road, St Michaels,
Tenterden, TN30 6SP
T: (01233) 850321
F: (01233) 850647
E: enquiries@little-silver.co.uk
I: www.little-silver.co.uk

Bedrooms: 5 double, 3 twin, 1 triple, 1 family room
Bathrooms: 10 en suite

Lunch available
EM 1830 (LO 2200)
Parking for 50
CC: Amex, Barclaycard, Delta, Mastercard, Solo, Switch, Visa, Visa Electron

B&B per night:
S £60.00–£85.00
D £85.00–£120.00

HB per person:
DY £60.00–£80.00

OPEN All year round

Quality accommodation in Tudor-style country house hotel. Four-poster, brass bedded, family, disabled facilities (all en suite). Personal service in a truly delightful and unique atmosphere. Landscaped gardens.

🄴🄿🆂🄸🅃 150 ⛎♿ SC SP T

★★★★
Gold
Award

Dale Hill is situated in an Area of Outstanding Natural Beauty. Our bedrooms offer comfort and luxury and many have magnificent views overlooking the Kentish Weald. Dale Hill boasts new leisure facilities and two 18-hole golf courses, one of which was designed by Ian Woosnam to USGA championship specifications.

DALE HILL HOTEL & GOLF CLUB

Ticehurst, Wadhurst, East Sussex TN5 7DQ
T: (01580) 200112
F: (01580) 201249
E: info@dalehill.co.uk
I: www.dalehill.co.uk

Bedrooms: 6 double, 20 twin; suite available
Bathrooms: 26 en suite

Lunch available
EM 1900 (LO 2145)
Parking for 220
CC: Amex, Barclaycard, Delta, Eurocard, JCB, Maestro, Mastercard, Switch, Visa

B&B per night:
S £80.00–£99.00
D £110.00–£130.00

HB per person:
DY £65.00–£80.00

OPEN All year round

🄴🄿🆂🄸🅃 TV 80 SP T

TOWN INDEX

This can be found at the back of the guide. If you know where you want to stay, the index will give you the page number listing accommodation in your chosen town, city or village.

A brief guide to the main Towns and Villages offering accommodation in # SOUTH EAST ENGLAND

A **ASHFORD, KENT** - Once a market centre for the farmers of the Weald of Kent and Romney Marsh. The town centre has a number of Tudor and Georgian houses and a museum. Eurostar trains stop at Ashford International station.

B **BOGNOR REGIS, WEST SUSSEX** - Five miles of firm, flat sand have made the town a popular family resort. Well supplied with gardens.

● **BRIGHTON & HOVE** - Brighton's attractions include the Royal Pavilion, Volks Electric Railway, Sea Life Centre and Marina Village, "The Lanes", Conference Centre and several theatres.

C **CAMBERLEY, SURREY** - Well-known for the Royal Staff College and the nearby Royal Military Academy, Sandhurst.

● **CANTERBURY, KENT** - Place of pilgrimage since the martyrdom of Becket in 1170 and the site of Canterbury Cathedral. Visit St Augustine's Abbey, St Martin's (the oldest church in England) and the Canterbury Tales. Nearby is Howletts Wild Animal Park. Good shopping centre.

● **CUCKFIELD, WEST SUSSEX** - The High Street is lined with Elizabethan and Georgian shops, inns and houses and was once part of the London to Brighton coach road. Nearby Nymans (National Trust) is a 30-acre garden with fine topiary work.

D **DARTFORD, KENT** - Industrial town probably most famous for the Dartford Tunnel and the Queen Elizabeth II bridge across the Thames. Large Orchard Theatre has a fine variety of entertainment.

● **DEAL, KENT** - Coastal town and popular holiday resort. Deal Castle was built by Henry VIII as a fort and the museum is devoted to finds excavated in the area. Also the Time Ball Tower museum. Angling available from both beach and pier.

● **DORKING, SURREY** - Ancient market town and a good centre for walking, delightfully set between Box Hill and the Downs. Denbies Wine Estate - England's largest vineyard - is situated here.

● **DOVER, KENT** - A Cinque Port and busiest passenger port in the world. Still a historic town and seaside resort beside the famous White Cliffs. The White Cliffs Experience attraction traces the town's history through the Roman, Saxon, Norman and Victorian periods.

E **EASTBOURNE, EAST SUSSEX** - One of the finest, most elegant resorts on the south-east coast situated beside Beachy Head. Long promenade, well known Carpet Gardens on the seafront, Devonshire Park tennis and indoor leisure complex, theatres, Towner Art Gallery, "How We Lived Then" Museum of Shops and Social History.

● **EGHAM, SURREY** - In attractive and historic area beside the Thames, adjoining Runnymede and near Windsor, Thorpe Park and Savill Garden. Convenient for Heathrow Airport and good base for London, Wisley Gardens and Hampton Court Palace.

F **FARNHAM, SURREY** - Town noted for its Georgian houses. Willmer House (now a museum) has a facade of cut and moulded brick with fine carving and panelling in the interior. The 12th C castle has been occupied by Bishops of both Winchester and Guildford.

H **HASTINGS, EAST SUSSEX** - Ancient town which became famous as the base from which William the Conqueror set out to fight the Battle of Hastings. Later became one of the Cinque Ports, now a leading resort. Castle, Hastings Embroidery inspired by the Bayeux Tapestry and Sea Life Centre.

● **HAYWARDS HEATH, WEST SUSSEX** - Busy town and administrative centre of mid-Sussex, with some interesting old buildings and a modern shopping centre.

● **HORLEY, SURREY** - Town on the London to Brighton road, just north of Gatwick Airport, with an ancient parish church and 15th C inn.

● **HYTHE, KENT** - Once one of the Cinque Ports, the town today stands back from the sea. The Royal Military Canal is the scene of a summer pageant, the Romney, Hythe and Dymchurch Railway terminates here and Port Lympne Wild Animal Park, Mansion and Gardens is nearby.

L **LEWES, EAST SUSSEX** - Historic county town with Norman castle. The steep High Street has mainly Georgian buildings. There is a folk museum at Anne of Cleves House and the archaeological museum is in Barbican House.

M **MAIDSTONE, KENT** - Busy county town of Kent on the River Medway has many interesting features and is an excellent centre for excursions. Museum of Carriages, Museum and Art Gallery, Mote Park.

● **MARGATE, KENT** - Oldest and most famous resort in Kent. Many Regency and Victorian buildings survive from the town's early days. There are 9 miles of sandy beach. "Dreamland" is a 20-acre amusement park and the Winter Gardens offer concert hall entertainment.

N **NEW ROMNEY, KENT** - Capital of Romney Marsh. Now a mile from the sea, it was one of the original Cinque Ports. Romney, Hythe and Dymchurch Railway's main station is here.

R **RAMSGATE, KENT** - Popular holiday resort with good sandy beaches. At Pegwell Bay is a replica of a Viking longship.

● **ROCHESTER, KENT** - Ancient cathedral city on the River Medway. Has many places of interest connected with Charles Dickens (who lived nearby) including the fascinating Dickens Centre. Also massive castle overlooking the river and Guildhall Museum.

● **RYE, EAST SUSSEX** - Cobbled, hilly streets and fine old buildings make Rye, once a Cinque Port, a most picturesque town. Noted for its church with ancient clock, potteries and antique shops. Town Model Sound and Light Show gives a good introduction to the town.

S **STEYNING, WEST SUSSEX** - An important market town and thriving port before the Norman Conquest, lying at the foot of the South Downs. Retains a picturesque charm with fascinating timber-framed and stone buildings.

T **TENTERDEN, KENT** - Most attractive market town with a broad main street full of 16th C houses and shops. The tower of the 15th C parish church is the finest in Kent. Fine antiques centre.

CENTRAL RESERVATIONS OFFICES

The symbol **CR** and a group name in an entry indicate that bookings can be made through a central reservations office. These are listed in a separate section towards the back of this guide.

Ratings you can trust

When you're looking for a place to stay, you need a rating system you can trust. The **English Tourism Council's** ratings are your clear guide to what to expect, in an easy-to-understand form. Properties are visited annually by our trained, impartial assessors, so you can have confidence that your accommodation has been thoroughly checked and rated for quality before you make a booking.

Based on the internationally recognised rating of One to Five Stars, the system puts great emphasis on quality and is based on research which shows exactly what consumers are looking for when choosing an hotel.

Ratings are awarded from One to Five Stars - the more Stars, the higher the quality and the greater the range of facilities and level of services provided.

Look out, too, for the English Tourism Council's Gold and Silver Awards, which are awarded to properties achieving the highest levels of quality within their Star rating. While the overall rating is based on a combination of facilities and quality, the Gold and Silver Awards are based solely on quality.

The ratings are your sign of quality assurance, giving you the confidence to book the accommodation that meets your expectations.

English Tourism Council
Assessed Accommodation

English Tourism Council

★ ★ ★
HOTEL

On the following pages you will find an exclusive listing of *every hotel in England that has been assessed for quality by the English Tourism Council.*

The information includes brief contact details for each place to stay, together with its Star rating, and quality award if appropriate. The listing also shows if an establishment is taking part in the Welcome Host scheme ⊛, and if it has a National Accessible rating (see the front of the guide for further information).

More detailed information on all the places shown in blue can be found in the regional sections (where establishments have paid to have their details included). To find these entries please refer to the appropriate regional section, or look in the town index at the back of this guide.

The list which follows was compiled slightly later than the regional sections. For this reason you may find that, in a few instances, a Star rating and quality award may differ between the two sections. This list contains the most up-to-date information and was correct at the time of going to press.

INNER LONDON
E1
Thistle Tower ★★★★
St Katharine's Way, London
E1W 1LD
T: (020) 7481 2575
F: (020) 7488 4106
E: tower.businesscentre@
thistle.co.uk
I: www.thistlehotels.com

E10
Sleeping Beauty Motel
Travel Accommodation
543 Lea Bridge Road, Leyton,
London E10 7EB
T: (020) 8556 8080
F: (020) 8556 8080

EC1
Thistle City Barbican
Rating Applied For
Central Street, Clerkenwell,
London EC1V 8DS
T: (020) 7956 6000
F: (020) 7253 1005
E: barbican@thistle.co.uk
I: www.thistlehotels.com

N1
Great Northern Hotel ★★★
King's Cross, London N1 9AN
T: (020) 7837 5454
F: (020) 7278 5270
E: gnres@compasshotels.co.uk
I: www.compasshotels.co.uk

Jurys London Inn ★★★
60 Pentonville Road, Islington,
London N1 9LA
T: (020) 7282 5500
F: (020) 7282 5511
E: padhraic_flavin@jurys.com
I: www.jurys.com

N4
Spring Park Hotel ★
400 Seven Sisters Road, London
N4 2LX
T: (020) 8800 6030
F: (020) 8802 5652
E: sphotel400@aol.com
I: www.smoothhound.co.
uk/hotels/springpa.html

NW1
The Landmark London
★★★★★ GOLD AWARD
222 Marylebone Road, London
NW1 6JQ
T: (020) 7631 8000
F: (020) 7631 8080
E: reservations@thelandmark.
co.uk
I: www.landmarklondon.co.uk

Melia White House ★★★★
Albany Street, Regent's Park,
London NW1 3UP
T: (020) 7387 1200
F: (020) 7388 0091
E: melia.white.house@solmelia.
es
I: www.solmelia.es

Regent's Park Hotel ★★
154-156 Gloucester Place,
London NW1 6DT
T: (020) 7258 1911
F: (020) 7258 0288

Thistle Euston
Rating Applied For
43 Cardington Street, Euston,
London NW1 2LP
T: (020) 7387 4400
F: (020) 7387 5122
E: euston@thistle.co.uk

NW4
**Hendon Hall, (A Thistle
Country House Hotel)★★★★**
Ashley Lane, off Parson Street,
Hendon, London NW4 1HF
T: (020) 8203 3341
F: (020) 8203 9709
E: hendon.hall@thistle.co.uk

SE1
**London Marriott Hotel, County
Hall ★★★★★ SILVER AWARD**
The County Hall, London
SE1 7PB
T: (020) 7928 5200
F: (020) 7928 5300
I: www.mariott.
com/marriott/lonch

The Mad Hatter ★★
3-7 Stamford Street, London
SE1 9NY
T: (020) 7401 9222
F: (020) 7401 7111
E: madhatter@fullers.co.uk

Novotel London Waterloo
113 Lambeth Road, London
SE1 7LS
T: (020) 7793 1010
F: (020) 7793 0202
E: h1785@accor-hotels.com
I: www.novotel.com

SE3
Bardon Lodge Hotel ★★★
15-17 Stratheden Road,
Blackheath, London SE3 7TH
T: (020) 8853 4051
F: (020) 8858 7387
E: bardonlodge@btclick.com
I: www.bardonlodgehotel.com

Clarendon Hotel ★★
8-16 Montpelier Row,
Blackheath, London SE3 0RW
T: (020) 8318 4321
F: (020) 8318 4378

SE10
Hamilton House Hotel
Rating Applied For
14 West Grove, Greenwich,
London SE10 8QT
T: (020) 8694 9899
F: (020) 8694 2370
E: reception@
hamiltonhousehotel.co.uk
I: www.hamiltonhousehotel.co.
uk

SE16
**Holiday Inn Nelson Dock
★★★★**
265 Rotherhithe Street, London
SE16 5HW
T: (020) 7231 1001
F: (020) 7231 0599
E: reservations@holidayinnnd.
co.uk

SW1
Dolphin Square Hotel ★★★★
Dolphin Square, Chichester
Street, London SW1V 3LX
T: (020) 7834 3800 &
0800 616607
F: (020) 7798 8735
E: reservations@
dolphinsquarehotel.co.uk
I: www.dolphinsquarehotel.co.
uk

The Goring Hotel
★★★★ GOLD AWARD
15 Beeston Place, Grosvenor
Gardens, London SW1W 0JW
T: (020) 7396 9000
F: (020) 7834 4393
E: reception@goringhotel.co.uk
I: www.goringhotel.co.uk

Hyatt Carlton Tower
★★★★★ GOLD AWARD
Cadogan Place, London
SW1X 9PY
T: (020) 7235 1234
F: (020) 7235 9129
E: ctower@hytlondon.co.uk
I: www.london.hyatt.com

New England Hotel
Rating Applied For
20 St George's Drive, London
SW1V 4BN
T: (020) 7834 1595 & 7834 8351
F: (020) 7834 9000
E: stay@newenglandhotel.com
I: www.newenglandhotel.com

**Royal Horseguards Thistle
Hotel★★★★ SILVER AWARD**
2 Whitehall Court, London
SW1A 2EJ
T: (020) 7839 3400
F: (020) 7930 3269
E: royal.horseguards@thistle.co.
uk
I: www.thistlehotels.com

Sheraton Park Tower
★★★★★ SILVER AWARD
101 Knightsbridge, London
SW1X 7RN
T: (020) 7235 8050
F: (020) 7235 8231
E: morten_ebbesen@sheraton.
com
I: www.luxurycollection.
com/parktowerlondon

Thistle Victoria
★★★★ SILVER AWARD
101 Buckingham Palace Road,
London SW1W 0SJ
T: (020) 7834 9494
F: (020) 7630 1978
E: grosvenor@thistle.co.uk

Thistle Westminster ★★★★
49 Buckingham Palace Road,
Victoria, London SW1W 0QT
T: (020) 7834 1821
F: (020) 7931 7542
E: royalwestminster@cix.co.uk
I: www.cix.co.uk/

SW3
The Basil Street Hotel ★★★
Basil Street, Knightsbridge,
London SW3 1AH
T: (020) 7581 3311
F: (020) 7581 3693
E: info@thebasil.com
I: www.thebasil.com

SW4
**Windmill on the Common
★★★**
Southside, Clapham Common,
London SW4 9DE
T: (020) 8673 4578
F: (020) 8675 1486

SW5
**Barkston Gardens Hotel,
Kensington ★★**
34-44 Barkston Gardens,
London SW5 0EW
T: (020) 7373 7851
F: (020) 7370 6570
E: barkston@hotmail.com
I: www.cairn.hotels.co.uk

The Burns Hotel ★★★
18-26 Barkston Gardens,
Kensington, London SW5 0EN
T: (020) 7373 3151
F: (020) 7370 4090
E: burnshotel@vienna-group.
co.uk
I: www.vienna-group.co.uk

Hogarth Hotel ★★★
33 Hogarth Road, Kensington,
London SW5 0QQ
T: (020) 7370 6831
F: (020) 7373 6179
E: hogarth@marstonhotels.co.
uk
I: www.marstonhotels.co.uk

**Twenty Nevern Square
★★★★**
Townhouse
20 Nevern Square, London
SW5 9PD
T: (020) 7565 9444
F: (020) 7565 9444
E: hotel@twentynevernsquare.
co.uk

SW7
Forum Hotel London ★★★★
97 Cromwell Road, London
SW7 4DN
T: (020) 7370 5757
F: (020) 7373 1448
E: forumlondon@interconti.
com
I: www.interconti.com

Jarvis Kensington ★★★
31-33 Queen's Gate, London
SW7 5JA
T: (020) 7584 7222
F: (020) 7589 3910
I: www.jarvis.co.uk

Millennium Gloucester London
★★★★ SILVER AWARD
4-18 Harrington Gardens,
London SW7 4LH
T: (020) 7373 6030
F: (020) 7373 0409
E: sales.gloucester@mill-cop.
com
I: www.mill-cop.com

Montana Hotel ★★
67-69 Gloucester Road, London
SW7 4PG
T: (020) 7584 7654
F: (020) 7581 3109
I: www.montanahotel.co.uk

Establishments printed in blue have a detailed entry in this guide

SW19

Cannizaro House, (A Thistle Country House Hotel)
★★★ SILVER AWARD
Westside, Wimbledon Common, London SW19 4UE
T: (020) 8879 1464
F: (020) 8879 7338
E: cannizaro.house@thistle.co.uk

W1

The Berners Hotel
★★★★ SILVER AWARD
10 Berners Street, London W1A 3BE
T: (020) 7666 2000
F: (020) 7666 2001
E: berners@berners.co.uk
I: www.thebernershotel.co.uk
⊕

Blandford Hotel
Rating Applied For
80 Chiltern Street, London W1M 1PS
T: (020) 7486 3103
F: (020) 7487 2786
E: blandfordhotel@dial.pipex.com
I: www.capricornhotels.co.uk

The Dorchester
★★★★★ GOLD AWARD
Park Lane, London W1A 2HJ
T: (020) 7629 8888
F: (020) 7409 0114
E: reservations@dorchesterhotel.com
I: www.dorchesterhotel.com

The Leonard
★★★★ GOLD AWARD
Townhouse
15 Seymour Street, London W1H 5AA
T: (020) 7935 2010
F: (020) 7935 6700
E: the.leonard@dial.pipex.com
I: www.theleonard.com

London Hilton
★★★★★ SILVER AWARD
22 Park Lane, London W1Y 4BE
T: (020) 7493 8000
F: (020) 7208 4136
E: sales_park_lane@hilton.com
I: www.hilton.com

May Fair Inter-Continental London ★★★★★
Stratton Street, London W1A 2AN
T: (020) 7629 7777
F: (020) 7629 1459
E: mayfair@interconti.com
I: www.interconti.com

Le Meridien Grosvenor House ★★★★★
Park Lane, London W1A 3AA
T: 0870 400 8500
F: (020) 7493 3341
E: grosvenor.reservations@forte-hotels.com

Le Meridien Piccadilly
★★★★★ SILVER AWARD
21 Piccadilly, London W1V 0BH
T: 0870 400 8400
F: (020) 7437 3574
E: lmpiccres@forte-hotels.com
I: www.forte-hotels.com

Hotel La Place
Rating Applied For
17 Nottingham Place, London W1M 3FF
T: (020) 7486 2323
F: (020) 7486 4335
E: reservations@hotellaplace.com
I: www.hotellaplace.com

The Selfridge, A Thistle Hotel
★★★★ SILVER AWARD
Orchard Street, London W1H 0JS
T: (020) 7408 2080
F: (020) 7629 8849
E: markbarrett@thistle.co.uk
I: www.thistlehotels.co.uk

Thistle Marble Arch
★★★★ SILVER AWARD
Bryanston Street, Marble Arch, London W1A 4UR
T: (020) 7629 8040
F: (020) 7499 7792
E: marble.arch@thistle.co.uk
I: www.thistlehotels.com

W2

The Abbey Court ★★★★
Townhouse
20 Pembridge Gardens, Kensington, London W2 4DU
T: (020) 7221 7518
F: (020) 7792 0858
E: info@abbeycourthotel.co.uk
I: www.abbeycourthotel.co.uk

Athena Hotel
Rating Applied For
110-114 Sussex Gardens, London W2 1UA
T: (020) 7706 3866
F: (020) 7262 6143
E: athena@stavrouhotels.co.uk
I: www.stavrouhotels.co.uk

Central Park Hotel ★★★
49 Queensborough Terrace, London W2 3SS
T: (020) 7229 2424
F: (020) 7229 2904
E: cph@centralparklondon.co.uk
I: www.centralparklondon.co.uk

The Delmere Hotel ★★
128-130 Sussex Gardens, Hyde Park, London W2 1UB
T: (020) 7706 3344
F: (020) 7262 1863
E: delmerehotel@compuserve.com
I: www.delmerehotels.com

Royal Lancaster Hotel ★★★★
Lancaster Terrace, London W2 2TY
T: (020) 7262 6737
F: (020) 7724 3191
E: book@royallancaster.com
I: www.royallancaster.com
⊕

Royal Sussex Hotel ★★
78-84 Sussex Gardens, London W2 1UH
T: (020) 7723 7723
F: (020) 7402 6318
E: info@royalsussexhotel.co.uk
I: www.royalsussexhotel.co.uk

Springfield Hotel
Rating Applied For
154 Sussex Gardens, London W2 1UD
T: (020) 7723 9898
F: (020) 7723 9898

Thistle Hyde Park ★★★★
90-92 Lancaster Gate, London W2 3NR
T: (020) 7262 2711
F: (020) 7262 2147
I: hyde.park@thistle.co.uk

Thistle Kensington Gardens
Rating Applied For
104 Bayswater Road, London W2 3HL
T: (020) 7262 4461
F: (020) 7706 4560
I: kensington.gardens@thistle.co.uk
⊕

Thistle Lancaster Gate
Rating Applied For
75-89 Lancaster Gate, London W2 3NN
T: (020) 7402 4272
F: (020) 7706 4156
E: lancaster.gate@thistle.co.uk
I: www.thistlehotels.com

Westland Hotel ★★
154 Bayswater Road, London W2 4HP
T: (020) 7229 9191
F: (020) 7727 1054
E: reservations@westlandhotel.co.uk
I: www.westlandhotel.co.uk
⊕

W3

Acton Park Hotel ★
116 The Vale, Acton, London W3 7JT
T: (020) 8743 9417
F: (020) 8743 9417

W4

Chiswick Hotel ★★★
73 High Road, London W4 2LS
T: (020) 8994 1712
F: (020) 8742 2585
E: Chishot@clara.net

W5

Jarvis International, Ealing ★★★★
Ealing Common, London W5 3HN
T: (020) 8896 8400
F: (020) 8992 7082
I: www.jarvis.co.uk

W8

London Lodge Hotel ★★★
134-136 Lexham Gardens, London W8 6JE
T: (020) 7244 8444
F: (020) 7373 6661
E: info@londonlodgehotel.com
I: www.londonlodgehotel.com

The Milestone Hotel and Apartments
★★★★★ GOLD AWARD
1 Kensington Court, London W8 5DL
T: (020) 7917 1000
F: (020) 7917 1010
E: guestservices@milestone.redcarnationhotels.com
I: www.themilestone.com

Thistle Kensington Palace
Rating Applied For
De Vere Gardens, London W8 5AF
T: (020) 7937 8121
F: (020) 7937 2816

W9

Colonnade Town House Hotel
★★★★ SILVER AWARD
Townhouse
2 Warrington Crescent, London W9 1ER
T: (020) 7289 2167
F: (020) 7286 1057
E: res_colonnade@etontownhouse.com
I: www.etontownhouse.com

W11

London Kensington Hilton
★★★★ SILVER AWARD
179-199 Holland Park Avenue, London W11 4UL
T: (020) 7603 3355
F: (020) 7602 9397
E: sales_kensington@hilton.com
I: www.kensington-hilton.com

W14

The Kensington
★★★★ SILVER AWARD
Kensington House, Richmond Way, London W14 0AX
T: (020) 7674 1000
F: (020) 7674 1050
E: reservations@thekensington.co.uk
I: www.thekensington.co.uk

WC1

Blooms Townhouse Hotel
★★★★
Townhouse
7 Montague Street, London WC1B 5BP
T: (020) 7323 1717
F: (020) 7636 6498
E: blooms@mermaid.co.uk
I: www.bloomshotel.co.uk

Bloomsbury Park Hotel
Rating Applied For
126 Southampton Row, London WC1B 5AD
T: (020) 7430 0434
F: (020) 7242 0665

The Bonnington in Bloomsbury
★★★
92 Southampton Row, London WC1B 4BH
T: (020) 7242 2828
F: (020) 7831 9170
E: sales@bonnington.com
I: www.bonnington.com
⊕ ♿

London Ryan Hotel
Rating Applied For
Gwynne Place, King's Cross Road, King's Cross, London WC1X 9QN
T: (020) 7278 2480
F: (020) 7837 3776
E: london.ryan@thistle.co.uk

The Montague on the Gardens
★★★★ SILVER AWARD
15 Montague Street, Bloomsbury, London WC1B 5BJ
T: (020) 7637 1001
F: (020) 7637 2516
E: sales@montague.redcarnationhotels.com
I: www.redcarnationhotels.com
⊕

myhotel Bloomsbury
Rating Applied For
11-13 Bayley Street, Bedford
Square, London WC1B 3HD
T: (020) 7667 6000
F: (020) 7667 6044
E: guest_services@myhotels.co.
uk
I: www.myhotels.co.uk

Thistle Bloomsbury ★★★★
Bloomsbury Way, London
WC1A 2SD
T: (020) 7242 5881
F: (020) 7831 0225
E: bloomsbury@thistle.co.uk
I: www.thistlehotels.com

Thistle Kings Cross
Rating Applied For
100 King's Cross Road, London
WC1X 9DT
T: (020) 7278 2434
F: (020) 7833 0798

Waverley House Hotel ★★★
130-134 Southampton Row,
London WC1B 5AG
T: (020) 7833 3691
F: (020) 7837 3485
E: waverleyhs@aol.com
I: www.aquarius-hotels.com

WC2

Le Meridien Waldorf
★★★★★
Aldwych, London WC2B 4DD
T: 0870 400 8484
F: (020) 7836 7244
I: www.lemeridien-hotels.com

**Radisson Edwardian
Hampshire Hotel**
★★★★ SILVER AWARD
31-36 Leicester Square, London
WC2H 7LH
T: (020) 7839 9399
F: (020) 7930 8122
E: hpbcentre@radisson.com
I: www.radissonedwardian.com

The Savoy
★★★★★ GOLD AWARD
The Strand, London WC2R 0EU
T: (020) 7836 4343
F: (020) 7240 6040
E: info@the-savoy.co.uk
I: www.savoy-group.co.uk

Thistle Charing Cross
★★★★ SILVER AWARD
Strand, London WC2N 5HX
T: (020) 7839 7282
F: (020) 7747 8454
E: charing.x@thistle.co.uk

Thistle Trafalgar Square
Rating Applied For
Whitcomb Street, London
WC2H 7HG
T: (020) 7930 4477
F: (020) 7925 2149
E: trafalgar.square@thistle.co.
uk
I: www.thistlehotels.com

OUTER LONDON
BARNET

West Lodge Park
★★★★ SILVER AWARD
Cockfosters Road, Hadley Wood,
Barnet, Hertfordshire EN4 0PY
T: (020) 8216 3900
F: (020) 8216 3937
E: beales_westlodgepark@
compuserve.com
I: www.bealeshotels.co.uk

BEXLEYHEATH

Swallow Hotel
★★★★ SILVER AWARD
1 Broadway, Bexleyheath, Kent
DA6 7JZ
T: (020) 8298 1000
F: (020) 8298 1234
E: bexleyheath@
swallow-hotels.co.uk
I: www.swallowhotels.com

CROYDON

Coulsdon Manor
★★★★ SILVER AWARD
Coulsdon Court Road, Coulsdon,
Croydon, Surrey CR5 2LL
T: (020) 8668 0414
F: (020) 8668 3118
E: coulsdonmanor@
marstonhotels.co.uk
I: www.marstonhotels.co.uk

Hayesthorpe Hotel ★★
48-52 St Augustine's Avenue,
Croydon, CR2 6JJ
T: (020) 8688 8120
F: (020) 8680 1099

**Markington Hotel and
Conference Centre★★**
9 Haling Park Road, South
Croydon, Surrey CR2 6NG
T: (020) 8681 6494
F: (020) 8688 6530
E: rooms@markingtonhotel.
ndirect.co.uk
I: www.markingtonhotel.com

Selsdon Park
★★★★ SILVER AWARD
Addington Road, Sanderstead,
South Croydon, Surrey CR2 8YA
T: (020) 8657 8811
F: (020) 8651 6171
E: caroline.chardon@
principalhotels.co.uk
I: www.principalhotels.co.uk

ENFIELD

Enfield Hotel ★★
52 Rowantree Road, Enfield,
Middlesex EN2 8PW
T: (020) 8366 3511
F: (020) 8366 2432
E: enfieldhotel@
meridianleisure.com
I: www.meridianleisure.
com/enfield

Oak Lodge Hotel
★★ SILVER AWARD
80 Village Road, Bush Hill Park,
Enfield, Middlesex EN1 2EU
T: (020) 8360 7082
I: www.oaklodgehotel.co.uk

HAMPTON COURT

Carlton Mitre Hotel ★★★★
Hampton Court Road, Hampton
Court, Surrey KT8 9BN
T: (020) 8979 9988
F: (020) 8979 9777
E: mitre@carltonhotels.co.uk
I: www.carltonhotels.co.uk

HARROW

Cumberland Hotel ★★★
St John's Road, Harrow,
Middlesex HA1 2EF
T: (020) 8863 4111
F: (020) 8861 5668
I: www.cumberlandhotel.co.uk

Grim's Dyke Hotel ★★★★
Old Redding, Harrow Weald,
Harrow, Middlesex HA3 6SH
T: (020) 8954 4227 & 8385 3100
F: (020) 8954 4560
E: enquiries@grimsdyke.com
I: www.grimsdyke.com

HOUNSLOW

Channins Hounslow Hotel ★
41 Hounslow Road, Feltham,
Middlesex TW14 0AU
T: (020) 8890 2358
F: (020) 8751 6103

Jarvis International Heathrow
★★★
Bath Road, Cranford, Hounslow,
Middlesex TW5 9QE
T: (020) 8897 2121 & 8897 3079
F: (020) 8897 7014
E: reservations@jarvis.co.uk

KINGSTON UPON THAMES

Hotel Antoinette of Kingston
★★
Beaufort Road, Kingston upon
Thames, Surrey KT1 2TQ
T: (020) 8546 1044
F: (020) 8547 2595
E: hotelantoinette@btinternet.
com
I: www.hotelantoinette.co.uk

Chase Lodge Hotel ★★
10 Park Road, Hampton Wick,
Kingston upon Thames, Surrey
KT1 4AS
T: (020) 8943 1862
F: (020) 8943 9363
E: chaselodge@aol.com
I: www.chaselodgehotel.com

ORPINGTON

The Mary Rose Hotel ★
40-50 High Street, St Mary Cray,
Orpington, Kent BR5 3NJ
T: (01689) 871917 & 875369
F: (01689) 839445
I: www.maryrose.co.uk/

SUTTON

Thatched House Hotel ★★
135-141 Cheam Road, Sutton,
Surrey SM1 2BN
T: (020) 8642 3131
F: (020) 8770 0684

WEST DRAYTON

Heathrow Park Hotel
Rating Applied For
Bath Road, Longford, West
Drayton, Middlesex UB7 0EQ
T: (020) 8759 2400
F: (020) 8759 5278
E: heathrow.park@thistle.co.uk
I: www.thistlehotels.
com/heathrow_park/

WOODFORD GREEN

Packfords Hotel ★★
16 Snakes Lane West, Woodford
Green, Essex IG8 0BX
T: (020) 8504 2642
F: (020) 8505 5778
E: simon.packford@virgin.net
I: www.eppingforest.co.
uk/packford

CUMBRIA

ALSTON
Cumbria

**Lovelady Shield Country House
Hotel★★★**
Nenthead Road, Alston, Cumbria
CA9 3LF
T: (01434) 381203 & 381305
F: (01434) 381515
E: enquiries@lovelady.co.uk
I: www.lovelady.co.uk

**Lowbyer Manor Country House
Hotel ★★**
Alston, Cumbria CA9 3JX
T: (01434) 381230
F: (01434) 382937

Nent Hall Country House Hotel
★★ SILVER AWARD
Nenthall, Alston, Cumbria
CA9 3LQ
T: (01434) 381584
F: (01434) 382668

AMBLESIDE
Cumbria

**The Ambleside Salutation
Hotel ★★★**
Lake Road, Ambleside, Cumbria
LA22 9BX
T: (015394) 32244
F: (015394) 34157
E: reservations@
hotelambleside.uk.com
I: www.hotelambleside.uk.com

Fisherbeck Hotel
★★ SILVER AWARD
Lake Road, Ambleside, Cumbria
LA22 0DH
T: (015394) 33215
F: (015394) 33600

**Langdale Hotel and Country
Club ★★★ SILVER AWARD**
Great Langdale, Ambleside,
Cumbria LA22 9JD
T: (015394) 37302
F: (015394) 37130
E: itsgreat@langdale.co.uk
I: www.langdale.co.uk

Laurel Villa ★★
Lake Road, Ambleside, Cumbria
LA22 0DB
T: (015394) 33240
E: laurelvilla@hotel-ambleside.
co.uk
I: www.hotel-ambleside.co.uk

Establishments printed in blue have a detailed entry in this guide

Nanny Brow Country House Hotel★★★ SILVER AWARD
Clappersgate, Ambleside,
Cumbria LA22 9NF
T: (015394) 32036
F: (015394) 32450
⊕

Queens Hotel ★★
Market Place, Ambleside,
Cumbria LA22 9BU
T: (015394) 32206
F: (015394) 32721
I: www.smoothhound.co.
uk/hotels/quecum.html

The Regent Hotel ★★★ SILVER AWARD
Waterhead Bay, Ambleside,
Cumbria LA22 0ES
T: (015394) 32254
F: (015394) 31474
E: lile@regentlakes.co.uk
I: www.regentlakes.co.uk
⊕

Rothay Garth Hotel ★★
Rothay Road, Ambleside,
Cumbria LA22 0EE
T: (015394) 32217
F: (015394) 34400
E: enquiries@rothay-garth.co.
uk
I: www.rothay-garth.co.uk
⊕

Rothay Manor Hotel ★★★ SILVER AWARD
Rothay Bridge, Ambleside,
Cumbria LA22 0EH
T: (015394) 33605
F: (015394) 33607
E: hotel@rothaymanor.co.uk
I: www.rothaymanor.co.uk

Smallwood House Hotel ★★
Compston Road, Ambleside,
Cumbria LA22 9DJ
T: (015394) 32330
F: (015394) 33764
E: enq@smallwoodhotel.co.uk
I: www.smallwoodhotel.co.uk
⊕

Wateredge Hotel ★★★ SILVER AWARD
Waterhead Bay, Ambleside,
Cumbria LA22 0EP
T: (015394) 32332
F: (015394) 31878
E: contact@wateredgehotel.co.
uk
I: www.wateredgehotel.co.uk

APPLEBY-IN-WESTMORLAND
Cumbria

Appleby Manor Country House Hotel ★★★ SILVER AWARD
Roman Road, Appleby-in-
Westmorland, Cumbria
CA16 6JB
T: (017683) 51571 & 51570
F: (017683) 52888
E: nswinscoe@bigfoot.com
I: www.applebymanor.co.uk

Royal Oak Inn ★★
Bongate, Appleby-in-
Westmorland, Cumbria
CA16 6UN
T: (017683) 51463
F: (017683) 52300
E: m.m.royaloak@btinternet.
com
I: www.mortal-man-inns.co.
uk/royaloak

BARROW-IN-FURNESS
Cumbria

Abbey House Hotel ★★★
Abbey Road, Barrow-in-Furness,
Cumbria LA13 0PA
T: (01229) 838282
F: (01229) 820403
E: resv@abbeyhh.freeserve.co.
uk
I: www.abbeyhousehotel.com

Hotel Majestic ★★
Duke Street, Barrow-in-Furness,
Cumbria LA14 1HP
T: (01229) 870448
F: (01229) 870448

BASSENTHWAITE
Cumbria

Ravenstone Hotel ★★
Bassenthwaite, Keswick,
Cumbria CA12 4QG
T: (017687) 76240
F: (017687) 76733
E: ravenstonehotel@aol.com
I: www.kesnet.co.uk

BASSENTHWAITE LAKE
Cumbria

Ouse Bridge Hotel ★★
Dubwath, Bassenthwaite Lake,
Cockermouth, Cumbria
CA13 9YD
T: (017687) 76322

The Pheasant ★★
Bassenthwaite Lake,
Cockermouth, Cumbria
CA13 9YE
T: (017687) 76234
F: (017687) 76002
🏚

BORROWDALE
Cumbria

Leathes Head Hotel and Restaurant ★★★
Borrowdale, Keswick, Cumbria
CA12 5UY
T: (017687) 77247
F: (017687) 77363
E: enq@leatheshead.co.uk
I: www.leatheshead.co.uk

Mary Mount Hotel ★★
Borrowdale, Keswick, Cumbria
CA12 5UU
T: (017687) 77223 & 77381
E: marymount@bigfoot.com
I: visitweb.com/marymount

BRAITHWAITE
Cumbria

Middle Ruddings Hotel ★★
Braithwaite, Keswick, Cumbria
CA12 5RY
T: (017687) 78436
F: (017687) 78438
E: reception@middleruddings.
com
I: www.middleruddings.com

BRAMPTON
Cumbria

Kirby Moor Country House Hotel and Bella Vissta Restaurant★★
Longtown Road, Brampton,
Cumbria CA8 2AB
T: (016977) 3893
F: (016977) 41847
E: info@kirbymoor-hotel.com
I: www.kirbymoor-hotel.com

Sands House Hotel ★★
The Sands, Brampton, Cumbria
CA8 1UG
T: (016977) 3085
F: (016977) 3297

BUTTERMERE
Cumbria

Bridge Hotel ★★
Buttermere, Cockermouth,
Cumbria CA13 9UZ
T: (017687) 70252
F: (017687) 70215
E: enquiries@bridge-hotel.com
I: www.bridge-hotel.com

CALDBECK
Cumbria

Parkend Restaurant and Country Hotel★★
Parkend, Caldbeck, Wigton,
Cumbria CA7 8HH
T: (016974) 78494 &
07976 741005
F: (016974) 78580

CARLISLE
Cumbria

Central Plaza Hotel ★★★
Victoria Viaduct, Carlisle,
CA3 8AL
T: (01228) 520256
F: (01228) 514657
E: info@centralplazahotel.co.uk
I: www.centralplazahotel.co.uk

County Hotel ★★
9 Botchergate, Carlisle, Cumbria
CA1 1QP
T: (01228) 531316
F: (01228) 401805
E: counth@cairn-hotels.co.uk
I: www.cairn-hotels.co.uk

Crosby Lodge Country House Hotel and Restaurant ★★★ SILVER AWARD
High Crosby, Crosby-on-Eden,
Carlisle CA6 4QZ
T: (01228) 573618
F: (01228) 573428
E: crosbylodge@crosby-eden.
demon.co.uk

Pinegrove Hotel ★★
262 London Road, Carlisle,
CA1 2QS
T: (01228) 524828
F: (01228) 810941
⊕

Tarn End House Hotel ★★
Talkin Tarn, Brampton, Cumbria
CA8 1LS
T: (016977) 2340
F: (016977) 2089
⊕

Wallfoot Hotel and Restaurant ★★
Park Broom, Crosby-on-Eden,
Carlisle, CA6 4QH
T: (01228) 573696
F: (01228) 573240
E: frazer@wallfoot.freeserve.co.
uk

CARTMEL
Cumbria

Aynsome Manor Hotel ★★ SILVER AWARD
Cartmel, Grange-over-Sands,
Cumbria LA11 6HH
T: (015395) 36653
F: (015395) 36016
E: aynsome@aynsomemanorhotel.
co.uk
I: www.aynsomemanorhotel.co.
uk
⊕

CASTLERIGG
Cumbria

The Heights Hotel ★
Rakefoot Lane, Castlerigg,
Keswick, Cumbria CA12 4TE
T: (017687) 72251
E: info@theheightshotel.co.uk
I: www.theheightshotel.co.uk

CLEATOR
Cumbria

The Ennerdale Country House Hotel★★★
Cleator, Cumbria CA23 3DT
T: (01946) 813907
F: (01946) 815260
E: ennerdale@bestwestern.co.uk
I: www.feathers.uk.com
⊕

Grove Court ★★
Cleator Gate, Cleator, Cumbria
CA23 3DT
T: (01946) 810503
F: (01946) 815412

COCKERMOUTH
Cumbria

Allerdale Court Hotel ★★
Market Square, Cockermouth,
Cumbria CA13 9NQ
T: (01900) 823654
F: (01900) 823033
E: allerdalecourt@edirectory.co.
uk
I: www.edirectory.co.
uk/allerdalecourt

Broughton Craggs Hotel ★★
Craggs Road, Great Broughton,
Cockermouth, Cumbria
CA13 0XW
T: (01900) 824400
F: (01900) 825350
E: peter_john.caddy@virgin.net
I: www.smoothhound.
cojk/hotels/broughto.html

Manor House Hotel ★★★
Crown Street, Cockermouth,
Cumbria CA13 0EH
T: (01900) 828663
F: (01900) 828679

Trout Hotel ★★★
Crown Street, Cockermouth,
Cumbria CA13 0EJ
T: (01900) 823591
F: (01900) 827514
E: enquiries@trouthotel.co.uk
I: www.trouthotel.co.uk

CONISTON
Cumbria

Sun Hotel & 16th Century Inn ★★
Coniston, Cumbria LA21 8HQ
T: (015394) 41248
F: (015394) 41219
E: the sun@hotelconiston.com
I: www.smoothhound.co.
uk/hotels/sun.html

Waterhead Hotel ★
Coniston, Cumbria LA21 8AJ
T: (015394) 41244 & 41454
F: (015394) 41193
E: reception@waterheadhotel.
f9.co.uk

Yewdale Hotel ★★
Yewdale Road, Coniston,
Cumbria LA21 8DU
T: (015394) 41280
F: (015394) 41871
E: yewdale.hotel@virginnet
I: freespace.virgin.net/yewdale.
hotel/

EMBLETON
Cumbria

Derwent Lodge Hotel ★★
Embleton, Cockermouth,
Cumbria CA13 9YA
T: (017687) 76606
F: (017687) 76766
E: onlodge@aol.com
I: www.derwentlodge.co.uk

ENNERDALE
Cumbria

Shepherd's Arms Hotel ★★
Ennerdale Bridge, Cleator,
Cumbria CA23 3AR
T: (01946) 861249
F: (01946) 861249
E: enquiries@
shepherdsarmshotel.co.uk
I: shephardsarmshotel.co.uk

ESKDALE
Cumbria

Bower House Inn ★★
Eskdale, Cumbria CA19 1TD
T: (019467) 23244
F: (019467) 23308
E: info@bowerhouseinn.co.uk
I: bowerhousehotel.co.uk

Brook House Inn ★★
Boot, Holmrook, Cumbria
CA19 1TG
T: (019467) 23288
F: (019467) 23160
E: stay@brookhouseinn.co.uk
I: www.brookhouseinn.co.uk

GRANGE-OVER-SANDS
Cumbria

Clare House ★
Park Road, Grange-over-Sands,
Cumbria LA11 7HQ
T: (015395) 33026 & 34253

The Cumbria Grand Hotel ★
Lindale Road, Grange-over-
Sands, Cumbria LA11 6EN
T: (015395) 32331
F: (015395) 34534
E: cumbria@cgrandhotel.
freeserve.co.uk
I: www.scoot.co.uk/strathmore/

Grange Hotel ★★★
Station Square, Grange-over-
Sands, Cumbria LA11 6EJ
T: (015395) 33666
F: (015395) 35064
E: grange.hotel@cerbernet.co.
uk
I: www.grange-hotel.co.uk

**Graythwaite Manor Hotel
★★★**
Fernhill Road, Grange-over-
Sands, Cumbria LA11 7JE
T: (015395) 32001 & 33755
F: (015395) 35549
E: enquiries@
graythwaitemanor.co.uk
I: www.graythwaitemanor.co.uk

Hampsfell House Hotel ★★
Hampsfell Road, Grange-over-
Sands, Cumbria LA11 6BG
T: (015395) 32567
F: (015395) 35995
E: hampsfellhotel@msn.com

Kents Bank Hotel ★★
96 Kentsford Road, Kents Bank,
Grange-over-Sands, Cumbria
LA11 7BB
T: (015395) 32054

Netherwood Hotel ★★★
Grange-over-Sands, Cumbria
LA11 6ET
T: (015395) 32552
F: (015395) 34121
E: blawith@aol.com
I: www.netherwood-hotel.co.uk

GRASMERE
Cumbria

**Bridge House Hotel
★★ SILVER AWARD**
Church Bridge, Grasmere,
Ambleside, Cumbria LA22 9SN
T: (015394) 35425
F: (015394) 35523
E: stay@bridgehousegrasmere.
co.uk
I: www.bridgehousegrasmere.co.
uk

**Gold Rill Country House Hotel
★★★ SILVER AWARD**
Grasmere, Cumbria LA22 9PU
T: (015394) 35486
F: (015394) 35486
E: enquiries@gold-rill.com
I: www.gold-rill.com

The Grasmere Hotel ★★
Broadgate, Grasmere,
Ambleside, Cumbria LA22 9TA
T: (015394) 35277
F: (015394) 35277
E: enquiries@grasmerehotel.co.
uk
I: www.grasmerehotel.co.uk

**Grasmere Red Lion Hotel
★★★**
Red Lion Square, Grasmere,
Ambleside, Cumbria LA22 9SS
T: (015394) 35456
F: (015394) 35579
E: enquiries@hotelgrasmere.uk.
com
I: www.hotelgrasmere.uk.com

Moss Grove Hotel ★★
Grasmere, Ambleside, Cumbria
LA22 9SW
T: (015394) 35251
F: (015394) 35691
E: martinw@globalnet.co.uk
I: www.mossgrove.co.uk

**Oak Bank Hotel
★★ SILVER AWARD**
Broadgate, Grasmere,
Ambleside, Cumbria LA22 9TA
T: (015394) 35217
F: (015395) 35685
E: grasmereoakbank@
btinternet.com
I: www.lakedistricthotel.co.uk

**Rothay Garden Hotel
Rating Applied For**
Broadgate, Grasmere,
Ambleside, Cumbria LA22 9RJ
T: (015394) 35334
F: (015394) 35723
E: rothay@grasmere.com
I: www.grasmere.com

**Thistle Grasmere
Rating Applied For**
Keswick Road, Grasmere,
Ambleside, Cumbria LA22 9PR
T: (015394) 35666
F: (015394) 35565
E: grasmere@thistle.co.uk

GREAT LANGDALE
Cumbria

New Dungeon Ghyll Hotel ★★
Great Langdale, Ambleside,
Cumbria LA22 9JY
T: (015394) 37213
F: (015394) 37666
E: enquireis@dungeon-ghyll.
com
I: www.dungeon-ghyll.com

HAVERTHWAITE
Cumbria

**Rusland Pool Hotel and
Restaurant ★★★**
Haverthwaite, Ulverston,
Cumbria LA12 8AA
T: (01229) 861384
F: (01229) 861425
E: enquiries@rusland-pool.
ndirect.co.uk
I: www.rusland-pool.ndirect.co.
uk

HAWKSHEAD
Cumbria

**Highfield House Country Hotel
★★ SILVER AWARD**
Hawkshead Hill, Ambleside,
Cumbria LA22 0PN
T: (015394) 36344
F: (015394) 36793
E: Highfield.Hawkshead@
btinternet.com
I: www.lakes-pages.co.
uk/highsite.html

**Queens Head Hotel
★★ SILVER AWARD**
Main Street, Hawkshead,
Ambleside, Cumbria LA22 0NS
T: (015394) 36271
F: (015394) 36722
E: enquiries@queensheadhotel.
co.uk
I: www.queensheadhotel.co.uk

HEVERSHAM
Cumbria

**The Blue Bell at Heversham
★★ SILVER AWARD**
Princes Way, Heversham,
Milnthorpe, Cumbria LA7 7EE
T: (015395) 62018
F: (015395) 62455
E: bluebellhotel@aol.com
I: www.bluebellhotel.co.uk

KENDAL
Cumbria

The County Hotel ★
Station Road, Kendal, Cumbria
LA9 6BT
T: (01539) 722461
F: (01539) 732644

Garden House ★★
Fowl-Ing Lane, Kendal, Cumbria
LA9 6PH
T: (01539) 731131
F: (01539) 740064
E: gardenhouse.hotel@virgin.
net
I: www.gardenhousehotel.co.uk

Heaves Hotel ★
Kendal, Cumbria LA8 8EF
T: (015395) 60396
F: (015395) 60269
E: hotel@heaves.freeserve.co.uk

**MacDonald Riverside Hotel
★★★**
Stramongate Bridge, Kendal,
Cumbria LA9 4BZ
T: (01539) 734861
F: (015389) 734863
E: info@riverside.
macdonald-hotels.co.uk
I: www.macdonaldhotels.co.uk

**Roadchef Lodge
Rating Applied For**
Travel Accommodation
Killington Lake Motorway
Service Area, M6 Southbound,
Kendal, Cumbria LA8 0NW
T: (015396) 21666 & 20739
F: (015396) 21660
E: ian@roadchef.com

KESWICK
Cumbria

**Applethwaite Country House
Hotel★★ SILVER AWARD**
Applethwaite, Keswick, Cumbria
CA12 4PL
T: (017687) 72413
F: (017687) 75706
E: ryan@applethwaite.freeserve.
co.uk
I: www.applethwaite.freeserve.
co.uk

**Borrowdale Gates Country
House Hotel and Restaurant
★★★ SILVER AWARD**
Grange-in-Borrowdale, Keswick,
Cumbria CA12 5UQ
T: (017687) 77204
F: (017687) 77254
E: hotel@borrowdale-gates.com
I: www.borrowdale-gates.com

Borrowdale Hotel ★★★
Borrowdale, Keswick, Cumbria
CA12 5UY
T: (017687) 77224
F: (017687) 77338
E: theborrowdalehotel@yahoo.
com
I: theborrowdalehotel.co.uk

Castle Head House Hotel ★★
Borrowdale Road, Keswick,
Cumbria CA12 5DD
T: (017687) 72082
F: (017687) 74065

Crow Park Hotel ★★
The Heads, Keswick, Cumbria
CA12 5ER
T: (017687) 72208
F: (017687) 74776

**Dale Head Hall Lakeside Hotel
★★★ SILVER AWARD**
Thirlmere, Keswick, Cumbria
CA12 4TN
T: (017687) 72478
F: (017687) 71070
E: onthelakeside@
dale-head-hall.co.uk
I: www.dale-head-hall.co.uk

Derwentwater Hotel
★★★ SILVER AWARD
Portinscale, Keswick, Cumbria
CA12 5RE
T: (017687) 72538
F: (017687) 71002
E: reservations@
derwentwater-hotel.co.uk
I: ds.dial.pipex.
com/derwentwater.hotel

Highfield Hotel
★★ SILVER AWARD
The Heads, Keswick, Cumbria
CA12 5ER
T: (017687) 72508

The Keswick Country House Hotel ★★★
Station Road, Keswick, Cumbria
CA12 4NQ
T: (017687) 72020
F: (017687) 71300

Keswick Park Hotel ★★
33 Station Road, Keswick,
Cumbria CA12 4NA
T: (017687) 72072 &
07802 762536
F: (017687) 74816
I: www.keswickparkhotel.uk.com

King's Arms Hotel ★★
Main Street, Keswick, Cumbria
CA12 5BL
T: (017687) 72083 & 71108
F: (017687) 75550
E: info@kingsarmshotelkeswick.
co.uk
I: www.kingsarmshotelkeswick.
co.uk

Kings Head Hotel ★★★
Thirlspot, Keswick, Cumbria
CA12 4TN
T: (017687) 72393 &
0500 600725
F: (017687) 72309
I: www.lakelandsheart.demon.
co.uk

Ladstock Country House Hotel
★★
Thornthwaite, Keswick, Cumbria
CA12 5RZ
T: (017687) 78210 & 78249
F: (017687) 78088

Lairbeck Hotel
★★ SILVER AWARD
Vicarage Hill, Keswick, Cumbria
CA12 5QB
T: (017687) 73373
F: (017687) 73144
E: rogerc@lairbeck.demon.co.uk
I: www.lairbeck.demon.co.uk

Lyzzick Hall Hotel
★★ SILVER AWARD
Underskiddaw, Keswick, Cumbria
CA12 4PY
T: (017687) 72277
F: (017687) 72278
I: lyzzickhall@netscapeonline.
co.uk

Morrel's Restaurant and Rooms ★★
Lake Road, Keswick, Cumbria
CA12 5DQ
T: (017687) 72666
F: (017687) 74879
E: info@morrels.co.uk

Queen's Hotel ★★★
Main Street, Keswick, Cumbria
CA12 5JF
T: (017687) 73333
F: (017687) 71144
E: book@queenshotel.co.uk
I: www.queenshotel.co.uk

Skiddaw Hotel
★★★ SILVER AWARD
Market Square, Keswick,
Cumbria CA12 5BN
T: (017687) 72071
F: (017687) 74850
E: info@skiddawhotel.co.uk
I: www.skiddawhotel.co.uk

Swan Hotel and Country Inn
★★
Thornthwaite, Keswick, Cumbria
CA12 5SQ
T: (017687) 78256
F: (017687) 78080
E: bestswan@aol.com
I: www.swan-hotel-keswick.co.
uk

Swinside Lodge Hotel
★ GOLD AWARD
Grange Road, Newlands,
Keswick, Cumbria CA12 5UE
T: (017687) 72948 &
07887 930998
F: (017687) 72948
E: stay@swinsidelodge.
fsbusiness.co.uk

Thwaite Howe Hotel ★★
Thornthwaite, Keswick, Cumbria
CA12 5SA
T: (017687) 78281
F: (017687) 78529

KIRKBY LONSDALE
Cumbria
Pheasant Inn ★★
Casterton, Kirkby Lonsdale,
Carnforth, Lancashire LA6 2RX
T: (015242) 71230
F: (015242) 71230
E: pheasant.casterton@
eggconnnect.net
I: www.pheasantinn.co.uk

Whoop Hall Inn ★★
Burrow with Burrow, Kirkby
Lonsdale, Carnforth, Lancashire
LA6 2HP
T: (01524) 271284
F: (01524) 272154
E: whoophall@cybernet.co.uk
I: www.whoophall.co.uk

LANGDALE
Cumbria
Britannia Inn ★
Elterwater, Ambleside, Cumbria
LA22 9HP
T: (015394) 37210
F: (015394) 37311
E: info@britinn.co.uk
I: www.britinn.co.uk

Eltermere Country House Hotel
★★
Elterwater, Ambleside, Cumbria
LA22 9HY
T: (015394) 37207
F: (015394) 37540
E: colin@hensington.demon.co.
uk
I: www.eltermere.co.uk

Three Shires Inn ★★
Little Langdale, Ambleside,
Cumbria LA22 9NZ
T: (015394) 37215
F: (015394) 37127
E: ian@threeshiresinn.co.uk
I: www.threeshiresinn.co.uk

LONGTOWN
Cumbria
Graham Arms Hotel ★★
English Street, Longtown,
Carlisle CA6 5SE
T: (01228) 791213
F: (01228) 791213
E: hotel@cumbria.com
I: www.cumbria.com/hotel

LUPTON
Cumbria
The Plough Hotel ★★
Cow Brow, Lupton, Cumbria
LA6 1PJ
T: (015395) 67227
F: (015395) 67848

MUNGRISDALE
Cumbria
The Mill Hotel ★
Mungrisdale, Penrith, Cumbria
CA11 0XR
T: (017687) 79659
F: (017687) 79155

NEWBY BRIDGE
Cumbria
Newby Bridge Hotel ★★★
Newby Bridge, Ulverston,
Cumbria LA12 8NA
T: (015395) 31222
F: (015395) 31868
E: newby.bridge.hotel@
kencomp.net
I: www.newbybridgehotel.co.uk

Swan Hotel ★★★★
Newby Bridge, Ulverston,
Cumbria LA12 8NB
T: (015395) 31681
F: (015395) 31917
E: swanhotel@aol.com
I: www.swanhotel.com

Whitewater Hotel ★★★
The Lakeland Village, Newby
Bridge, Cumbria LA12 8PX
T: (015395) 31133
F: (015395) 31881
E: smcintosh@btconnect.com
I: www.whitewater-hotel.co.uk

ORTON
Cumbria
Westmorland Hotel ★★★
Westmorland Place, Orton,
Penrith, Cumbria CA10 3SB
T: (015396) 24351
F: (015396) 24354
I: www.westmorland.com

PENRITH
Cumbria
Clifton Hill Hotel and Motel
★★
Clifton, Penrith, Cumbria
CA10 2EJ
T: (01768) 862717
F: (01768) 867182

RAVENSTONEDALE
Cumbria
The Black Swan Hotel ★★
Ravenstonedale, Kirkby Stephen,
Cumbria CA17 4NG
T: (015396) 23204
F: (015396) 23604
E: reservations@
balckswanhotel.com
I: www.blackswanhotel.com

The Fat Lamb ★★
Crossbank, Ravenstonedale,
Kirkby Stephen, Cumbria
CA17 4LL
T: (015396) 23242
F: (015396) 23285
E: fatlamb@cumbria.com
I: www.fatlamb.co.uk

ST BEES
Cumbria
Seacote Hotel
Rating Applied For
Beach Road, St Bees, Cumbria
CA27 0ES
T: (01946) 822777
F: (01946) 824442

SAWREY
Cumbria
Sawrey Hotel ★★
Far Sawrey, Ambleside, Cumbria
LA22 0LQ
T: (015394) 43425
F: (015394) 43425

SHAP
Cumbria
Shap Wells Hotel ★★★
Shap, Penrith, Cumbria
CA10 3QU
T: (01931) 716628
F: (01931) 716377
E: manager@shapwells.com
I: www.shapwells.com

SILLOTH
Cumbria
Skinburness Hotel ★★★
Silloth, Carlisle, Cumbria
CA5 4QY
T: (016973) 32332
F: (016973) 32549

THRELKELD
Cumbria
Horse and Farrier Inn ★★
Threlkeld, Keswick, Cumbria
CA12 4SQ
T: (017687) 79688
F: (017687) 79824

TROUTBECK
Cumbria
Broadoaks Country House
★★ SILVER AWARD
Bridge Lane, Troutbeck,
Windermere, Cumbria LA23 1LA
T: (015394) 45566
F: (015394) 88766
E: broadoaks.com@virgin.net
I: www.travel.to/broadoaks

CUMBRIA

Mortal Man Hotel ★★
Troutbeck, Windermere, Cumbria
LA23 1PL
T: (015394) 33193
F: (015394) 31261
E: the-mortalman@btinternet.com
I: www.the_mortal_man_inns.com

ULLSWATER
Cumbria

Patterdale Hotel ★★
Patterdale, Lake Ullswater,
Penrith, Cumbria CA11 0NN
T: (017684) 82329
F: (017684) 82440

ULVERSTON
Cumbria

Lonsdale House Hotel
Rating Applied For
11 Daltongate, Ulverston,
Cumbria LA12 7BD
T: (01229) 582598
F: (01229) 581260
E: lonsdale.house.hotel@kencomp.net
I: www.lonsdalehousehotel.co.uk

WIGTON
Cumbria

The Kelsey Hotel ★★
Mealsgate, Wigton, Cumbria
CA5 1JP
T: (016973) 71229 & 71372
F: (016973) 71372
E: the kelseyhotel@aol.com

WINDERMERE
Cumbria

The Belsfield ★★★
Bowness-on-Windermere,
Windermere, Cumbria LA23 3EL
T: (015394) 42448
F: (015394) 46397
E: belsfield@regalhotels.co.uk
I: www.corushotels.com
⊕

**Briery Wood Country House
★★**
Ambleside Road, Windermere,
Cumbria LA23 1ES
T: (015394) 33316
F: (015394) 34258
⊕

Burnside Hotel ★★★
Kendal Road, Bowness-on-
Windermere, Windermere,
Cumbria LA23 3EP
T: (015394) 42211 & 44530
F: (015394) 43824
E: stay@burnsidehotel.com
I: www.burnsidehotel.com
⊕ ⓖ

**Cedar Manor Hotel
★★ SILVER AWARD**
Ambleside Road, Windermere,
Cumbria LA23 1AX
T: (015394) 43192
F: (015394) 45970
E: cedarmanor@fsbdial.co.uk
I: www.cedarmanor.co.uk

**Crag Brow Cottage Hotel
★★ SILVER AWARD**
Helm Road, Bowness-on-
Windermere, Cumbria LA23 3BU
T: (015394) 44080
F: (015394) 46003
E: cragbrow@aol.com

**Cragwood Country House
Hotel and Restaurant★★★**
Eccelrigg, Windermere, Cumbria
LA23 1LQ
T: (015394) 88177
F: (015394) 47263

Cranleigh Hotel ★★
Kendal Road, Bowness-on-
Windermere, Windermere,
Cumbria LA23 3EW
T: (015394) 43293
F: (015394) 47283
E: mike@thecranleigh.com
I: www.thecranleigh.com

Dalegarth Private Hotel ★★
Lake Road, Windermere,
Cumbria LA23 2EQ
T: (015394) 45052
F: (015394) 46702
E: enquiries@dalegarthe.demon.co.uk
I: www.dalegarthe.demon.co.uk

Damson Dene Hotel
Rating Applied For
Crosthwaite, Kendal, Cumbria
LA8 8JE
T: (015395) 68676
F: (015395) 68227
E: info@damsondene.co.uk
I: www.damsondene.co.uk

**Fayrer Garden House Hotel
★★★ SILVER AWARD**
Lyth Valley Road, Bowness-on-
Windermere, Windermere,
Cumbria LA23 3JP
T: (015394) 88195
F: (015394) 45986
E: lakescene@fayrergarden.com
I: www.fayrergarden.com
⊕

**Gilpin Lodge Country House
Hotel and Restaurant
★★★ GOLD AWARD**
Crook Road, Windermere,
Cumbria LA23 3NE
T: (015394) 88818
F: (015394) 88058
E: hotel@gilpin-lodge.co.uk
I: www.gilpin-lodge.co.uk

Grey Walls Hotel ★
Elleray Road, Windermere,
Cumbria LA23 1AG
T: (015394) 43741
F: (015394) 47546

Hideaway Hotel ★★
Phoenix Way, Windermere,
Cumbria LA23 1DB
T: (015394) 43070
F: (015394) 48664

Hillthwaite House ★★★
Thornbarrow Road, Windermere,
Cumbria LA23 2DF
T: (015394) 43636 & 46691
F: (015394) 88660
E: reception@hillthwaite.com
I: homepages.kencomp.net/hillthwaite/home.htm

**Holbeck Ghyll Country House
Hotel and Restaurant
★★★ GOLD AWARD**
Holbeck Lane, Windermere,
Cumbria LA23 1LU
T: (015394) 32375
F: (015394) 34743
E: accommodation@holbeck-ghyll.co.uk
I: www.holbeck-ghyll.co.uk

**Lakeside Hotel on Lake
Windermere
★★★★ SILVER AWARD**
Newby Bridge, Ulverston,
Cumbria LA12 8AT
T: (015395) 31207
F: (015395) 31699
E: sales@lakesidehotel.co.uk
I: www.lakesidehotel.co.uk

Langdale Chase Hotel ★★★
Windermere, Cumbria LA23 1LW
T: (015394) 32201
F: (015394) 32604
E: sales@langdalechase.co.uk
I: www.langdalechase.co.uk

**Lindeth Fell Country House
Hotel ★★ GOLD AWARD**
Lyth Valley Road, Bowness-on-
Windermere, Windermere,
Cumbria LA23 3JP
T: (015394) 43286 & 44287
F: (015394) 47455
E: kennedy@lindethfell.co.uk
I: www.lindethfell.co.uk

**Lindeth Howe Country House
Hotel ★★★ SILVER AWARD**
Lindeth Drive, Longtail Hill,
Bowness-on-Windermere,
Windermere, Cumbria LA23 3JF
T: (015394) 45759
F: (015394) 46368
E: lindeth.howe@kencomp.net
I: www.lakes-pages.co.uk
⊕ ⓖ

**Linthwaite House Hotel
★★★ GOLD AWARD**
Crook Road, Bowness-on-
Windermere, Windermere,
Cumbria LA23 3JA
T: (015394) 88600
F: (015394) 88601
E: admin@linthwaite.com.
I: www.linthwaite.com
⊕ ⓧ

**Merewood Country House
Hotel ★★ SILVER AWARD**
Eccelrigg, Windermere, Cumbria
LA23 1LH
T: (015394) 46484
F: (015394) 42128
E: merewood.hotel@impact-dtg.com

Mountain Ash Hotel ★★★
Ambleside Road, Windermere,
Cumbria LA23 1AT
T: (015394) 43715
F: (015394) 88480
E: john_fawbert@msn.com
I: www.mountainashhotel.co.uk

The Old England ★★★
Church Street, Bowness-on-
Windermere, Windermere,
Cumbria LA23 3DF
T: 0870 400 8130
F: (015394) 43432

Ravensworth Hotel ★★
Ambleside Road, Windermere,
Cumbria LA23 1BA
T: (015394) 43747
F: (015394) 43670
E: raveswth@aol.com
I: www.ravensworthhotel.co.uk

**South View
★★ SILVER AWARD**
Cross Street, Windermere,
Cumbria LA23 1AE
T: (015394) 42951
F: (015394) 45669
E: sthviewhotel@btconnect.com
I: www.smooothhound.co.uk/hotels/southvie.html

The Willowsmere Hotel ★
Ambleside Road, Windermere,
Cumbria LA23 1ES
T: (015394) 43575 & 44962
F: (015394) 44962
E: willowsmerehotel@hotmail.com

Windermere Manor ★★
Rayrigg Road, Windermere,
Cumbria LA23 1ES
T: (015394) 45801
F: (015394) 48397
E: windermere@aflop.org
⊕

Woodlands ★★ SILVER AWARD
New Road, Windermere,
Cumbria LA23 2EE
T: (015394) 43915
F: (015394) 48558
⊕

WITHERSLACK
Cumbria

**The Old Vicarage Country
House Hotel
★★ SILVER AWARD**
Church Road, Witherslack,
Grange-over-Sands, Cumbria
LA11 6RS
T: (015395) 52381
F: (015395) 52373
E: hotel@old-vic.demon.co.uk
I: www.oldvicarage.com
⊕

WORKINGTON
Cumbria

Hunday Manor Hotel ★★★
Hunday, Workington, Cumbria
CA14 4JF
T: (01900) 61798
F: (01900) 601202

**The Washington Central Hotel
★★★**
Washington Street, Workington,
Cumbria CA14 3AY
T: (01900) 65772
F: (01900) 68770

Establishments printed in blue have a detailed entry in this guide

NORTHUMBRIA

ALLENSFORD
Durham

The Royal Derwent Hotel
Rating Applied For
Hole Row, Allensford, Newcastle
upon Tyne, Northumberland
DH8 9BB
T: (01207) 592000
F: (01207) 502472
E: info@royalderwent.
macdonald-hotels.co.uk
I: www.macdonaldhotels.co.uk

ALNMOUTH
Northumberland

Saddle Hotel ★★
24-25 Northumberland Street,
Alnmouth, Alnwick,
Northumberland NE66 2RA
T: (01665) 830476

ALNWICK
Northumberland

Hotspur Hotel ★★
Bondgate Without, Alnwick,
Northumberland NE66 1PR
T: (01665) 510101
F: (01665) 605033
I: www.city2000.
com/tl/hotspur-alnwick.html

White Swan Hotel ★★
Bondgate Within, Alnwick,
Northumberland NE66 1TD
T: (01665) 602109
F: (01665) 510400
I: www.macdonaldhotels.co.
uk/white-swan-hotel

BAMBURGH
Northumberland

Lord Crewe Arms Hotel ★★
Front Street, Bamburgh,
Northumberland NE69 7BL
T: (01668) 214243 & 214393
F: (01668) 214273
E: lca@tinyonline.co.uk

Sunningdale Hotel ★★
Lucker Road, Bamburgh,
Northumberland NE69 7BS
T: (01668) 214334

Victoria Hotel ★★
Front Street, Bamburgh,
Northumberland NE69 7BP
T: (01668) 214431
F: (01668) 214404
E: victoria@bestwestern.co.uk
I: www.bestwestern.co.uk

Waren House Hotel ★★★
Waren Mill, Belford,
Northumberland NE70 7EE
T: (01668) 214581
F: (01668) 214484
E: enquiries@warenhousehotel.
co.uk
I: www.warenhousehotel.co.uk

BARNARD CASTLE
Durham

Jersey Farm Hotel ★★★
Darlington Road, Barnard Castle,
County Durham DL12 8TA
T: (01833) 638223
F: (01833) 631988
E: jerseyfarmhotel@enta.net
I: www.jerseyfarmhotel.enta.net

**The Morritt Arms Hotel &
Restaurant ★★★**
Greta Bridge, Barnard Castle,
County Durham DL12 9SE
T: (01833) 627232
F: (01833) 627392
E: relax@themorritt.co.uk
I: www//relax@the morritt.co.
uk

**Rose & Crown Hotel
★★ SILVER AWARD**
Romaldkirk, Barnard Castle,
County Durham DL12 9EB
T: (01833) 650213
F: (01833) 650828
E: hotel@rose-and-crown.co.uk
I: www.rose-and-crown.co.uk

BELFORD
Northumberland

Blue Bell Hotel ★★★
Market Place, Belford,
Northumberland NE70 7NE
T: (01668) 213543
F: (01668) 213787
E: bluebel@globalnet.co.uk

BELLINGHAM
Northumberland

Riverdale Hall Hotel ★★
Bellingham, Hexham,
Northumberland NE48 2JT
T: (01434) 220254
F: (01434) 220457
E: iben@riverdalehall.demon.co.
uk

BERWICK-UPON-TWEED
Northumberland

Kings Arms Hotel ★★
43 Hide Hill, Berwick-upon-
Tweed, Northumberland
TD15 1EJ
T: (01289) 307454
F: (01289) 308867
E: king's_arms.hotel@virgin.co.
uk

**Marshall Meadows Country
House Hotel ★★★**
Berwick-upon-Tweed,
Northumberland TD15 1UT
T: (01289) 331133
F: (01289) 331438
E: stay@marshallmeadows.co.
uk
I: www.marshallmeadows.co.uk

Queens Head Hotel ★
Sandgate, Berwick-upon-Tweed,
Northumberland TD15 1EP
T: (01289) 307852
F: (01289) 307858

BLANCHLAND
Northumberland

Lord Crewe Arms Hotel ★★
Blanchland, Consett, County
Durham DH8 9SP
T: (01434) 675251
F: (01434) 675337
E: lord@crewearms.freeserve.co.
uk
I: stay-at.
com/lordcrewe/welcome.html

CORBRIDGE
Northumberland

Angel Inn ★★
Main Street, Corbridge,
Northumberland NE45 5LA
T: (01434) 632119
F: (01434) 632119

Lion of Corbridge Hotel ★★
Bridge End, Corbridge,
Northumberland NE45 5AX
T: (01434) 632504
F: (01434) 632571
E: lionofcorbridge@talk21.com
I: freespace.virgin.net/rodeo.
visual/thelion.htm

CORNHILL-ON-TWEED
Northumberland

**Tillmouth Park Country House
Hotel ★★★ SILVER AWARD**
Cornhill-on-Tweed,
Northumberland TD12 4UU
T: (01890) 882255
F: (01890) 882540
E: igl@tillmouthpark.force9.co.
uk
I: www.tillmouthpark.co.uk

CROOK
Durham

Helme Park Hall Hotel ★★★
Fir Tree, Crook, County Durham
DL13 4NW
T: (01388) 730970
F: (01388) 730970

DARLINGTON
Durham

Blackwell Grange Hotel ★★★
Blackwell Grange, Darlington,
County Durham DL3 8QH
T: (01325) 509955
F: (01325) 380899
I: www.corushotels.com

Headlam Hall Hotel ★★★
Headlam, Gainford, Darlington,
County Durham DL2 3HA
T: (01325) 730238
F: (01325) 730790
E: admin@headlamhall.co.uk
I: www.headlamhall.co.uk

**The New Grange Hotel and
Maxine's Restaurant ★★**
Southend Avenue, Darlington,
County Durham DL3 7HZ
T: (01325) 365859 & 365858
F: (01325) 487111

**Newbus Arms Hotel and
Restaurant★★**
Newbus Arms, Neasham,
Darlington, County Durham
DL2 1PE
T: (01325) 721071
F: (01325) 721770

Quality Kings Head ★★★
Priestgate, Darlington, County
Durham DL1 1NW
T: (01325) 380222
F: (01325) 382006

St George Hotel ★★★
Teesside Airport, Darlington,
County Durham DL2 1RH
T: (01325) 332631
F: (01325) 333851

**Stanwick House Airport Hotel
★**
Stanwick House, Teesside
International Airport,
Darlington, County Durham
DL2 1PD
T: (01325) 333353
E: enquiries@stanwick-house.
co.uk
I: www.stanwick-house.co.uk

DURHAM
Durham

Bowburn Hall Hotel ★★★
Bowburn, Durham DH6 5NH
T: (0191) 377 0311
F: (0191) 377 3459

Hallgarth Manor Hotel ★★
Pittington, Durham DH6 1AB
T: (0191) 372 1188
F: (0191) 372 1249

Kensington Hall Hotel ★★
Kensington Terrace, Willington,
Crook, County Durham DL15 0PJ
T: (01388) 745071
F: (01388) 745800
E: kensingtonhall@cs.com
I: ourworld.cs.
com/kensingtonhall

**Lumley Castle Hotel
★★★ SILVER AWARD**
Chester-le-Street, County
Durham DH3 4NX
T: (0191) 389 1111
F: (0191) 389 1881
I: www.lumleycastle.com

The Newton Grange Hotel
Rating Applied For
Finchal Road, Brasside, Durham
DH1 5SA
T: (0191) 386 0872
F: (0191) 386 0872

Ramside Hall Hotel ★★★
Carrville, Durham DH1 1TD
T: (0191) 386 5282
F: (0191) 386 0399
E: ramsidehal@aol.com

**Royal County Hotel
★★★★ SILVER AWARD**
Old Elvet, Durham, DH1 3JN
T: (0191) 386 6821
F: (0191) 386 0704
E: royal.county@
swallow-hotels.co.uk
I: www.swallowhotels.com

EAGLESCLIFFE
Tees Valley

Sunnyside Hotel ★★
580-582 Yarm Road,
Eaglescliffe, Stockton-on-Tees,
Cleveland TS16 0DF
T: (01642) 780075
F: (01642) 783789

HARTLEPOOL
Tees Valley

Grand Hotel ★★★
Swainson Street, Hartlepool,
Cleveland TS24 8AA
T: (01429) 266345
F: (01429) 265217

307

Ryedale Moor Hotel ★★
3 Beaconsfield Street, Headland,
Hartlepool, Cleveland TS24 0NX
T: (01429) 231436 & 288051
F: (01429) 288053
E: ryedalemoore@hotelo.
demon.co.uk
I: www.hotel-hartlepool.co.uk

HEXHAM
Northumberland

Beaumont Hotel ★★★
Beaumont Street, Hexham,
Northumberland NE46 3LT
T: (01434) 602331
F: (01434) 606184
E: beaumont.hotel@btinternet.
com
I: www.beaumont-hotel.co.uk

Langley Castle ★★★
Langley-on-Tyne, Hexham,
Northumberland NE47 5LU
T: (01434) 688888
F: (01434) 684019
E: manager@langleycastle.com
I: www.langleycastle.com

HOLY ISLAND
Northumberland

Lindisfarne Hotel ★
Holy Island, Berwick-upon-
Tweed, Northumberland
TD15 2SQ
T: (01289) 389273
F: (01289) 389284

HOUGHTON-LE-SPRING
Tyne and Wear

**Chilton Lodge Country Pub &
Hotel★★**
Black Boy Road, Fencehouses,
Houghton-le-Spring, Tyne and
Wear DH4 6PY
T: (0191) 385 2694
F: (0191) 385 6762

KIRKWHELPINGTON
Northumberland

Knowesgate Inn ★★
Knowesgate, Kirkwhelpington,
Newcastle upon Tyne,
Northumberland NE19 2SH
T: (01830) 540336
F: (01830) 540449

LONGFRAMLINGTON
Northumberland

Embleton Hall ★★★
Longframlington, Morpeth,
Northumberland NE65 8DT
T: (01665) 570206 & 570249
F: (01665) 570056

MATFEN
Northumberland

Matfen Hall ★★★
Matfen, Newcastle upon Tyne
NE20 0RH
T: (01661) 886500
F: (01661) 886055
E: info@matfenhall.com
I: www.matfenhall.com

MIDDLESBROUGH
Tees Valley

Baltimore Hotel ★★★
250 Marton Road,
Middlesbrough, Cleveland
TS4 2EZ
T: (01642) 224111
F: (01642) 226156
E: info@lincoln-group.co.uk

TAD Centre ★★★
Ormesby Road, Middlesbrough,
Cleveland TS3 7SF
T: (01642) 203000
E: info@tad-centre.co.uk
I: www.tad-centre.co.uk

**Thistle Middlesbrough
Rating Applied For**
Fry Street, Middlesbrough,
Cleveland TS1 1JH
T: (01642) 232000
F: (01642) 232655

MORPETH
Northumberland

Linden Hall ★★★
Longhorsley, Morpeth,
Northumberland NE65 8XF
T: (01670) 500000
F: (01670) 500001
E: stay@lindenhall.co.uk
I: www.lindenhall.co.uk

Longhirst Hall ★★★
Longhirst, Morpeth,
Northumberland NE61 3LL
T: (01670) 791348
F: (01670) 791385
E: enquiries@longhirst.co.uk
I: www.longhirst.co.uk

NEWCASTLE UPON TYNE
Tyne and Wear

Cairn Hotel ★★
97-103 Osborne Road, Jesmond,
Newcastle upon Tyne NE2 2TJ
T: (0191) 281 1358
F: (0191) 281 9031
E: arvanhanda@aol.com
I: www.cairn-hotels.co.uk

Caledonian Hotel ★★★
Osborne Road, Jesmond,
Newcastle upon Tyne NE2 2AT
T: (0191) 281 7881
F: (0191) 281 6241
E: caledonian.hotel@lineone.net
I: www.peelhotel.com

Comfort Inn Carlton ★★
82-86 Osborne Road, Jesmond,
Newcastle upon Tyne NE2 2AP
T: (0191) 281 3361
F: (0191) 281 7722

**The Copthorne Newcastle
★★★★**
The Close, Quayside, Newcastle
upon Tyne, Tyne & Wear
NE1 3RT
T: (0191) 222 0333
F: (0191) 230 1111
E: sales.newcastle@mill-cop.
com
I: www.stay.with-us.com

Ferncourt ★★★
Osborne Road, Jesmond,
Newcastle upon Tyne NE2 2AJ
T: (0191) 281 5377 & 281 5418
F: (0191) 212 0783
I: www.ferncourthotel.co.uk

George Hotel ★★
88 Osborne Road, Jesmond,
Newcastle upon Tyne NE2 2AP
T: (0191) 281 4442 & 281 2943
F: (0191) 281 8300
E: georgehotel@dial.pipex.com

Grosvenor Hotel ★★
Grosvenor Road, Jesmond,
Newcastle upon Tyne NE2 2RR
T: (0191) 281 0543
F: (0191) 281 9217
E: info@grosvenor-hotel.com
I: www.grosvenor-hotel.com

Grove Hotel ★
134 Brighton Grove, Newcastle
upon Tyne, Tyne and Wear
NE4 5NT
T: (0191) 273 8248
F: (0191) 272 5649
I: www.grove-hotel.co.uk

Hadrian Lodge Hotel ★
Hadrian Road, Wallsend,
Newcastle upon Tyne, Tyne &
Wear NE28 6HH
T: (0191) 262 7733
F: (0191) 263 0714
I: www.hadrianlodgehotel.co.uk

Jarvis Springfield Hotel ★★★
Durham Road, Gateshead, Tyne
and Wear NE9 5BT
T: (0191) 477 4121
F: (0191) 477 7213
I: www.jarvis-co.uk

Kenilworth Hotel ★★
44 Osborne Road, Jesmond,
Newcastle upon Tyne NE2 2AL
T: (0191) 281 8111
F: (0191) 281 9476

New Kent Hotel ★★
127 Osborne Road, Jesmond,
Newcastle upon Tyne NE2 2TB
T: (0191) 281 7711
F: (0191) 281 3369

Novotel Newcastle ★★★
Ponteland Road, Kenton,
Newcastle upon Tyne NE3 3HZ
T: (0191) 214 0303
F: (0191) 214 0633
E: h1118@accor-hotels.com
I: www.novotel.com

Osborne Hotel ★★
13-15 Osborne Road, Jesmond,
Newcastle upon Tyne NE2 2AE
T: (0191) 281 3385
F: (0191) 281 7717

**Posthouse Newcastle upon
Tyne ★★★**
New Bridge Street, Newcastle
upon Tyne, Tyne and Wear
NE1 8BS
T: 08704 009 058
F: (0191) 222 0375
E: gm1727@forte-hotels.com
I: www.posthouse-hotels.co.uk

Royal Station Hotel ★★★
Neville Street, Newcastle upon
Tyne, Tyne and Wear NE1 5DH
T: (0191) 232 0781
F: (0191) 222 0786
E: royalsttn@hotmail.com
I: www.cairn-hotels.co.uk

**Ryton Park Country House
Hotel ★★**
Holburn Lane, Ryton, Tyne and
Wear NE40 3PF
T: (0191) 413 3535
F: (0191) 413 6582

Surtees Hotel Ltd
★★★ SILVER AWARD
12-16 Dean Street, Newcastle
upon Tyne, NE1 1PG
T: (0191) 261 7771
F: (0191) 230 1322
I: www.scoot.co.uk/surteeshotel

Swallow Gosforth Park Hotel
★★★★ SILVER AWARD
High Gosforth Park, Newcastle
upon Tyne, NE3 5HN
T: (0191) 236 4111
F: (0191) 236 8192

**Thistle Newcastle
Rating Applied For**
Neville Street, Newcastle upon
Tyne, NE99 1AH
T: (0191) 232 2471
F: (0191) 232 1285
E: newcastle@thistle.co.uk

Whites Hotel ★★
38-42 Osborne Road, Jesmond,
Newcastle upon Tyne NE2 2AL
T: (0191) 281 5126
F: (0191) 281 9953
E: WhitesHotel@aol.com

NEWTON AYCLIFFE
Darlington

Redworth Hall
★★★★ SILVER AWARD
Redworth, Newton Aycliffe,
County Durham DL5 6NL
T: (01388) 772442
F: (01388) 775112
E: redworthhall@
paramount-hotels.co.uk
I: www.paramount.hotels.co.uk

OTTERBURN
Northumberland

Percy Arms Hotel ★★
Otterburn, Newcastle upon Tyne
NE19 1NR
T: (01830) 520261
F: (01830) 520567
E: percyarms@bestwestern.co.
uk

The Tower
★★★ SILVER AWARD
Otterburn, Newcastle upon Tyne
NE19 1NS
T: (01830) 520620
F: (01830) 520620
E: reservations@
otterburntower.co.uk
I: www.otterburntower.co.uk

RYTON
Tyne and Wear

**Hedgefield Country House
Hotel ★**
Old Hexham Road, Ryton, Tyne
and Wear NE21 4LU
T: (0191) 413 2921
F: (0191) 413 6356

SALTBURN-BY-THE-SEA
Tees Valley

Grinkle Park Hotel ★★★
Easington-Loftus, Saltburn-by-
the-Sea, Cleveland TS13 4UB
T: (01287) 640515
F: (01287) 641278
E: grinkle.parkhotel@bass.com
I: www.grinklepark.co.uk

Establishments printed in blue have a detailed entry in this guide

Hunley Hall Golf Club and Hotel ★★
Brotton, Saltburn-by-the-Sea, North Yorkshire TS12 2QQ
T: (01287) 676216
F: (01287) 678250
E: enquiries@hunleyhall.co.uk
I: www.hunleyhall.com

SEAHOUSES
Northumberland
Bamburgh Castle Hotel ★★
Seahouses, Northumberland NE68 7SQ
T: (01665) 720283
F: (01665) 720848
I: www.bamburghcastlehotel.ntb.org.uk
⊚

Beach House Hotel ★★
Sea Front, Seahouses, Northumberland NE68 7SR
T: (01665) 720337
F: (01665) 720921
E: beach.house.hotel.seahouses@tinyonline.co.uk
I: www.beachhousehotel.co.uk

Links Hotel ★★
8 King Street, Seahouses, Northumberland NE68 7XP
T: (01665) 720062
F: (01665) 721305
E: linkshotel@supanet.com
I: www.smoothhound.co.uk/hotels/links4.html

Longstone House Hotel ★★
182 Main Street, Seahouses, Northumberland NE68 7UA
T: (01665) 720212

Olde Ship Hotel ★★
Seahouses, Northumberland NE68 7RD
T: (01665) 720200
F: (01665) 721383
E: theoldeship@seahouses.co.uk
I: www.smoothhound.co.uk/hotels/oldeship.htmlwww.seahouses.co.uk
⊚

SEATON CAREW
Tees Valley
The Staincliffe Hotel ★★★
The Cliff, Seaton Carew, Hartlepool, Cleveland TS25 1AB
T: (01429) 264301
F: (01429) 421366
⊚

SEDGEFIELD
Durham
Hardwick Hall Hotel ★★★
Sedgefield, Stockton-on-Tees, Cleveland TS21 2EH
T: (01740) 620253
F: (01740) 622771

SLALEY
Northumberland
De Vere Slaley Hall
★★★★ SILVER AWARD
Slaley, Hexham, Northumberland NE47 0BY
T: (01434) 673350
F: (01434) 673962
E: slaley.hall@devere-hotels.com
I: www.devere.com
⊚

SOUTH SHIELDS
Tyne and Wear
Little Haven Hotel ★★★
River Drive, Littlehaven, South Shields, Tyne and Wear NE33 1LH
T: (0191) 455 4455
F: (0191) 455 4466

Sea Hotel ★★★
Sea Road, South Shields, Tyne and Wear NE33 2LD
T: (0191) 427 0999
F: (0191) 454 0500
E: seahotel@fsmail.net
I: www.seahotel.co.uk

SPENNYMOOR
Durham
Whitworth Hall Hotel ★★★
Whitworth Hall Estates Ltd., Stanners Lane, Spennymoor, County Durham DL16 7QX
T: (01388) 811772
F: (01388) 818669
E: hotel@whithall.freeserve.co.uk
I: www.infotel.co.uk/hotels/21281.htm
⊚

STOCKTON-ON-TEES
Tees Valley
Parkmore Hotel and Leisure Club ★★★
636 Yarm Road, Eaglescliffe, Stockton-on-Tees, Cleveland TS16 0DH
T: (01642) 786815
F: (01642) 790485
E: enquiries@parkmorehotel.co.uk
I: www.parkmorehotel.co.uk
⊚

SUNDERLAND
Tyne and Wear
George Washington County Hotel Golf & Country Club ★★★
Stone Cellar Road, High Usworth, District 12, Washington, Tyne and Wear NE37 1PH
T: (0191) 402 9988
F: (0191) 415 1166

Mowbray Park Hotel ★★
Borough Road, Sunderland, SR1 1PR
T: (0191) 567 8221
F: (0191) 510 2572
E: reception@mowbray-park-hotel.co.uk
I: mowbray-park-hotel.co.uk

Quality Hotel ★★★
Junction A19/A184, Witney Way, Boldon, Sunderland, Tyne & Wear NE35 9PE
T: (0191) 519 1999
F: (0191) 519 0655
E: admin@gb621.u-net.com
I: www.choicehotelseurope.com
⊚ &

Quinceys Premier Lodge Rating Applied For
Timber Beach Road, Off Wessington Road, Sunderland, SR5 3XG
T: (0191) 516 9009
F: (0191) 549 8669

Swallow Hotel
★★★★ SILVER AWARD
Queens Parade, Seaburn, Sunderland, Tyne & Wear SR6 8DB
T: (0191) 529 2041
F: (0191) 529 4227
E: sunderland@swallow-hotels.co.uk
⊚ 🐾

THORNABY
Tees Valley
Posthouse Teesside ★★★
Low Lane, Stainton Village, Thornaby, Stockton-on-Tees, Cleveland TS17 9LW
T: 0870 400 9081
F: (01642) 594989
E: gm1221@forte-hotels.com

TYNEMOUTH
Tyne and Wear
Grand Hotel ★★★
Grand Parade, Tynemouth, North Shields, Tyne and Wear NE30 4ER
T: (0191) 293 6666
F: (0191) 293 6665
E: info@grand-hotel.demon.co.uk
I: www.grand-hotel.demon.co.uk

WARK
Northumberland
Black Bull Hotel
Rating Applied For
Main Street, Wark, Hexham, Northumberland NE48 3LG
T: (01434) 230239
F: (01434) 230239

WARKWORTH
Northumberland
Sun Hotel ★★
6 Castle Terrace, Warkworth, Alnwick, Northumberland NE65 0UP
T: (01665) 711259
F: (01665) 711833

Warkworth House Hotel ★★
16 Bridge Street, Warkworth, Morpeth, Northumberland NE65 0XB
T: (01665) 711276
F: (01665) 713323
E: welcome@warkworthhousehotel.co.uk
I: www.warkworthhousehotel.co.uk
⊚ &

WASHINGTON
Tyne and Wear
Posthouse Washington ★★★
Emerson District 5, Washington, Tyne and Wear NE37 1LB
T: 0870 400 9084
F: (0191) 415 3371
E: gm1232@forte-hotels.com
I: www.posthouse-hotels.com

WEST AUCKLAND
Durham
Manor House Hotel and Country Club ★★★
The Green, Front Street, West Auckland, Bishop Auckland, County Durham DL14 9HW
T: (01388) 834834
F: (01388) 833566

WEST RAINTON
Durham
Rainton Lodge Hotel ★★
West Rainton, Houghton-le-Spring, Tyne and Wear DH4 6QY
T: (0191) 512 0540
F: (0191) 584 1221

WHICKHAM
Tyne and Wear
Gibside Hotel ★★★
Front Street, Whickham, Newcastle upon Tyne NE16 4JG
T: (0191) 488 9292
F: (0191) 488 8000
E: reception@gibside-hotel.co.uk
I: www.gibside-hotel.co.uk

WHITLEY BAY
Tyne and Wear
Avalon Hotel ★★
26 South Parade, Whitley Bay, Tyne and Wear NE26 2RG
T: (0191) 251 0080
F: (0191) 251 0100
E: reception@avalon-hotel.freeserve.co.uk
I: www.avalon-hotel.freeserve.co.uk

The Esplanade Hotel ★★
The Esplanade, Whitley Bay, Tyne and Wear NE26 2AW
T: (0191) 252 1111
F: (0191) 252 0101
E: esplanade.hotel@btinternet.com
I: www.esplanade-hotel.freeserve.co.uk

High Point Hotel ★★
The Promenade, Whitley Bay, Tyne and Wear NE26 2NJ
T: (0191) 251 7782
F: (0191) 251 6318
E: highpointhotel@aol.com

Park Lodge Hotel ★★
162-164 Park Avenue, Whitley Bay, Tyne and Wear NE26 1AU
T: (0191) 252 6879 & 253 0288
F: (0191) 297 1006
E: parklodgehotel@hotmail.com
I: www.theparklodgehotel.co.uk

Rex Hotel ★★★
The Promenade, Whitley Bay, Tyne and Wear NE26 2RL
T: (0191) 252 3201
F: (0191) 251 4663
E: rex-hotel.freeserve.co.uk
I: www.rex-hotel.freeserve.co.uk

Windsor Hotel ★★★
South Parade, Whitley Bay, Tyne and Wear NE26 2RF
T: (0191) 2518888
F: (0191) 2970272
E: info@windsor-hotel.demon.co.uk

WOOLER
Northumberland
Tankerville Arms Hotel
★★ SILVER AWARD
22 Cottage Road, Wooler, Northumberland NE71 6AD
T: (01668) 281581
F: (01668) 281387
E: tankervillehotel.co.uk
I: www.tankervillehotel.co.uk
⊚

NORTH WEST

ALDERLEY EDGE
Cheshire
The Alderley Edge Hotel
★★★ SILVER AWARD
Macclesfield Road, Alderley
Edge, Cheshire SK9 7BJ
T: (01625) 583033
F: (01625) 586343
E: sales@alderley-edge-hotel.
co.uk
I: www.alderley-edge-hotel.co.
uk

ALSAGER
Cheshire
The Manor House Hotel ★★★
Audley Road, Alsager, Stoke-on-
Trent, Cheshire ST7 2QQ
T: (01270) 884000
F: (01270) 882483
E: mmres@compassmotels.co.
uk
I: www.compasshotels.co.uk

ALTRINCHAM
Greater Manchester
Cresta Court Hotel ★★★
Church Street, Altrincham,
Cheshire WA14 4DP
T: (0161) 927 7272
F: (0161) 926 9194
E: info@cresta-court.co.uk
I: www.cresta-court.co.uk

Oasis Hotel ★★
46-48 Barrington Road,
Altrincham, Cheshire WA14 1HN
T: (0161) 928 4523 & 929 9046
F: (0161) 928 1055
E: enquiries@oasishotel.co.uk
I: www.oasishotel.co.uk

Woodland Park Hotel ★★★
Wellington Road, Timperley,
Altrincham, Cheshire WA15 7RG
T: (0161) 928 8631
F: (0161) 941 2821
E: info@woodlandpark.co.uk
I: www.woodlandpark.co.uk

BIRKENHEAD
Merseyside
Central Hotel ★
Clifton Crescent, Birkenhead,
Merseyside CH41 2QH
T: (0151) 647 6347 &
07989 881331
F: (0151) 647 5476

Riverhill Hotel
Rating Applied For
Talbot Road, Oxton, Birkenhead,
Merseyside CH43 2HJ
T: (0151) 653 3773
F: (0151) 653 7162

BLACKBURN
Lancashire
Northcote Manor Hotel
★★★ GOLD AWARD
Northcote Road, Old Langho,
Blackburn BB6 8BE
T: (01254) 240555
F: (01254) 246568
E: admin@ncotemanor.demon.
co.uk
I: ncotemanor.demon.co.uk

BLACKPOOL
Lancashire
The Bond Hotel ★★
112-120 Bond Street, Blackpool,
FY4 1HG
T: (01253) 341218
F: (01253) 349452
E: reception@bondhotel.co.uk
I: www.bondhotel.co.uk

Brabyns Hotel ★★
1-5 Shaftesbury Avenue,
Blackpool, FY2 9QQ
T: (01253) 354263 & 352163
F: (01253) 352915
E: brabynshotel@
netscapeonline.co.uk

Carlton Hotel ★★
282-286 North Promenade,
Blackpool, FY1 2EZ
T: (01253) 628966 & 621494
F: (01253) 752587

Doric Hotel ★★
48-52 Queens Promenade,
Blackpool, FY2 9RP
T: (01253) 352640 & 351751
F: (01253) 596842
E: info@dorichotel-blackpool.
net
I: dorichotel.blackpool.net

The Headlands ★★
611-613 South Promenade,
Blackpool, FY4 1NJ
T: (01253) 341179
F: (01253) 342047
E: headland@blackpool.net
I: www.theheadlands.blackpool.
net

New Mayfair ★★
673-677 New South Promenade,
Blackpool, Lancashire FY4 1RN
T: (01253) 347543
F: (01253) 349678

Park House Hotel ★★
308 North Promenade,
Blackpool, FY1 2HA
T: (01253) 620081
F: (01253) 290181

Ruskin Hotel ★★
Albert Road, Blackpool, FY1 4PW
T: (01253) 624063
F: (01253) 623571
E: ruskinhotel@aol.com
I: ruskinhotel.com

St Chads Hotel ★★
317-327 Promenade, Blackpool,
FY1 6BN
T: (01253) 346348 & 344669
F: (01253) 348240

Savoy Hotel ★★★
Queens Promenade, Blackpool,
FY2 9SJ
T: (01253) 352561
F: (01253) 595549

Shellard Hotel ★
18-20 Dean Street, Blackpool,
FY4 1AU
T: (01253) 342679
F: (01253) 342433
E: robert@shellardhotel.
freeserve.co.uk
I: www.shellardhotel.freeserve.
co.uk

Stretton Hotel ★★
206-214 North Promenade,
Blackpool, FY1 1RU
T: (01253) 625688
F: (01253) 624075
E: strettonhotel@btconnect.
com
I: www.strettonhotel.co.uk

BOLTON
Greater Manchester
Bolton Moat House ★★★
1 Higher Bridge Street, Bolton,
Greater Manchester BL1 2EW
T: (01204) 879988
F: (01204) 380777
E: cbbol@queensmoat.co.uk

Jarvis International Hotel
★★★
Manchester Road, Blackrod,
Bolton BL6 5RU
T: (01942) 814598
F: (01942) 816026

Last Drop Village Hotel
★★★★
Hospital Road, Bromley Cross,
Bolton BL7 9PZ
T: (01204) 591131
F: (01204) 304122
E: info@lastdrop.
macdonald-hotels.co.uk
I: www.macdonaldhotels.co.uk

BROMBOROUGH
Merseyside
Village Hotel and Leisure Club
★★★
Pool Lane, Bromborough, Wirral,
Merseyside CH62 4UE
T: (0151) 643 1616
F: (0151) 643 1420
E: tom.hendry@village-hotels.
com
I: www.vlh.co.uk

BURNLEY
Lancashire
Alexander Hotel ★★
2 Tarleton Avenue, Todmorden
Road, Burnley, Lancashire
BB11 3ET
T: (01282) 422684
F: (01282) 424094
E: phleisure@aol.com
I: www.thealexanderhotel.co.uk

Sparrowhawk Hotel ★★★
Church Street, Burnley,
Lancashire BB11 2DN
T: (01282) 421551
F: (01282) 456506
I: www.sparrowhawkhotel.co.uk

BURWARDSLEY
Cheshire
The Pheasant Inn ★★
Higher Burwardsley, Tattenhall,
Chester CH3 9PF
T: (01829) 770434
F: (01829) 771097
E: dave1pheas@aol.com
I: www.trad-inns.co.uk

BURY
Greater Manchester
**The Old Mill Hotel and
Restaurant**★★
Springwood, Ramsbottom, Bury,
Lancashire BL0 9DS
T: (01706) 822991
F: (01706) 822291
E: oldmill.hot@netscapeonline.
co.uk

Red Hall Hotel & Restaurant
★★★
Manchester Road, Walmersley,
Bury, Lancashire BL9 5NA
T: (01706) 822476
F: (01706) 828086
I: www.redhall.co.uk

CARNFORTH
Lancashire
The County Hotel and Lodge
★★
Lancaster Road, Carnforth,
Lancashire LA5 9LD
T: (01524) 732469
F: (01524) 720142
E: info@thecountyhotel.co.uk
I: www.thecountyhotel.co.uk

Royal Station Hotel ★★
Market Street, Carnforth,
Lancashire LA5 9BT
T: (01524) 732033 & 733636
F: (01524) 720267
E: j.thornber@arol.com

CASTLETON
Greater Manchester
The Royal Toby Hotel ★★★
Manchester Road, Castleton,
Rochdale, Lancashire OL11 3HF
T: (01706) 861861
F: (01706) 869428

CHESTER
Cheshire
Abbey Court Hotel ★★
Liverpool Road, Chester,
CH2 1AG
T: (01244) 374100
F: (01244) 379240
I: www.macdonaldhotels.co.
uk/abbeycourthotel/

**Carden Park Hotel Golf Resort
Spa** ★★★★ SILVER AWARD
Carden Park, Chester, Cheshire
CH3 9DQ
T: (01829) 731000
F: (01829) 731032
E: reservations@cardenpark.co.
uk
I: www.cardenpark.co.uk

The Chester Grosvenor
★★★★★ GOLD AWARD
Eastgate, Chester, CH1 1LT
T: (01244) 324024 & 895614
F: (01244) 313246
E: chesgrov@chestergrosvenor.
co.uk
I: www.chestergrosvenor.co.uk

Chester Moat House ★★★★
Trinity Street, Chester, CH1 2BD
T: (01244) 899988
F: (01244) 316118
E: revchs@queensmoat.co.uk
I: www.moathousehotels.com

Establishments printed in blue have a detailed entry in this guide

Crabwall Manor Hotel and Restaurant
★★★★ SILVER AWARD
Parkgate Road, Mollington, Chester CH1 6NE
T: (01244) 851666
F: (01244) 851400
E: louise@crabwall.com
I: www.crabwall.com

Curzon Hotel ★★
52-54 Hough Green, Chester, CH4 8JQ
T: (01244) 678581
F: (01244) 680866
E: curzon.chester@virgin.net
I: www.chestercurzonhotel.co.uk

Dene Hotel ★★
Hoole Road, Chester, CH2 3ND
T: (01244) 321165
F: (01244) 350277
E: denehotel@btconnect.com
I: www.denehotel.com
◉ ⛗

Green Bough Hotel and Restaurant
★★★ SILVER AWARD
60 Hoole Road, Chester, CH2 3NL
T: (01244) 326241 & 07710 353370
F: (01244) 326265
E: greenboughhotel@cwcom.net
I: www.smoothhound.co.uk/hotels/greenbo.html
◉ ⛗

Grosvenor-Pulford Hotel
★★★
Wrexham Road, Pulford, Chester CH4 9DG
T: (01244) 570560
F: (01244) 570809
E: enquiries@grosvenorpulfordhotel.co.uk
I: www.grosvenorpulfordhotel.co.uk

The Limes Hotel
Rating Applied For
12 Hoole Road, Hoole, Chester CH2 3NJ
T: (01244) 328239
F: 07968 404105
E: rhowardbraydon@btinternet.com

Mollington Banastre Hotel
★★★★
Parkgate Road, Mollington, Chester CH1 6NN
T: (01244) 851471
F: (01244) 851242

Queen Hotel ★★★★
City Road, Chester, CH1 3AH
T: (01244) 305000
F: (01244) 318483
E: richard.hopson-cossey@principalhotels.co.uk
I: www.principalhotels.co.uk

Hotel Romano ★★★
51 Lower Bridge Street, Chester, CH1 1RS
T: (01244) 325091 & 320841
F: (01244) 315628

Rowton Hall Hotel ★★★
Whitchurch Road, Rowton, Chester CH3 6AD
T: (01244) 335262
F: (01244) 335464
E: rowtonhall@rowtonhall.co.uk
⛗

Stafford Hotel ★★
City Road, Chester, CH1 3AE
T: (01244) 326052 & 302695
F: (01244) 311403
E: stafhotel.l@aol.com

Westminster Hotel ★★
City Road, Chester, CH1 3AF
T: (01244) 317341
F: (01244) 325369
E: westminsterhotel@feathers.uk.com
I: www.feathers.uk.com

CHIPPING
Lancashire

Gibbon Bridge Hotel
★★★★ SILVER AWARD
Chipping, Preston PR3 2TQ
T: (01995) 61456
F: (01995) 61277
E: reception@gibbon-bridge.co.uk
I: www.gibbon-bridge.co.uk
◉ ⛗

CHORLEY
Lancashire

Park Hall Hotel, Leisure and Conference Centre★★★
Park Hall Road, Charnock Richard, Chorley, Preston PR7 5LP
T: (01257) 452090 & 455000
F: (01257) 451838
E: conf@parkhall-hotel.co.uk
I: www.parkhall-hotel.co.uk
◉

CLAYTON-LE-MOORS
Lancashire

Sparth House Hotel ★★★
Whalley Road, Clayton-le-Moors, Accrington, Lancashire BB5 5RP
T: (01254) 872263
F: (01254) 872263
◉

CLITHEROE
Lancashire

Shireburn Arms Hotel ★★
Whalley Road, Hurst Green, Clitheroe, Lancashire BB7 9QJ
T: (01254) 826518
F: (01254) 826208
E: sales@shireburn-hotel.co.uk
I: www.shireburn-hotel.co.uk

DARWEN
Lancashire

Astley Bank ★★★
Bolton Road, Darwen, Blackburn, Lancashire BB3 2QB
T: (01254) 777700
F: (01254) 777707

Whitehall Hotel & Country Club★★★
Spring Bank, Whitehall, Darwen, Lancashire BB3 2JU
T: (01254) 701595
F: (01254) 773426
E: hotel@thewhitehallhotel.freeserve.co.uk

ECCLES
Greater Manchester

Wendover Hotel ★★
118 Monton Road, Monton, Eccles, Manchester M30 9HG
T: (0161) 789 7811
F: (0161) 787 7609
E: wendover.hotel@virgin.net
I: www.wendover-hotel.co.uk

FLEETWOOD
Lancashire

North Euston Hotel
★★★ SILVER AWARD
Esplanade, Fleetwood, Lancashire FY7 6BN
T: (01253) 876525
F: (01253) 777842
E: admin@northeustonhotel.co.uk
I: www.northeustonhotel.co.uk

FORMBY
Merseyside

Tree Tops Restaurant and Hotel
★★★
Southport Old Road, Formby, Merseyside L37 0AB
T: (01704) 572430
F: (01704) 572430

FRODSHAM
Cheshire

Forest Hills Hotel ★★★
Overton Hill, Frodsham, Warrington, Cheshire WA6 6HH
T: (01928) 735255
F: (01928) 735517
E: info@foresthillshotel.com
I: www.foresthillshotel.com
◉

GARSTANG
Lancashire

Crofters Hotel ★★★
A6, Cabus, Garstang, Preston PR3 1PH
T: (01995) 604128
F: (01995) 601646

Garstang Country Hotel and Golf Club★★★
Garstang Road, Bowgreave, Garstang, Preston PR3 1YE
T: (01995) 600100
F: (01995) 600950
E: reception@garstanghotelandgolf.co.uk
I: www.garstanghotelandgolf.co.uk

GISBURN
Lancashire

Stirk House Hotel ★★★
Gisburn, Clitheroe, Lancashire BB7 4LJ
T: (01200) 445581
F: (01200) 445744
E: stirk-house@hotmail.com

HAYDOCK
Merseyside

Thistle Haydock ★★★★
Penny Lane, Haydock, St Helens, Merseyside WA11 9SG
T: (01942) 272000
F: (01942) 711092
E: haydock@thistle.co.uk
I: www.thistlehotels.com
◉

HEYWOOD
Greater Manchester

Birch Hotel ★★
Manchester Road, Birch, Heywood, Lancashire OL10 2QD
T: (01706) 360965 & 366137
F: (01706) 621000
E: thebirch@globalnet.co.uk
I: www.hotels-manchester.co.uk

HOYLAKE
Merseyside

King's Gap Court Hotel ★
The King's Gap, Hoylake, Wirral, Merseyside CH47 1HE
T: (0151) 632 2073
F: (0151) 632 0247
E: kingsgapcourt@aol.com
I: www.scoot.co.uk/kings-gap/
◉

KNUTSFORD
Cheshire

Longview Hotel and Restaurant★★
Manchester Road, Knutsford, Cheshire WA16 0LX
T: (01565) 632119
F: (01565) 652402
E: longview_hotel@compuserve.com
I: www.longviewhotel@freeserve.com

Mere Court Hotel ★★★★
Mere, Knutsford, Cheshire WA16 0RW
T: (01565) 831000
F: (01565) 831001
E: sales@merecourt.co.uk
I: www.merecourt.co.uk
◉

LANCASTER
Lancashire

The Greaves Hotel ★★
Greaves Road, Lancaster, LA1 4UW
T: (01524) 63943
F: (01524) 382679

Hampson House Hotel ★★
Hampson Lane, Hampson Green, Lancaster, LA2 0JB
T: (01524) 751158 & 751189
F: (01524) 751779

Scarthwaite Hotel ★
Crook O'Lune, Caton, Lancaster LA2 9HR
T: (01524) 770267
F: (01524) 770711

Thurnham Mill Hotel ★★
Thurnham, Lancaster LA2 0BD
T: (01524) 752852
F: (01524) 752477
⛗

LANGHO
Lancashire

Mytton Fold Hotel and Golf Complex ★★★
Whalley Road, Langho, Blackburn BB6 8AB
T: (01254) 240662
F: (01254) 248119
E: mytton_fold.hotel@virgin.net
I: www.smoothhound.co.uk/hotels/mytton.html
⛗

LEIGH
Greater Manchester

Jarvis Greyhound Hotel ★★
Warrington Road, Leigh, Lancashire WN7 3XQ
T: (01942) 671256
F: (01942) 261949
I: www.jarvis.co.uk

LEYLAND
Lancashire

Jarvis Leyland Hotel ★★
Leyland Way, Leyland, Preston PR5 2JX
T: (01772) 422922
F: (01772) 622282

LIVERPOOL
Merseyside

The Devonshire House Hotel and Conference Centre★★★
293-297 Edge Lane, Liverpool, L7 9LD
T: (0151) 264 6600
F: (0151) 263 2109
E: sales@devonshirehousehotel.co.uk
I: www.devonshirehousehotel.co.uk

Gateacre Hall Hotel ★★★
The Nook, Halewood Road, Liverpool, L25 5PG
T: (0151) 428 6322
F: (0151) 428 4302

Green Park Hotel ★
4-6 Green Bank Drive, Liverpool, L17 1AW
T: (0151) 733 3382
F: (0151) 734 1161

Liverpool Moat House ★★★★
Paradise Street, Liverpool, L1 8JD
T: (0151) 471 9988 & 709 1937
F: (0151) 709 2706
⊛

Park Hotel ★★
Dunningsbridge Road, Netherton, Liverpool L30 6YN
T: (0151) 525 7555
F: (0151) 525 2481
E: enquiries@parkhotelliverpool.co.uk
I: www.parkhotelliverpool.co.uk

Rockland Hotel ★
View Road, Rainhill, Prescot, Merseyside L35 0LG
T: (0151) 426 4603
F: (0151) 426 0107

Royal Hotel ★
Marine Terrace, Waterloo, Liverpool L22 5PR
T: (0151) 928 2332
F: (0151) 949 0320
E: royalhotel@compuserve.com
I: www.s-h-systems.co.uk/hotels/royal

Thistle Liverpool
Rating Applied For
Chapel Street, Liverpool, L3 9RE
T: (0151) 227 4444
F: (0151) 236 3973
E: liverpool@cix.co.uk

LONGRIDGE
Lancashire

Ferraris Country House Limited Hotel & Restaurant★★
Chipping Road, Thornley, Longridge, Preston PR3 2TB
T: (01772) 783148
F: (01772) 786174
E: alferrari@compuserve.com
⊛

LYMM
Cheshire

Statham Lodge Country House Hotel ★★★
Warrington Road, Statham, Lymm, Cheshire WA13 9BP
T: (01925) 752204
F: (01925) 757406
E: statham_lodge@btconnect.com
I: www.statham-lodge.co.uk

LYTHAM ST ANNES
Lancashire

Chadwick Hotel ★★★
South Promenade, Lytham St Annes, Lancashire FY8 1NP
T: (01253) 720061
F: (01253) 714455
E: sales@chadwickhotel.com
I: www.chadwickhotel.com
🏃

Clifton Arms Hotel ★★★★
West Beach, Lytham St Annes, Lancashire FY8 5QJ
T: (01253) 739898 & 730657
F: (01253) 730657
E: info@cliftonarms.demon.co.uk
I: www.@cliftonarms.demon.co.uk

Dalmeny Hotel ★★★
19-33 South Promenade, Lytham St Annes, Lancashire FY8 1LX
T: (01253) 712236
F: (01253) 724447
E: info@dalmenyhotel.com
I: www.dalmenyhotel.com

The Grand Hotel ★★★
South Promenade, Lytham St Annes, Lancashire FY8 1NB
T: (01253) 721288 & 0800 731 2208
F: (01253) 714459
E: book@the-grand.co.uk
I: www.the-grand.co.uk
⊛

Langdales Hotel ★★
318-328 Clifton Drive North, Lytham St Annes, Lancashire FY8 2PB
T: (01253) 721342
F: (01253) 729517

Lindum Hotel ★★
63-67 South Promenade, Lytham St Annes, Lancashire FY8 1LZ
T: (01253) 721534 & 722516
F: (01253) 721364
E: info@lindumhotel.co.uk
I: www.lindomhotel.co.uk

St Ives Hotel ★★
7 South Promenade, Lytham St Annes, Lancashire FY8 1LS
T: (01253) 720011
F: (01253) 722873

MACCLESFIELD
Cheshire

Shrigley Hall Hotel Golf and Country Club★★★★
Shrigley Park, Pott Shrigley, Macclesfield, Cheshire SK10 5SB
T: (01625) 575757
F: (01625) 573323
E: shrigleyhall@paramount-hotels.co.uk
I: www.paramount-hotels.co.uk

MANCHESTER
Greater Manchester

Albany Hotel ★★
21 Albany Road, Chorlton-cum-Hardy, Manchester, M21 0AY
T: (0161) 881 6774
F: (0161) 862 9405

Castlefield Hotel ★★★
Liverpool Road, Castlefield, Manchester, M3 4JR
T: (0161) 832 7073
F: (0161) 839 0326
E: info@castlefield-hotel.co.uk
I: www.castlefield-hotel.co.uk
⊛

Copthorne Manchester ★★★★ SILVER AWARD
Clippers Quay, Salford Quays, Manchester, M5 2XP
T: (0161) 873 7321
F: (0161) 873 7318
E: manchester@mill-cop.com
I: www.mill-cop.com

Crowne Plaza Manchester–The Midland ★★★★ SILVER AWARD
Peter Street, Manchester, M60 2DS
T: (0161) 236 3333
F: (0161) 932 4100
E: sales@mhccl.demon.co.uk
I: www.crowneplaza.com
⊛

Elm Grange Hotel ★
559-561 Wilmslow Road, Withington, Manchester M20 4GJ
T: (0161) 445 3336
F: (0161) 445 3336
E: elmgrange.hotel@tvc.org.uk
I: www.hotelmanchester.com

Gardens Hotel ★★★
55 Piccadilly, Manchester, M1 2AP
T: (0161) 236 5155
F: (0161) 228 7287
E: gardens@hotmail.com

Jurys Manchester Inn ★★★
56 Great Bridgewater Street, Manchester, M1 5LE
T: (0161) 953 8888
F: (0161) 953 9090
I: www.jurys.com

Manchester Conference Centre and Hotel★★★
The Weston Building, Sackville Street, Manchester, M1 3BB
T: (0161) 955 8000
F: (0161) 955 8050
E: weston@umist.ac.uk
I: www.meeting.co.uk

Novotel Manchester West ★★★
Worsley Brow, Worsley, Manchester M28 2YA
T: (0161) 799 3535
F: (0161) 703 8207
E: h0907@accor-hotels.com
I: www.novotel.com
♿

The Palace Hotel ★★★★
Oxford Street, Manchester, M60 7HA
T: (0161) 288 1111
F: (0161) 288 2222
I: www.principalhotels.co.uk

Princess Hotel ★★★
101 Portland Street, Manchester, M1 6DF
T: (0161) 236 5122
F: (0161) 236 4468
E: admin@princesshotels.co.uk
I: www.scoot.co.uk/princess-hotel

Quality Hotel Manchester ★★★ SILVER AWARD
Waters Reach, Trafford Park, Manchester, M17 1WS
T: (0161) 873 8899
F: (0161) 872 6556
E: info@qualitymanchester.co.uk
I: www.qualitymanchester.co.uk

Radisson SAS Hotel Manchester Airport★★★★
Chicago Avenue, Manchester Airport, Manchester, M90 3RA
T: (0161) 490 5000
F: (0161) 490 5100
E: sales@manzq.rdsas.com
I: www.radissonsas.com

Swallow Four Seasons ★★★★
Manchester Airport, Hale Road, Halebarns, Altrincham, Cheshire WA15 8XW
T: (0161) 904 0301
F: (0161) 980 1787
E: sfsh@lineone.net
I: www.swallowhotels.com

Thistle Manchester ★★★★
3-5 Portland Street, Piccadilly Gardens, Manchester, M1 6DP
T: (0161) 228 3400
F: (0161) 228 6347
E: sales.manchester@thistle.co.uk
I: www.thistlehotels.com
⊛

Village Leisure Hotel ★★★
George Street, Sedgley Park, Prestwich, Manchester M25 9WS
T: (0161) 798 8905
F: (0161) 773 5562
E: village.prestwich@village-hotels.com
I: www.vlh.co.uk

The Waterside Hotel and Galleon Leisure Club★★★
Wilmslow Road, Didsbury, Manchester, M20 5WZ
T: (0161) 445 0225
F: (0161) 446 2090
E: office@watersidehotel.co.uk
I: www.watersidehotel.co.uk
🏃

MAWDESLEY
Lancashire

Mawdsleys Eating House and Hotel★★★
Hall Lane, Mawdesley, Ormskirk, Lancashire L40 2QZ
T: (01704) 822552 & 821874
F: (01704) 822096
E: mawdsleyeh@aol.com
I: www.mawdsleyeh.co.uk

MIDDLEWICH
Cheshire

The Kinderton House Hotel ★★
Kinderton Street, Middlewich, Cheshire CW10 0JE
T: (01606) 834325
F: (01606) 834325

MORECAMBE
Lancashire

The Auckland Hotel ★★
313-315 Marine Road, Central Promenade, Morecambe, Lancashire LA4 5AA
T: (01524) 412565
F: (01524) 400862

Establishments printed in blue have a detailed entry in this guide

Broadway Hotel ★★
East Promenade, Morecambe,
Lancashire LA4 5AR
T: (01524) 410777
F: (01524) 417573
I: www.morecambe.
net/broadwayhotel

Clarendon Hotel ★
76 Marine Road West,
Morecambe, Lancashire LA4 4EP
T: (01524) 410180
F: (01524) 421616

Elms Hotel ★★★
Bare Village, Morecambe,
Lancashire LA4 6DD
T: (01524) 411501
F: (01524) 831979

Headway Hotel ★★★
Marine Road, East Promenade,
Morecambe, Lancashire
LA4 5AW
T: (01524) 412525
F: (01524) 832630
E: admin@headway.net1.co.uk
I: www.headwayhotel.co.uk

Lothersdale Hotel ★★
320-323 Marine Road, Central
Promenade, Morecambe,
Lancashire LA4 5AA
T: (01524) 416404
F: (01524) 416 4000
E: info@lothersdale.com
I: www.lothersdale.com
◎ ⛫

Seacrest
Rating Applied For
9-13 West End Road,
Morecambe, Lancashire LA4 4DJ
T: (01524) 411006

MORETON
Merseyside

Leasowe Castle Hotel ★★★
Leasowe Road, Moreton, Wirral,
Merseyside CH46 3RF
T: (0151) 606 9191
F: (0151) 678 5551
E: leasowe.castle@mail.cybase.
co.uk

NANTWICH
Cheshire

Rookery Hall
★★★ GOLD AWARD
Main Road, Worleston,
Nantwich, Cheshire CW5 6DQ
T: (01270) 610016
F: (01270) 626027
I: www.mywebpage.
net/rookeryhall
♿

NEWTON-LE-WILLOWS
Merseyside

Kirkfield Hotel ★★
2-4 Church Street, Newton-le-
Willows, Merseyside WA12 9SU
T: (01925) 228196
F: (01925) 291540

NORTHWICH
Cheshire

Oaklands Country House Hotel
★★
Millington Lane, Gorstage,
Northwich, Cheshire CW8 2SU
T: (01606) 853249
F: (01606) 852419

Quality Hotel ★★★
London Road, Northwich,
Cheshire CW9 5HD
T: (01606) 44443
F: (01606) 42596
E: admin@gb618.u.net.com
I: www.choicehotelseurope.com
⛫

OLD TRAFFORD
Greater Manchester

Old Trafford Lodge
Rating Applied For
Travel Accommodation
Lancashire County Cricket Club,
Old Trafford, Manchester
M16 0PX
T: (0161) 874 3333
F: (0161) 874 3399
E: sales.lancs@ecb.co.uk
I: www.lccc.co.uk
◎

OLDHAM
Greater Manchester

Hotel Smokies Park ★★★
Ashton Road, Bardsley, Oldham,
Lancashire OL8 3HX
T: (0161) 785 5000
F: (0161) 785 5010

ORMSKIRK
Lancashire

Beaufort Hotel ★★★
High Lane, Burscough, Ormskirk,
Lancashire L40 7SN
T: (01704) 892655
F: (01704) 895135
E: info@beaufort.uk.com
I: www.beaufort.uk.com
⛫

PARKGATE
Cheshire

Ship Hotel ★★
The Parade, Parkgate, South
Wirral, Cheshire CH64 6SA
T: (0151) 336 3931
F: (0151) 336 3931

PILLING
Lancashire

Springfield House Hotel and
Restaurant★★★
Wheel Lane, Pilling, Preston
PR3 6HL
T: (01253) 790301
F: (01253) 790907
E: recep@springfieldhouse.uk.
com
I: www.springfieldhouse.uk.com
◎

PRESTBURY
Cheshire

The White House Manor
★★★★ SILVER AWARD
Townhouse
The Village, Prestbury,
Macclesfield, Cheshire SK10 4HP
T: (01625) 829376
F: (01625) 828627
⛫

PRESTON
Lancashire

Novotel Preston ★★★
Reedfield Place, Walton Summit,
Preston, PR5 6AA
T: (01772) 313331
F: (01772) 627868
E: h0838@accor.hotels.com
I: www.novotel.com
⛫

Tickled Trout Hotel ★★★
Preston New Road, Samlesbury,
Preston PR5 0UJ
T: (01772) 877671
F: (01772) 877463
E: info@tickledtrout.macdonald.
hotels.co.uk
I: www.macdonaldhotels.co.uk

SADDLEWORTH
Greater Manchester

La Pergola Hotel and
Restaurant ★★★
Rochdale Road, Denshaw,
Oldham OL3 5UE
T: (01457) 871040
F: (01457) 873804
E: reception@lapergola.
freeserve.co.uk
I: www.hotel.restaurant.co.uk

SALE
Greater Manchester

Lennox Lea Hotel ★★
Irlam Road, Sale, Cheshire
M33 2BH
T: (0161) 973 1764
F: (0161) 969 6059
E: info@lennoxlea.co.uk
I: www.lennoxlea.co.uk

SANDBACH
Cheshire

Chimney House Hotel ★★★
Congleton Road, Sandbach,
Cheshire CW11 4ST
T: (01270) 764141
F: (01270) 768961

Saxon Cross Hotel ★★
M6 junction 17, Holmes Chapel
Road, Sandbach, Cheshire
CW11 1SE
T: (01270) 763281
F: (01270) 768723
⛫

SOUTHPORT
Merseyside

Cambridge House Hotel ★★
4 Cambridge Road, Southport,
Merseyside PR9 9NG
T: (01704) 538372
F: (01704) 547183

Crimond Hotel ★★
28-30 Knowsley Road,
Southport, Merseyside PR9 0HN
T: (01704) 536456
F: (01704) 548643
E: dtarl10164@aol.com
I: www.crimondhotel.com

Dukes Folly Hotel ★★
11 Duke Street, Southport,
Merseyside PR8 1LS
T: (01704) 533355
F: (01704) 530065

Metropole Hotel ★★
3 Portland Street, Southport,
Merseyside PR8 1LL
T: (01704) 536836
F: (01704) 549041
E: metropole.southport@
btinternet.com
I: www.btinternet.
com/§metropole.southport

Scarisbrick Hotel ★★★
239 Lord Street, Southport,
Merseyside PR8 1NZ
T: (01704) 543000
F: (01704) 533335
E: scarisbrickhotel@talk21.com
I: www.scarisbrickhotel.com
⛫

Stutelea Hotel and Leisure
Club★★★
Alexandra Road, Southport,
Merseyside PR9 0NB
T: (01704) 544220
F: (01704) 500232
E: info@stutelea.co.uk
I: www.stutelea.co.uk
◎

STANDISH
Greater Manchester

Wigan/Standish Moat House
★★★
Almond Brook Road, Standish,
Wigan, Lancashire WN6 0SR
T: (01257) 499988
F: (01257) 427327
E: gmwig@queensmoat.co.uk
I: www.moathousehotels.com

STOCKPORT
Greater Manchester

Saxon Holme Hotel ★★
230 Wellington Road North,
Stockport, SK4 2QN
T: (0161) 432 2335
F: (0161) 431 8076
⛫

SUTTON
Cheshire

Sutton Hall ★★
Bullocks Lane, Sutton,
Macclesfield, Cheshire SK11 0HE
T: (01260) 253211
F: (01260) 252538

TARPORLEY
Cheshire

Willington Hall Hotel ★★★
Willington, Tarporley, Cheshire
CW6 0NB
T: (01829) 752321
F: (01829) 752596
E: enquiries@willingtonhall.co.
uk
I: www.willingtonhall.co.uk

THORNTON HOUGH
Merseyside

Thornton Hall Hotel & Country
Health Club★★★
Neston Road, Thornton Hough,
Wirral, Merseyside CH63 1JF
T: (0151) 336 3938
F: (0151) 336 7864
E: thorntonhallhotel@
btinternet.com
I: www.thornton-hall.co.uk
⛫

UPHOLLAND
Lancashire

Holland Hall Hotel ★★★
6 Lafford Lane, Upholland,
Skelmersdale, Lancashire
WN8 0QZ
T: (01695) 624426
F: (01695) 622433

URMSTON
Greater Manchester

Manor Hey Hotel ★★
130 Stretford Road, Urmston,
Manchester M41 9LT
T: (0161) 748 3896
F: (0161) 746 7183

WADDINGTON
Lancashire

The Moorcock Inn ★★
Slaidburn Road, Waddington,
Clitheroe, Lancashire BB7 3AA
T: (01200) 422333
F: (01200) 429184

NORTH WEST

WARRINGTON
Cheshire
The Park Royal International Hotel, Health and Leisure Spa ★★★★
Stretton Road, Stretton, Warrington, Cheshire WA4 4NS
T: (01925) 730706
F: (01925) 730740
E: hotel@park-royal-int.co.uk
🖼

WHITTLE-LE-WOODS
Lancashire
Shaw Hill Hotel Golf & Country Club★★★
Preston Road, Whittle-le-Woods, Chorley, Lancashire PR6 7PP
T: (01257) 269221 & 226821
F: (01257) 261223

WIDNES
Cheshire
Hillcrest Hotel ★★★
Cronton Lane, Widnes, Cheshire WA8 9AR
T: (0151) 424 1616
F: (0151) 495 1348
🖼

WIGAN
Greater Manchester
Burridges Hotel and Restaurant ★★★
Standishgate, Wigan, Lancashire WN1 1XA
T: (01942) 741674
F: (01942) 741683
E: info@burridges.co.uk
I: www.burridges.co.uk

Kilhey Court Hotel ★★★★ SILVER AWARD
Chorley Road, Standish, Wigan, Lancashire WN1 2XN
T: (01257) 472100
F: (01257) 422401
E: reservations@kilhey.co.uk
🖼

Quality Oak Wigan ★★★
Riverway, Wigan, Greater Manchester WN1 3SS
T: (01942) 826888
F: (01942) 825800
E: admin@gb058.u-net.com
I: www.choicehotelseurope.com
🖼

WILMSLOW
Cheshire
Stanneylands Hotel ★★★ SILVER AWARD
Stanneylands Road, Wilmslow, Cheshire SK9 4EY
T: (01625) 525225
F: (01625) 537282
E: email@stanneylands.co.uk
I: www.stanneylandshotel.co.uk

Thistle Manchester Airport Rating Applied For
Wilmslow Road, Handforth, Wilmslow, Cheshire SK9 3LG
T: (01625) 529211
F: (01625) 536812

WINCHAM
Cheshire
Wincham Hall ★★
Hall Lane, Wincham, Northwich, Cheshire CW9 6DG
T: (01606) 43453
F: (01606) 40128
E: jane@winchamhall.co.uk
I: www.winchamhall.co.uk

WORSLEY
Greater Manchester
Marriott Manchester Hotel and Country Club
★★★★ SILVER AWARD
Worsley Park, Worsley, Manchester M28 2QT
T: (0161) 975 2000
F: (0161) 799 6341
I: www.marriott.com

WREA GREEN
Lancashire
The Villa ★★★
Moss Side Lane, Wrea Green, Preston PR4 2PE
T: (01772) 684347
F: (01772) 687647

YORKSHIRE

APPLETON-LE-MOORS
North Yorkshire
Appleton Hall Country House Hotel ★★
Appleton-le-Moors, York YO62 6TF
T: (01751) 417227 & 417452
F: (01751) 417540

ASKRIGG
North Yorkshire
Winville Hotel & Restaurant ★
Main Street, Askrigg, Leyburn, North Yorkshire DL8 3HG
T: (01969) 650515
F: (01969) 650594

AYSGARTH
North Yorkshire
The George & Dragon Inn
◆◆◆
Aysgarth, Leyburn, North Yorkshire DL8 3AD
T: (01969) 663358
F: (01969) 663773

Wheatsheaf Hotel ★
Carperby, Leyburn, North Yorkshire DL8 4DF
T: (01969) 663216
F: (01969) 663019
E: wheatsheaf@paulmit.globalnet.co.uk

BARNSLEY
South Yorkshire
Ardsley House Hotel and Health Club
★★★ SILVER AWARD
Doncaster Road, Ardsley, Barnsley, South Yorkshire S71 5EH
T: (01226) 309955
F: (01226) 205374
E: sales@ardsley-house.co.uk
I: ardsley-house.co.uk

Tankersley Manor Hotel
★★★ SILVER AWARD
Church Lane, Upper Tankersley, Tankersley, Barnsley, South Yorkshire S75 3DQ
T: (01226) 744700
F: (01226) 745405
E: info@tankersleymanor.co.uk
I: www.tankersleymanor.co.uk

BEDALE
North Yorkshire
White Rose Hotel ★★
Bedale Road, Leeming Bar, Northallerton, North Yorkshire DL7 9AY
T: (01677) 422707 & 424941
F: (01677) 425123
E: royston@whiterosehotel.co.uk
I: www.whiterosehotel.co.uk

BEVERLEY
East Riding of Yorkshire
Manor House ★★
Newbald Road, Northlands, Walkington, Beverley, East Riding of Yorkshire HU17 8RT
T: (01482) 881645
F: (01482) 866501
E: nicola@the-manor-house.co.uk

Tickton Grange Hotel & Restaurant★★★
Tickton Grange, Tickton, Beverley, East Riding of Yorkshire HU17 9SH
T: (01964) 543666
F: (01964) 542556
E: maggy@tickton-grange.demon.co.uk
I: www.ticktongrange.co.uk
🖼

BINGLEY
West Yorkshire
Jarvis Bankfield Hotel ★★★
Bradford Road, Bingley, West Yorkshire BD16 1TU
T: (01274) 567123
F: (01274) 551331
E: bankfield@jarvis.co.uk

BISHOP THORNTON
North Yorkshire
Chequers Inn Country Hotel and Restaurant★
Fountain's Abbey Road, Bishop Thornton, Harrogate, North Yorkshire HG3 3JN
T: (01423) 770173 & 771544
F: (01423) 770049

BOROUGHBRIDGE
North Yorkshire
Crown Hotel ★★★
Horsefair, Boroughbridge, York YO51 9LB
T: (01423) 322328
F: (01423) 324512
🖼

Rose Manor Hotel ★★★
Horsefair, Boroughbridge, York YO51 9LL
T: (01423) 322245
F: (01423) 324920
E: rosemanorhotel@boroughbridge.fsnet.co.uk
I: ww.smoothhound.co.uk/

BOSTON SPA
West Yorkshire
The Royal ★★
182 High Street, Boston Spa, Wetherby, West Yorkshire LS23 6BT
T: (01937) 842142
F: (01937) 541036
E: royalhotel-bostonspa.com
I: www.royalhotel-bostonspa.com

BRADFORD
West Yorkshire
Cartwright Hotel ★★
308 Manningham Lane, Manningham, Bradford, West Yorkshire BD8 7AX
T: (01274) 499908
F: (01274) 481309
E: info@cartwrighthotel.co.uk
I: www.cartwrighthotel.co.uk

Castle Hotel
Rating Applied For
20 Grattan Road, Bradford, West Yorkshire BD1 2LU
T: (01274) 393166
F: (01274) 393200
E: rooms@castle-bfd.freeserve.co.uk
I: www.thecastlehotel.britain-uk.con

Cedar Court Hotel Bradford
★★★★ SILVER AWARD
Mayo Avenue (top of the M606), Off Rooley Lane, Bradford, West Yorkshire BD5 8HZ
T: (01274) 406606
F: (01274) 406600
E: sales@cedarcourt-hotelbradford.co.uk
I: www.cedarcourt-hotel-bradford.co.uk
🖼

Hilton Bradford ★★★
Hall Ings, Bradford, West Yorkshire BD1 5SH
T: (01274) 734734
F: (01274) 306146

Midland Hotel ★★★
Forster Square, Bradford, West Yorkshire BD1 4HU
T: (01274) 735735
F: (01274) 720003
I: www.peelhotel.com

Novotel Bradford ★★★
Adjacent M606, 6 Roydsdale Way, Bradford, West Yorkshire BD4 6SA
T: (01274) 683683
F: (01274) 651342
E: h0510@accor-hotels.com
I: www.novotel.com
🖼

Park Drive Hotel ★★
12 Park Drive, Heaton, Bradford, West Yorkshire BD9 4DR
T: (01274) 480194
F: (01274) 484869
E: sales@parkdrivehotel.co.uk
I: www.parkdrivehotel.co.uk

Establishments printed in blue have a detailed entry in this guide

Park Grove Hotel and Restaurant ★★
Park Grove, Frizinghall, Bradford, West Yorkshire BD9 4JY
T: (01274) 543444
F: (01274) 495619
E: enquiries@parkgrovehotel.co.uk
I: www.parkgrovehotel.co.uk

Quality Victoria Hotel, Bradford ★★★
Bridge Street, Bradford, West Yorkshire BD1 1JX
T: (01274) 728706
F: (01274) 736358
E: admin@gb654.u-net.com
◉

BRAMLEY
West Yorkshire

Corn Mill Lodge Hotel ★★★
Pudsey Road, Bramley, Leeds LS13 4JA
T: (0113) 257 9059
F: (0113) 257 6665

BRANDESBURTON
East Riding of Yorkshire

Burton Lodge Hotel ★★
Brandesburton, Driffield, East Yorkshire YO25 8RU
T: (01964) 542847
F: (01964) 544771
E: burton@lodge5755.freeserve.co.uk

BRIDLINGTON
East Riding of Yorkshire

Expanse Hotel ★★★
North Marine Drive, Bridlington, East Riding of Yorkshire YO15 2LS
T: (01262) 675347
F: (01262) 604928
E: expanse@brid.demon.co.uk
I: www.expanse.co.uk

Manor Court Hotel & Restaurant★★★
53 Main Street, Carnaby, Bridlington, East Riding of Yorkshire YO16 4UJ
T: (01262) 606468
F: (01262) 400217
E: manorc@aol.com.
I: www.nmanorcourt.co.uk

BUCKDEN
North Yorkshire

The Buck Inn ★★
Buckden, Skipton, North Yorkshire BD23 5JA
T: (01756) 760228 & 760416
F: (01756) 760227
E: thebuckinn@yorks.net
I: www.thebuckinn.yorks.net

CLAPHAM

Flying Horseshoe Hotel ★★
Clapham Station, Clapham, Lancaster LA2 8ES
T: (015242) 51229
F: (015242) 51229
E: alan@laughing-gravy.co.uk
I: www.laughing-gravy.co.uk

DARLEY
North Yorkshire

Wellington Inn ★★
Darley, Harrogate, North Yorkshire HG3 2QQ
T: (01423) 780362 & 781445
F: (01423) 781534

DEWSBURY
West Yorkshire

Heath Cottage Hotel & Restaurant★★★
Wakefield Road, Dewsbury, West Yorkshire WF12 8ET
T: (01924) 465399
F: (01924) 459405

DONCASTER
South Yorkshire

Regent Hotel ★★★
Regent Square, Doncaster, South Yorkshire DN1 2DS
T: (01302) 364180 & 364336
F: (01302) 322331
E: admin@theregenthotel.co.uk
I: www.theregenthotel.co.uk

DRIFFIELD

The Bell In Driffield ★★★
Market Place, Driffield, East Yorkshire YO25 6AN
T: (01377) 256661
F: (01377) 253228
(&)

EASINGWOLD
North Yorkshire

The George at Easingwold ★★
Market Place, Easingwold, York YO61 3AD
T: (01347) 821698
F: (01347) 823448
E: info@the-george-hotel.co.uk
I: www.the-george-hotel.co.uk

Old Farmhouse Country Hotel & Restaurant★★
Raskelf, York YO61 3LF
T: (01347) 821971
F: (01347) 822392

ECCLESHILL
West Yorkshire

Prince of Wales
Rating Applied For
91-93 Harrogate Road, Eccleshill, Bradford, West Yorkshire BD2 3ES
T: (01274) 638729
F: (01274) 627145

FILEY
North Yorkshire

The Downcliffe House Hotel
★★ SILVER AWARD
The Beach, Filey, North Yorkshire YO14 9LA
T: (01723) 513310
F: (01723) 513773
E: onyx.net.co.uk

Sea Brink Hotel ★★
3 The Beach, Filey, North Yorkshire YO14 9LA
T: (01723) 513257
F: (01723) 514139
E: seabrink@supanet.com
I: www.seabrink.supanet.com

White Lodge Hotel ★★★
The Crescent, Filey, North Yorkshire YO14 9JX
T: (01723) 514771
F: (01723) 516590
E: white.lodge@lineone.net
◉

FLAMBOROUGH
East Riding of Yorkshire

Flaneburg Hotel ★★
North Marine Road, Flamborough, Bridlington, East Riding of Yorkshire YO15 1LF
T: (01262) 850284
F: (01262) 850284

North Star Hotel
★★ SILVER AWARD
North Marine Road, Flamborough, Bridlington, East Riding of Yorkshire YO15 1BL
T: (01262) 850379
F: (01262) 850379

GILLAMOOR
North Yorkshire

Royal Oak Inn ★★
Gillamoor, York YO62 7HX
T: (01751) 431414
F: (01751) 431414

GOATHLAND
North Yorkshire

Mallyan Spout Hotel ★★
The Common, Goathland, Whitby, North Yorkshire YO22 5AN
T: (01947) 896486 & 896206
F: (01947) 896327
E: mallyan@ukgateway.net
I: www.mywebpage.net/mallyanspout
◉

Whitfield House Hotel ★★
Darnholm, Goathland, Whitby, North Yorkshire YO22 5LA
T: (01947) 896215 & 896214
◉

GOMERSAL
West Yorkshire

The Gomersal Lodge Hotel ★★
Spen Lane, Gomersal, Cleckheaton, West Yorkshire BD19 4PJ
T: (01274) 861111
F: (01274) 861111

GOOLE
East Riding of Yorkshire

Clifton Hotel
★★ SILVER AWARD
Boothferry Road, Goole, East Riding of Yorkshire DN14 6AL
T: (01405) 761336
F: (01405) 762350
E: cliftonhotel@telinco.co.uk
I: www.s-h-systems.co.uk/hotels/cliftong.html

GRASSINGTON
North Yorkshire

Black Horse Hotel ★★
Garrs Lane, Grassington, Skipton, North Yorkshire BD23 5AT
T: (01756) 752770
F: (01756) 753425
I: www.grassington.net.

Grassington House Hotel and Restaurant★★
5 The Square, Grassington, Skipton, North Yorkshire BD23 5AQ
T: (01756) 752406
F: (01756) 752135

Tennant Arms Hotel ★★
Kilnsey, Skipton, North Yorkshire BD23 5PS
T: (01756) 752301

GRIMSBY
North East Lincolnshire

Millfields ★★★
53 Bargate, Grimsby, North East Lincolnshire DN34 5AD
T: (01472) 356068
F: (01472) 250286
E: info@millfieldshotel.co.uk
I: www.millfieldshotel.co.uk
◉ (↑)

HALIFAX
West Yorkshire

The Hobbit Hotel ★★
Hob Lane, Norland, Halifax, West Yorkshire HX6 3QL
T: (01422) 832202
F: (01422) 835381
E: info@hobbit-hotel
I: www.hobbit-hotel.co.uk

Milan's Hotel and Conference Suite ★★
6-8 Carlton Place, Halifax, West Yorkshire HX1 2SB
T: (01422) 330539
F: (01422) 381873

The Quays Premier Lodge
Travel Accommodation
Salterhebble Hill, Huddersfield Road, Halifax, West Yorkshire HX3 0QT
T: (01422) 347700 & 0800 118833
F: (01422) 320793

Rock Inn Hotel & Churchills Restaurant★★★
Holywell Green, Halifax, West Yorkshire HX4 9BS
T: (01422) 379721
F: (01422) 379110
E: therock@dial.pipex.com
I: www.rockinnhotel.com

White Swan Hotel ★★
Princess Street, Halifax, West Yorkshire HX1 1TS
T: (01422) 355541
F: (01422) 357311
E: whiteswan@clara.net
I: www.whiteswan.clara.net

HARROGATE
North Yorkshire

Ascot House Hotel
★★ SILVER AWARD
53 Kings Road, Harrogate, North Yorkshire HG1 5HJ
T: (01423) 531005
F: (01423) 503523
E: admin@ascothouse.com
I: www.harrogate.com/ascot

Balmoral Hotel ★★★★
Franklin Mount, Harrogate, North Yorkshire HG1 5EJ
T: (01423) 508208
F: (01423) 530652
E: info@balmoralhotel.co.uk
I: www.balmoralhotel.co.uk
◉

The Boar's Head Hotel
★★★ SILVER AWARD
Ripley Castle Estate, Ripley, Harrogate, North Yorkshire HG3 3AY
T: (01423) 771888
F: (01423) 771509
E: reservations@boarsheadripley.co.uk
I: www.boarsheadripley.co.uk
◉ (↑)

Cairn Hotel ★★★
Ripon Road, Harrogate, North Yorkshire HG1 2JD
T: (01423) 504005
F: (01423) 500056
E: cairnhot@aol.com

Grants Hotel and Chimney Pots Bistro★★★
Swan Road, Harrogate, North Yorkshire HG1 2SS
T: (01423) 560666
F: (01423) 502550
E: enquiries@grantshotel-harrogate.com
I: www.grantshotel-harrogate.com

Harrogate Spa Hotel ★★★
Prospect Place, West Park, Harrogate, North Yorkshire HG1 1LB
T: (01423) 564601
F: (01423) 507508

Imperial Hotel ★★★
Prospect Place, Harrogate, North Yorkshire HG1 1LA
T: (01423) 565071
F: (01423) 500082

The Langham ★★
21-27 Valley Drive, Harrogate, North Yorkshire HG2 0JL
T: (01423) 502179
F: (01423) 502347

Low Hall Hotel and Restaurant ★★
Ripon Road, Killinghall, Harrogate, North Yorkshire HG3 2AY
T: (01423) 508598
F: (01423) 560848
E: lowhall@fsbusiness.co.uk

The Majestic ★★★★
Ripon Road, Harrogate, North Yorkshire HG1 2HU
T: (01423) 700300
F: (01423) 502283
E: swhite@paramount-hotels.co.uk
I: www.paramount-hotels.co.uk

Rudding Park House and Hotel ★★★★ SILVER AWARD
Rudding Park, Follifoot, Harrogate, North Yorkshire HG3 1JH
T: (01423) 871350
F: (01423) 872286
E: sales@rudding-park.co.uk
I: www.rudding-park.co.uk

Studley Hotel and Le Breton Restaurant★★★
Swan Road, Harrogate, North Yorkshire HG1 2SE
T: (01423) 560425
F: (01423) 530967
E: studleyhotel@hotels.activebooking.com

White Hart Hotel ★★★
Cold Bath Road, Harrogate, North Yorkshire HG2 0NF
T: (01423) 505681
F: (01423) 568354
E: pwalker@whithart.net
I: www.whitehart.net

HAWES
North Yorkshire

Stone House Hotel ★★
Sedbusk, Hawes, North Yorkshire DL8 3PT
T: (01969) 667571
F: (01969) 667720
E: daleshotel@aol.com
I: www.stonehousehotel.com

HAWORTH
West Yorkshire

Old White Lion Hotel ★★
Main Street, Haworth, Keighley, West Yorkshire BD22 8DU
T: (01535) 642313
F: (01535) 646222
E: enquiries@oldwhitelionhotel.com
I: www.oldwhitelionhotel.com

HEBDEN BRIDGE
West Yorkshire

Carlton Hotel ★★★
Albert Street, Hebden Bridge, West Yorkshire HX7 8ES
T: (01422) 844400
F: (01422) 843117
E: ctonhotel@aol.com

Hebden Lodge Hotel ★★
6-10 New Road, Hebden Bridge, West Yorkshire HX7 8AD
T: (01422) 845272 & 844233
F: (01422) 845272
I: www.hebdenlodgehotel.fsnet.co.uk

HELMSLEY
North Yorkshire

Carlton Lodge ★★
Bondgate, Helmsley, York YO62 5EY
T: (01439) 770557
F: (01439) 770623
E: carlton.lodge@dial.pipex.com
I: dspace.dial.pipex.com/carlton.lodge

The Crown Hotel ★★
Market Place, Helmsley, York YO62 5BJ
T: (01439) 770297
F: (01439) 771595

Feathers Hotel ★★
Market Place, Helmsley, York YO62 5BH
T: (01439) 770275
F: (01439) 771101
E: feathers@zen.co.uk
I: www.feathershotel.co.uk

Pheasant Hotel ★★★
Harome, Helmsley, YO62 5JG
T: (01439) 771241
F: (01439) 771744

HOLME UPON SPALDING MOOR
East Riding of Yorkshire

Ye Olde Red Lion ★★
Old Road, Holme upon Spalding Moor, York YO43 4AD
T: (01430) 860220
F: (01430) 861471

HOLMFIRTH
West Yorkshire

Old Bridge Hotel ★★★
Off Victoria Street, Holmfirth, Huddersfield HD7 1DA
T: (01484) 681212
F: (01484) 687978
E: oldbridgehotel@enterprise.net
I: www.oldbridgehotel.co.uk

HOVINGHAM
North Yorkshire

Worsley Arms Hotel ★★★
Hovingham, York YO62 4LA
T: (01653) 628234
F: (01653) 628130
E: worsleyarms@aol.com
I: fine-individual-hotels.co.uk

HOWDEN
East Riding of Yorkshire

Wellington Hotel ★
31 Bridgegate, Howden, East Yorkshire DN14 7JG
T: (01430) 430258 & (01763) 287663
F: (01430) 432139

HUDDERSFIELD
West Yorkshire

Briar Court Hotel ★★★
Halifax Road, Birchencliffe, Huddersfield, HD3 3NT
T: (01484) 519902 & 519978
F: (01484) 431812
E: briarcourthotel@btconnect.com
I: www.briaracourthotel.co.uk

Elm Crest Hotel ★
2 Queens Road, Edgerton, Huddersfield, HD2 2AG
T: (01484) 530990 & 07721 458479
F: (01484) 516227
E: derek.gee@talk21.com
I: www.elm-crest.co.uk

The George Hotel ★★★
St George's Square, Huddersfield, HD1 1JA
T: (01484) 515444
F: (01484) 435056
E: stuart.mcmanus@principalhotels.co.uk
I: www.principalhotels.co.uk

Hanover International Hotel Huddersfield★★★
Penistone Road, Kirkburton, Huddersfield HD8 0PE
T: (01484) 607788
F: (01484) 607961
I: www.hanover.international.com

Hilton National Huddersfield/Halifax★★★
M62 Exit 24, Ainley Top, Huddersfield HD3 3RH
T: (01422) 375431
F: (01422) 310067

Huddersfield Hotel and Rosemary Lane Bistro★★★
33-47 Kirkgate, Huddersfield, HD1 1QT
T: (01484) 512111
F: (01484) 435262
E: enquiries@huddersfieldhotel.com
I: www.huddersfieldhotel.com

The Lodge Hotel ★★
48 Birkby Lodge Road, Birkby, Huddersfield HD2 2BG
T: (01484) 431001
F: (01484) 421590

HULL

Cornmill Hotel ★
Mount Pleasant, Holderness Road, Hull, HU9 1LA
T: (01482) 589000
F: (01482) 586447
E: ops@cornmill.globalnet.co.uk
I: www.webmarketing.co.uk/cornmill/html/wedding.htm.

Jarvis International Hotel ★★★
Grange Park Lane, Willerby, Hull, East Yorkshire HU10 6EA
T: (01482) 656488
F: (01482) 655848
I: www.jarvis.co.uk

Pearson Park Hotel ★★
Pearson Park, Hull, HU5 2TQ
T: (01482) 343043
F: (01482) 447679

ILKLEY
West Yorkshire

The Crescent Hotel ★★★
Brook Street, Ilkley, West Yorkshire LS29 8DG
T: (01943) 600012
F: (01943) 601513
E: creschot@dialstaart.net
I: www.crescenthotelilkley.co.uk

Moorview Hotel ★
104 Skipton Road, Ilkley, West Yorkshire LS29 9HE
T: (01943) 600156 & 816572
F: (01943) 817313

Riverside Hotel ★
Riverside Gardens, Bride Lane, Ilkley, West Yorkshire LS29 9EU
T: (01943) 607338 & 432021
F: (01943) 607338

Rombalds Hotel and Restaurant ★★★ SILVER AWARD
West View, Wells Road, Ilkley, West Yorkshire LS29 9JG
T: (01943) 603201
F: (01943) 816586
E: reception@rombalds.demon.co.uk
I: www.rombalds.co.uk

KEIGHLEY
West Yorkshire

Dalesgate Hotel ★★
406 Skipton Road, Utley, Keighley, West Yorkshire BD20 6HP
T: (01535) 664930
F: (01535) 611253
E: stephen.e.atha@btinternet.com
I: www.dalesgate.co.uk

KIRKBYMOORSIDE
North Yorkshire

George & Dragon Hotel ★★
Market Place, Kirkbymoorside, York YO62 6AA
T: (01751) 433334
F: (01751) 432933

Kings Head Hotel ★★
Market Place, Kirkbymoorside, York YO62 6AT
T: (01751) 431340
F: (01751) 431340

Establishments printed in blue have a detailed entry in this guide

KNARESBOROUGH
North Yorkshire
General Tarleton Inn ★★★
Boroughbridge Road, Ferrensby,
Knaresborough, North Yorkshire
HG5 0QB
T: (01423) 340284
F: (01423) 340288
E: gti@generaltarleton.co.uk
I: www.generaltarleton.co.uk

LEEDS
West Yorkshire
Aragon Hotel ★★
250 Stainbeck Lane, Meanwood,
Leeds, LS7 2PS
T: (0113) 275 9306
F: (0113) 275 7166

Ascot Grange Hotel ★★
126-130 Otley Road,
Headingley, Leeds LS16 5JX
T: (0113) 293 4444
F: (0113) 293 5555

The Butlers Hotel ★★★
Cardigan Road, Headingley,
Leeds LS6 3AG
T: (0113) 274 4755
F: (0113) 274 4755
E: info@butlershotel.co.uk
I: www.butlershotel.co.uk

De Vere Oulton Hall
★★★★★ SILVER AWARD
Rothwell Lane, Oulton,
Woodlesford, Leeds LS26 8HN
T: (0113) 282 1000
F: (0113) 282 8066
E: oulton.hall@devere-hotel.com
I: www.devereonline.co.uk

The Hotel Metropole ★★★★
King Street, Leeds, LS1 2HQ
T: (0113) 245 0841
F: (0113) 242 5156
I: www.principalhotels.co.uk

Jarvis Leeds North ★★★
Ring Road, Mill Green View,
Seacroft, Leeds LS14 5QF
T: (0113) 273 2323
F: (0113) 232 3018
I: www.jarvis.co.uk

Jarvis Parkway Hotel and Country Club★★★
Otley Road, Bramhope, Leeds
LS16 8AG
T: (0113) 269 9000
F: (0113) 267 4410
E: parkway@jarvis.co.uk
I: www.jarvis.co.uk

Le Meridien Queens ★★★★
City Square, Leeds, LS1 1PL
T: 0870 400 8696
F: (0113) 242 5154
I: www.lemeridien-hotels.com

Travelodge
Travel Accommodation
Blayds Court, Blayds Yard, Leeds,
LS1 4AG
T: (0113) 244 5793 & 247 0076
I: www.travelodge.co.uk

Weetwood Hall ★★★★
Otley Road, Headingley, Leeds
LS16 5PS
T: (0113) 230 6000
F: (0113) 230 6095
E: sales@weetwood.co.uk
I: www.weetwood.co.uk

LEYBURN
North Yorkshire
Golden Lion Hotel & Licensed Restaurant★
Market Place, Leyburn, North
Yorkshire DL8 5AS
T: (01969) 622161
F: (01969) 623836
E: annegoldenlion@aol.com

LITTLE WEIGHTON
East Riding of Yorkshire
Rowley Manor ★★
Little Weighton, Cottingham,
East Riding of Yorkshire
HU20 3XR
T: (01482) 848248 & 843132
F: (01482) 849900

LIVERSEDGE
West Yorkshire
Geordie Pride Lodge Hotel ★★
112 Roberttown Lane,
Roberttown, Liversedge, West
Yorkshire WF15 7LZ
T: (01924) 402069
F: (01924) 410136

Heals Hall Hotel ★★
Leeds Road, Liversedge, West
Yorkshire WF15 6JA
T: (01924) 409112
F: (01924) 401895
E: healdshall@ndirect.co.uk

LONG PRESTON
North Yorkshire
Plough Inn ★★
Wigglesworth, Skipton, North
Yorkshire BD23 4RJ
T: (01729) 840243 & 840638
F: (01729) 840243
I: www.the-plough-wigglesworth-freeserve.co.uk

MALHAM
North Yorkshire
Buck Inn ★★
Malham, Skipton, North
Yorkshire BD23 4DA
T: (01729) 830317
F: (01729) 830670

MALTON
North Yorkshire
The Green Man ★★★
15 Market Street, Malton, North
Yorkshire YO17 7LY
T: (01653) 600370
F: (01653) 696006
E: greenman@englishhousehotels.co.uk

Talbot Hotel ★★
Yorkersgate, Malton, North
Yorkshire YO17 7AJ
T: (01653) 694031
F: (01653) 693355
E: talbot@englishrosehotels.co.uk
I: www.englishrosehotels.co.uk

Wentworth Arms Hotel ★
Town Street, Old Malton,
Malton, North Yorkshire
YO17 7HD
T: (01653) 692618

MARKINGTON
North Yorkshire
Hob Green ★★★
Markington, Harrogate, North
Yorkshire HG3 3PJ
T: (01423) 770031
F: (01423) 771589

MELTHAM
West Yorkshire
Durker Roods Hotel ★★
Bishops Way, Meltham,
Huddersfield HD7 3AG
T: (01484) 851413
F: (01484) 851843
E: spencer@durkerroodshotel.co.uk
I: www.durkerroodshotel.co.uk

MIDDLEHAM
North Yorkshire
Millers House Hotel ★★
Middleham, Leyburn, North
Yorkshire DL8 4NR
T: (01969) 622630
F: (01969) 623570
E: hotel@millershouse.demon.co.uk
I: www.hotelwensleydale.com

MONK FRYSTON
North Yorkshire
Monk Fryston Hall ★★★
Monk Fryston, Leeds LS25 5DU
T: (01977) 682369
F: (01977) 683544
E: reception@monkfryston-hotel.com
I: www.monkfryston-hotel.com

MORLEY
West Yorkshire
The Old Vicarage ★★
Bruntcliffe Road, Morley, Leeds
LS27 0JZ
T: (0113) 253 2174
F: (0113) 253 3549
E: oldvicarage@btinternet.com
I: www.oldvicaragehotel.co.uk

NEWBY WISKE
North Yorkshire
Solberge Hall ★★★
Newby Wiske, Northallerton,
North Yorkshire DL7 9ER
T: (01609) 779191
F: (01609) 780472
E: hotel@solberge.freeserve.co.uk
I: www.smoothhound.com

NIDD
North Yorkshire
Nidd Hall ★★
Nidd, Harrogate, North Yorkshire
HG3 3BN
T: (01423) 771598
F: (01423) 770931

NUNNINGTON
North Yorkshire
Ryedale Country Lodge ★★
Nunnington, York YO62 5XB
T: (01439) 748246
F: (01439) 748346

OSSETT
West Yorkshire
Mews Hotel ★★
Dale Street, Ossett, West
Yorkshire WF5 9HN
T: (01924) 273982 & 07973 137547
F: (01924) 279389
E: enquiries@mews-hotel.co.uk
I: www.mews-hotel.co.uk

OTLEY
West Yorkshire
Chevin Lodge Country Park Hotel★★★
Yorkgate, Otley, West Yorkshire
LS21 3NU
T: (01943) 467818
F: (01943) 850335
E: reception@chevinlodge.co.uk
I: www.chevinlodge.co.uk

PATELEY BRIDGE
North Yorkshire
Grassfields Country House Hotel★★
Low Wath Road, Pateley Bridge,
Harrogate, North Yorkshire
HG3 5HL
T: (01423) 711412 & 712844
F: (01423) 712844
E: grassfields@nidderdale.com.uk
I: www.nidderdale.co.uk

Sportsmans Arms Hotel ★★
Wath-in-Nidderdale, Pateley
Bridge, Harrogate, North
Yorkshire HG3 5PP
T: (01423) 711306
F: (01423) 712524

Yorke Arms Hotel
★★ SILVER AWARD
Ramsgill, Harrogate, North
Yorkshire HG3 5RL
T: (01423) 755243
F: (01423) 755330
E: enquiries/york-arms.co.uk
I: www.yorke-arms.co.uk

PECKFIELD
West Yorkshire
Best Western Milford Lodge Hotel ★★★
A1 Great North Road, Peckfield,
Leeds LS25 5LQ
T: (01977) 681800
F: (01977) 681245
E: enquiries@mlh.co.uk
I: www.mlh.co.uk

PICKERING
North Yorkshire
Beansheaf Restaurant Hotel and Restaurant★★
Malton Road, Pickering, North
Yorkshire YO17 6UE
T: (01653) 668614
F: (01653) 686370

Crossways Hotel ★★
Eastgate, Pickering, North
Yorkshire YO18 7DW
T: (01751) 472804
F: (01751) 472804

Forest & Vale Hotel ★★★
Malton Road, Pickering, North
Yorkshire YO18 7DL
T: (01751) 472722
F: (01751) 472972

White Swan Hotel
★★ SILVER AWARD
Market Place, Pickering, North
Yorkshire YO18 7AA
T: (01751) 472288
F: (01751) 475554
E: welcome@white-swan.co.uk
I: www.white-swan.co.uk

PONTEFRACT
West Yorkshire
Rogerthorpe Manor Country Hotel ★★★
Thorpe Lane, Badsworth,
Pontefract, West Yorkshire
WF9 1AB
T: (01977) 643839
F: (01977) 641571
E: ops@rogerthorpemanor.co.uk
I: www.rogerthorpemanor.co.uk

POOL IN WHARFEDALE
West Yorkshire
Monkman's Bistro with Bedrooms ★★
Pool Bank, Pool in Wharfedale,
Otley, West Yorkshire LS21 1EH
T: (0113) 284 1105
F: (0113) 284 3115
E: monkmans@clara.co.uk
I: www.monkmans.co.uk

RICHMOND
North Yorkshire
Bridge House Hotel ★★
Catterick Bridge, Richmond,
North Yorkshire DL10 7PE
T: (01748) 818331
F: (01748) 818331
E: bridge_house@hotmail.com

Frenchgate Hotel ★★
59-61 Frenchgate, Richmond,
North Yorkshire DL10 7AE
T: (01748) 822087 & 823596
F: (01748) 823596
I: www.richmond.org

King's Head Hotel ★★
Market Place, Richmond, North
Yorkshire DL10 4HS
T: (01748) 850220
F: (01748) 850635
E: res@kingsheadrichmond.co.uk
I: www.kingsheadrichmond.co.uk

RIPON
North Yorkshire
Ripon Spa Hotel ★★★
Park Street, Ripon, North
Yorkshire HG4 2BU
T: (01765) 602172
F: (01765) 690770
E: spahotel@bronco.co.uk
I: www.stemsys.co.uk/spa

Unicorn Hotel ★★
Market Place, Ripon, North
Yorkshire HG4 1BP
T: (01765) 602202
F: (01765) 690734
E: info@unicorn-hotel.co.uk
I: www.unicorn-hotel.co.uk

ROSEDALE ABBEY
North Yorkshire
Blacksmiths Country Inn ★★★
Hartoft End, Rosedale Abbey,
Pickering, North Yorkshire
YO18 8EN
T: (01751) 417331
F: (01751) 417167
E: blacksmiths.rosedale@virgin.net
I: www.blacksmithsinn-rosedale.co.uk

Milburn Arms Hotel ★★
Rosedale Abbey, Pickering,
North Yorkshire YO18 8RA
T: (01751) 417312
F: (01751) 417312
E: info@milburnarms.com
I: www.milburnarms.com

White Horse Farm Hotel ★★
Rosedale Abbey, Pickering,
North Yorkshire YO18 8SE
T: (01751) 417239
F: (01751) 417781
E: sarah@midnorth.fsnet.co.uk

ROTHERHAM
South Yorkshire
Best Western Elton Hotel ★★★
Main Street, Bramley,
Rotherham, South Yorkshire
S66 2SF
T: (01709) 545681
F: (01709) 549100
E: bestwestern.eltonhotel@btinternet.com
I: www.bestwestern.co.uk

Consort Hotel ★★★
Brampton Road, Thurcroft,
Rotherham, South Yorkshire
S66 9JA
T: (01709) 530022
F: (01709) 531529
I: www.consorthotel.com

Hellaby Hall ★★★★ SILVER AWARD
Old Hellaby Lane, Hellaby,
Rotherham, South Yorkshire
S66 8SN
T: (01709) 702701
F: (01709) 700979
E: stay@paramount-hotels.co.uk
I: www.paramount-hotels.co.uk

Swallow Hotel ★★★
West Bawtry Road, Rotherham,
South Yorkshire S60 4NA
T: (01709) 830630
F: (01709) 830549

SCARBOROUGH
North Yorkshire
Ambassador Hotel ★★★
Centre of the Esplanade,
Scarborough, North Yorkshire
YO11 2AY
T: (01723) 362841
F: (01723) 366166

Beiderbecke's Hotel and Restaurant ★★★
1-3 The Crescent, Scarborough,
North Yorkshire YO11 2PW
T: (01723) 365766
F: (01723) 367433
E: info@beiderbeckes.com
I: www.beiderbeckes.com

Brooklands Hotel ★★
7-11 Esplanade Gardens,
Scarborough, North Yorkshire
YO11 2AW
T: (01723) 376576 & 890314
F: (01723) 376576
E: stay@brooklandshotel.co.uk

The Clifton Hotel ★★★
Queens Parade, North Cliff,
Scarborough, North Yorkshire
YO12 7HX
T: (01723) 375691
F: (01723) 364203
E: cliftonhotel@englishrosehotels.co.uk
I: www.englishrosehotels.co.uk

Crown Hotel ★★★
The Esplanade, Scarborough,
North Yorkshire YO11 2AG
T: (01723) 373491
F: (01723) 362271
E: richardfrank@scarboroughhotel.com
I: scarboroughhotel.com

East Ayton Lodge Country Hotel and Restaurant ★★★
Moor Lane, East Ayton,
Scarborough, North Yorkshire
YO13 9EW
T: (01723) 864227
F: (01723) 862680
E: eastaytonlodge@hotmail.com

Esplanade Hotel ★★★
Belmont Road, Scarborough,
North Yorkshire YO11 2AA
T: (01723) 360382
F: (01723) 376137

Gridleys Crescent Hotel ★★ SILVER AWARD
The Crescent, Scarborough,
North Yorkshire YO11 2PP
T: (01723) 360929 & 507507
F: (01723) 354126
E: reception@crescent-hotel.co.uk
I: www.crescent-hotel.co.uk

Hackness Grange Country House Hotel ★★★
North York Moors National Park,
Hackness, Scarborough, North
Yorkshire YO13 0JW
T: (01723) 882345
F: (01723) 882391
E: hacknessgrange@englishrosehotels.co.uk
I: www.englishrosehotels.co.uk

La Baia Hotel ★★
24 Blenheim Terrace,
Scarborough, North Yorkshire
YO12 7HD
T: (01723) 370780

Londesborough Arms Hotel ★★
24 Main Street, Seamer,
Scarborough, North Yorkshire
YO12 4PS
T: (01723) 863230
F: (01723) 863230
E: londesborough@scarborough.co.uk
I: www.scarborough.co.uk/londesborough

Lynton Private Hotel ★★
104 Columbus Ravine,
Scarborough, North Yorkshire
YO12 7QZ
T: (01723) 374240
E: enquiries@lynton-hotel.fsnet.co.uk
I: www.lynton-hotel.fsnet.co.uk

Hotel Majestic ★★
57 Northstead Manor Drive,
Scarborough, North Yorkshire
YO12 6AG
T: (01723) 363806
F: (01723) 363806
E: hotelmajestic@bt-internet.com
I: www.bt.internet.com/§hotelmajestic

Manor Heath Hotel ★★
67 Northstead Manor Drive,
Scarborough, North Yorkshire
YO12 6AF
T: (01723) 365720
F: (01723) 365720
E: enquiries@manorheath.freeserve.co.uk
I: www.manorheath.freeserve.co.uk

Mount Hotel ★★ SILVER AWARD
Cliff Bridge Terrace, Saint
Nicholas Cliff, Scarborough,
North Yorkshire YO11 2HA
T: (01723) 360961
F: (01723) 375850

Norbreck Hotel Rating Applied For
Castle Road, Scarborough, North
Yorkshire YO11 1HY
T: (01723) 366607
F: (01723) 500984

Norlands Hotel ★★
10 Weydale Avenue,
Scarborough, North Yorkshire
YO12 6BA
T: (01723) 362606
F: (01723) 362606

Ox Pasture Hall ★★★
Lady Ediths Drive, Throxenby,
Scarborough, North Yorkshire
YO15 5TD
T: (01723) 365295
F: (01723) 355156

Palm Court Hotel ★★★
St Nicholas Cliff, Scarborough,
North Yorkshire YO11 2ES
T: (01723) 368161
F: (01723) 371547

Red Lea Hotel ★★
Prince of Wales Terrace,
Scarborough, North Yorkshire
YO11 2AJ
T: (01723) 362431
F: (01723) 371230
E: redlea@globalnet.co.uk
I: www.redleahotel.co.uk

Ryndle Court Private Hotel ★★
47 Northstead Manor Drive,
Scarborough, North Yorkshire
YO12 6AF
T: (01723) 375188 & 07860 711517
F: (01723) 375188
E: enquiries@ryndlecourt.co.uk
I: www.ryndlecourt.co.uk

Establishments printed in blue have a detailed entry in this guide

Scarborough Travel and Holiday Lodge
Travel Accommodation
33 Valley Road, Scarborough,
North Yorkshire YO11 2LX
T: (01723) 363537
F: (01723) 501239
E: scarborough.lodge@onyxnet.co.uk
I: www.scarborough-lodge.co.uk
🌐 🔨

Selbourne Hotel ★
4 West Street, South Cliff,
Scarborough, North Yorkshire
YO11 2QL
T: (01723) 372822 & 373240
F: (01723) 372822
🌐

Southlands Hotel ★★
West Street, South Cliff,
Scarborough, North Yorkshire
YO11 2QW
T: (01723) 361461
F: (01723) 376035

Hotel St Nicholas ★★★
St Nicholas Cliff, Scarborough,
North Yorkshire YO11 2EU
T: (01723) 364101
F: (01723) 500538
🌐

Sunningdale Hotel ★★
105 Peasholm Drive,
Scarborough, North Yorkshire
YO12 7NB
T: (01723) 372041 &
07850 784347
F: (01723) 354691
E: sunningdale@barclay.net
I: www.
sunningdale-scarborough.co.uk

Wrea Head Country House Hotel ★★★
Barmoor Lane, Scalby,
Scarborough, North Yorkshire
YO13 0PB
T: (01723) 378211
F: (01723) 355936

The Beeches Hotel ★★★
42 Waltham Road, Scartho,
Grimsby, South Humberside
DN33 2LX
T: (01472) 278830
F: (01472) 752880

Bagden Hall ★★★
Wakefield Road, Scissett,
Huddersfield HD8 9LE
T: (01484) 865330
F: (01484) 861001
E: info@bagdenhall.demon.co.uk
I: www.bagdenhall.demon.co.uk

Quality Scotch Corner Hotel ★★★
A1/A66 Junction, Scotch Corner,
Richmond, North Yorkshire
DL10 6NR
T: (01748) 850900
F: (01748) 825417
E: admin@gb609.u-net.com.
I: www.choicehotels.com

The Bridge House Hotel ★
Station Road, Scunthorpe, North
Lincolnshire DN15 6PY
T: (01724) 847590
F: (01724) 861708
E: www.lincs.co.uk
🌐

Forest Pines Hotel, Golf Course and Spa
★★★★ SILVER AWARD
Ermine Street, Broughton, Brigg,
North Lincolnshire DN20 0AQ
T: (01652) 650770 & 650756
F: (01652) 650495
E: enquiries@forestpines.co.uk
I: www.forestpines.co.uk
🌐

Wortley House Hotel ★★★
Rowland Road, Scunthorpe,
North Lincolnshire DN16 1SU
T: (01724) 842223
F: (01724) 280646
E: wortley.hotel@virgin.net

Loftsome Bridge Coaching House Ltd
★★★ SILVER AWARD
Loftsome Bridge, Wressle, Selby,
North Yorkshire YO8 6EN
T: (01757) 630070
F: (01757) 630070
E: reception@loftsomebridge.co.uk
I: www.loftsomebridge-hotel.co.uk

Bowerley Hotel and Conference Centre ★★
Langcliffe, Settle, North
Yorkshire BD24 9LY
T: (01729) 823811
F: (01729) 822317
E: bowerley_hotel@aol.com

Falcon Manor Hotel ★★★
Skipton Road, Settle, North
Yorkshire BD24 9BD
T: (01729) 823814
F: (01729) 822087
E: enquiries@thefalconmanor.com
I: www.thefalconmanor.com

New Inn Hotel ★★
Clapham, Lancaster, North
Yorkshire LA2 8HH
T: (015242) 51203
F: (015242) 51496
E: newinn@compuserve.com
I: www.trad-inns.com.co.uk/newinn-clapham

Royal Oak Hotel ★★
Market Place, Settle, North
Yorkshire BD24 9ED
T: (01729) 822561
F: (01729) 823102
I: www.yorkshirenet.co.uk/stayat/royaloak

Hotel Bristol ★★★
Blonk Street, Sheffield, S1 2AU
T: (0114) 220 4000
F: (0114) 220 3900
E: sheffield@bhg.co.uk
I: www.bhg.co.uk

Cutlers Hotel ★★
George Street, Sheffield, South
Yorkshire S1 2PF
T: (0114) 273 9939
F: (0114) 276 8332
E: enquiries@cutlershotel.co.uk
I: www.cutlershotel.co.uk

The Hillsborough Hotel ★★
54-58 Langsett Road,
Hillsborough, Sheffield, S6 2UB
T: (0114) 232 2100
F: (0114) 232 2100
E: hillsboro@railway@globalnet.uk

Novotel Sheffield ★★★
Arundel Gate, Sheffield, S1 2PR
T: (0114) 278 1781
F: (0114) 278 7744
E: H1348@accorhotels.com
🔨

Whitley Hall Hotel
★★★ SILVER AWARD
Elliott Lane, Grenoside, Sheffield
S35 8NR
T: (0114) 245 4444
F: (0114) 245 5414
E: reservations@whitleyhall.com
I: www.whitleyhall.com

Coniston Hall Lodge and Restaurant ★★★
Coniston Cold, Skipton, North
Yorkshire BD23 4EB
T: (01756) 748080
F: (01756) 749487
E: conistonhall@clara.net
I: www.conistonhall.co.uk

Hanover International Hotel & Club Skipton ★★★
Keighley Road, Skipton, North
Yorkshire BD23 2TA
T: (01756) 700100
F: (01756) 700107
E: luciadonizetti
I: www.hihskipton@totalise.co.uk
🌐 🔨

Highfield Hotel ★★
58 Keighley Road, Skipton,
North Yorkshire BD23 2NB
T: (01756) 793182 & 798834
F: (01756) 793182

Unicorn Hotel ★★
Devonshire Place, Keighley Road,
Skipton, North Yorkshire
BD23 2LP
T: (01756) 794146 & 793376
F: (01756) 793376
E: christine@unicornhotel.freeserve.co.uk

Sneaton Hall Hotel ★★
Sneaton, Whitby, North
Yorkshire YO22 5HP
T: (01947) 605929
F: (01947) 820177

Posthouse Leeds/Selby ★★★
Junction A1/A63, South Milford,
Leeds LS25 5LF
T: 0870 400 9050
F: (01977) 685462

Stallingborough Grange Hotel ★★★
Riby Road, Stallingborough,
Grimsby, North East Lincolnshire
DN41 8BU
T: (01469) 561302
F: (01469) 561338
I: www.stallingborough-grange.com

Steeton Hall Hotel
Rating Applied For
Station Road, Steeton, Keighley,
West Yorkshire BD20 6RY
T: (01535) 655676
F: (01535) 655663
I: www.steetonhallhotel.co.uk

Wainstones Hotel ★★★
High Street, Great Broughton,
Stokesley, Middlesbrough,
Cleveland TS9 7EW
T: (01642) 712268
F: (01642) 711560
E: wstones@netcomuk.co.uk
I: www.wainstoneshotel.co.uk
🌐

Hazlewood Castle
★★★ GOLD AWARD
Paradise Lane, Hazlewood,
Tadcaster, North Yorkshire
LS24 9NJ
T: (01937) 535353 & 535310
F: (01937) 535316
E: info@hazlewood-castle.co.uk
I: www.hazlewood-castle.co.uk

Angel Inn ★★
Long Street, Topcliffe, Thirsk,
North Yorkshire YO7 3RW
T: (01845) 577237
F: (01845) 578000

Golden Fleece
★★ SILVER AWARD
Market Place, Thirsk, North
Yorkshire YO7 1LL
T: (01845) 523108
F: (01845) 523996
I: www@bestwestern.co.uk

Sheppards Hotel Restaurant and Bistro ★★
Front Street, Sowerby, Thirsk,
North Yorkshire YO7 1JF
T: (01845) 523655
F: (01845) 524720
E: sheppards@thirskny.freeserve.co.uk

Three Tuns Hotel ★★
Market Place, Thirsk, North
Yorkshire YO7 1LH
T: (01845) 523124
F: (01845) 52612
E: threetuns@talk121.com

Treetops Hotel ★★
Sutton Road, Thirsk, North
Yorkshire YO7 2ER
T: (01845) 522293
F: (01845) 522579
E: treetops.hotel@virginnet.co.uk
I: www.treetops-hotel.com

Establishments printed in blue have a detailed entry in this guide

THORNE
South Yorkshire
Belmont Hotel ★★
Horsefair Green, Thorne,
Doncaster, South Yorkshire
DN8 5EE
T: (01405) 812320
F: (01405) 740508
E: belmonthotel@compuserve.
com
⊛

THORNTON WATLASS
North Yorkshire
The Buck Inn ★
Thornton Watlass, Ripon, North
Yorkshire HG4 4AH
T: (01677) 422461
F: (01677) 422447

WAKEFIELD
West Yorkshire
Bank House Hotel ★★
11 Bank Street, Westgate,
Wakefield, West Yorkshire
WF1 1EH
T: (01924) 368248
F: (01924) 363724

**Billy Budd Hotel & Restaurant
★★**
10 Drury Lane, Wakefield, West
Yorkshire WF1 2TE
T: (01924) 372069 & 299368
F: (01924) 374787

Cedar Court Hotel ★★★★
Denby Dale Road, Calder Grove,
Wakefield, West Yorkshire
WF4 3QZ
T: (01924) 276310 & 261459
F: (01924) 280221

**Dimple Well Lodge Hotel
★★ SILVER AWARD**
The Green, Ossett, West
Yorkshire WF5 8JX
T: (01924) 264352
F: (01924) 274024
E: joandsandy@
dimple-well-lodge-hotel.co.uk
I: www.dimple-well-lodge-hotel.
co.uk

Parklands Hotel ★★
143 Horbury Road, Wakefield,
West Yorkshire WF2 8TY
T: (01924) 377407
F: (01924) 290348
E: steve@parklands23.fsnet.co.
uk

**Hotel St Pierre
★★★ SILVER AWARD**
733 Barnsley Road,
Newmillerdam, Wakefield, West
Yorkshire WF2 6QG
T: (01924) 255596
F: (01924) 252746
E: sales@hotelstpierre.co.uk
I: www.hotelstpierre.co.uk

WALSHFORD
North Yorkshire
Bridge Inn Hotel ★★★
Walshford, Wetherby, Yorkshire
LS22 5HS
T: (01937) 580115
F: (01937) 580556
E: bridge.walshford@virgin.net
I: www.thebridgeinnhotel.co.uk
⊛

WENTBRIDGE
West Yorkshire
**Wentbridge House Hotel
★★★ SILVER AWARD**
Wentbridge, Pontefract, West
Yorkshire WF8 3JJ
T: (01977) 620444
F: (01977) 620148
E: wentbridgehouse@
wentbridge.fsbusiness.co.uk
I: www.wentbridgehouse.co.uk

WEST WITTON
North Yorkshire
Wensleydale Heifer ★★
West Witton, Leyburn, North
Yorkshire DL8 4LS
T: (01969) 622322
F: (01969) 624183
E: info@wensleydaleheifer.co.uk
I: www.wensleydaleheifer.co.uk

WETHERBY
West Yorkshire
Jarvis Wetherby Hotel ★★★
Leeds Road, Wetherby, West
Yorkshire LS22 5HE
T: (01937) 583881
F: (01937) 580062
I: www.jarvis.co.uk

Wood Hall Hotel ★★★
Trip Lane, Linton, Wetherby,
West Yorkshire LS22 4JA
T: (01937) 587271
F: (01937) 584353

WHITBY
North Yorkshire
**Bagdale Hall & Bagdale Lodge
★★★**
1 Bagdale, Whitby, North
Yorkshire YO21 1QL
T: (01947) 602958
F: (01947) 820714
I: www.smoothhound.co.
uk/hotels/bagdale.html

**Dunsley Hall Country House
Hotel and Leisure Club
★★★ SILVER AWARD**
Dunsley, Whitby, North
Yorkshire YO21 3TL
T: (01947) 893437
F: (01947) 893505
E: reception@dunsleyhall.com
I: www.dunsleyhall.com

**Royal Hotel
Rating Applied For**
West Cliff, Whitby, North
Yorkshire YO21 3HA
T: (01947) 602234
F: (01947) 820355

Saxonville Hotel ★★
Ladysmith Avenue, Whitby,
North Yorkshire YO21 3HX
T: (01947) 602631 & 0800 019
1147
F: (01947) 820523
E: saxonville@onyxnet.co.uk
I: www.whitshirenet.co.
uk/saxonville

**Stakesby Manor
★★ SILVER AWARD**
Manor Close, High Stakesby,
Whitby, North Yorkshire
YO21 1HL
T: (01947) 602773
F: (01947) 602140
E: relax@stakesby-manor.co.uk
I: www.stakesby-manor.co.uk
⊛

White House Hotel ★★
Upgang Lane, West Cliff, Whitby,
North Yorkshire YO21 3JJ
T: (01947) 600469
F: (01947) 821600
E: 101745.1440@compuserve.
com
I: www.s-h-systems.co.
uk/hotels/whitehse.html

WHITLEY
West Yorkshire
**The Woolpack Country Inn
Hotel & Restaurant★★★**
Whitley Road, Whitley,
Dewsbury, West Yorkshire
WF12 0LZ
T: (01924) 499999 &
07930 418311
F: (01924) 495289
I: www.woolpackhotel.co.uk

WILLERBY
East Riding of Yorkshire
**Willerby Manor Hotel
★★★ SILVER AWARD**
Well Lane, Willerby, Hull
HU10 6ER
T: (01482) 652616
F: (01482) 653901
E: info@willerbymanor.co.uk
I: www.willerbymanor.co.uk

YORK
North Yorkshire
Abbots Mews Hotel ★★
6 Marygate Lane, Bootham,
York, YO30 7DE
T: (01904) 634866 & 622395
F: (01904) 612848

**Aldwark Manor Hotel, Golf
and Country Club★★★**
Aldwark, Alne, York YO61 1UF
T: (01347) 838146
F: (01347) 838867
E: reception@aldwarkmanor.co.
uk
I: www.aldwarkmanor.co.uk

Alhambra Court Hotel ★★
31 St Mary's, Bootham, York,
YO30 7DD
T: (01904) 628474 & 647427
F: (01904) 610690
⊛

Ambassador ★★★
123-125 The Mount, York,
YO24 1DU
T: (01904) 641316
F: (01904) 640259
E: stay@ambassadorhotel.co.uk
I: www.ambassadorhotel.co.uk
⊛

Ashcroft Hotel ★★
294 Bishopthorpe Road, York,
YO23 1LH
T: (01904) 659286 & 629543
F: (01904) 640107

Beechwood Close Hotel ★★
19 Shipton Road, Clifton, York
YO30 5RE
T: (01904) 658378
F: (01904) 647124
E: bch@selcom.co.uk
I: www.beechwood-close.co.uk

Black Bull Hotel ★★
Hull Road, York, YO10 3LF
T: (01904) 411856
F: (01904) 430667

The Churchill ★★★
65 Bootham, York, YO30 7DQ
T: (01904) 644456
F: (01904) 652447
E: churchillh@aol.com
I: churchillhotel.com

Clifton Bridge Hotel ★★
Water End, Clifton, York
YO30 6LL
T: (01904) 610510
F: (01904) 640208
E: enq@cliftonbridgehotel.co.uk
I: www.cliftonbridgehotel.co.uk
⊛ ⟨⟩

Coach House Hotel ★★
20-22 Marygate, Bootham, York,
YO30 7BH
T: (01904) 652780
F: (01904) 679943

Cottage Hotel ★★
1 Clifton Green, York, YO30 6LH
T: (01904) 643711
F: (01904) 611230

**Dean Court Hotel
★★★ SILVER AWARD**
Duncombe Place, York, YO1 7EF
T: (01904) 625082
F: (01904) 620305
E: info@deancourt-york.co.uk
I: www.deancourt-york.co.uk
⊛

Elliotts ★★
Sycamore Place, Bootham
Terrace, York, YO30 7DW
T: (01904) 623333
F: (01904) 654908
E: elliottshotel@aol.com

Elmbank ★★
The Mount, York, YO24 1GE
T: (01904) 610653
F: (01904) 627139

Granby Lodge Hotel ★
41-43 Scarcroft Road, York,
YO24 1DB
T: (01904) 653291
F: (01904) 653291

**The Grange Hotel
★★★ SILVER AWARD**
1 Clifton, York, YO30 6AA
T: (01904) 644744
F: (01904) 612453
E: info@grangehotel.co.uk
I: www.grangehotel.co.uk
⟨⟩

Hedley House ★★
3-4 Bootham Terrace, York,
North Yorkshire YO30 7DH
T: (01904) 637404
F: (01904) 639774
E: h.h@mcmail.com
I: www.hedleyhouse.com

Hilton York ★★★★
1 Tower Street, York, YO1 9WD
T: (01904) 648111
F: (01904) 610317
E: reservation@stakis.york.co.uk
I: www.hilton.com
⟨⟩

Holgate Hill Hotel ★★
124 Holgate Road, York,
YO24 4BB
T: (01904) 653786
F: (01904) 643223
E: hhhhh01904@tesco.net
⊛

Establishments printed in blue have a detailed entry in this guide

Jacobean Lodge Hotel ★★
Plainville Lane, Wigginton, York
YO32 2RG
T: (01904) 762749
F: (01904) 768403

Jarvis Abbey Park ★★★
77 The Mount, York, YO24 1BN
T: (01904) 658301
F: (01904) 621224
I: www.jarvis.co.uk
◎

**Jarvis International Hotel
★★★**
Shipton Road, Skelton, York,
YO30 1XW
T: (01904) 670222
F: (01904) 670311
I: www.jarvis.co.uk

Jorvik Hotel ★★
50-52 Marygate, Bootham, York,
YO30 7BH
T: (01904) 653511
F: (01904) 627009
I: freespace.virgin.net/jorvik.
hotel

**Judges Lodging
★★★ SILVER AWARD**
9 Lendal, York, YO1 8AQ
T: (01904) 623587 & 638733
F: (01904) 679947
E: judgeshotel@aol.com

Kilima Hotel ★★
129 Holgate Road, York,
YO24 4AZ
T: (01904) 625787
F: (01904) 612083
E: sales@kilima.co.uk
I: www.kilima.co.uk

Knavesmire Manor Hotel ★★
302 Tadcaster Road, York,
YO24 1HE
T: (01904) 702941
F: (01904) 709274
E: knavesmire@easynet.co.uk
I: www.knavesmire-manor.co.uk
◎

**Lady Anne Middleton's Hotel
★★**
Skeldergate, York, YO1 6DS
T: (01904) 611570
F: (01904) 613043
E: bookings@ladyannes.co.uk
I: www.ladyannes.co.uk

Meadowcroft Hotel ★
84 Bootham, York, YO30 7DF
T: (01904) 655194
F: (01904) 651384
E: mcroftyork@aol.com
I: www.scoot.co.
uk/meadowcroft

Monkbar Hotel ★★★
St Maurice's Road, York,
YO31 7JA
T: (01904) 638086
F: (01904) 629195
E: colin-gardner@
monkbar-york.freeserve.co.uk

Mount Royale Hotel ★★★
The Mount, York, YO24 1GU
T: (01904) 628856
F: (01904) 611171
E: reservations@mountroyale.
co.uk
I: www.mountroyale.co.uk

Newington Hotel ★★
147-157 Mount Vale, York,
YO24 1DJ
T: (01904) 625173 & 623090
F: (01904) 679937
E: bookings@ladyannes.co.uk
I: www.ladyannes.co.uk

Novotel York ★★★
Fishergate, York, YO10 4FD
T: (01904) 611660
F: (01904) 610925
E: h0949-gm@accor-hotel.com
⏏

Orchard Court Hotel ★★
4 St Peter's Grove, Bootham,
York, YO30 6AQ
T: (01904) 653964
F: (01904) 653964
◎

**The Parsonage Country House
Hotel ★★★**
York Road, Escrick, York
YO19 6LF
T: (01904) 728111
F: (01904) 728151
E: reservations.parsonagehotel.
co.uk
I: www.parsonagehotel.co.uk

Queens Hotel
Travel Accommodation
Queens Staith Road,
Skeldergate, York, YO32 5XF
T: (01904) 611321

Royal York Hotel ★★★★
Station Road, York, YO24 1AA
T: (01904) 653681
F: (01904) 623503
E: julia.bodmer@principalhotels.
co.uk
I: www.principalhotels.co.uk
◎

Savages Hotel ★★
15 St Peter's Grove, Clifton, York
YO30 6AQ
T: (01904) 610818
F: (01904) 627729
⏏

**Swallow Hotel
★★★★ SILVER AWARD**
Tadcaster Road, Dringhouses,
York, YO24 2QQ
T: (01904) 701000 & 770600
F: (01904) 702308
E: york@swallow-hotels.co.uk
I: www.swallowhotels.com
◎ ♿

Wheatlands Lodge Hotel ★★
75-85 Scarcroft Road, York,
YO24 1DB
T: (01904) 654318
F: (01904) 654318
E: wheatlodge@aol.com
I: www.smoothhound.co.
uk/hotels/wheatlan.html

York Moat House ★★★
North Street, York, YO1 6JF
T: (01904) 459988
F: (01904) 641793
E: cbrk@queensmoat.co.uk
◎

York Pavilion Hotel ★★★
Main Street, Fulford, York
YO10 4PJ
T: (01904) 622099
F: (01904) 626939

HEART OF ENGLAND

**ABBOTS SALFORD
Warwickshire**

**Salford Hall Hotel
★★★ SILVER AWARD**
Abbots Salford, Evesham,
Worcestershire WR11 5UT
T: (01386) 871300
F: (01386) 871301
E: reception@salfordhall.co.uk
I: www.salfordhall.co.uk

**ALBRIGHTON
Shropshire**

**Lea Manor Hotel
★★★ SILVER AWARD**
Holyhead Road, Albrighton,
WV7 3BX
T: (01902) 373266
F: (01902) 372853
E: hotel@leamanor.co.uk
I: www.leamanor.co.uk

**ALCESTER
Warwickshire**

Kings Court Hotel ★★★
Kings Coughton, Stratford-
upon-Avon, Warwickshire
B49 5QQ
T: (01789) 763111
F: (01789) 400242
E: info@kingscourthotel.co.uk
I: www.kingscourthotel.co.uk

Throckmorton Arms Hotel ★★
Coughton, Alcester,
Warwickshire B49 5HX
T: (01789) 762879
F: (01789) 762654

**ALREWAS
Staffordshire**

**Claymar Hotel and Restaurant
★★**
118a Main Street, Alrewas,
Burton upon Trent, Staffordshire
DE13 7AE
T: (01283) 790202 & 791281
F: (01283) 791465

**ALTON
Staffordshire**

**Alton Bridge Hotel
Rating Applied For**
Station Road, Alton, Stoke-on-
Trent, Staffordshire ST10 4BX
T: (01538) 702338
F: (01538) 703303
E: altonbridge@mut.org.uk
I: www.touristnetuk.
com/wm/alton-bridge-hotel

**Alton Towers Hotel
★★★ SILVER AWARD**
Alton Towers, Alton, Stoke-on-
Trent, Staffordshire ST10 4DB
T: (01538) 704600
F: (01538) 704657

**ASHBOURNE
Derbyshire**

**The Bentley Brook Inn and
Fenny's Restaurant★**
Fenny Bentley, Ashbourne,
Derbyshire DE6 1LF
T: (01335) 350278
F: (01335) 350422
E: all@bentleybrookinn.co.uk
I: www.bentleybrookinn.co.uk

**Callow Hall Country House
Hotel & Restaurant
★★★ SILVER AWARD**
Mappleton, Ashbourne,
Derbyshire DE6 2AA
T: (01335) 300900 & 300900
F: (01335) 300512
E: RESERVATIONS@callowhall.
demon.co.uk
I: www.callowhall.co.uk

**BAKEWELL
Derbyshire**

Ashford Arms ★★
Church Street, Ashford in the
Water, Bakewell, Derbyshire
DE45 1QB
T: (01629) 812725
F: (01629) 814749

**The Croft Country House Hotel
★★ SILVER AWARD**
Great Longstone, Bakewell,
Derbyshire DE45 1TF
T: (01629) 640278
⏏

**East Lodge Country House
Hotel and Restaurant
★★★ SILVER AWARD**
Rowsley, Matlock, Derbyshire
DE4 2EF
T: (01629) 734474
F: (01629) 733949
E: info@eastlodge.com
I: www.eastlodge.com

Rutland Arms Hotel ★★★
The Square, Bakewell, Derbyshire
DE45 1BT
T: (01629) 812812
F: (01629) 812309
E: rutland@bakewell.demon.co.
uk
I: www.bakewell.demon.co.uk

**BALSALL COMMON
West Midlands**

**Haigs Hotel
Rating Applied For**
Kenilworth Road, Balsall
Common, Coventry CV7 7EL
T: (01676) 533004
F: (01676) 535132

BAMFORD
Derbyshire
Yorkshire Bridge Inn
★★ SILVER AWARD
Ashopton Road, Bamford, Hope
Valley S33 0AZ
T: (01433) 651361
F: (01433) 651361
E: mr@ybridge.force9.co.uk
I: www.yorkshire-bridge.co.uk

BARNBY MOOR
Nottinghamshire
Ye Olde Bell ★★★
Barnby Moor, Retford,
Nottinghamshire DN22 8QS
T: (01777) 705121
F: (01777) 860424

BASLOW
Derbyshire
Devonshire Arms Hotel ★★
Nether End, Baslow, Bakewell,
Derbyshire DE45 1SR
T: (01246) 582551
F: (01246) 582116
E: devonshirearms@btinternet.
com

Fischers Baslow Hall
★★ GOLD AWARD
Calver Road, Baslow, Bakewell,
Derbyshire DE45 1RR
T: (01246) 583259
F: (01246) 583818

BERKELEY
Gloucestershire
The Berkeley Arms Hotel ★★
Canonbury Street, Berkeley,
Gloucestershire GL13 9BG
T: (01453) 810291
F: (01453) 511334

Newport Towers Hotel ★★
Newport, Berkeley,
Gloucestershire GL13 9PX
T: (01453) 810575
F: (01453) 511062

Prince of Wales Hotel ★★★
Berkeley Road, Berkeley,
Gloucestershire GL13 9HD
T: (01453) 810474
F: (01453) 511370

BERKSWELL
West Midlands
**Nailcote Hall Hotel and
Restaurant★★★★★**
Nailcote Lane, Berkswell,
Coventry CV7 7DE
T: (024) 7646 6174
F: (024) 7647 0720
E: info@nailcotehall.co.uk
I: www.nailcotehall.co.uk

BEWDLEY
Worcestershire
**The Jarvis Heath Hotel and
Country Club★★★**
Habberley Road, Wribbenhall,
Bewdley, Kidderminster,
Worcestershire DY12 1LJ
T: (01299) 400900
F: (01299) 400921

BIBURY
Gloucestershire
The Swan Hotel
★★★ GOLD AWARD
Bibury, Cirencester,
Gloucestershire GL7 5NW
T: (01285) 740695
F: (01285) 740473
E: swanhot1@
swanhotel-cotswolds.co.uk
I: www.swanhotel.co.uk

BIGGIN-BY-HARTINGTON
Derbyshire
Biggin Hall ★★
★★★
Biggin-by-Hartington, Buxton,
Derbyshire SK17 0DH
T: (01298) 84451
F: (01298) 84681
E: bigginhall@compuserve.com
I: www.bigginhall.co.uk

BIRMINGHAM
West Midlands
Arden Hotel and Leisure Club
★★★
Coventry Road, Bickenhill,
Solihull, West Midlands B92 0EH
T: (01675) 443221
F: (01675) 443221
E: enquires@ardenhote.co.uk
I: www.ardenhotel.co.uk

The Burlington Hotel
★★★★ SILVER AWARD
Burlington Arcade, 126 New
Street, Birmingham, B2 4JQ
T: (0121) 643 9191
F: (0121) 643 5075
E: mail@Burlingtonhotel.com
I: www.burlingtonhotel.com

Chamberlain Hotel ★★
Alcester Street, Birmingham,
B12 0PJ
T: (0121) 606 9000
F: (0121) 606 9001
E: info@chamberlain.co.uk

The Copthorne Birmingham
★★★★ SILVER AWARD
Paradise Circus, Birmingham,
B3 3HJ
T: (0121) 200 2727
F: (0121) 200 1197
E: sales.birmingham@mill-cop
com
I: www.mill-cop.com

Fountain Court Hotel ★★
339-343 Hagley Road,
Edgbaston, Birmingham
B17 8NH
T: (0121) 429 1754
F: (0121) 429 1209
E: fountain-court@excite.co.uk

Old Farm Hotel ★★
108 Linden Road, Bournville,
Birmingham B30 1LA
T: (0121) 458 3146
F: (0121) 459 0607
E: oldfarmhotel@voogd.co.uk

Sheriden House Hotel ★★
82 Handsworth Wood Road,
Handsworth Wood, Birmingham,
B20 2PL
T: (0121) 523 5960 & 554 2185
F: (0121) 551 4761
E: g.f.harmon@btinternet.com
I: www.SmoothHound.co.
uk/hotels/sheriden.html

Swallow Hotel
★★★★★ GOLD AWARD
Hagley Road, Five Ways,
Birmingham, B16 8SJ
T: (0121) 452 1144
F: (0121) 456 3442

**Thistle Birmingham City
Rating Applied For**
St Chad's, Queensway,
Birmingham, B4 6HY
T: (0121) 236 4211
F: (0121) 233 2195

**Thistle Birmingham Edgbaston
Rating Applied For**
225 Hagley Road, Edgbaston,
Birmingham B16 9RY
T: (0121) 455 9777
F: (0121) 454 9432
E: birmingham.edgbaston@
thistle.co.uk
I: www.thistlehotels.com

Westbourne Lodge Hotel ★★
27-29 Fountain Road,
Edgbaston, Birmingham
B17 8NJ
T: (0121) 429 1003
F: (0121) 429 7436
E: westbourne@lodgehotel.
demon.co.uk

Westmead Hotel ★★★
Redditch Road, Hopwood,
Alvechurch, Birmingham
B48 7AL
T: (0121) 445 1202
F: (0121) 445 6163

BLYTH
Nottinghamshire
The Charnwood Hotel ★★★
Sheffield Road, Blyth, Worksop,
Nottinghamshire S81 8HF
T: (01909) 591610
F: (01909) 591429
E: info@charnwoodhotel.com
I: www.charnwoodhotel.com

BOSTON
Lincolnshire
Comfort Friendly Inn ★★
Junction A17/A52, Donnington
Road, Bicker Bar Roundabout,
Boston, Lincolnshire PE20 3AN
T: (01205) 820118
F: (01205) 820228
E: aminogb607.u-net-com
I: wwwv-net-com/hotelnet/
friendly/home/htm

BOURTON-ON-THE-WATER
Gloucestershire
Apple Pie House Hotel ★★★
Whiteshoots Hill, Bourton-on-
the-Water, Cheltenham,
Gloucestershire GL54 2LE
T: (01451) 820387
F: (01451) 812821
E: hotel@bourton.com
I: www.bourton.com

Chester House Hotel ★★
Victoria Street, Bourton-on-the-
Water, Cheltenham,
Gloucestershire GL54 2BU
T: (01451) 820286
F: (01451) 820471
E: juliand@chesterhouse.u-net.
com
I: www.bizare.demon.co.
uk/chester

Dial House ★★ SILVER AWARD
The Chestnuts, High Street,
Bourton-on-the-Water,
Cheltenham, Gloucestershire
GL54 2AN
T: (01451) 822244
F: (01451) 810126
E: info@dialhousehotel.com
I: www.dialhousehotel.com

Old Manse Hotel
★★ SILVER AWARD
Victoria Street, Bourton-on-the-
Water, Cheltenham,
Gloucestershire GL54 2BX
T: (01451) 820082
F: (01451) 810381
E: centralreservations@
oldenglishpub.co.uk
I: www.oldenglish.co.uk

BRETBY
Derbyshire
Stanhope Arms Hotel ★★
Ashby Road East, Bretby, Burton
upon Trent, Staffordshire
DE15 0PU
T: (01283) 217954
F: (01283) 226199

BRIDGNORTH
Shropshire
The Croft Hotel ★
St. Mary's Street, Bridgnorth,
Shropshire WV16 4DW
T: (01746) 762416 & 767155
F: (01746) 767431

Mill Hotel ★★★★
Alveley, Bridgnorth, Shropshire
WV15 6HL
T: (01746) 780437
F: (01746) 780850
I: www.theaa.co.
uk/region5/36837.html

Old Vicarage Hotel
★★★ GOLD AWARD
Worfield, Bridgnorth, Shropshire
WV15 5JZ
T: (01746) 716497 &
0800 0968010
F: (01746) 716552
E: admin@the-old-vicarage.
demon.co.uk
I: www.oldvicarageworfield.
demon.co.uk

BROADWAY
Worcestershire
Broadway Hotel
★★★ SILVER AWARD
The Green, Broadway,
Worcestershire WR12 7AA
T: (01386) 852401
F: (01386) 853879
E: Bookings@
cotswold-inns-hotels.co.uk
I: www.cotswold-inns-hotel.co.
uk

**Collin House Hotel &
Restaurant★★**
Collin Lane, Broadway,
Worcestershire WR12 7PB
T: (01386) 858354
F: (01386) 858697
E: collin.house@virgin.net
I: www.broadway-cotswolds.co.
uk/collin.html

Establishments printed in blue have a detailed entry in this guide

Dormy House
★★★ SILVER AWARD
Willersey Hill, Broadway,
Worcestershire WR12 7LF
T: (01386) 852711
F: (01386) 858636
E: reservation@dormyhouse.co.
uk

The Lygon Arms
★★★★ GOLD AWARD
Broadway, Worcestershire
WR12 7DU
T: (01386) 852255
F: (01386) 854470
E: info@the-lygon-arms.co.uk
I: www.savoy-group.co.uk

BROMSGROVE
Worcestershire

The Hilton Hotel
★★★★ SILVER AWARD
Birmingham Road, Bromsgrove,
Worcestershire B61 0JB
T: (0121) 447 7888
F: (0121) 447 7273
E: reservations@stakis.co.uk
I: www.stakisco.uk

Pine Lodge Hotel ★★★★
Kidderminster Road,
Bromsgrove, Worcestershire
B61 9AB
T: (01527) 576600
F: (01527) 878981
E: enquiries@pine-lodge-hotel.
co.uk

BUCKLAND
Gloucestershire

Buckland Manor
★★★ GOLD AWARD
Buckland, Broadway,
Worcestershire WR12 7LY
T: (01386) 852626
F: (01386) 853557
E: buckland-manor.uk@mon.
com
I: www.
relaischateaux-fr/buckland

BURTON UPON TRENT
Staffordshire

The Queens Hotel ★★★
One Bridge Street, Burton upon
Trent, Staffordshire DE14 1SY
T: (01283) 523800
F: (01283) 523823

The Riverboat Branston ★★★
Riverside Drive, Branston,
Burton upon Trent, Staffordshire
DE14 3EP
T: (01283) 511234
F: (01283) 511441

BUXTON
Derbyshire

Alison Park ★★
3 Temple Road, Buxton,
Derbyshire SK17 9BA
T: (01298) 22473
F: (01298) 72709
E: reservations@
alison-park-hotel.co.uk
I: www.alison-park-hotel.co.uk
♿

Buckingham Hotel ★★★
1 Burlington Road, Buxton,
Derbyshire SK17 9AS
T: (01298) 70481
F: (01298) 72186
E: fontdesk@buckinghamhotel.
co.uk
I: www.buckinghamhotel.co.uk

Old Hall Hotel ★★★
The Square, Buxton, Derbyshire
SK17 6BD
T: (01298) 22841
F: (01298) 72437
E: reception@
oldhallhotelbuxton.co.uk
I: www.oldhallhotelbuxton.co.uk

Palace Hotel ★★★★
Palace Road, Buxton, Derbyshire
SK17 6AG
T: (01298) 22001
F: (01298) 72131
◉

**Portland Hotel and Park
Restaurant** ★★
32 St John's Road, Buxton,
Derbyshire SK17 6XQ
T: (01298) 71493 & 22462
F: (01298) 27464
E: brian@portland-hotel.
freeserve.co.uk
I: www.highpeak/portland.co

CANNOCK
Staffordshire

Oak Farm Hotel ★★★
Watling Street, Hatherton,
Cannock, Staffordshire
WS11 1SF
T: (01543) 462045
F: (01543) 500257
I: N.
BANFORD@OAKFARMHOTEL.
FSBUSINESS.CO.UK

CASTLE DONINGTON
Leicestershire

Donington Manor Hotel ★★★
High Street, Castle Donington,
Derby DE74 2PP
T: (01332) 810253
F: (01332) 850330
E: cngrist@dmhgrist.demon.co.
uk
I: www.doningtonmanorhotel.
co.uk

Thistle East Midlands Airport
Rating Applied For
East Midlands Airport, Castle
Donington, Derby DE74 2SH
T: (01332) 850700
F: (01332) 850823
E: east.midlandsairport@thistle.
co.uk
I: www.thistlehotels.com
◉

CASTLETON
Derbyshire

Castle Hotel ★★
Castle Street, Castleton, Hope
Valley S33 8WG
T: (01433) 620578 &
07885 952810
F: (01433) 622902
I: www.webrover.co.uk/castle.
htm
◉

CHADDESLEY CORBETT
Worcestershire

Brockencote Hall
★★★ GOLD AWARD
Chaddesley Corbett,
Kidderminster, Worcestershire
DY10 4PY
T: (01562) 777876
F: (01562) 777872
E: info@brockencotehall.com
I: www.brockencotehall.com
◉

CHELTENHAM
Gloucestershire

Carlton Hotel ★★★
Parabola Road, Cheltenham,
Gloucestershire GL50 3AQ
T: (01242) 514453
F: (01242) 226487

Charlton Kings Hotel
★★★ SILVER AWARD
London Road, Charlton Kings,
Cheltenham, Gloucestershire
GL52 6UU
T: (01242) 231061
F: (01242) 241900

The Cheltenham Park Hotel
★★★★ SILVER AWARD
Cirencester Road, Charlton
Kings, Cheltenham,
Gloucestershire GL53 8EA
T: (01242) 222021
F: (01242) 254880
E: cheltenhampark@
paramount-hotels.co.uk
I: www.paramount-hotels.co.uk

Clarence Court Hotel
Rating Applied For
Clarence Square, Cheltenham,
Gloucestershire GL50 4JR
T: (01242) 580411
F: (01242) 224609
◉

Dumbleton Hall Hotel ★★★
Dumbleton, Evesham,
Worcestershire WR11 6TS
T: (01386) 881240
F: (01386) 882142
E: reception@
dumbletonhallforce9.co.uk
I: www.dumbletonhallforce9.co.
uk

North Hall Hotel ★★
Pittville Circus Road,
Cheltenham, Gloucestershire
GL52 2PZ
T: (01242) 520589
F: (01242) 261953
E: northhallhotel@btinternet.
com

Hotel On The Park
★★★ GOLD AWARD
38 Evesham Road, Cheltenham,
Gloucestershire GL52 2AH
T: (01242) 518898
F: (01242) 511526
E: stay@hotelonthepark.co.uk
I: www.hotelonthepark.co.uk

**The Prestbury House Hotel and
Restaurant** ★★★
The Burgage, Prestbury,
Cheltenham, Gloucestershire
GL52 3DN
T: (01242) 529533
F: (01242) 227076
I: www.smoothhound.co.
uk/hotels/prestbur.html
◉ ♿

Thistle Cheltenham
Rating Applied For
Gloucester Road, Cheltenham,
Gloucestershire GL51 0TS
T: (01242) 232 691
F: (01242) 221846
E: cheltenham@Thistle.co.uk
I: www.thistlehotels.com
◉

White House Hotel ★★★
Gloucester Road, Staverton,
Cheltenham, Gloucestershire
GL51 0ST
T: (01452) 713226
F: (01452) 857590
E: felicity@whitehousehotel.
freeserve.co.uk
I: www.smoothhound.co.uk

Willoughby House Hotel ★★★
1 Suffolk Square, Cheltenham,
Gloucestershire GL50 2DR
T: (01242) 522798
F: (01242) 256369
E: bookings@willoughbyhouse.
com
I: www.willoughbyhouse.co

CHESTERFIELD
Derbyshire

Portland Hotel ★★
West Bars, Chesterfield,
Derbyshire S40 1AY
T: (01246) 234502
F: (01246) 550915

The Sandpiper Hotel ★★★
Sheffield Road, Sheepbridge,
Chesterfield, Derbyshire S41 9EH
T: (01246) 450550
F: (01246) 452805
E: sandpiper.hotel@virgin.net
I: www.sandpiperhotel.co.uk
◉

The Tullamore Hotel
Rating Applied For
32 Springbank Road,
Chesterfield, Derbyshire S40 1NL
T: (01246) 550542

CHIPPING CAMPDEN
Gloucestershire

Noel Arms Hotel ★★★
High Street, Chipping Campden,
Gloucestershire GL55 6AT
T: (01386) 840317
F: (01386) 841136
E: bookings@
cotswold-inns-hotels.co.uk
I: www.cotswold-inns-hotels.co.
uk

Three Ways House ★★★
Chapel Lane, Mickleton,
Chipping Campden,
Gloucestershire GL55 6SB
T: (01386) 438429
F: (01386) 438118
E: threeways@puddingclub.com
I: www.puddingclub.com

CHURCH STRETTON
Shropshire

Longmynd Hotel ★★★
Cunnery Road, Church Stretton,
Shropshire SY6 6AG
T: (01694) 722244
F: (01694) 722718
E: reservations@longmynd.co.
uk
I: www.longmynd.co.uk

Mynd House Hotel ★★
Ludlow Road, Little Stretton,
Church Stretton, Shropshire
SY6 6RB
T: (01694) 722212
F: (01694) 724180
E: myndhouse@goz.co.uk
I: www.goz.co.uk/myndhouse

CIRENCESTER
Gloucestershire
Corinium Court Hotel
Rating Applied For
12 Gloucester Street,
Cirencester, Gloucestershire
GL7 2DG
T: (01285) 659711 &
07970 372208
F: (01285) 885807
E: timmcg@waitrose.com

Crown of Crucis ★★★
Ampney Crucis, Cirencester,
Gloucestershire GL7 5RS
T: (01285) 851806
F: (01285) 851735
E: info@thecrownofcrucis
I: www.thecrownofcrucis.co.uk

The Jarvis Fleece Hotel ★★
Market Place, Cirencester,
Gloucestershire GL7 2NZ
T: (01285) 658507
F: (01285) 651017

King's Head Hotel
Rating Applied For
Market Place, Cirencester,
Gloucestershire GL7 2NR
T: (01285) 653322
F: (01285) 655103
(⚲)

CLEARWELL
Gloucestershire
Wyndham Arms
★★★ SILVER AWARD
Clearwell, Coleford,
Gloucestershire GL16 8JT
T: (01594) 833666
F: (01594) 836450

CLEEVE HILL
Gloucestershire
Rising Sun Hotel ★★★
Cleeve Hill, Cheltenham,
Gloucestershire GL52 3PX
T: (01242) 676281 & 672002
F: (01242) 673069

CLEOBURY MORTIMER
Shropshire
The Redfern Hotel ★★
Cleobury Mortimer,
Kidderminster, Worcestershire
DY14 8AA
T: (01299) 270395
F: (01299) 271011
E: jon@redfern-hotel.co.uk
I: www.redfern-hotel.co.uk

COALVILLE
Leicestershire
Charnwood Arms ★★
Beveridge Lane, Bardon Hill,
Coalville, Leicester LE6 2TB
T: (01530) 813644
F: (01530) 815425

COLEFORD
Gloucestershire
The Lambsquay House Hotel
★★
Royal Forest of Dean, Coleford,
Gloucestershire GL16 8QB
T: (01594) 833127
F: (01594) 833127

The Speech House ★★★
Forest of Dean, Coleford,
Gloucestershire GL16 7EL
T: (01594) 822607
F: (01594) 823658
E: relax@thespeechhouse.
demon.co.uk
I: www.fweb.org.uk/speech
(⚲)

COLESHILL
Warwickshire
Coleshill Hotel ★★★
152 High Street, Coleshill,
Birmingham B46 3BG
T: (01675) 465527
F: (01675) 464013

Grimstock Country House
Hotel ★★★
Gilson Road, Coleshill,
Birmingham, Warwickshire
B46 1AJ
T: (01675) 462121 & 462161
F: (01675) 467646
E: grimstockhotel@easynet.co.
uk

CORLEY
West Midlands
Toffs Country House Hotel ★★
Wall Hill Hall, Wall Hill Road,
Corley, Coventry CV7 8AD
T: (02476) 332030
F: (02476) 332255
I: www.toffs-hotel.co.uk
(⚲)

COVENTRY
West Midlands
Coombe Abbey Hotel
★★★ GOLD AWARD
Brinklow Road, Binley, Coventry
CV3 2AB
T: (024) 7645 0450
F: (024) 7663 5101
E: ACCOMMODATION@
COMMBEABBEY.COM
I: WWW.COOMBEABBEY.COM

Coventry Holiday Inn Express
Travel Accommodation
Kenpass Highway, Coventry,
CV3 6PB
T: (024) 7641 7555
F: (024) 7641 3388

Merrick Lodge Hotel ★★
80-82 St Nicholas Street,
Coventry, CV1 4BP
T: (024) 7655 3940
F: (024) 7655 0112
I: www.merricklodge.co.uk

DARLEY DALE
Derbyshire
Dales and Peaks Hotel and
Restaurant ★★
Old Road, Darley Dale, Matlock,
Derbyshire DE4 2ER
T: (01629) 733775
F: (01629) 733775

DERBY
Derbyshire
International Hotel &
Restaurant ★★★
Burton Road (A5250), Derby,
DE23 6AD
T: (01332) 369321
F: (01332) 294430

Kedleston Country House
Hotel ★★
Kedleston Road, Derby,
DE52 2JD
T: (01332) 559202
F: (01332) 558822

Midland Hotel ★★★
Midland Road, Derby, DE1 2SQ
T: (01332) 345894
F: (01332) 293522
E: sales@midland-derby.co.uk
I: www.midland-derby.co.uk
(⚲)

Mundy Arms Hotel ★★★
Ashbourne Road, Mackworth,
Derby DE22 4LZ
T: (01332) 824254 & 824664
F: (01332) 824519
E: mr/p@msn.com
I: www.derbyhotel.com
(⚲)

DUDLEY
West Midlands
The Copthorne Merry Hill
★★★★
The Waterfront, Level Street,
Brierley Hill, Dudley, West
Midlands DY5 1UR
T: (01384) 482882
F: (01384) 482773
E: reservations@mill-cop.
com/marketing@mill-cop.com
I: www.mill-cop.com
(⚲)

ECCLESHALL
Staffordshire
The George Inn
Rating Applied For
Castle Street, Eccleshall, Stafford
ST21 6DF
T: (01785) 850300
F: (01785) 851452

EDGBASTON
West Midlands
Apollo Hotel ★★★
Hagley Road, Edgbaston,
Birmingham, West Midlands
B16 9RA
T: (0121) 455 0271
F: (0121) 456 2394

ETRURIA
Staffordshire
Stoke on Trent Moat House
★★★★
Etruria Hall, Festival Way,
Etruria, Stoke-on-Trent ST1 5BQ
T: (01782) 609988
F: (01782) 284500

EVESHAM
Worcestershire
Chequers Inn (Fladbury) Ltd
★★
Chequers Lane, Fladbury,
Pershore, Worcestershire
WR10 2PZ
T: (01386) 860276 & 860527
F: (01386) 861286
E: chequers_inn_fladbury@
hotmail.com

The Mill at Harvington
★★★ SILVER AWARD
Anchor Lane, Harvington,
Evesham, Worcestershire
WR11 5NR
T: (01386) 870688
F: (01386) 870688

Riverside Hotel ★★
The Parks, Offenham Road,
Evesham, Worcestershire
WR11 5JP
T: (01386) 446200
F: (01386) 40021

The Waterside Hotel ★★★
56 Waterside, Evesham,
Worcestershire WR11 6JZ
T: (01386) 442420
F: (01386) 446272

Wood Norton Hall and
Conference Centre
★★★★ GOLD AWARD
Evesham, Worcestershire
WR11 4YB
T: (01386) 420007 & 420000
F: (01386) 420190
E: woodnortonhall@bbc.co.uk
I: www.woodnortonhall.co.uk

FAIRFORD
Gloucestershire
Bull Hotel ★★
Market Place, Fairford,
Gloucestershire GL7 4AA
T: (01285) 712535 & 712217
F: (01285) 713782
E: mashd@markdudley.
freeserve.co.uk
I: www.smoothhound.co.uk/

FINEDON
Northamptonshire
Tudor Gate Hotel ★★
35 High Street, Finedon,
Wellingborough,
Northamptonshire NN9 5JN
T: (01933) 680408
F: (01933) 680745
E: info@tudorgate-hotel.co.uk
I: www.tudorgate-hotel.co.uk
(⚲)(⚲)

FOWNHOPE
Herefordshire
Green Man Inn ★★
Fownhope, Hereford HR1 4PE
T: (01432) 860243
F: (01432) 860207
I: www.smoothhound.co.
uk/Hotels/Greenman.html

GAINSBOROUGH
Lincolnshire
White Hart Hotel ★
Lord Street, Gainsborough,
Lincolnshire DN21 2DD
T: (01427) 612018
F: (01427) 811756
E: white.hart@tesco.net
(⚲)

GLOSSOP
Derbyshire
Wind in the Willows Hotel
★★ SILVER AWARD
Derbyshire Level, off Sheffield
Road, (A57), Glossop, Derbyshire
SK13 7PT
T: (01457) 868001
F: (01457) 853354
E: info@windinthewillows.co.uk
I: www.windinthewillows.co.uk

GLOUCESTER
Gloucestershire
Edward Hotel ★★
88 London Road, Gloucester,
GL1 3PG
T: (01452) 525865
F: (01452) 302165

Jarvis Bowden Hall Hotel and
Country Club ★★★
Bondend Lane, Upton St
Leonards, Gloucester GL4 8ED
T: (01452) 614121
F: (01452) 611885

Jarvis Gloucester Hotel and
Country Club ★★★
Matson Lane, Robinswood Hill,
Gloucester, GL4 6EA
T: (01452) 525653
F: (01452) 307212
I: www.jarvis.co.uk

Establishments printed in blue have a detailed entry in this guide

New County Hotel ★★★
44 Southgate Street, Gloucester,
GL1 2DU
T: (01452) 307000
F: (01452) 500487
E: newcountry@
meridianleisure.com
I: www.meridianleisure.com

Rotherfield House Hotel ★
5 Horton Road, Gloucester,
GL1 3PX
T: (01452) 410500
F: (01452) 381922

GOODRICH
Herefordshire
Ye Hostelrie Hotel ★★
Goodrich, Ross-on-Wye,
Herefordshire HR9 6HX
T: (01600) 890241
F: (01600) 890838
E: ye-hostelrie@lineone.net
I: ye-hostelrie.8k.com

GRANTHAM
Lincolnshire
Kings Hotel ★★★
North Parade, Grantham,
Lincolnshire NG31 8AU
T: (01476) 590800
F: (01476) 590800
E: kingshotel@compuserve.com

Swallow Hotel ★★★
Swingbridge Road, Grantham,
Lincolnshire NG31 7XT
T: (01476) 593000
F: (01476) 592592
I: www.swallowhotels.con

GRINDLEFORD
Derbyshire
Maynard Arms Hotel ★★★
Main Road, Grindleford, Hope
Valley S32 2HE
T: (01433) 630321
F: (01433) 630445

HARRINGWORTH
Northamptonshire
White Swan ★★
Seaton Road, Harringworth,
Corby, Northamptonshire
NN17 3AF
T: (01572) 747543
F: (01572) 747323
E: white.swan1@virgin.net
I: www.lookitup.co.
uk/whiteswan

HARTINGTON
Derbyshire
Charles Cotton Hotel ★
The Square, Hartington, Buxton,
Derbyshire SK17 0AL
T: (01298) 84229
F: (01298) 84301

HASSOP
Derbyshire
Hassop Hall Hotel ★★★
Hassop, Bakewell, Derbyshire
DE45 1NS
T: (01629) 640488
F: (01629) 640577
E: hassophallhotel@btinternet.
com

HATTON
Warwickshire
Haseley House Hotel and Brasserie ★★★
Haseley, Hatton, Warwick
CV35 7LS
T: (01926) 484222
F: (01926) 484227
E: info@haseleyhouse.co.uk
I: www.haseleyhouse.co.uk

HENLEY-IN-ARDEN
Warwickshire
Henley Hotel ★★
Tanworth Lane, Henley-in-
Arden, Warwickshire B95 5RA
T: (01564) 794551
F: (01564) 795044

HEREFORD
Herefordshire
Belmont Lodge and Golf Course★★★
Belmont, Hereford, HR2 9SA
T: (01432) 352666
F: (01432) 358090
E: info@belmontlodge.co.uk
I: www.belmontlodge.co.uk

Hopbine Hotel ★
The Hopbine, Roman Road,
Hereford, HR1 1LE
T: (01432) 268722
F: (01432) 268722

Merton Hotel ★★
Commercial Road, Hereford,
HR1 2BD
T: (01432) 265925 &
07860 550288
F: (01432) 354983
E: sales@mertonhotel.co.uk
I: www.mertonhotel.co.uk

The New Priory Hotel ★
Stretton Sugwas, Hereford
HR4 7AR
T: (01432) 760264 & 760183
F: (01432) 761809

Three Counties Hotel ★★★
Belmont Road, Hereford,
HR2 7BP
T: (01432) 299955
F: (01432) 275114
E: threecountieshotel@hotmail.
com

HIGHAM
Derbyshire
Santo's Higham Farm Hotel ★★★ SILVER AWARD
Main Road, Higham, Alfreton,
Derbyshire DE55 6EH
T: (01773) 833812
F: (01773) 520525
E: reception@
santoshighamfarm.demon.co.uk
I: www.santoshighamfarm.
demon.co.uk

HIMLEY
Staffordshire
Himley Country Hotel Rating Applied For
School Road, Himley, Dudley,
West Midlands DY3 4LG
T: (01902) 896716
F: (01902) 896668

HINCKLEY
Leicestershire
Sketchley Grange Hotel ★★★★
Sketchley Lane, Burbage,
Hinckley, Leicestershire
LE10 3HU
T: (01455) 251133
F: (01455) 631384
E: sketchleygrange@btinternet.
com
I: www.sketchleygrange.co.uk

HINDLIP
Worcestershire
Pear Tree Inn & Country Hotel ★★★ SILVER AWARD
Smite, Hindlip, Worcester
WR3 8SY
T: (01905) 756565
F: (01905) 756777
E: thepeartree@aol.com
I: www.thepeartree.co.uk

HOCKLEY HEATH
West Midlands
Nuthurst Grange Country House Hotel and Restaurant ★★★ GOLD AWARD
Nuthurst Grange Lane, Hockley
Heath, Warwickshire B94 5NL
T: (01564) 783972
F: (01564) 783919
E: info@nuthurst-grange.co.uk
I: www.theaa.co.uk/hotels

HORNCASTLE
Lincolnshire
Admiral Rodney Hotel ★★
North Street, Horncastle,
Lincolnshire LN9 5DX
T: (01507) 523131
F: (01507) 523104
E: admiralrodney@bestwestern.
co.uk

IRONBRIDGE
Shropshire
The Best Western Valley Hotel ★★★
Ironbridge, Telford, Shropshire
TF8 7DW
T: (01952) 432247
F: (01952) 432308
E: valley.hotel@ironbridge.fsnet.
co.uk
I: www.bestwestern.co.uk

KEGWORTH
Leicestershire
The Kegworth Hotel ★★
Packington Hill, Kegworth,
Derby DE74 2DF
T: (01509) 672427
F: (01509) 674664
E: info@kegworth-hotel.co.uk
I: www.kegworth-hotel.co.uk

Kegworth Lantern Hotel Rating Applied For
1 Market Place, Kegworth, Derby
DE74 2EE
T: (01509) 673989 & 672538
F: (01509) 670725

KENILWORTH
Warwickshire
Clarendon House Bar – Brasserie Hotel★★★
Old High Street, Kenilworth,
Warwickshire CV8 1LZ
T: (01926) 857668
F: (01926) 850669
E: info@clarendonhousehotel.
com
I: www.clarendonhousehotel.
com

Macdonald De Montfort ★★★★
The Square, Kenilworth,
Warwickshire CV8 1ED
T: (01926) 855944
F: (01926) 855952
E: info@demontfort.
macdonald-hotels.co.uk

Nightingales Hotel and Restaurant Rating Applied For
95-97 Warwick Road,
Kenilworth, Warwickshire
CV8 1HP
T: (01926) 853594
F: (01926) 853594

The Peacock Hotel ★★★
149 Warwick Road, Kenilworth,
Warwickshire CV8 1HY
T: (01926) 851156 & 964500
F: (01926) 864644
E:
peacockhotel@rafflesmalaysian.
com
I: www.peacockhotel.com

KIDDERMINSTER
Worcestershire
Cedars Hotel ★★
Mason Road, Kidderminster,
Worcestershire DY11 6AG
T: (01562) 515595
F: (01562) 751103
E: reservations@cedars-hotel.
co.uk

Gainsborough House Hotel ★★★
Bewdley Hill, Kidderminster,
Worcestershire DY11 6BS
T: (01562) 820041
F: (01562) 66179

The Granary Hotel and Restaurant★★★
Heath Lane, Shenstone,
Kidderminster, Worcestershire
DY10 4BS
T: (01562) 777535
F: (01562) 777722

KNIGHTWICK
Worcestershire
Talbot ★
Knightwick, Worcester WR6 5PH
T: (01886) 821235
F: (01886) 821060

LANGAR
Nottinghamshire
Langar Hall ★★★ SILVER AWARD
Langar, Nottingham NG13 9HG
T: (01949) 860559
F: (01949) 861045
E: langarhall-hotel@ndirect.co.
uk
I: www.langarhall.com

LEAMINGTON SPA
Warwickshire

Angel Hotel ★★★
143 Regent Street, Leamington
Spa, Warwickshire CV32 4NZ
T: (01926) 881296
F: (01926) 881296

Eaton Court Hotel ★★★
1-7 St Marks Road, Leamington
Spa, Warwickshire CV32 6DL
T: (01926) 885848
F: (01926) 885848
E: eatoncourt@cascade-uk.net

Falstaff Hotel ★★★
16-20 Warwick New Road,
Leamington Spa, Warwickshire
CV32 5JQ
T: (01926) 312044
F: (01926) 450574
E: falstaff@meridianleisure.com
I: meridianleisure.com

Lansdowne Hotel
★ SILVER AWARD
87 Clarendon Street,
Leamington Spa, Warwickshire
CV32 4PF
T: (01926) 450505
F: (01926) 421313

Leamington Hotel and Bistro
★★★ SILVER AWARD
64 Upper Holly Walk,
Leamington Spa, Warwickshire
CV32 4JL
T: (01926) 883777
F: (01926) 330467
E: leamington@bestwestern.
com

Manor House Hotel
Rating Applied For
Avenue Road, Leamington Spa,
Warwickshire CV31 3NJ
T: (01926) 423251
F: (01926) 425933
I: www.corushotels.com

LEDBURY
Herefordshire

Feathers Hotel
★★★ SILVER AWARD
High Street, Ledbury,
Herefordshire HR8 1DS
T: (01531) 635266
F: (01531) 638955
E: mary@feathers-ledbury.co.uk
I: www.feathers-ledbury.co.uk

Leadon House Hotel ★★
Ross Road, Ledbury,
Herefordshire HR8 2LP
T: (01531) 631199 & 632880
F: (01531) 631476
E: leadonho@lineone.net

The Talbot ★★
New Street, Ledbury,
Herefordshire HR8 2DX
T: (01531) 632963
F: (01531) 633796
E: susan.talbot@dial.pipex.com
I: www.smoothhound.co.
uk/hotels/talbot.html

LEEK
Staffordshire

The Jester Hotel ★★
81-83 Mill Street, Leek,
Staffordshire ST13 8EU
T: (01538) 382880
F: (01538) 398288

**Three Horseshoes Inn and
Restaurant★★**
Buxton Road, Blackshaw Moor,
Leek, Staffordshire ST13 8TW
T: (01538) 300296
F: (01538) 300320

LEICESTER
Leicestershire

**Chase Hotel and Leisure
Complex ★★**
The Racecourse, Oadby, Leicester
LE2 3QH
T: (0116) 270 3920 & 270 2323
F: (0116) 270 0008

The Grand Hotel ★★★
Granby Street, Leicester, LE1 6ES
T: (0116) 255 5599
F: (0116) 254 4736
I: www.jarvis.co.uk

Holiday Inn Leicester ★★★★
129 St Nicholas Circle, Leicester,
LE1 5LX
T: (0116) 253 1161
F: (0116) 251 3169
I: www.holiday-inn.com

**Kabalou's Hotel and
Restaurant ★★**
23-25 Loughborough Road,
Leicester, LE4 5LD
T: (0116) 2682626
F: (0116) 2682641

Mill on the Soar Hotel ★★
Coventry Road, Sutton in the
Elms, Leicestershire LE9 6QD
T: (01455) 282419
F: (01455) 285937

The Red Cow ★★
Hinckley Road, Leicester Forest
East, Leicester LE3 3PG
T: (0116) 238 7878
F: (0116) 238 6539
E: alanjudd@msn.com

Scotia Hotel
Rating Applied For
10 Westcotes Drive, Leicester,
LE3 0QR
T: (0116) 254 9200
F: (0116) 254 9200

LEOMINSTER
Herefordshire

Royal Oak Hotel ★★
South Street, Leominster,
Herefordshire HR6 8JA
T: (01568) 612610
F: (01568) 612710

Talbot Hotel ★★★
West Street, Leominster,
Herefordshire HR6 8EP
T: (01568) 616347
F: (01568) 614880

LICHFIELD
Staffordshire

Jarvis George Hotel ★★★
Bird Street, Lichfield,
Staffordshire WS13 6PR
T: (01543) 414822
F: (01543) 415817

Little Barrow Hotel ★★★
Beacon Street, Lichfield,
Staffordshire WS13 7AR
T: (01543) 414500
F: (01543) 415734
E: hinecjp@netscapeonline.co.
uk

Oakleigh House Hotel ★★
25 St. Chad's Road, Lichfield,
Staffordshire WS13 7LZ
T: (01543) 262688 & 255573
F: (01543) 418556
E: info@oakleighhouse.co.uk
I: www.oakleighhouse.co.uk

**The Olde Corner House Hotel
★★**
Walsall Road, Muckley Corner,
Lichfield, Staffordshire
WS14 0BG
T: (01543) 372182
F: (01543) 372211

Swinfen Hall Hotel ★★★
Swinfen, Lichfield, Staffordshire
WS14 9RS
T: (01543) 481494
F: (01543) 480341
E: swinfen.hall@virgin.net

LINCOLN
Lincolnshire

**The Bentley Hotel & Leisure
Club ★★★**
Newark Road, South Hykeham,
Lincoln, LN6 9NH
T: (01522) 878000
F: (01522) 878001
I: www.thebentleyhotel.uk.com

Branston Hall Hotel ★★★
Lincoln Road, Branston, Lincoln
LN4 1PD
T: (01522) 793305
F: (01522) 790549
E: brahal@enterprise.net
I: www.mercuryin.es/branston

Castle Hotel ★★
Westgate, Lincoln, LN1 3AS
T: (01522) 538801
F: (01522) 575457

Grand Hotel ★★★
St Mary's Street, Lincoln,
LN5 7EP
T: (01522) 524211
F: (01522) 537661
I: www.thegrandhotel.com

Hillcrest Hotel ★★
15 Lindum Terrace, Lincoln,
LN2 5RT
T: (01522) 510182
F: (01522) 510182
E: jennifer@hillcresthotel.
freeserve.co.uk
I: www.hillcrest-hotel.com

Moor Lodge Hotel ★★
Sleaford Road, Branston, Lincoln
LN4 1HU
T: (01522) 791366
F: (01522) 794389

LONG COMPTON
Warwickshire

The Red Lion Hotel ★★
Main Street, Long Compton,
Shipston-on-Stour,
Warwickshire CV36 5JS
T: (01608) 684221
F: (01608) 684221

LONG EATON
Derbyshire

**Jarvis Nottingham Hotel
★★★**
Bostock Lane, Long Eaton,
Nottingham NG10 5NL
T: (0115) 946 0000
F: (0115) 946 0726

LOUGHBOROUGH
Leicestershire

**Jarvis Loughborough Hotel
★★★**
High Street, Loughborough,
Leicestershire LE11 2QL
T: (01509) 233222
F: (01509) 262911

LOUTH
Lincolnshire

The Beaumont Hotel ★★★
Victoria Road, Louth,
Lincolnshire LN11 0BX
T: (01507) 605005
F: (01507) 607768

**Brackenborough Arms Hotel &
Restaurant★★★**
Cordeaux Corner,
Brackenborough, Louth,
Lincolnshire LN11 0SZ
T: (01507) 609169
F: (01507) 609413
E: info@brackenborough.co.uk
I: www.brackenborough.co.uk

**Kenwick Park Hotel & Leisure
Club★★★**
Kenwick Park, Kenwick, Louth,
Lincolnshire LN11 8NR
T: (01507) 608806
F: (01507) 608027
E: enquiries@kenwick-park.com
I: www.kenwick-park.co.uk

LOWER SLAUGHTER
Gloucestershire

Lower Slaughter Manor
★★★ GOLD AWARD
Lower Slaughter, Cheltenham,
Gloucestershire GL54 2HP
T: (01451) 820456
F: (01451) 822150
E: lowsmanor@aol.com
I: www.lowerslaughter.co.uk

Washbourne Court Hotel
★★★ SILVER AWARD
Lower Slaughter, Cheltenham,
Gloucestershire GL54 2HS
T: (01451) 822143
F: (01451) 821045
E: washbourne@msn.com

LUDLOW
Shropshire

**Dinham Hall Hotel and
Restaurant★★**
Dinham, By The Castle, Ludlow,
Shropshire SY8 1EJ
T: (01584) 876464
F: (01584) 876019

The Feathers at Ludlow ★★★
Bull Ring, Ludlow, Shropshire
SY8 1AA
T: (01584) 875261
F: (01584) 876030
I: www.corushotels.com

Overton Grange Hotel
★★★ SILVER AWARD
Old Hereford Road, Ludlow,
Shropshire SY8 4AD
T: (01584) 873500
F: (01584) 873524
I: www.goz.uk/overtongrange

Establishments printed in blue have a detailed entry in this guide

LYDNEY
Gloucestershire
Parkend House Hotel ★★
Parkend, Lydney, Gloucestershire
GL15 4HH
T: (01594) 563666
F: (01594) 564631
E: ajl@cix.co.uk
I: www.cix.co.uk/§mutts/

MALVERN
Worcestershire
Colwall Park Hotel
★★★ GOLD AWARD
Walwyn Road, Colwall, Malvern,
Worcestershire WR13 6QG
T: (01684) 540206 & 541033
F: (01684) 540847
E: hotel@colwall.com
I: www.colwall.com
◉

Cotford Hotel ★★
Graham Road, Malvern,
Worcestershire WR14 2HU
T: (01684) 572427
F: (01684) 572952

The Cottage in the Wood Hotel
★★★ SILVER AWARD
Holywell Road, Malvern Wells,
Malvern, Worcestershire
WR14 4LG
T: (01684) 575859
F: (01684) 560662
E: proprietor@
cottageinthewood.co.uk
I: www.cottageinthewood.co.uk
◉

Great Malvern Hotel ★★
Graham Road, Malvern,
Worcestershire WR14 2HN
T: (01684) 563411
F: (01684) 560514
E: sutton@great-malvern-hotel.
co.uk
I: www.great-malvern-hotel.co.
uk

Holdfast Cottage Hotel
★★ SILVER AWARD
Marlbank Road, Little Malvern,
Malvern, Worcestershire
WR13 6NA
T: (01684) 310288
F: (01684) 311117
E: holdcothot@aol.com
I: www.holdfast-cottage.co.uk

Malvern Hills Hotel ★★
Wynds Point, British Camp,
Malvern, Worcestershire
WR13 6DW
T: (01684) 540690
F: (01684) 540327
E: malhilhotl@aol.com

Mount Pleasant Hotel ★★
Belle Vue Terrace, Malvern,
Worcestershire WR14 4PZ
T: (01684) 561837
F: (01684) 569968

Thornbury House Hotel ★★
Avenue Road, Malvern,
Worcestershire WR14 3AR
T: (01684) 572278
F: (01684) 577042
E: thornburyhousehotel@
compuserve.com

MANSFIELD
Nottinghamshire
Pine Lodge Hotel ★★
281-283 Nottingham Road,
Mansfield, Nottinghamshire
NG18 4SE
T: (01623) 622308
F: (01623) 656819
E: plhotel@aol.com

Portland Hall Hotel ★★
Carr Bank Park, Windmill Lane,
Mansfield, Nottinghamshire
NG18 2AL
T: (01623) 452525
F: (01623) 452550
E: enquiries@portlandhallhotel.
co.uk
I: www.portlandhallhotel.co.uk

MARKET DEEPING
Lincolnshire
The Towngate Inn Motel ★★
3 Towngate East, Market
Deeping, Peterborough PE6 8DP
T: (01778) 348000 & 348000
F: (01778) 347947
E: towngateinn@
marketdeepinglincs.freeserve.co.
uk

MARKET DRAYTON
Shropshire
The Bear Hotel ★★
Hodnet, Market Drayton,
Shropshire TF9 3NH
T: (01630) 685214 & 685788
F: (01630) 685787

**Rosehill Manor Hotel &
Restaurant★★**
Tern Hill, Market Drayton,
Shropshire TF9 2JF
T: (01630) 638532 & 637000
F: (01630) 637008

MARKFIELD
Leicestershire
Field Head Hotel ★★
Markfield Lane, Markfield,
Leicester LE67 9PS
T: (01530) 245454
F: (01530) 243740
E: fieldhead.hotel@virgin.net
◉

MATLOCK
Derbyshire
The Red House Hotel ★★
Old Road, Darley Dale, Matlock,
Derbyshire DE4 2ER
T: (01629) 734854
F: (01629) 734885
E: Redhoose@aol.com

Riber Hall
★★★ SILVER AWARD
Riber, Matlock, Derbyshire
DE4 5JU
T: (01629) 582795
F: (01629) 580475
E: info@riber-hall.co.uk
I: www.riber-hall.co.uk

MELTON MOWBRAY
Leicestershire
Quorn Lodge Hotel ★★
46 Asfordby Road, Melton
Mowbray, Leicestershire
LE13 0HR
T: (01664) 566660 & 562590
F: (01664) 480660
E: quornlodge@aol.com
I: www.quornlodge.co.uk

Sysonby Knoll Hotel ★★★
Asfordby Road, Melton
Mowbray, Leicestershire
LE13 0HP
T: (01664) 563563
F: (01664) 410364
E: sysonby.knoll@btinternet.
com
I: www.sysonby.knoll.btinternet.
co.uk

MERIDEN
West Midlands
**Strawberry Bank Restaurant
and Hotel★★★**
Main Road, Meriden, Coventry,
Warwickshire CV7 7NF
T: (01676) 522117
F: (01676) 523804

MORETON-IN-MARSH
Gloucestershire
Manor House Hotel ★★★
High Street, Moreton-in-Marsh,
Gloucestershire GL56 0LJ
T: (01608) 650501
F: (01608) 651481

The White Hart Royal ★★
High Street, Moreton-in-Marsh,
Gloucestershire GL56 0BA
T: (01608) 650731
F: (01608) 650880
E: whitehart@demon.co.uk

NAILSWORTH
Gloucestershire
Egypt Mill ★★
Nailsworth, Stroud,
Gloucestershire GL6 0AE
T: (01453) 833449
F: (01453) 836098
◉

NESSCLIFFE
Shropshire
The Nesscliffe Hotel ★★
Nesscliffe, Shrewsbury SY4 1DB
T: (01743) 741430
F: (01743) 741104
E: enquiries@nesscliffe-hotel.
co.uk

NEWARK
Nottinghamshire
South Parade Hotel ★★
117 Balderton Gate, Newark,
Nottinghamshire NG24 1RY
T: (01636) 703008 & 703030
F: (01636) 605593
E: thesouthparadehotel@tesco.
net
I: homepages.tesco.
net/§thesouthparadehotel

NEWTON SOLNEY
Derbyshire
**Jarvis Newton Park Hotel
★★★**
Newton Solney, Burton upon
Trent, Staffordshire DE15 0SS
T: (01283) 703568
F: (01283) 703214

NORTHAMPTON
Northamptonshire
**Broomhill Country House
Hotel and Restaurant★★★**
Holdenby Road, Spratton,
Northampton NN6 8LD
T: (01604) 845959
F: (01604) 845834
◉

Grand Hotel ★★★
Gold Street, Northampton,
NN1 1RE
T: (01604) 250511
F: (01604) 234534
E: grand@zoffanyhotels.co.uk
I: www.zoffanyhotels.co.uk

Lime Trees Hotel
★★★ SILVER AWARD
8 Langham Place, Barrack Road,
Northampton, NN2 6AA
T: (01604) 632188
F: (01604) 233012
E: info@limetreeshotel.co.uk
I: www.limetreeshotel.co.uk

Swallow Hotel
★★★★ SILVER AWARD
Eagle Drive, Northampton,
NN4 7HW
T: (01604) 768700 & 667617
F: (01604) 769011
◉ ⌂

NOTTINGHAM
Nottinghamshire
**The Nottingham Gateway
Hotel ★★★**
Nuthall Road, Nottingham,
NG8 6AZ
T: (0115) 979 4949
F: (0115) 979 4744
E: nottmgateway@btconnect.
com
⌂

Quality Hotel George ★★
George Street, Nottingham,
NG1 3BP
T: (0115) 947 5641
F: (0115) 948 3292
E: admin@gb620.u-net.com
I: www.choicehotelseurope.com
⌂

**Swans Hotel and Restaurant
★★★**
84-90 Radcliffe Road, West
Bridgford, Nottingham
NG2 5HH
T: (0115) 981 4042
F: (0115) 945 5745
E: swanshotel@aol.com
I: www.smoothhound.co.uk/

OAKHAM
Leicestershire
Barnsdale Lodge Hotel
★★★ SILVER AWARD
The Avenue, Rutland Water,
Exton, Oakham, Leicestershire
LE15 8AH
T: (01572) 724678
F: (01572) 724961

**Boultons Country Town House
Hotel and Restaurants★★★**
4 Catmos Street, Oakham,
Leicestershire LE15 6HW
T: (01572) 722844
F: (01572) 724473
◉

The Whipper-in Hotel ★★★
Market Place, Oakham, Rutland
LE15 6DT
T: (01572) 756971
F: (01572) 757759
E: mairead@brook-hotels.
demon.co.uk
I: www.brook-hotels.co.uk
◉

OLLERTON
Nottinghamshire
Hop Pole Hotel ★★
Ollerton, Newark,
Nottinghamshire NG22 9AD
T: (01623) 822573 & 822305

OSWESTRY
Shropshire
**Pen-y-Dyffryn Country Hotel
★★★ SILVER AWARD**
Rhyd-y-Croesau, Oswestry,
Shropshire SY10 7JD
T: (01691) 653700
F: (01691) 650066
E: peny.d@virginnet.co.uk
I: www.go2.co.uk/penydyffryn

**Sweeney Hall Hotel
★★ SILVER AWARD**
Morda, Oswestry, Shropshire
SY10 9EU
T: (01691) 652450
F: (01691) 652805

PAINSWICK
Gloucestershire
The Falcon Hotel ★★
New Street, Painswick, Stroud,
Gloucestershire GL6 6UN
T: (01452) 814222 & 812228
F: (01452) 813377
E: bleninns@clara.net
I: www.poinswick.co.uk

**Painswick Hotel
★★★ SILVER AWARD**
Kemps Lane, Painswick, Stroud,
Gloucestershire GL6 6YB
T: (01452) 812160
F: (01452) 814059
E: reservations@painswickhotel.
com
I: www.painswickhotel.com

PENKRIDGE
Staffordshire
**Quality Hotel Stafford &
Hatherton Leisure Club★★**
Pinfold Lane, Penkridge,
Stafford, Staffordshire ST19 5QP
T: (01785) 712459
F: (01785) 715532

PERRY BARR
West Midlands
**Park Hotel
Rating Applied For**
131 Aldridge Road, Perry Barr,
Birmingham B24 2ET
T: (0121) 3560707
F: (0121) 3314450
E: parkhoteldavidsue@hotmail.
com
I: www.members.xoom.
com/thehussar/

PERSHORE
Worcestershire
**Angel Inn & Posting House
★★★**
9 High Street, Pershore,
Worcestershire WR10 1AF
T: (01386) 552046
F: (01386) 552581

QUORN
Leicestershire
**Quorn Country Hotel
★★★★ SILVER AWARD**
66 Leicester Road, Quorn,
Loughborough, Leicestershire
LE12 8BB
T: (01509) 415050
F: (01509) 415557

**Quorn Grange Hotel and
Restaurant★★★**
Quorn Grange, 88 Wood Lane,
Quorn, Loughborough,
Leicestershire LE12 8DB
T: (01509) 412167
F: (01509) 415621

REDDITCH
Worcestershire
**Campanile Hotel and
Restaurant ★**
Far Moor Lane, Winyates Green,
Redditch, B98 0SD
T: (01527) 510710
F: (01527) 517269
I: www.campanile-fr

Quality Hotel Redditch ★★★
Pool Bank, Southcrest, Redditch,
Worcestershire B97 4JS
T: (01527) 541511
F: (01527) 402600
E: admin@gb6646.u-net.com
I: www.choicehotelseurope.com

RISLEY
Derbyshire
**Risley Hall Hotel Limited
★★★ SILVER AWARD**
Derby Road, Risley, Draycott,
Derbyshire DE72 3SS
T: (0115) 939 9000
F: (0115) 939 7766

ROSS-ON-WYE
Herefordshire
Bridge House Hotel ★★
Wilton, Ross-on-Wye,
Herefordshire HR9 6AA
T: (01989) 562655
F: (01989) 567652
E: alison@bhhotel.fsnet.co.uk

Castle Lodge Hotel ★★
Wilton, Ross-on-Wye,
Herefordshire HR9 6AD
T: (01989) 562234
F: (01989) 768322

**The Chase Hotel
★★★ SILVER AWARD**
Gloucester Road, Ross-on-Wye,
Herefordshire HR9 5LH
T: (01989) 763161
F: (01989) 768330
E: info@chasehotel.co.uk
I: www.chasehotel.co.uk

Glewstone Court Hotel ★★
Glewstone, Ross-on-Wye,
Herefordshire HR9 6AW
T: (01989) 770367
F: (01989) 770282
E: glewstone@aol.com
I: www.smoothhound.co.
uk/hotels/glewston.html

**Orles Barn Hotel & Restaurant
★★**
Wilton, Ross-on-Wye,
Herefordshire HR9 6AE
T: (01989) 562155
F: (01989) 768470
E: orles.barn@clara.net
I: www.orles.barn.clara.net

**Pencraig Court Hotel
★★★ SILVER AWARD**
Pencraig, Ross-on-Wye,
Herefordshire HR9 6HR
T: (01989) 770306 & 770416
F: (01989) 770040
E: mike@pencraig-court.co.uk.
I: www.pencraig-court.co.uk

Rosswyn Hotel ★
17 High Street, Ross-on-Wye,
Herefordshire HR9 5BZ
T: (01989) 562733
F: (01989) 562733

The Royal ★★★
Palace Pound, Ross-on-Wye,
Herefordshire HR9 5HZ
T: (01989) 565105
F: (01989) 768058

Wilton Court Hotel ★★
Wilton Lane, Wilton, Ross-on-
Wye, Herefordshire HR9 6AQ
T: (01989) 562569
F: (01989) 768460
I: www.visitus.co.
uk/bnbhtm/wilton.htm

ROWSLEY
Derbyshire
Peacock Hotel ★★★
Bakewell Road, Rowsley,
Matlock, Derbyshire DE4 2EB
T: (01629) 733518
F: (01629) 732671
I: www.jarvis.co.uk

RUGBY
Warwickshire
Brownsover Hall ★★★
Brownsover Lane, Old
Brownsover, Rugby,
Warwickshire CV21 1HU
T: (01788) 546100
F: (01788) 579241
I: www.corushotels.com

Express By Holiday Inn
Travel Accommodation
Brownsover Road, Rugby,
Warwickshire CV21 1HL
T: (01788) 550333 & 569466
F: (01788) 547531

**The Grosvenor Hotel
Rating Applied For**
81-87 Clifton Road, Rugby,
Warwickshire CV21 3QQ
T: (01788) 535686
F: (01788) 541297
E: therugbygrosvenorhotel@
freeserve.co.uk

ST BRIAVELS
Gloucestershire
**The Florence Country Hotel
★★**
Bigsweir, Lower Wye Valley, St
Briavels, Lydney, Gloucestershire
GL15 6QQ
T: (01594) 530830
F: (01594) 531198
I: www.florencehotel.co.uk

SHIPSTON-ON-STOUR
Warwickshire
The Old Mill Hotel ★★
Mill Street, Shipston-on-Stour,
Warwickshire CV36 4AW
T: (01608) 661880
F: (01608) 661880
E: enquiries@old-mill-hotel.co.
uk
I: www.old-mill-hotel.co.uk

SHREWSBURY
Shropshire
Abbot's Mead Hotel ★★
9-10 St. Julian Friars,
Shrewsbury, Shropshire SY1 1XL
T: (01743) 235281
F: (01743) 369133
E: abbotsmead@shotel@
orginnet.co.uk
I: www.freespace.orginnet.co.
uk/abbotsmead.hotel

**Albright Hussey Hotel and
Restaurant
★★★ SILVER AWARD**
Ellesmere Road, Shrewsbury,
Shropshire SY4 3AF
T: (01939) 290571 & 290523
F: (01939) 291143
E: abhhotel@aol.com
I: www.albright-hussey.co.uk

**Hawkstone Park Hotel, Golf
and Leisure Centre
★★★ SILVER AWARD**
Weston-under-Redcastle,
Shrewsbury SY4 5UY
T: (01939) 200611 & 200204
F: (01939) 200311
E: info@hawkstone.co.uk /
reservations@hawkstone.co.uk
I: www.hawkstone.co.uk

Lion and Pheasant Hotel ★★
49-50 Wyle Cop, Shrewsbury,
SY1 1XJ
T: (01743) 236288
F: (01743) 244475

Shelton Hall Hotel ★★
Shelton, Shrewsbury SY3 8BH
T: (01743) 343982
F: (01743) 241515

SKEGNESS
Lincolnshire
Grosvenor House Hotel ★
North Parade, Skegness,
Lincolnshire PE25 2TE
T: (01754) 763376
F: (01754) 764650

Savoy Hotel ★★
12 North Parade, Skegness,
Lincolnshire PE25 2UB
T: (01754) 763371
F: (01754) 761256

The Vine ★★★
Vine Road, Seacroft, Skegness,
Lincolnshire PE25 3DB
T: (01754) 610611 & 763018
F: (01754) 769845

SLEAFORD
Lincolnshire
Carre Arms Hotel ★★
Mareham Lane, Sleaford,
Lincolnshire NG34 7JP
T: (01529) 303156
F: (01529) 303139

**The Lincolnshire Oak Hotel
★★★**
East Road, Sleaford, Lincolnshire
NG34 7EH
T: (01529) 413807
F: (01529) 413710
E: lincs.oak@pipermedia.co.uk
I: www.sleaford.co.
uk/lincolnshire-oak

Establishments printed in blue have a detailed entry in this guide

SOLIHULL
West Midlands

The Forest Hotel ★★
Station Approach, Dorridge,
Solihull, West Midlands B93 8JA
T: (01564) 772120
F: (01564) 770677
E: forest-hotel.sagehost.co.uk

Regency Hotel ★★★
Stratford Road, Shirley, Solihull,
West Midlands B90 4EB
T: (0121) 745 6119 & 745 0400
F: (0121) 733 3801
E: regencyhotel.regalhotel@
pop3.hiway.co.uk
I: www.corushotels.com

**Swallow St John's Hotel
★★★★ SILVER AWARD**
651 Warwick Road, Solihull,
West Midlands B91 1AT
T: (0121) 711 3000
F: (0121) 705 6629

SOUTH NORMANTON
Derbyshire

**The Boundary Lodge
Rating Applied For**
Lea Vale, Broadmeadows, South
Normanton, Alfreton, Derbyshire
DE55 3NA
T: (01773) 819066

**Swallow Hotel
★★★★ SILVER AWARD**
Carter Lane East, Junction 28 of
M1, South Normanton, Alfreton,
Derbyshire DE55 2EH
T: (01773) 812000
F: (01773) 580032

SPALDING
Lincolnshire

Cley Hall Hotel ★★
22 High Street, Spalding,
Lincolnshire PE11 1TX
T: (01775) 725157
F: (01775) 710785
E: cleyhall@enterprise.net
I: homepages.enterprise.
net/cleyhall

STAFFORD
Staffordshire

Abbey Hotel ★★
65-68 Lichfield Road, Stafford,
Staffordshire ST17 4LW
T: (01785) 258531
F: (01785) 246875

Albridge Private Hotel ★
73 Wolverhampton Road,
Stafford, Staffordshire
ST17 4AW
T: (01785) 254100
F: (01785) 223895

**Aviemore Hotel
Rating Applied For**
4A Lloyd Street, Stafford,
ST16 3AS
T: (01785) 211986
F: (01785) 226143
E: aviemore@kid99.freeserve.co.
uk

STAMFORD
Lincolnshire

Crown Hotel ★★
All Saints Place, Stamford,
Lincolnshire PE9 2AG
T: (01780) 763136
F: (01780) 756111
E: thecrownhotel@excite.com

Garden House Hotel ★★★
St Martins, Stamford,
Lincolnshire PE9 2LP
T: (01780) 763359
F: (01780) 763339
E: gardenhousehotel@
stamford60.freeserve.co.uk
I: stamford.co.uk

**George of Stamford
★★★ SILVER AWARD**
71 St Martins, Stamford,
Lincolnshire PE9 2LB
T: (01780) 750750 & 750700
F: (01780) 750701
E: reservations@
georgehotelofstamford.com
I: www.georgehotelofstamford.
com

STAPENHILL
Staffordshire

Redhill Hotel ★
66 Stanton Road, Stapenhill,
Burton upon Trent, Staffordshire
DE15 9RS
T: (01283) 564629 & 565078
F: (01283) 564629

STOKE-ON-TRENT
Staffordshire

**George Hotel
★★★ SILVER AWARD**
Swan Square, Burslem, Stoke-
on-Trent ST6 2AE
T: (01782) 577544
F: (01782) 837496
E: georgestoke@btinternet.com
I: www.georgehotelstoke.cwc.
net

**Jarvis Clayton Lodge Hotel
★★★**
Clayton Road, Newcastle-under-
Lyme, Staffordshire ST5 4AF
T: (01782) 613093
F: (01782) 711896
I: www.jarvis.co.uk

The North Stafford ★★★
Station Road, Stoke-on-Trent,
ST4 2AE
T: (01782) 744477
F: (01782) 744580
E: claireportas@principalhotels.
co.uk
I: www.principalhotels.co.uk

**The Plough Motel and
Restaurant
Rating Applied For**
Campbell Road, Stoke-on-Trent,
ST4 4EN
T: (01782) 414685
F: (01782) 414669
E: info@ploughmotel.co.uk
I: www.ploughmotel.co.uk

**Tollgate Hotel and Leisure
★★★**
Ripon Road, Blurton, Stoke-on-
Trent, ST3 3BS
T: (01782) 313029
F: (01782) 593959
E: adrian@tollgate.co.uk
I: www.tollgate.co.uk

The Weathervane Lodge ★★
Lysander Road, Meir Park, Stoke-
on-Trent, ST3 7TW
T: (01782) 388799 & 388803
F: (01782) 388804

STONE
Worcestershire

Stone Manor Hotel ★★★★
Stone, Kidderminster,
Worcestershire DY10 4PJ
T: (01562) 777555
F: (01562) 777834
E: beverleywstonemanor.
freeserve.co.uk

STOURBRIDGE
West Midlands

**Talbot Hotel
Rating Applied For**
High Street, Stourbridge, West
Midlands DY8 1DW
T: (01384) 394350
F: (01384) 371318
I: WWW.OLDENGLISH.CO.UK

STOW-ON-THE-WOLD
Gloucestershire

Auld Stocks Hotel ★★
The Square, Stow-on-the-Wold,
Cheltenham, Gloucestershire
GL54 1AF
T: (01451) 830666
F: (01451) 870014

The Farmers Arms Hotel ★★
Fosse Way, Stow-on-the-Wold,
Cheltenham, Gloucestershire
GL54 1JX
T: (01451) 870539
F: (01451) 870639

**Fosse Manor Hotel
★★★ SILVER AWARD**
Stow-on-the-Wold,
Cheltenham, Gloucestershire
GL54 1JX
T: (01451) 830354
F: (01451) 832486
E: fossemanor@bestwestern.co.
uk

**Grapevine Hotel
★★★ SILVER AWARD**
Sheep Street, Stow-on-the-
Wold, Gloucestershire GL54 1AU
T: (01451) 830344
F: (01451) 832278
E: wts@vines.co.uk
I: www.vines.co.uk/

Old Farmhouse Hotel ★★
Lower Swell, Stow-on-the-Wold,
Cheltenham, Gloucestershire
GL54 1LF
T: (01451) 830232 &
0800 0561150
F: (01451) 870962
E: oldfarm@globalnet.co.uk
I: www.scws.
com/webcraft/hotels/
Old_Farmhouse

Stow Lodge Hotel ★★★
The Square, Stow-on-the-Wold,
Cheltenham, Gloucestershire
GL54 1AB
T: (01451) 830485
F: (01451) 831671
E: chris@stowlodge.com
I: www.stowlodge.com

The Unicorn Hotel ★★★
Sheep Street, Stow-on-the-
Wold, Cheltenham,
Gloucestershire GL54 1HQ
T: (01451) 830257
F: (01451) 831090

STRATFORD-UPON-AVON
Warwickshire

**Charlecote Pheasant Country
Hotel★★★**
Charlecote, Warwickshire
CV35 9EW
T: (01789) 279954
F: (01789) 470222
E: www.corushotels.com

**Ettington Park
★★★★ GOLD AWARD**
Alderminster, Stratford-upon-
Avon, Warwickshire CV37 8BU
T: (01789) 450123
F: (01789) 450472

Falcon Hotel ★★★
Chapel Street, Stratford-upon-
Avon, Warwickshire CV37 6HA
T: (01789) 279953
F: (01789) 414260
E: www.corushotels.com

Grosvenor Hotel ★★★
Warwick Road, Stratford-upon-
Avon, Warwickshire CV37 6YT
T: (01789) 269213
F: (01789) 266087
I: www.patenhotels.co.uk

The New Inn ★★
Clifford Chambers, Stratford-
upon-Avon, Warwickshire
CV37 8HR
T: (01789) 293402
F: (01789) 293402
E: thenewinn65@aol.com
I: www.stratford-upon-avon.co.
uk

Stratford Court Hotel ★★
20 Avenue Road, Stratford-
upon-Avon, Warwickshire
CV37 6UX
T: (01789) 297799
F: (01789) 262449
E: stratfordcourt@easynet.co.uk
I: www.stratford-upon-avon.co.
uk/stratcrt.htm

**Stratford Manor Hotel
★★★★**
Warwick Road, Stratford-upon-
Avon, Warwickshire CV37 0PY
T: (01789) 731173
F: (01789) 731131
E: stratfordmanor@
marstonhotels.co.uk
I: www.marstonhotels.co.uk

**Stratford Victoria
★★★★ SILVER AWARD**
Arden Street, Stratford-upon-
Avon, Warwickshire CV37 6QQ
T: (01789) 271000
F: (01789) 271001
E: stratfordvictoria@
compuserve.com
I: www.stratfordvictoria.co.uk

**Thistle Stratford-upon-Avon
Rating Applied For**
Waterside, Stratford-upon-
Avon, Warwickshire CV37 6BA
T: (01789) 294949
F: (01789) 415874
E: stratford.uponavon@thistle.
co.uk
I: www.demon.co.
uk/quinsolve/arden/htm

Establishments printed in blue have a detailed entry in this guide

Welcome Hotel and Golf Course★★★★ SILVER AWARD
Warwick Road, Stratford-upon-Avon, Warwickshire CV37 0NR
T: (01789) 295252
F: (01789) 414666
E: sales@welcombe.co.uk
I: www.welcombe.co.uk
⊚ ⏏

The White Swan ★★★
Rother Street, Stratford-upon-Avon, Warwickshire CV37 6NH
T: (01789) 297022
F: (01789) 268773

STRENSHAM
Worcestershire
Roadchef Lodge
Rating Applied For
Strensham Motorway Services, M5 Service Area, Strensham, Worcester WR8 0BZ
T: 0800 834719 &
(01684) 293004
F: (01684) 273606

STRETTON UNDER FOSSE
Warwickshire
Ashton Lodge Country Hotel and Restaurant
Rating Applied For
Stretton under Fosse, Rugby, Warwickshire CV23 0PJ
T: (01788) 832278
F: (01788) 833497
E: enquiries@ashtonlodgehotel.co.uk
I: www.ashtonlodgehotel.co.uk

STROUD
Gloucestershire
Bear of Rodborough Hotel ★★★
Rodborough Common, Stroud, Gloucestershire GL5 5DE
T: (01453) 878522
F: (01453) 872523
E: bookings@
cotswold-inns-hotels.co.uk
I: www.cotswold-inns-hotels.co.uk

Bell Hotel and Restaurant ★★
Wallbridge, Stroud, Gloucestershire GL5 3JS
T: (01453) 763556
F: (01453) 758611

SUTTON COLDFIELD
West Midlands
Jarvis Penns Hall Hotel and Country Club★★★
Penns Lane, Walmley, Sutton Coldfield, West Midlands B76 1LH
T: (0121) 351 3111
F: (0121) 313 1297
I: www.jarvis.co.uk

Marston Farm Hotel ★★★
Bodymoor Heath, Sutton Coldfield, Warwickshire B76 9JD
T: (01827) 872133
F: (01827) 875043
I: www.brook-hotels.co.uk

New Hall (A Thistle Country House Hotel)
Rating Applied For
Walmley Road, Sutton Coldfield, West Midlands B76 1QX
T: (0121) 378 2442
F: (0121) 378 4637
E: new.hall@thistle.co.uk

SUTTON-ON-SEA
Lincolnshire
Bacchus Hotel
Rating Applied For
High Street, Sutton-on-Sea, Mablethorpe, Lincolnshire LN12 2EY
T: (01507) 441204
F: (01507) 441204

SWINSCOE
Staffordshire
The Dog and Partridge Country Inn with Rooms in the Grounds ★★
Swinscoe, Ashbourne, Derbyshire DE6 2HS
T: (01335) 343183
F: (01335) 342742

SYMONDS YAT EAST
Herefordshire
Forest View Hotel ★★ SILVER AWARD
Symonds Yat East, Ross-on-Wye, Herefordshire HR9 6JL
T: (01600) 890210
F: (01600) 890210

Royal Hotel ★★
Symonds Yat East, Ross-on-Wye, Herefordshire HR9 6JL
T: (01600) 890238
F: (01600) 890238

SYMONDS YAT WEST
Herefordshire
Old Court Hotel ★
Symonds Yat West, Ross-on-Wye, Herefordshire HR9 6DA
T: (01600) 890367
F: (01600) 890964
E: oldcourt@aol.com
I: www.SmoothHound.co.uk/hotels/oldcourt.html

Woodlea Country Hotel ★★
Symonds Yat West, Ross-on-Wye, Herefordshire HR9 6BL
T: (01600) 890206
F: (01600) 890206
E: woodlea_hotel@compuserve.com

TELFORD
Shropshire
Arleston Inn Hotel ★★
Arleston Lane, Wellington, Telford, Shropshire TF1 2LA
T: (01952) 501881
F: (01952) 506429

Buckatree Hall Hotel ★★★
The Wrekin, Wellington, Telford, Shropshire TF6 5AL
T: (01952) 641821
F: (01952) 247540
E: info@buckatree.macdonald-hotels.co.uk
I: www.macdonaldhotels.co.uk

Hadley Park House Hotel and Bistro ★★★ SILVER AWARD
Hadley Park, Telford, Shropshire TF1 4AF
T: (01952) 677269
F: (01952) 676938
⊚

The Oaks at Redhill ★★
Redhill, St Georges, Telford, Shropshire TF2 9NZ
T: (01952) 620126
F: (01952) 620257
I: www.scoot.oaks/uk.co

TETBURY
Gloucestershire
Calcot Manor
★★★ GOLD AWARD
Beverston, Tetbury, Gloucestershire GL8 8YJ
T: (01666) 890391
F: (01666) 890394
E: reception@calcotmanor.co.uk
I: www.calcotmanor.co.uk

TETTENHALL WOOD
West Midlands
Jarvis Mount Hotel ★★★
Mount Road, Tettenhall Wood, Wolverhampton WV6 8HL
T: (01902) 752055
F: (01902) 745263
E: www.jarvis.co.uk
⊚

TEWKESBURY
Gloucestershire
Corse Lawn House Hotel ★★★
Corse Lawn, Gloucester GL19 4LZ
T: (01452) 780771
F: (01452) 780840
E: hotel@corselawnhouse.u-net.com
I: www.corselawnhousehotel.co.uk

Hilton Puckrup Hall Hotel ★★★★
Puckrup, Tewkesbury, Gloucestershire GL20 6EL
T: (01684) 296200
F: (01684) 850788
E: general.manager@puckruphall.stakis.co.uk

Tewkesbury Park Hotel Country Club★★★
Lincoln Green Lane, Tewkesbury, Gloucestershire GL20 7DN
T: (01684) 295405
F: (01684) 292386

THURLASTON
Warwickshire
Whitefields Hotel and Golf Complex Limited★★★
Coventry Road, Thurlaston, Rugby, Warwickshire CV23 9JR
T: (01788) 521800
F: (01788) 521695
E: mail@whitefields-hotel.co.uk
I: www.whitefield-hotel.co.uk

TOWCESTER
Northamptonshire
Plum Park Hotel
Rating Applied For
Watling Street, Towcester, Northamptonshire NN12 6LG
T: (01327) 811515 & 811727
F: (01327) 811723

TUTBURY
Staffordshire
Ye Olde Dog & Partridge Hotel ★★★
High Street, Tutbury, Burton upon Trent, Staffordshire DE13 9LS
T: (01283) 813030
F: (01283) 813178

ULLINGSWICK
Herefordshire
The Steppes
★★ SILVER AWARD
Ullingswick, Hereford HR1 3JG
T: (01432) 820424
F: (01432) 820042
E: bookings@steppeshotel.fsbusiness.co.uk
I: www.steppeshotel.fsbusiness.co.uk

UPPER SLAUGHTER
Gloucestershire
Lords of the Manor Hotel
★★★ GOLD AWARD
Upper Slaughter, Cheltenham, Gloucestershire GL54 2JD
T: (01451) 820243
F: (01451) 820696
E: lordsofthemanor@btinternet.com
I: lordofthemanor.com

UPPINGHAM
Leicestershire
Lake Isle Hotel
★★ SILVER AWARD
16 High Street East, Uppingham, Oakham, Leicestershire LE15 9PZ
T: (01572) 822951
F: (01572) 822951

UPTON ST LEONARDS
Gloucestershire
Hatton Court Hotel
★★★ SILVER AWARD
Upton Hill, Upton St Leonards, Gloucester GL4 8DE
T: (01452) 617412
F: (01452) 612945
E: Res@hatton-court.co.uk
I: www.hatton-hotels.co.uk

UPTON-UPON-SEVERN
Worcestershire
White Lion Hotel ★★★
21 High Street, Upton-upon-Severn, Worcester WR8 0HJ
T: (01684) 592551
F: (01684) 59333
E: info@whitelionhotel.demon.co.uk
I: www.whitelion.demon.co.uk

WALSALL
West Midlands
Beverley Hotel ★★★
58 Lichfield Road, (A461), Walsall, WS4 2DJ
T: (01922) 622999 & 614967
F: (01922) 724187

WARWICK
Warwickshire
Chesford Grange Hotel ★★★
Chesford Bridge, Kenilworth, Warwick, Warwickshire CV8 2LD
T: (01926) 859331
F: (01926) 859075
E: samanthabrown@principalhotels
I: www.principalhotels.co.uk

Crown and Castle Inn
Rating Applied For
2-4 Coventry Road, Warwick, CV34 4NT
T: (01926) 492087
F: (01926) 410638

Establishments printed in blue have a detailed entry in this guide

The Glebe at Barford ★★★
Church Street, Barford, Warwick
CV35 8BS
T: (01926) 624218
F: (01926) 624625
E: GLEBE_HOTEL@YAHOO.CO.
UK
I: WWW.SMOOTHHOUND.CO.
UK/

Hilton Warwick ★★★★
A429 Stratford Road, (Junction
15 of M40), Warwick, CV34 6RE
T: (01926) 499555
F: (01926) 410020

**The Lord Leycester Hotel
★★★**
17 Jury Street, Warwick,
CV34 4EJ
T: (01926) 491481
F: (01926) 491561
E: reception@lord-leycester.co.
uk
I: www.lord-leycester.co.uk

**The Old Fourpenny Shop Hotel
★★**
27-29 Crompton Street,
Warwick, CV34 6HJ
T: (01926) 491360
F: (01926) 411892

Warwick Arms Hotel ★★
17 High Street, Warwick,
CV34 4AT
T: (01926) 492759
F: (01926) 410587

WATERHOUSES
Staffordshire
**Old Beams Restaurant with
Rooms★★ SILVER AWARD**
Leek Road, Waterhouses, Stoke-
on-Trent ST10 3HW
T: (01538) 308254
F: (01538) 308157
I: www.oldbeamsrestaurant

WEEDON
Northamptonshire
Globe Hotel ★★
High Street, Weedon,
Northampton NN7 4QD
T: (01327) 340336
F: (01327) 349058
E: llct@tinyworld.co.uk
I: djl-hotel.co.uk.

WELLINGBOROUGH
Northamptonshire
High View Hotel ★★
156 Midland Road,
Wellingborough,
Northamptonshire NN8 1NG
T: (01933) 278733
F: (01933) 225948

WEOBLEY
Herefordshire
The Salutation Inn ★★
Market Pitch, Weobley, Hereford
HR4 8SJ
T: (01544) 318443
F: (01544) 318216
E: info@salutationinn.com
I: www.aitch.net/salutation/

WHATTON
Nottinghamshire
The Haven ★★
Grantham Road, Whatton,
Nottingham NG13 9EU
T: (01949) 850800
F: (01949) 851454

WHITCHURCH
Shropshire
**Terrick Hall Hotel & Restaurant
★★★**
Terrick Road, Hill Valley,
Whitchurch, Shropshire
SY13 4JZ
T: (01948) 663031
F: (01948) 663020

WHITNEY-ON-WYE
Worcestershire
The Rhydspence Inn ★★
Whitney-on-Wye, Hereford
HR3 6EU
T: (01497) 831262
F: (01497) 831751

WISHAW
Warwickshire
**The Belfry
★★★★ SILVER AWARD**
Wishaw, Warwickshire B76 9PR
T: (01675) 470301 & 470033
F: (01675) 470256
E: enquiries@thebelfry.com
I: www.thebelfry.com

Moxhull Hall Hotel ★★
Holly Lane, Wishaw, Sutton
Coldfield, West Midlands
B76 9PE
T: (0121) 329 2056
F: (0121) 311 1980
E: john@moxhull-hall.demon.
co.uk

WOLVERHAMPTON
West Midlands
**Fox Hotel (Wolverhampton)
★★**
118 School Street,
Wolverhampton, WV3 0NR
T: (01902) 421680
F: (01902) 711654
E: sales@foxhotel.co.uk
I: www.foxhotel.co.uk

**Novotel Wolverhampton
★★★**
Union Street, Wolverhampton,
West Midlands WV1 3JN
T: (01902) 871100
F: (01902) 870054

**Park Hall Hotel and
Conference Centre★★★**
Park Drive, Goldthorn Park,
Wolverhampton WV4 5AJ
T: (01902) 331121
F: (01902) 344760
E: enquiries@parkhallhotel.co.
uk
I: www.parkhallhotel.co.uk

**Patshull Park Hotel, Golf and
Country Club★★★**
Patshull Park, Pattingham,
Wolverhampton, WV6 7HR
T: (01902) 700100
F: (01902) 700874
E: sales@patshull-park.co.uk
I: www.patshull-park.co.uk

WOODHALL SPA
Lincolnshire
The Dower House Hotel ★★
The Manor Estate, Woodhall Spa,
Lincolnshire LN10 6PY
T: (01526) 352588
F: (01526) 352588
E: info@dowerhousehotel.co.uk
I: www.web-marketing.co.
uk/dowerhouse

Eagle Lodge Hotel ★★
The Broadway, Woodhall Spa,
Lincolnshire LN10 6ST
T: (01526) 353231
F: (01526) 352797

The Golf Hotel ★★★
The Broadway, Woodhall Spa,
Lincolnshire LN10 6SG
T: (01526) 353535
F: (01526) 353096
I: www.principalhotels.co.uk

Petwood Hotel ★★★
Stixwould Road, Woodhall Spa,
Lincolnshire LN10 6QF
T: (01526) 352411
F: (01526) 353473
E: reception@petwood.co.uk
I: www.petwood.co.uk

WORCESTER
Worcestershire
Diglis House Hotel ★★
Riverside, Severn Street,
Worcester, WR1 2NF
T: (01905) 353518
F: (01905) 767772
E: diglis@england.com
I: www.jks.org/diglis

Five Ways Hotel ★★
Angel Place, Worcester,
WR1 3QN
T: (01905) 616980 & 29666
F: (01905) 616344

**The Hadley Bowling Green Inn
& Country Hotel★★**
Hadley Heath, Droitwich,
Worcestershire WR9 0AR
T: (01905) 620294
F: (01905) 620771
E: hbginn@backissues.freeserve.
co.uk
I: www.english-inns.co.
uk/HadleyBowlingGreen

**The Maximillian Hotel
Rating Applied For**
Shrub Hill Road, Shrub Hill,
Worcester, WR4 9EF
T: (01905) 23867 & 21694
F: (01905) 724935

Severn View Hotel ★★
Newport Street, Worcester,
WR1 3NS
T: (01905) 27600
F: (01905) 612643

Ye Olde Talbot Hotel ★★
Friar Street, Worcester,
WR1 2NA
T: (01905) 23573
F: (01905) 612760

WORKSOP
Nottinghamshire
**Lion Hotel and Restaurant
★★★**
112 Bridge Street, Worksop,
Nottinghamshire S80 1HT
T: (01909) 477925
F: (01909) 479038
E: lionhotel@hotmail.com

EAST OF ENGLAND

ALDEBURGH
Suffolk
The Brudenell Hotel ★★★
The Parade, Aldeburgh, Suffolk
IP15 5BU
T: (01728) 452071
F: (01728) 454082

Uplands Hotel ★★
Victoria Road, Aldeburgh,
Suffolk IP15 5DX
T: (01728) 452420
F: (01728) 454872
I: www.smoothound.co.
uk/hotels/uplands.html

**Wentworth Hotel
★★★ SILVER AWARD**
Wentworth Road, Aldeburgh,
Suffolk IP15 5BD
T: (01728) 452312
F: (01728) 454343
E: wentworth.hotel@anglianet.
co.uk
I: www.wentworthhotel.com

White Lion Hotel ★★★
Market Cross Place, Aldeburgh,
Suffolk IP15 5BJ
T: (01728) 452720
F: (01728) 452986
E: whitelionaldeburgh@
btinternet.com
I: www.whitelion.co.uk

AYLMERTON
Norfolk
Roman Camp Inn ★★
Holt Road, Aylmerton, Norwich
NR11 8QD
T: (01263) 838291
F: (01263) 837071

BASILDON
Essex
Campanile Hotel ★★
A127 Southend Arterial Road,
Pipps Hill, Basildon, Essex
SS14 3AE
T: (01268) 530810
F: (01268) 286710

The Chichester Hotel ★★★
Old London Road, Wickford,
Essex SS11 8UE
T: (01268) 560555
F: (01268) 560580

Establishments printed in blue have a detailed entry in this guide

BEDFORD
Bedfordshire
Bedford Swan Hotel ★★★
The Embankment, Bedford,
MK40 1RW
T: (01234) 346565
F: (01234) 212009
I: www.patenhotels.co.uk

BLACK NOTLEY
Essex
Woodlands Manor Hotel ★★
Upper London Road, Black
Notley, Braintree, Essex
CM7 8QN
T: (01245) 361502 & 363201
F: (01245) 363209
I: www.business.thisisessex.co.
uk/woodlands

BLAKENEY
Norfolk
Morston Hall
★★ GOLD AWARD
Morston, Holt, Norfolk
NR25 7AA
T: (01263) 741041
F: (01263) 740419
E: reception@morstonhall.com.
uk
I: www.morstonhall.com.uk

The Pheasant Hotel ★★
The Coast Road, Kelling, Holt,
Norfolk NR25 7EG
T: (01263) 588382
F: (01263) 588101
E: enquiries@
pheasanthotelnorfolk.co.uk
I: www.pheasanthotelnorfolk.co.
uk

BRAINTREE
Essex
White Hart Hotel ★★★
Bocking End, Braintree, Essex
CM7 9AB
T: (01376) 321401
F: (01376) 552628
E: geaves@cix.co.uk.
I: www.thewhiteharthotel.
freeserve.co.uk

BRANCASTER STAITHE
Norfolk
The White Horse ★★
Main Road, Brancaster Staithe,
King's Lynn, Norfolk PE31 8BW
T: (01485) 210262
F: (01485) 210930
E: whitehorse.brancaster@
virgin.net
I: www.whitehorsebrancaster.co.
uk

BRENTWOOD
Essex
Marygreen Manor Hotel
★★★★ SILVER AWARD
London Road, Brentwood, Essex
CM14 4NR
T: (01277) 225252
F: (01277) 262809
E: info@marygreenmanor.co.uk
I: www.marygreenmanor.co.uk

New World Hotel ★★
Great Warley Street, Great
Warley, Brentwood, Essex
CM13 3JP
T: (01277) 226418 & 220483
F: (01277) 229795

BUCKDEN
Cambridgeshire
Lion Hotel ★★★
High Street, Buckden, St Neots,
Huntingdon, Cambridgeshire
PE18 9XA
T: (01480) 810313
F: (01480) 811070

BUNGAY
Suffolk
The Kings Head Hotel ★
Market Place, Bungay, Suffolk
NR35 1AF
T: (01986) 893583 & 893582
F: (01986) 893583
I: www.
admin@vintagealecompany.co.
uk

BURNHAM MARKET
Norfolk
The Hoste Arms
★★ SILVER AWARD
The Green, Burnham Market,
King's Lynn, Norfolk PE31 8HD
T: (01328) 738777 & 738257
F: (01328) 730103
E: thehostearms@compuserve.
com
I: www.hostearms.co.uk

BURY ST EDMUNDS
Suffolk
Angel Hotel ★★★
Angel Hill, Bury St Edmunds,
Suffolk IP33 1LT
T: (01284) 753926
F: (01284) 750092
E: sales@theangel.co.uk
I: www.theangel.co.uk

Butterfly Hotel ★★★
A14 Bury East Exit, Moreton
Hall, Bury St Edmunds, Suffolk
IP32 7BW
T: (01284) 760884
F: (01284) 755476
E: burybutterfly@lineone.net
I: www.butterflyhotels.co.uk

The Grange Hotel ★★
Barton Road, Thurston, Bury St
Edmunds, Suffolk IP31 3PQ
T: (01359) 231260
F: (01359) 231387
E: info@thegrangehotel.uk.com
I: www.thegrangehotel.uk.com

Priory Hotel and Restaurant
★★★
Fornham Road, Tollgate, Bury St
Edmunds, Suffolk IP32 6EH
T: (01284) 766181
F: (01284) 767604
E: reservations@prioryhotel.co.
uk
I: www.prioryhotel.co.uk

CAMBRIDGE
Cambridgeshire
Arundel House Hotel
★★ SILVER AWARD
Chesterton Road, Cambridge,
Cambridgeshire CB4 3AN
T: (01223) 367701
F: (01223) 367721

Bridge Hotel (Motel) ★
Clayhythe, Waterbeach,
Cambridge CB5 9NZ
T: (01223) 860252
F: (01223) 440448

Centennial Hotel ★★
63-71 Hills Road, Cambridge,
CB2 1PG
T: (01223) 314652
F: (01223) 315443
I: centennialhotel@barclays.net

Duxford Lodge Hotel and Le
Paradis Restaurant
★★★ GOLD AWARD
Ickleton Road, Duxford,
Cambridge CB2 4RU
T: (01223) 836444
F: (01223) 832271
E: duxford@btclick.com
I: www.touristnetuk.
com/em/duxford

Gonville Hotel
★★★ SILVER AWARD
Gonville Place, Cambridge,
CB1 1LY
T: (01223) 366611 & 221111
F: (01223) 315470
E: enq@gonvillehotel.co.uk
I: www.gonvillehotel.co.uk

Royal Cambridge Hotel ★★★
Trumpington Street, Cambridge,
Cambridgeshire CB2 1PY
T: (01223) 351631
F: (01223) 352972
E: royalcambridge@
2offanyhotels.co.uk
I: www.2offanyhotels.co.uk

CHATTERIS
Cambridgeshire
Cross Keys Inn Hotel ★
12-16 Market Hill, Chatteris,
Cambridgeshire PE16 6BA
T: (01354) 693036 & 692644
F: (01354) 694454

CHELMSFORD
Essex
Atlantic Hotel ★★★
Brook Street, Off New Street,
Chelmsford, CM1 1PP
T: (01245) 268168
F: (01245) 268169
E: info@atlantichotel.co.uk
I: www.atlantichotel.co.uk

County Hotel
★★★ SILVER AWARD
Rainsford Road, Chelmsford,
CM1 2PZ
T: (01245) 455700
F: (01245) 492762
E: sales@countyhotel-essex.co.
uk
I: www.countyhotel.co.uk

Miami Hotel ★★
Princes Road, Chelmsford,
CM2 9AJ
T: (01245) 264848 & 269603
F: (01245) 259860
E: miamihotel@hotmail.com
I: www.miamihotel.co.uk

Pontlands Park Country Hotel
and Conservatory Restaurant
★★★ SILVER AWARD
West Hanningfield Road, Great
Baddow, Chelmsford CM2 8HR
T: (01245) 476444 & 478999
F: (01245) 478393
E: sales@pontlandsparkhotel.co.
uk
I: www.pontlandsparkhotel.co.
uk

Saracens Head Hotel ★★
3-5 High Street, Chelmsford,
CM1 1BE
T: (01245) 262368
F: (01245) 262418

Snows Hotel ★
240 Springfield Road,
Chelmsford, CM2 6BP
T: (01245) 352004
F: (01245) 356675
E: sales@snowshotel.com
I: www.snowshotel.com

CHESHUNT
Hertfordshire
Cheshunt Marriott Hotel
★★★
Halfhide Lane, Turnford,
Broxbourne, Hertfordshire
EN10 6NG
T: (01992) 451245
F: (01992) 440120
I: www.marriott.com

CLACTON-ON-SEA
Essex
Chudleigh Hotel ★
Agate Road, Marine Parade
West, Clacton-on-Sea, Essex
CO15 1RA
T: (01255) 425407
F: (01255) 470280

Esplanade Hotel ★★
27-29 Marine Parade East,
Clacton-on-Sea, Essex
CO15 1UU
T: (01255) 220450
F: (01255) 221800

CLARE
Suffolk
The Plough Inn ★★
Brockley Green, Hundon,
Sudbury, Suffolk CO10 8DT
T: (01440) 786789
F: (01440) 786710

CODICOTE
Hertfordshire
The Bell Motel ★★
High Street, Codicote,
Hertfordshire SG4 8XD
T: (01438) 820278
F: (01438) 821671

COGGESHALL
Essex
The White Hart Hotel ★★
Market End, Coggeshall,
Colchester CO6 1NH
T: (01376) 561654
F: (01376) 561789
E: wharthotel@ndirect.co.uk
I: www.oldenglish.co.uk

COLCHESTER
Essex
Butterfly Hotel ★★★
A12-A120 Ardleigh Junction,
Old Ipswich Road, Colchester,
Essex CO7 7QY
T: (01206) 230900
F: (01206) 231095
E: colbutterfly@lineone.net
I: www.butterflyhotels.co.uk

George Hotel
★★★ SILVER AWARD
116 High Street, Colchester,
Essex CO1 1TD
T: (01206) 578494
F: (01206) 761732
E: george@keme.co.uk
I: www.esspro.co.uk/george

Establishments printed in blue have a detailed entry in this guide

The Lodge ★★
The Essex Golf & Country Club,
Earls Colne, Colchester CO6 2NS
T: (01787) 224466
F: (01787) 224410
I: www.the essex.co.uk

Rose & Crown ★★★
East Street, Colchester, Essex
CO1 2TZ
T: (01206) 866677
F: (01206) 866616
E: info@rose-and-crown.com
I: www.rose-and-crown.com

Wivenhoe House Hotel and Conference Centre★★★
Wivenhoe Park, Colchester,
CO4 3SQ
T: (01206) 863666
F: (01206) 868532
E: fossy@essex.ac.uk
I: www.essex.ac.uk/wivenhoe-house/main.html

COLTISHALL
Norfolk
The Norfolk Mead Hotel
★★ SILVER AWARD
Church Loke, Coltishall, Norwich
NR12 7DN
T: (01603) 737531
F: (01603) 737521
E: norfolkmead@aol.com.uk

CROMER
Norfolk
Cliftonville Hotel ★★
Seafront, Runton Road, Cromer,
Norfolk NR27 9AS
T: (01263) 512543
F: (01263) 515700
E: reservation@cliftonvillehotel.co.uk
I: www.cliftonvillehotel.co.uk

Ye Olde Red Lion Hotel ★★
Brook Street, Cromer, Norfolk
NR27 9HD
T: (01263) 514964
F: (01263) 512834

DISS
Norfolk
The Park Hotel ★★
29 Denmark Street, Diss, Norfolk
IP22 4LE
T: (01379) 642244
F: (01379) 644218
E: park.hotel@btinternet.com
I: www.eurotrail.com

Scole Inn ★★
Scole, Diss IP21 4DR
T: (01379) 740481
F: (01379) 740762

DOVERCOURT
Essex
Tower Hotel ★★
Main Road, Dovercourt,
Harwich, Essex CO12 3PJ
T: (01255) 504952
F: (01255) 504952
E: admin@towerharwich.fsnet.co.uk

DOWNHAM MARKET
Norfolk
Castle Hotel ★★
High Street, Downham Market,
Norfolk PE38 9HF
T: (01366) 384311
F: (01366) 384311
E: howard@castle-hotel.com
I: www.castle-hotel.com

DUNSTABLE
Bedfordshire
Old Palace Lodge Hotel ★★★
Church Street, Dunstable,
Bedfordshire LU5 4RT
T: (01582) 662201 & 470774
F: (01582) 696422

EAST DEREHAM
Norfolk
The Phoenix Hotel ★★
Church Street, East Dereham,
Norfolk NR19 1DL
T: (01362) 692276
F: (01362) 691752

EPPING
Essex
The Parsonage Ltd
★★ SILVER AWARD
Abridge Road, Theydon Bois,
Epping, Essex CM16 7NN
T: (01992) 814242
F: (01992) 812170
E: reception@theparsonage.co.uk
I: www.theparsonage.co.uk

EYE
Suffolk
The Cornwallis Country Hotel and Restaurant★★★
Brome, Eye, Suffolk IP23 8AJ
T: (01379) 870326
F: (01379) 870051
E: info@thecornwallis.com
I: www.thecornwallis.com

FAKENHAM
Norfolk
Wensum Lodge Hotel ★★
Bridge Street, Fakenham,
Norfolk NR21 9AY
T: (01328) 862100
F: (01328) 863365
I: www.scoot.co.uk/wensum_lodge_hotel/

FELIXSTOWE
Suffolk
Brook Hotel and Carvery ★★
Orwell Road, Felixstowe, Suffolk
IP11 7PF
T: (01394) 278441
F: (01394) 670422

Marlborough Hotel ★★
Sea Front, Felixstowe, Suffolk
IP11 2BJ
T: (01394) 285621
F: (01394) 670724

Waverley Hotel ★★
Wolsey Gardens, Felixstowe,
Suffolk IP11 7DF
T: (01394) 282811
F: (01394) 670185

FRINTON-ON-SEA
Essex
The Rock Hotel ★★
The Esplanade, Frinton-on-Sea,
Essex CO13 9EQ
T: (01255) 677194 & 0800 0187194
F: (01255) 675173
E: enquiries@therockhotel.co.uk
I: www.rockhotel.co.uk

GISSING
Norfolk
Gissing Hall ★★
Gissing, Diss, Norfolk IP22 5UN
T: (01379) 677291
F: (01379) 674117

GORLESTON-ON-SEA
Norfolk
Cliff Hotel ★★★
Cliff Hill, Gorleston-on-Sea,
Great Yarmouth, Norfolk
NR31 6BN
T: (01493) 662179
F: (01493) 653617

Pier Hotel ★★
Harbour Mouth, Gorleston-on-Sea, Great Yarmouth, Norfolk
NR31 6PL
T: (01493) 662631
F: (01493) 440263

GREAT CHESTERFORD
Essex
Crown House ★★
Great Chesterford, Saffron
Walden, Essex CB10 1NY
T: (01799) 530515
F: (01799) 530683
I: www.virtlialhotels.com/crown-house

GREAT YARMOUTH
Norfolk
Burlington Palm Court Hotel ★★
North Drive, Great Yarmouth,
Norfolk NR30 1EG
T: (01493) 844568
F: (01493) 331848
E: enquiries@burlington-hotel.co.uk
I: www.burlington-hotel.co.uk

Hotel Elizabeth ★★
1 Marine Parade, Great
Yarmouth, Norfolk NR30 3AG
T: (01493) 855551
F: (01493) 853338

Embassy Hotel ★★
38-41 Camperdown, Great
Yarmouth, Norfolk NR30 3JB
T: (01493) 843135
F: (01493) 331064

Furzedown Private Hotel ★★
19-20 North Drive, Great
Yarmouth, Norfolk NR30 4EW
T: (01493) 844138
F: (01493) 844138

Hadleigh Gables Hotel
Rating Applied For
6-7 North Drive, Great
Yarmouth, Norfolk NR30 1ED
T: (01493) 843078
F: (01493) 843078
E: mike@hadleigh-gables.co.uk
I: www.hadleigh-gables.co.uk

Horse & Groom Motel ★★
Rollesby, Great Yarmouth,
Norfolk NR29 5ER
T: (01493) 740624
F: (01493) 740022
E: chris@groommotel.freeserve.co.uk

Imperial Hotel
★★★ SILVER AWARD
North Drive, Great Yarmouth,
Norfolk NR30 1EQ
T: (01493) 851113
F: (01493) 852229
E: imperial@scs-datacom.co.uk
I: www.imperialhotel.co.uk

Regency Dolphin Hotel ★★★
Albert Square, Great Yarmouth,
Norfolk NR30 3JH
T: (01493) 855070
F: (01493) 853798
E: regency@meridianleisure.com
I: www.meridianleisure.com

Regency Private Hotel ★★
5 North Drive, Great Yarmouth,
Norfolk NR30 1ED
T: (01493) 843759
F: (01493) 330411

HARLOW
Essex
Swallow Churchgate Hotel ★★★
Churchgate Street Village, Old
Harlow, Harlow, Essex CM17 0JT
T: (01279) 420246
F: (01279) 437720
E: churchgate.mann-@swallow.hotels.co.uk
I: www.swallowhotels.com

HARPENDEN
Hertfordshire
Glen Eagle Hotel ★★★
Luton Road, Harpenden,
Hertfordshire AL5 2PX
T: (01582) 464513
F: (01582) 460819

HARWICH
Essex
Cliff Hotel ★★
Marine Parade, Dovercourt,
Harwich, Essex CO12 3RE
T: (01255) 503345 & 507373
F: (01255) 240358

The Hotel Continental ★★
28-29 Marine Parade,
Dovercourt, Harwich, Essex
CO12 3RG
T: (01255) 551298 & 07770 308976
F: (01255) 551698
E: hotconti@aol.com
I: www.hotelcontinental-harwich.co.uk

The Pier at Harwich ★★★
The Quay, Harwich, Essex
CO12 3HH
T: (01255) 241212
F: (01255) 551922
E: info@thepieratharwich.co.uk
I: www.talbooth.com

HATFIELD
Hertfordshire
Hatfield Lodge Hotel ★★★
Comet Way, Hatfield,
Hertfordshire AL10 9NG
T: (01707) 288500
F: (01707) 256282
E: beales-hatfieldlodge@compuserve.com
I: www.bealeshotels.co.uk

Jarvis International Hotel ★★★
301 St Albans Road West,
Hatfield, Hertfordshire
AL10 9RH
T: (01707) 265411
F: (01707) 264019

Quality Hotel Hatfield ★★★
Roehyde Way, Hatfield,
Hertfordshire AL10 9AF
T: (01707) 275701
F: (01707) 266033
E: admin@gb059.u-net.com
I: www.choicehotelseurope.com
◉

HATFIELD HEATH
Essex

**Down Hall Country House
Hotel** ★★★★
Hatfield Heath, Bishop's
Stortford, Hertfordshire
CM22 7AS
T: (01279) 731441
F: (01279) 730416
◉

HERTFORD
Hertfordshire

Salisbury Arms Hotel ★★
Fore Street, Hertford,
Hertfordshire SG14 1BZ
T: (01992) 583091
F: (01992) 552510

HILLINGTON
Norfolk

Ffolkes Arms Hotel ★★
Lynn Road, Hillington, King's
Lynn, Norfolk PE31 6BJ
T: (01485) 600210
F: (01485) 601196
E: ffolkespub@aol.com
I: www.ffolkes-arms-hotel.co.uk
⚘

HINTLESHAM
Suffolk

Hintlesham Hall
★★★★ GOLD AWARD
Hintlesham, Ipswich, Suffolk
IP8 3NS
T: (01473) 652334 & 652268
F: (01473) 652463
E: reservations@
hintlesham-hall.co.uk
I: www.hintlesham-hall.co.uk

HITCHIN
Hertfordshire

Firs Hotel ★
83 Bedford Road, Hitchin,
Hertfordshire SG5 2TY
T: (01462) 422322
F: (01462) 432051
E: firshotel@freewayuk.com
I: www.firshotel.co.uk

Thistle Stevenage
Rating Applied For
Blakemore End Road, Little
Wymondley, Hitchin,
Hertfordshire SG4 7JJ
T: (01438) 355821
F: (01438) 742114
E: stevenage@thistle.co.uk
I: www.thistlehotels.com

HORNING
Norfolk

Petersfield House Hotel ★★★
Lower Street, Horning, Norwich
NR12 8PF
T: (01692) 630741
F: (01692) 630745
E: reception@petersfield.co.uk
I: www.petersfieldhotel.co.uk

HUNSTANTON
Norfolk

**Caley Hall Motel and
Restaurant**★★
Old Hunstanton, Hunstanton,
Norfolk PE36 6HH
T: (01485) 533486
F: (01485) 533348
⚘

The Golden Lion Hotel ★★
The Green, Hunstanton, Norfolk
PE36 6BH
T: (01485) 532688
F: (01485) 535310
E: golden-lion.co.uk

Le Strange Arms Hotel ★★★
Golf Course Road, Old
Hunstanton, Hunstanton,
Norfolk PE36 6JJ
T: (01485) 534411
F: (01485) 534724
E: lestrangearms@netmatters.
co.uk

**The Linksway Country House
Hotel**★★
Golf Course Road, Old
Hunstanton, Hunstanton,
Norfolk PE36 6JE
T: (01485) 532209 &
07860 330178
F: (01485) 532209

The Lodge Hotel ★★
Old Hunstanton, Hunstanton,
Norfolk PE36 6HX
T: (01485) 532896
F: (01485) 535007
E: reception@thelodge-hotel.co.
uk
I: www.thelodge-hotel.co.uk

HUNTINGDON
Cambridgeshire

Old Bridge Hotel
★★★ SILVER AWARD
1 High Street, Huntingdon,
Cambridgeshire PE18 6TQ
T: (01480) 452681
F: (01480) 411017

Swallow Hotel
★★★★ SILVER AWARD
Kingfisher Way, Hinchingbrooke
Business Park, Huntingdon,
Cambridgeshire PE18 8FL
T: (01480) 446000
F: (01480) 451111
E: info@swallowhotels.com
I: www.swallowhotels.com
◉ ⚘

INGATESTONE
Essex

The Heybridge Hotel ★★★
Roman Road, Ingatestone, Essex
CM4 9AB
T: (01277) 355355
F: (01277) 353288
⚘

IPSWICH
Suffolk

**Claydon Country House Hotel
and Restaurant**★★
Ipswich Road, Claydon, Ipswich
IP6 0AR
T: (01473) 830382
F: (01473) 832476
E: kayshotels@yahoo.com
I: www.bestwestern.co.uk

Courtyard By Marriott Ipswich
★★★ SILVER AWARD
The Havens, Ransomes Europark,
Ipswich, IP3 9SJ
T: (01473) 272244
F: (01473) 272484
I: www.marriotthotels.com
⚘

Ipswich County Hotel ★★★
London Road, Copdock, Ipswich,
Suffolk IP8 3JD
T: (01473) 209988
F: (01473) 730801
E: 114506,3671@compuserve.
com
I: www.ipswichcounty.co.uk
⚘

The Marlborough at Ipswich
★★★ SILVER AWARD
Henley Road, Ipswich, IP1 3SP
T: (01473) 257677
F: (01473) 226927
E: reception@themarlborough.
co.uk
I:·www.the marlborough.co.uk

Novotel Ipswich ★★★
Greyfriars Road, Ipswich, Suffolk
IP1 1UP
T: (01473) 232400
F: (01473) 232414
⚘

KING'S LYNN
Norfolk

Butterfly Hotel ★★★
A10-A47 Roundabout, Hardwick
Narrows, King's Lynn, Norfolk
PE30 4NB
T: (01553) 771707
F: (01553) 768027
E: kingsbutterfly@lineone.net
I: www.butterflyhotels.com

**Congham Hall Country House
Hotel**★★★ GOLD AWARD
Lynn Road, Grimston, King's
Lynn, Norfolk PE32 1AH
T: (01485) 600250
F: (01485) 601191
E: reception@conghamhotel.
demon.co.uk
I: www.prideofbritainhotels.com

Knights Hill Hotel ★★★
South Wootton, King's Lynn,
Norfolk PE30 3HQ
T: (01553) 675566
F: (01553) 675568
E: reception@knightshill.co.uk
I: www.abacushotels.co.uk

Park View Hotel ★★
Blackfriars Street, King's Lynn,
Norfolk PE30 1NN
T: (01553) 775146
F: (01553) 766957

Stuart House Hotel ★★
35 Goodwins Road, King's Lynn,
Norfolk PE30 5QX
T: (01553) 772169
F: (01553) 774788
E: stuarthousehotel@btinternet.
com
I: www.stuart-house-hotel-co.
uk
◉

The Tudor Rose Hotel ★★
St Nicholas Street, Off Tuesday
Market Place, King's Lynn,
Norfolk PE30 1LR
T: (01553) 762824
F: (01553) 764894
E: kltudorrose@aol.com
I: www.tudorrose-hotel.co.uk

LEAVENHEATH
Suffolk

**The Stoke by Nayland Club
Hotel**
Rating Applied For
Keepers Lane, Leavenheath,
Colchester, Essex CO6 4PZ
T: (01206) 262836
F: (01206) 263356
E: info@golf-club.co.uk
I: www.stokebynaylandclub.co.
uk

LEISTON
Suffolk

White Horse Hotel ★
Station Road, Leiston, Suffolk
IP16 4HD
T: (01728) 830694
F: (01728) 833105
E: whihorse@globalnet.co.uk
I: www.whitehorsehotel.co.uk

LETCHWORTH
Hertfordshire

Letchworth Hall Hotel ★★★
Letchworth Lane, Letchworth,
Hertfordshire SG6 3NP
T: (01462) 683747
F: (01462) 481540
I: www.aquarius-hotels.com

LOWESTOFT
Suffolk

Hotel Hatfield ★★★
The Esplanade, Lowestoft,
Suffolk NR33 0QP
T: (01502) 565337
F: (01502) 511885

Hotel Victoria
★★★ SILVER AWARD
Kirkley Cliff, Lowestoft, Suffolk
NR33 0BZ
T: (01502) 574433
F: (01502) 501529
⚘

LUTON
Bedfordshire

Thistle Luton
Rating Applied For
Arndale Centre, Luton,
Bedfordshire LU1 2TR
T: (01582) 734199
F: (01582) 402528
E: luton@thistle.co.uk
I: www.thistlehotels.com
◉ ⚘

MALDON
Essex

**Five Lakes Hotel, Golf and
Country Club and Spa**
★★★★ SILVER AWARD
Colchester Road, Tolleshunt
Knights, Maldon, Essex CM9 8HX
T: (01621) 868888
F: (01621) 869696
E: enquiries@fivelakes.co.uk
I: www.fivelakes.co.uk
◉

MARCH
Cambridgeshire
Olde Griffin Hotel Ltd ★★
High Street, March,
Cambridgeshire PE15 9JS
T: (01354) 652517
F: (01354) 650086

MARKS TEY
Essex
Marks Tey Hotel ★★★
London Road, Marks Tey,
Colchester, Essex CO6 1DU
T: (01206) 210001
F: (01206) 212167
I: www.virtualhotels.
com/marks-tey

MILDENHALL
Suffolk
Riverside Hotel ★★★
Mill Street, Mildenhall, Bury St
Edmunds, Suffolk IP28 7DP
T: (01638) 717274
F: (01638) 715997
E: cameronhotels@
riversidehotel.freeserve.co.uk
I: www.riversidehotel-net

The Smoke House ★★★
Beck Row, Bury St Edmunds,
Suffolk IP28 8DH
T: (01638) 713223
F: (01638) 712202
E: enquiries@smoke-house.co.
uk
I: www.smoke-house.co.uk

NEEDHAM MARKET
Suffolk
The Limes Hotel ★★
High Street, Needham Market,
Ipswich IP6 8DQ
T: (01449) 720305
F: (01449) 722233
E: limes@enterprise.net

NEWMARKET
Suffolk
Heath Court Hotel ★★★
Moulton Road, Newmarket,
Suffolk CB8 8DY
T: (01638) 667171
F: (01638) 666533
E: quality@heathcourt-hotel.co.
uk
I: www.heathcourt-hotel.co.uk

Rutland Arms ★★★
High Street, Newmarket, Suffolk
CB8 8NB
T: (01638) 664251
F: (01638) 666298
I: www.virtualhotels.
com/rutland-arms

**Swynford Paddocks Hotel
★★★**
Six Mile Bottom, Newmarket,
Suffolk CB8 0UE
T: (01638) 570234
F: (01638) 570283
E: sales@swynfordpaddocks.
com
I: www.swynfordpaddocks.com

NORTH WALSHAM
Norfolk
**Beechwood Hotel
★★ SILVER AWARD**
20 Cromer Road, North
Walsham, Norfolk NR28 0HD
T: (01692) 403231
F: (01692) 407284

**Elderton Lodge Hotel and
Langtry Restaurant★★**
Gunton Park, Thorpe Market,
Norwich NR11 8TZ
T: (01263) 833547
F: (01263) 834673
E: enquiries@eldertonlodge.co.
uk
I: www.eldertonlodge.co.uk

Kings Arms Hotel ★★
Kings Arms Street, North
Walsham, Norfolk NR28 9JX
T: (01692) 403054
F: (01692) 500095
E: kahotel@fsbdml.co.uk

**Scarborough Hill Country
House Hotel★★**
Old Yarmouth Road, North
Walsham, Norfolk NR28 9NA
T: (01692) 402151
F: (01692) 406686

NORWICH
Norfolk
Annesley House Hotel ★★
6 Newmarket Road, Norwich,
Norfolk NR2 2LA
T: (01603) 624553
F: (01603) 621577

**Barnham Broom Hotel, Golf,
Conference & Leisure Centre
★★★**
Honingham Road, Barnham
Broom, Norwich NR9 4DD
T: (01603) 759393 & 759552
F: (01603) 758224
E: enquiry@
barnhambroomhotel.co.uk
I: www.barnham-broom.co.uk

**Beeches Hotel
★★ SILVER AWARD**
2-6 Earlham Road, Norwich,
NR2 3DB
T: (01603) 621167 & 667357
F: (01603) 620151
E: reception@beeches.co.uk
I: www.beeches.co.uk

Dunston Hall Hotel ★★★★
Ipswich Road, Norwich,
NR14 8PQ
T: (01508) 470444
F: (01508) 471499
E: dhreception@devere-hotels.
com
I: www.devereonline.co.uk

Garden House Hotel ★
Salhouse Road, Rackheath,
Norwich NR13 6AA
T: (01603) 720007
F: (01603) 720019
E: ghotel@globalnet.co.uk
I: www.norfolkbroads.
com/gardenhousehotel

The Georgian House Hotel ★★
32-34 Unthank Road, Norwich,
Norfolk NR2 2RB
T: (01603) 615655
F: (01603) 765689
E: reception@georgian-hotel.
co.uk
I: georgian-hotel.co.uk

Old Rectory ★★
North Walsham Road,
Crostwick, Norwich, Norfolk
NR12 7BG
T: (01603) 738513
F: (01603) 738712
I: www.accomodata.co.
uk/020896.htm

**The Old Rectory
★★ SILVER AWARD**
103 Yarmouth Road, Thorpe St
Andrew, Norwich, NR7 0HF
T: (01603) 700772
F: (01603) 300772
E: rectoryh@aol.com

**Park Farm Country Hotel &
Leisure ★★★**
Hethersett, Norwich NR9 3DL
T: (01603) 810264
F: (01603) 812104
E: enq@parkfarm-hotel.co.uk

Pearl Continental Hotel ★★
116 Thorpe Road, Norwich,
NR1 1RU
T: (01603) 620302
F: (01603) 761706

Quality Hotel ★★★
2 Barnard Road, Bowthorpe,
Norwich, NR5 9JB
T: (01603) 741161
F: (01603) 741500
E: admin@gb619.u-net.com
I: www.choicehotelseurope.com

**Swallow Sprowston Manor
Hotel ★★★★ SILVER AWARD**
Sprowston Park, Wroxham Road,
Norwich, Norfolk NR7 8RP
T: (01603) 410871
F: (01603) 423911
I: www.swallowhotels.com

OULTON BROAD
Suffolk
Broadlands Hotel ★★
Bridge Road, Oulton Broad,
Lowestoft, Suffolk NR32 3LN
T: (01502) 516031 & 572157
F: (01502) 501454

**Ivy House Farm Hotel
★★★ SILVER AWARD**
Ivy Lane, Oulton Broad,
Lowestoft, Suffolk NR33 8HY
T: (01502) 501353 & 588144
F: (01502) 501539
E: IvyHouseFm@aol.com
I: ivyhousefarm.co.uk

OVERSTRAND
Norfolk
Sea Marge Hotel ★★★
16 High Street, Overstrand,
Cromer, Norfolk NR27 0AB
T: (01263) 579579
F: (01263) 579524
E: seamarge.hotel@virgin.net

PAPWORTH EVERARD
Cambridgeshire
Papworth Hotel ★★
Ermine Street South, Papworth
Everard, Cambridge CB3 8PB
T: (01954) 718851
F: (01954) 718069

PETERBOROUGH
Cambridgeshire
The Bell Inn Hotel ★★★
Great North Road, Stilton,
Peterborough, Cambridge
PE7 3RA
T: (01733) 241066
F: (01733) 245173
E: reception@thebellstilton.co.
uk
I: www.thebellstilton.co.uk

Butterfly Hotel ★★★
Thorpe Meadows, Off
Longthorpe Parkway,
Peterborough, PE3 6GA
T: (01733) 564240
F: (01733) 565538
E: peterbutterfly@lineone.net
I: www.butterflyhotels.co.uk

**Da Rosalia Hotel
Rating Applied For**
25 Burghley Road,
Peterborough, PE1 2QA
T: (01733) 568020 & 553331
F: (01733) 897816
E: darosaliahotel.1@virginnet.
co.uk

**Newark Hotel
Rating Applied For**
239-241 Eastfield Road,
Peterborough, PE1 4BH
T: (01733) 569811
F: (01733) 312550

Orton Hall Hotel ★★★
The Village, Orton Longueville,
Peterborough, Cambridgeshire
PE2 7DN
T: (01733) 391111
F: (01733) 231912
E: reception@ortonhall.co.uk
I: www.ortonhall.co.uk

**Peterborough Moat House
★★★**
Thorpe Wood, Peterborough,
Cambridgeshire PE3 6SG
T: (01733) 289988
F: (01733) 262737

Queensgate Hotel ★★
5 Fletton Avenue, Peterborough,
PE2 8AX
T: (01733) 562572 & 553181
F: (01733) 558982

Swallow Hotel ★★★★
Peterborough Business Park,
Lynch Wood, Peterborough,
Cambridgeshire PE2 6GB
T: (01733) 371111 & 375527
F: (01733) 236725
E: peterborough@
swallow-hotels.co.uk
I: www.swallowhotels.com

Talbot Hotel ★★★
New Street, Oundle,
Peterborough, PE8 4EA
T: (01832) 273621
F: (01832) 274545

Thomas Cook Bluebell Lodge Leisure Centre ★★
P O Box 36, Thorpe Wood,
Peterborough, PE3 6SB
T: (01733) 502555 & 503008
F: (01733) 502020

PETTISTREE
Suffolk

The Three Tuns Coaching Inn
Rating Applied For
Main Road, Pettistree,
Woodbridge, Suffolk IP13 0HW
T: (01728) 747979 & 746244
F: (01728) 746244
E: jon@threetuns-coachinginn.
co.uk
I: www.threetuns-coachinginn.
co.uk

PUCKERIDGE
Hertfordshire

The Vintage Court Hotel ★★★
Puckeridge, Ware, Hertfordshire
SG11 1SA
T: (01920) 822722
F: (01920) 822877

ST ALBANS
Hertfordshire

The Apples Hotel ★★
133 London Road, St Albans,
Hertfordshire AL1 1TA
T: (01727) 844111
F: (01727) 861100

Ardmore House ★★
54 Lemsford Road, St Albans,
Hertfordshire AL1 3PP
T: (01727) 859313
F: (01727) 859313
E: 106376.2353@compuserve.
com
I: www.stalbans.gou/ardmore/

Avalon Hotel ★★
260 London Road, St Albans,
Hertfordshire AL1 1TJ
T: (01727) 856757
F: (01727) 856750

Jarvis International Hotel
★★★
Hemel Hempstead Road,
Redbourn, St Albans,
Hertfordshire AL3 7AF
T: (01582) 792105
F: (01582) 792001
I: www.jarvis.co.uk

Nonna Rosa Hotel ★
3 Manor Road, St Albans,
AL1 3ST
T: (01727) 853613 & 831700
F: (01727) 853613

**Saint Michaels Manor St
Michaels Village**
★★★ SILVER AWARD
Fishpool Street, St Albans,
Hertfordshire AL3 4RY
T: (01727) 864444
F: (01727) 848909
E: smmanor@globalnet.co.uk
I: www.stmichaelsmanor.com

**Sopwell House Hotel and
Country Club** ★★★★
Cottonmill Lane, Sopwell, St
Albans, Hertfordshire AL1 2HQ
T: (01727) 864477
F: (01727) 844741
E: enquiries@sopwellhouse.co.
uk
I: www.sopwellhouse.co.uk

Thistle St Albans ★★★★
Watford Road, St Albans,
Hertfordshire AL2 3DS
T: (01727) 854252
F: (01727) 841906
E: st.albans@thistle.co.uk
I: www.thistlehotels.com

ST IVES
Cambridgeshire

The Dolphin Hotel ★★★
Bridgefoot, London Road, St
Ives, Huntingdon,
Cambridgeshire PE17 4EP
T: (01480) 466966 & 497497
F: (01480) 495597

The Golden Lion Hotel ★
Market Hill, St Ives, Huntingdon,
Cambridgeshire PE27 5AL
T: (01480) 492100
F: (01480) 497109

Olivers Lodge Hotel ★★★
Needingworth Road, St Ives,
Huntingdon, Cambridgeshire
PE27 5JP
T: (01480) 463252
F: (01480) 461150
E: reception@oliverslodge.co.uk
I: www.oliverslodge.co.uk

Slepe Hall Hotel ★★★
Ramsey Road, St Ives,
Huntingdon, Cambridgeshire
PE27 5RB
T: (01480) 463122
F: (01480) 300706
E: mail@slepehall.co.uk
I: www.slepehall.co.uk

ST NEOTS
Cambridgeshire

**Abbotsley Golf Hotel &
Country Club** ★★
Eynesbury Hardwicke, St Neots,
Huntingdon, Cambridgeshire
PE19 4XN
T: (01480) 474000
F: (01480) 471018

SAWBRIDGEWORTH
Hertfordshire

**The Manor of Groves Hotel
Golf and Country Club** ★★★
High Wych, Sawbridgeworth,
Hertfordshire CM21 0LA
T: (01279) 600777 & 722333
F: (01279) 600374
E: manor@brook-hotels.demon.
uk
I: www.brook-hotels.co.uk

SHERINGHAM
Norfolk

Beaumaris Hotel ★★
15 South Street, Sheringham,
Norfolk NR26 8LL
T: (01263) 822370
F: (01263) 821421
E: beauhotel@aol.com.
I: www.ecn.co.uk/beaumaris/

Southlands Hotel ★★
South Street, Sheringham,
Norfolk NR26 8LL
T: (01263) 822679
F: (01263) 822679

SHOTTISHAM
Suffolk

**Wood Hall Country House
Hotel** ★★★
Shottisham, Woodbridge,
Suffolk IP12 3EG
T: (01394) 411283
F: (01394) 410007
I: www.woodhall.uk.com

SOUTHEND-ON-SEA
Essex

Balmoral Hotel ★★
32-36 Valkyrie Road, Southend-
on-Sea, Essex SS0 8BU
T: (01702) 342947
F: (01702) 337828
E: balmoralhotel@
netscapeonline.co.uk

Camelia Hotel and Restaurant
★★ SILVER AWARD
178 Eastern Esplanade, Thorpe
Bay, Southend-on-Sea, SS1 3AA
T: (01702) 587917
F: (01702) 585704
E: cameliahotel@fsbdial.co.uk
I: www.cameliahotel.com

The County Hotel ★★★
Aviation Way, Southend-on-Sea,
SS2 6UN
T: (01702) 279955
F: (01702) 541961
E: enquiries@countysouthend.
co.uk
I: www.countysouthend.co.uk

Roslin Hotel ★★★
Thorpe Esplanade, Thorpe Bay,
Southend-on-Sea, Essex
SS1 3BG
T: (01702) 586375
F: (01702) 586663
I: www.roslinhotel.com

Tower Hotel and Restaurant
★★
146 Alexandra Road, Southend-
on-Sea, SS1 1HE
T: (01702) 348635
F: (01702) 433044

SOUTHWOLD
Suffolk

The Crown ★★
High Street, Southwold, Suffolk
IP18 6DP
T: (01502) 722275
F: (01502) 727263
E: crownreception@adnams.co.
uk

Swan Hotel
★★ SILVER AWARD
Market Place, Southwold,
Suffolk IP18 6EG
T: (01502) 722186
F: (01502) 724800
E: swan.hotel@adnams.co.uk

STEVENAGE
Hertfordshire

Novotel ★★★
Knebworth Park, Stevenage,
Hertfordshire SG1 2AX
T: (01438) 346100
F: (01438) 723872
E: h0992@accor-hotels.com
I: www.novotel.com

STOWMARKET
Suffolk

Cedars Hotel ★★
Needham Road, Stowmarket,
Suffolk IP14 2AJ
T: (01449) 612668
F: (01449) 674704
E: enquiries@cedarshotel.co.uk
I: www.cedarshotel.co.uk

SWAFFHAM
Norfolk

George Hotel ★★★
Station Street, Swaffham,
Norfolk PE37 7LJ
T: (01760) 721238
F: (01760) 725333
E: reception@
geprgehotelswaffham.freeserve.
co.uk
I: www.bestwestern.co.uk

Lydney House Hotel ★★
Norwich Road, Swaffham,
Norfolk PE37 7QS
T: (01760) 723355
F: (01760) 721410
E: rooms@lydney-house.
demon.co.uk
I: www.lydney-house.demon.co.
uk

TAVERHAM
Norfolk

**Wensum Valley Golf & Country
Club** ★★
Beech Avenue, Taverham,
Norwich NR8 6HP
T: (01603) 261012
F: (01603) 261664
E: enqs@wensumvalley.
freeserve.co.uk
I: www.wensumvalley.freeserve.
co.uk

THETFORD
Norfolk

The Bell Hotel ★★★
King Street, Thetford, Norfolk
IP24 2AZ
T: (01842) 754455
F: (01842) 755552
E: thetbell@aol.com
I: www.oldenglish.co.uk

The Thomas Paine Hotel ★★
White Hart Street, Thetford,
Norfolk IP24 1AA
T: (01842) 755631
F: (01842) 766505
E: thomaspainehotel@www.
hotmail.com
I: www.ecn.co.
uk/thomaspainehotel./

THORNHAM
Norfolk

The Lifeboat Inn ★★
Ship Lane, Thornham,
Hunstanton, Norfolk PE36 6LT
T: (01485) 512236
F: (01485) 512323
E: reception@lifeboatinn.co.uk
I: www.lifeboatinn.co.uk

THORPENESS
Suffolk

Thorpeness Hotel & Golf Club
★★
Lakeside Avenue, Thorpeness,
Leiston, Suffolk IP16 4NH
T: (01728) 452176 & 454926
F: (01728) 453868
E: info@thorpeness.co.uk
I: www.thorpeness.co.uk

Establishments printed in blue have a detailed entry in this guide

TITCHWELL
Norfolk

Briarfields Hotel ★★
Main Street, Titchwell, King's Lynn, Norfolk PE31 8BB
T: (01485) 210742
F: (01485) 210933
E: briarfields@norfolk-hotels.co.uk

Titchwell Manor Hotel
★★ SILVER AWARD
Titchwell, King's Lynn, Norfolk PE31 8BB
T: (01485) 210221
F: (01485) 210104
E: margaret@titchwellmanor.co.uk
I: www.titchwellmanor.co.uk

TIVETSHALL ST MARY
Norfolk

The Old Ram Coaching Inn
★★ SILVER AWARD
Ipswich Road, Tivetshall St Mary, Norwich, Norfolk NR15 2DE
T: (01379) 676794
F: (01379) 608399
E: theoldram@btinternet.com
I: www.theoldram.com

UPPER SHERINGHAM
Norfolk

The Dales Hotel
Rating Applied For
Lodge Hill, Upper Sheringham, Sheringham, Norfolk NR26 8TJ
T: (01263) 822225

WALTHAM ABBEY
Essex

Swallow Hotel ★★★★
Old Shire Lane, Waltham Abbey, Essex EN9 3LX
T: (01992) 717170
F: (01992) 711841
E: waltham.abbey@swallow-hotels.co.uk
I: www.swallowhotels.com

WANSFORD
Cambridgeshire

Haycock Hotel ★★★
Wansford, Peterborough PE8 6JA
T: (01780) 782223
F: (01780) 783508
E: haycockhotel@hotmail.com

WARE
Hertfordshire

Briggens House Hotel ★★★★
Briggens Park, Stanstead Road (A414), Stanstead Abbotts, Ware, Hertfordshire SG12 8LD
T: (01279) 829955
F: (01279) 793685
E: reservations@corushotels.com
I: www.corushotels.com

Marriott Hanbury Manor Hotel & Country Club
★★★★★ GOLD AWARD
Ware, Herts SG12 0SD
T: (01920) 487722
F: (01920) 487692
I: www.marriott.com

Roebuck Hotel ★★★
Baldock Street, Ware, Hertfordshire SG12 9DR
T: (01920) 409955
F: (01920) 468016
E: roebuck@zoffanyhotels.co.uk
I: www.zoffanyhotels.co.uk

WEST RUNTON
Norfolk

Dormy House Hotel ★★
Cromer Road, West Runton, Norfolk NR27 9QA
T: (01263) 837537
F: (01263) 837537
E: j.jarvis@freenetname.co.uk

The Links Country Park Hotel and Golf Club★★★
Sandy Lane, West Runton, Cromer, Norfolk NR27 9QH
T: (01263) 838383
F: (01263) 838264
E: sales@links-hotel.co.uk
I: www.links-hotel.co.uk

WESTCLIFF-ON-SEA
Essex

Erlsmere Hotel ★★
24-32 Pembury Road, Westcliff-on-Sea, Essex SS0 8DS
T: (01702) 349025
F: (01702) 337724
E: www.erlsmere.com

Westcliff Hotel ★★★
Westcliff Parade, Westcliff-on-Sea, Essex SS0 7QW
T: (01702) 345247
F: (01702) 431814
E: westcliff@msihotels.co.uk
I: www.msihotels.co.uk

WHITTLESFORD
Cambridgeshire

Red Lion Hotel ★
Station Road East, Whittlesford, Cambridge CB2 4NL
T: (01223) 832047 & 832115
F: (01223) 837576

WISBECH
Cambridgeshire

Crown Lodge Hotel ★★
Downham Road, Outwell, Wisbech, Cambridgeshire PE14 8SE
T: (01945) 773391
F: (01945) 772668
I: www.smoothound.co.uk/hotels/crownl.html

WITHAM
Essex

Jarvis Rivenhall Hotel ★★★
Rivenhall End, Witham, Essex CM8 3HB
T: (01376) 516969
F: (01376) 513674
E: 0345 303040

WOBURN
Bedfordshire

The Bedford Arms ★★★
George Street, Woburn, Milton Keynes MK17 9PX
T: (01525) 290441
F: (01525) 290432

WOODBRIDGE
Suffolk

Bull Hotel ★★
Market Hill, Woodbridge, Suffolk IP12 4LR
T: (01394) 382089 & 385688
F: (01394) 384902
E: reception@bullhotel.co.uk
I: wwwbullhotel.co.uk

Seckford Hall Hotel
★★★ SILVER AWARD
Woodbridge, Suffolk IP13 6NU
T: (01394) 385678
F: (01394) 380610
E: reception@seckford.co.uk
I: www.seckford.co.uk

Ufford Park Hotel Golf & Leisure ★★★ SILVER AWARD
Yarmouth Road, Ufford, Woodbridge, Suffolk IP12 1QW
T: (01394) 383555
F: (01394) 383582
E: uffordparkltd@btinternet.com
I: uffordpark.co.uk

WROXHAM
Norfolk

The Broads Hotel ★★
Station Road, Wroxham, Norwich NR12 8UR
T: (01603) 782869 & 784157
F: (01603) 784066

Hotel Wroxham ★★
The Bridge, Wroxham, Norwich NR12 8AJ
T: (01603) 782061
F: (01603) 784279
I: www.smoothound.co.uk/hotels/hotelwro.html

WYMONDHAM
Norfolk

Wymondham Consort Hotel ★★
28 Market Street, Wymondham, Norfolk NR18 0BB
T: (01953) 606721
F: (01953) 601361
E: wymondham@bestwestern.co.uk
I: www.hotelnet.co.uk/wymondham

YOXFORD
Suffolk

Satis House Hotel and Restaurant★★
Yoxford, Saxmundham, Suffolk IP17 3EX
T: (01728) 668418
F: (01728) 668640
E: y.blackmore@aol.com

SOUTH WEST

ALCOMBE
Somerset

Alcombe House Hotel
★★ SILVER AWARD
Bircham Road, Alcombe, Minehead, Somerset TA24 6BG
T: (01643) 705130
F: (01643) 705130
E: alcombe.house@virgin.net
I: www.visitus.co.uk/minehead

ASHWATER
Devon

Blagdon Manor Country Hotel
★★ SILVER AWARD
Ashwater, Devon EX21 5DF
T: (01409) 211224
F: (01409) 211634
E: stay@blagdon.com
I: www.blagdon.com

ASH
Somerset

Ash House Country Hotel
★★★ SILVER AWARD
41 Main Street, Ash, Martock, Somerset TA12 6PB
T: (01935) 822036 & 823126
F: (01935) 822992
E: jacquie@ashhouehotel.freeserve.co.uk

AXMINSTER
Devon

Lea Hill Hotel
★★ SILVER AWARD
Membury, Axminster, Devon EX13 7AQ
T: (01404) 881881 & 881388
F: (01404) 881890
I: www.leahillhotel.co.uk

BADMINTON
South Gloucestershire

Petty France Hotel ★★★
A46, Dunkirk, Badminton GL9 1AF
T: (01454) 238361
F: (01454) 238768
E: hotel@pettyfrance.telme.com
I: ds.dial.pipex.com/pettyfrance/

BARNSTAPLE
Devon

Barnstaple Hotel ★★★
Braunton Road, Barnstaple, Devon EX31 1LE
T: (01271) 376221
F: (01271) 324101

Establishments printed in blue have a detailed entry in this guide

Downrew House Hotel and Restaurant ★★
Bishop's Tawton, Barnstaple, Devon EX32 0DY
T: (01271) 342497 & 346673
F: (01271) 323947
E: downrew@globalnet.co.uk
I: www.downrew.co.uk

The Imperial
★★★★ SILVER AWARD
Taw Vale Parade, Barnstaple, Devon EX32 8NB
T: (01271) 345861
F: (01271) 324448
E: info-imperial.co.uk
I: www.brendimperial.co.uk

The Park Hotel ★★★
Taw Vale, Barnstaple, Devon EX32 8NJ
T: (01271) 372166
F: (01271) 323157
E: sales@brend-hotels.co.uk
I: www.brend-hotels.co.uk

Royal and Fortescue Hotel ★★★
Boutport Street, Barnstaple, Devon EX31 1HG
T: (01271) 342289
F: (01271) 342289
E: info@royalfortescue.co.uk
I: www.brend-hotels.co.uk

BATH
Bath & North East Somerset

The Abbey Hotel ★★★
North Parade, Bath, BA1 1LF
T: (01225) 461603
F: (01225) 447758
E: ahres@compasshotels.co.uk

Ashley Villa Hotel
Rating Applied For
26 Newbridge Road, Bath, BA1 3JZ
T: (01225) 421683 & 428887
F: (01225) 313604
E: ashleyvilla@clearface.co.uk
I: www.ashleyvilla.sagenet.co.uk

The Bath Tasburgh Hotel ★★
Warminster Road, Bath, BA2 6SH
T: (01225) 425096
F: (01225) 463842
E: reservations@bathtasburgh.demon.co.uk
I: www.bathtasburgh.co.uk

Cliffe Hotel
★★★ SILVER AWARD
Crowe Hill, Limpley Stoke, Bath BA3 6HY
T: (01225) 723226
F: (01225) 723871
E: cliffe.hotel@virgin.net

Combe Grove Manor Hotel and Country Club
★★★★ SILVER AWARD
Brassknocker Hill, Monkton Combe, Bath BA2 7HS
T: (01225) 834644 & 835533
F: (01225) 834961
E: james.parker@combegrovemanor.com
I: www.scoot.co.uk/combe-grove

Dukes Hotel ★★★
Great Pulteney Street, Bath, BA2 4DN
T: (01225) 463512
F: (01225) 483733

George's Hotel ★★
2 South Parade, Bath, BA2 4AA
T: (01225) 464923
F: (01225) 425471
E: info@georgeshotel.co.uk
I: www.georgeshotel.co.uk

Haringtons Hotel
★★ SILVER AWARD
8-10 Queen Street, Bath, BA1 1HE
T: (01225) 461728
F: (01225) 444804
E: post@haringtonshotel.co.uk
I: www.haringtonshotel.co.uk

Lansdown Grove Hotel
★★★ SILVER AWARD
Lansdown Road, Bath, BA1 5EH
T: (01225) 483888
F: (01225) 483838
E: lansdown@marstonhotels.co.uk
I: www.marstonhotels.co.uk

Lucknam Park
★★★★ GOLD AWARD
Colerne, Chippenham, Wiltshire SN14 8AZ
T: (01225) 742777
F: (01225) 743536
E: reservations@lucknampark.co.uk
I: www.lucknampark.co.uk

Old Malt House Hotel ★★
Radford, Timsbury, Bath BA3 1QF
T: (01761) 470106
F: (01761) 472726
E: hotel@oldmalthouse.co.uk
I: www.oldmalthouse.co.uk

The Old Mill Hotel
★★ SILVER AWARD
Tollbridge Road, Batheaston, Bath BA1 7DE
T: (01225) 858576
F: (01225) 852600
E: oldmill@batheaston1.freeserve.co.uk
I: www.pr-inns.freeserve.co.uk

Queensberry Hotel
★★★ GOLD AWARD
Russel Street, Bath, BA1 2QF
T: (01225) 447928
F: (01225) 446065
E: queensberry@dial.pipex.com
I: www.bathqueensberry.com

Royal Hotel ★★
Manvers Street, Bath, BA1 1JP
T: (01225) 463134
F: (01225) 442931
E: royal@rhotel.freeserve.co.uk
I: www.pr-inns.freeserve.co.uk

Rudloe Hall Hotel
Rating Applied For
Leafy Lane, Box, Corsham, Wiltshire SN13 0PA
T: (01225) 810555
F: (01225) 811412
E: mail@rudloehall.co.uk
I: www.rudloehall.co.uk

BIDEFORD
Devon

The Orchard Hill Hotel ★★
Orchard Hill, Bideford, Devon EX39 2QY
T: (01237) 472872
F: (01237) 423803

Riversford Hotel ★★
Limers Lane, Bideford, Devon EX39 2RG
T: (01237) 474239
F: (01237) 421661
E: riversford@aol.com
I: www.riversford.co.uk

Royal Hotel ★★★
Barnstaple Street, Bideford, Devon EX39 4AE
T: (01237) 472005
F: (01237) 478957
E: royalbid@btinternet.com
I: www.brend-hotels.co.uk

Tanton's Hotel ★★★
New Road, Bideford, Devon EX39 2HR
T: (01237) 473317
F: (01237) 473387

Yeoldon House Hotel
★★ SILVER AWARD
Durrant Lane, Northam, Bideford, Devon EX39 2RL
T: (01237) 474400
F: (01237) 476618
E: yeoldonhouse@aol.com

BIGBURY-ON-SEA
Devon

The Henley Hotel
★★ SILVER AWARD
Folly Hill, Bigbury-on-Sea, Kingsbridge, Devon TQ7 4AR
T: (01548) 810240
F: (01548) 810240

BILBROOK
Somerset

The Dragon House Hotel & Restaurant ★★
Dragon's Cross, Bilbrook, Minehead, Somerset TA24 6HQ
T: (01984) 640215
F: (01984) 641340
E: info@dragonhouse.co.uk
I: www.dragonhouse.co.uk

BOSCASTLE
Cornwall

Bottreaux House Hotel and Restaurant ★★ SILVER AWARD
Boscastle, Cornwall PL35 0BG
T: (01840) 250231
F: (01840) 250170
E: bothotel@dircon.co.uk
I: www.chycor.co.uk/bottreaux

The Wellington Hotel ★★
Old Road, Boscastle, Cornwall PL35 0AQ
T: (01840) 250202
F: (01840) 250621
E: vtbutt@enterprise.net
I: www.enterprise.net/wellington-hotel

BOVEY TRACEY
Devon

Coombe Cross Hotel ★★
Bovey Tracey, Newton Abbot, Devon TQ13 9EY
T: (01626) 832476
F: (01626) 835298

Edgemoor Hotel
★★★ SILVER AWARD
Haytor Road, Lowerdown Cross, Bovey Tracey, Devon TQ13 9LE
T: (01626) 832466
F: (01626) 834760
E: edgemoor@btinternet.com
I: www.edgemoor.co.uk

BOWER HINTON
Somerset

The Hollies ★★★
Bower Hinton, Martock, Somerset TA12 6LG
T: (01935) 822232
F: (01935) 822249
E: thehollieshotel@ukonline.co.uk
I: web.ukonline.co.uk/thehollieshotel.

BRIDGWATER
Somerset

Friarn Court Hotel ★★
37 St Mary Street, Bridgwater, Somerset TA6 3LX
T: (01278) 452859
F: (01278) 452988

Walnut Tree Hotel ★★★
North Petherton, Bridgwater, Somerset TA6 6QA
T: (01278) 662255
F: (01278) 663946
E: sales.walnuttree@btinternet.com

BRIDPORT
Dorset

Haddon House Hotel ★★★
West Bay, Bridport, Dorset DT6 4EL
T: (01308) 423626 & 425323
F: (01308) 427348

Roundham House Hotel
★★ SILVER AWARD
Roundham Gardens, West Bay Road, Bridport, Dorset DT6 4BD
T: (01308) 422753
F: (01308) 421500

BRISTOL

Clifton Hotel ★★
St Paul's Road, Clifton, Bristol BS8 1LX
T: (0117) 9736882
F: (0117) 9741082

Courtlands Hotel ★★
1 Redland Court Road, Redland, Bristol BS6 7EE
T: (0117) 9424432
F: (0117) 9232432

Glenroy Hotel ★★
Victoria Square, Clifton, Bristol BS8 4EW
T: (0117) 9739058
F: (0117) 9739058
E: reservations@glenroyhotel.demon.co.uk
I: www.glenroyhotel.demon.co.uk

Henbury Lodge Hotel ★★★
Station Road, Henbury, Bristol BS10 7QQ
T: (0117) 950 2615
F: (0117) 950 9532

Jarvis Grange Hotel and Country Club★★★
Northwoods, Winterbourne, Bristol BS36 1RP
T: (01454) 777333
F: (01454) 777447
I: www.jarvis.co.uk

Establishments printed in blue have a detailed entry in this guide

The Old Bowl Inn and Lilies Restaurant ★★
16 Church Road, Lower Almondsbury, Almondsbury, Bristol BS32 4DT
T: (01454) 612757
F: (01454) 619910
E: thebowl@3wa.co.uk

Redwood Lodge Hotel and Country Club
Rating Applied For
Beggar Bush Lane, Failand, Bristol BS8 3TG
T: (01275) 393901
F: (01275) 392104
E: redwood.lodge@virgin.net
I: www.conshotels.com/hotels/BRIRED.htm

Rodney Hotel ★★
4 Rodney Place, Clifton, Bristol BS8 4HY
T: (0117) 9735422
F: (0117) 9467092

Swallow Royal Hotel ★★★★ GOLD AWARD
College Green, Bristol, BS1 5TA
T: (0117) 9255100 & 9255200
F: (0117) 9251515

Thistle Bristol
Rating Applied For
Broad Street, Bristol, BS1 2EL
T: (0117) 929 1645
F: (0117) 922 7619
E: bristol@thistle.co.uk
I: www.thistle.co.uk

The Town and Country Lodge ★★★
A38 Bridgwater Road, Bristol, BS13 8AG
T: (01275) 392441
F: (01275) 393362
E: reservations@tclodge.co.uk
I: www.tclodge.co.uk

BRIXHAM
Devon
The Berry Head Hotel ★★★
Berry Head Road, Brixham, Devon TQ5 9AJ
T: (01803) 853225
F: (01803) 882084
E: berryhd@aol.com
I: www.scoot.co.uk/berry-head-hotel

BUDE
Cornwall
Atlantic House Hotel ★★
Summerleaze Crescent, Bude, Cornwall EX23 8HJ
T: (01288) 352451
F: (01288) 356666
E: ahbude@aol.com
I: www.atlantic-house-hotel.co.uk

Edgcumbe Hotel ★★
19 Summerleaze Cres, Bude, Cornwall EX23 8HJ
T: (01288) 353846
F: (01288) 355256
E: hotel@edgecumbe.force9.co.uk
I: www.north-cornwall.co.uk/client/edgecumbe-hotel

The Falcon Hotel ★★★
Breakwater Road, Bude, Cornwall EX23 8SD
T: (01288) 352005
F: (01288) 356359

Inn on the Green ★★
Crooklets Beach, Bude, Cornwall EX23 8NF
T: (01288) 356013
F: (01288) 356244
E: bude@innonthegreen46.freeserve.co.uk
I: www.innonthegreen46.freeserve.co.uk

Maer Lodge Hotel ★★
Maer Down Road, Crooklets Beach, Bude, Cornwall EX23 8NG
T: (01288) 353306
F: (01288) 354005
E: maerlodgehotel@btinternet.com
I: www.westcountry-hotels.co.uk/maerlodge

BURNHAM-ON-SEA
Somerset
Laburnum House Lodge Hotel ★★
Sloway Lane, West Huntspill, Burnham-on-Sea, Somerset TA9 3RJ
T: (01278) 781830
F: (01278) 781612
E: laburnumh@aol.com

BURRINGTON
Devon
Northcote Manor Hotel ★★★ SILVER AWARD
Burrington, Umberleigh, Devon EX37 9LZ
T: (01769) 560501
F: (01769) 560770
E: rest@northcotemanor.co.uk
I: www.northcotemanor.co.uk

CAMBORNE
Cornwall
Tyacks Hotel ★★★
Commercial Street, Camborne, Cornwall TR14 8LD
T: (01209) 612424
F: (01209) 612435

CARLYON BAY
Cornwall
Carlyon Bay Hotel ★★★★ SILVER AWARD
Sea Road, Carlyon Bay, St Austell, Cornwall PL25 3RD
T: (01726) 812304
F: (01726) 814938
E: info@carlyonbay.co.uk
I: www.carlyonbay.co.uk

CHAGFORD
Devon
Easton Court Hotel ★★
Easton Cross, Chagford, Newton Abbot, Devon TQ13 8JL
T: (01647) 433469
F: (01647) 433654
E: stay@easton.co.uk

Gidleigh Park ★★★ GOLD AWARD
Chagford, Devon TQ13 8HH
T: (01647) 432367
F: (01647) 432574
E: gidleighpark@gidleigh.co.uk
I: www.gidleigh.com

Mill End ★★★
Sandy Park, Dartmoor National Park, Chagford, Devon TQ13 8JN
T: (01647) 432282
F: (01647) 433106

Three Crowns Hotel ★★
High Street, Chagford, Newton Abbot, Devon TQ13 8AJ
T: (01647) 433444
F: (01647) 433117
E: threecrowns@msn.com
I: www.chagford-accom.co.uk

CHARD
Somerset
Lordleaze Hotel ★★★
Henderson Drive, Off Forton Road, Chard, Somerset TA20 2HW
T: (01460) 61066
F: (01460) 66468
E: lordleaze@fsbdial.co.uk

CHARLESTOWN
Cornwall
Pier House Hotel ★★
Harbour Front, Charlestown, St Austell, Cornwall PL25 3NJ
T: (01726) 67955
F: (01726) 69246
I: www.cornishriviera.co.uk/pierhouse.asp

CHARMOUTH
Dorset
Hensleigh Hotel ★★
Lower Sea Lane, Charmouth, Bridport, Dorset DT6 6LW
T: (01297) 560830
F: (01297) 560830

Queen's Arms Hotel ★★
The Street, Charmouth, Bridport, Dorset DT6 6QF
T: (01297) 560339
F: (01297) 560339
E: peterm@netcomuk.co.uk

The White House Hotel ★★ SILVER AWARD
2 Hillside, The Street, Charmouth, Bridport, Dorset DT6 6PJ
T: (01297) 560411
F: (01297) 560702
E: white-house@lineone.net

CHIDEOCK
Dorset
Chideock House Hotel ★★
Main Street, Chideock, Bridport, Dorset DT6 6JN
T: (01297) 489242
F: (01297) 489184
E: enquiries@Chideockhousehotel.com
I: www.chideockhousehotel.com

CHILLINGTON
Devon
White House Hotel ★★ SILVER AWARD
Chillington, Kingsbridge, Devon TQ7 2JX
T: (01548) 580580
F: (01548) 581124
E: tinawhthse@cs.com

CHITTLEHAMHOLT
Devon
Highbullen Hotel ★★★
Chittlehamholt, Umberleigh, Devon EX37 9HD
T: (01769) 540561
F: (01769) 540492
E: info@highbullen.co.uk
I: www.highbullen.co.uk

CHOLDERTON
Hampshire
The Red House Hotel ★★
Parkhouse Cross, Cholderton, Salisbury, Wiltshire SP4 0EG
T: (01980) 629542
F: (01980) 629481

CHURCHILL
Bath & North East Somerset
Lyncombe Lodge ★★
Lyncombe Drive, Churchill, North Somerset BS25 5PQ
T: (01934) 852335
F: (01934) 853314
E: info@highaction.co.uk
I: www.highaction.co.uk

Winston Manor Hotel ★★
Bristol Road, Churchill, Winscombe BS25 5NL
T: (01934) 852348
F: (01934) 852033
E: enquiries@winston-manor.co.uk
I: www.winston-manor.co.uk

CLIFTON
Seeley's Hotel ★★
17/27 St Paul's Road, Clifton, Bristol BS8 1LX
T: (0117) 9738544
F: (0117) 9732406
E: admin@seeleys.demon.co.uk
I: www.seeleys.demon.co.uk

CLOVELLY
Devon
The New Inn ★★
High Street, Clovelly, Bideford, Devon EX39 5TQ
T: (01237) 431303
F: (01237) 431636
E: newinnatclovelly.co.uk

Red Lion Hotel ★★
The Quay, Clovelly, Bideford, Devon EX39 5TF
T: (01237) 431237
F: (01237) 431044
E: redliionatclovelly.co.uk

COMBE MARTIN
Devon
Sandy Cove Hotel ★★★
Old Coast Road, Berrynarbor, Ilfracombe, Devon EX34 9SR
T: (01271) 882243 & 882888
F: (01271) 883830
I: www.exmoor-hospitality-inns.co.uk

CONSTANTINE
Cornwall
Trengilly Wartha Inn ★★
Nancenoy, Constantine, Falmouth, Cornwall TR11 5RP
T: (01326) 340332
F: (01326) 340332
E: trengilly@compuserve.com
I: www.trengilly.co.uk

CRICKLADE
Wiltshire
White Hart Hotel ★★
High Street, Cricklade, Swindon, Wiltshire SN6 6AA
T: (01793) 750206
F: (01793) 750650

CULLOMPTON
Devon

The Manor Hotel ★★
2/4 Fore Street, Cullompton,
Devon EX15 1JL
T: (01884) 32281
F: (01884) 38344

DARTMOUTH
Devon

Little Admiral Hotel ★★
27-29 Victoria Road, Dartmouth,
Devon TQ6 9RT
T: (01803) 832572
F: (01803) 835815
E: info@little-admiral.co.uk
I: www.little-admiral.co.uk

Royal Castle Hotel
★★★ SILVER AWARD
11 The Quay, Dartmouth, Devon
TQ6 9PS
T: (01803) 833033
F: (01803) 835445
E: enquiry@royalcastle.co.uk
I: www.royalcastle.co.uk

Stoke Lodge Hotel ★★★
Stoke Fleming, Dartmouth,
Devon TQ6 0RA
T: (01803) 770523
F: (01803) 770851
E: mail@stokelodge.co.uk
I: www.stokelodge.co.uk

Townstal Farmhouse ★★
Townstal Road, Dartmouth,
Devon TQ6 9HY
T: (01803) 832300
F: (01803) 835428

DAWLISH
Devon

Radfords Country Hotel ★★
Lower Dawlish Water, Dawlish,
Devon EX7 0QN
T: (01626) 863322
F: (01626) 888515
E: radfords@eclipse.co.uk
I: www.eclipse.co.uk/radfords

DEVIZES
Wiltshire

Black Swan Hotel ★★
Market Place, Devizes, Wiltshire
SN10 1JQ
T: (01380) 723259
F: (01380) 729966
E: lugg@blackswanhotel.fsnet.
co.uk
I: www.blackswanhotel.fsnet.co.
uk

DORCHESTER
Dorset

Wessex Royale Hotel ★★★
32 High West Street, Dorchester,
Dorset DT1 1UP
T: (01305) 262660
F: (01305) 251941

DUNSTER
Somerset

Yarn Market Hotel (Exmoor)
★★★
25 High Street, Dunster,
Minehead, Somerset TA24 6SF
T: (01643) 821425
F: (01643) 821475
E: yarnmarket.hotel@virgin.net
I: www.s-h-systems.co.
uk/hotels/yarnmkt

EXETER
Devon

Buckerell Lodge ★★★
Topsham Road, Exeter, Devon
EX2 4SQ
T: (01392) 221111
F: (01392) 491111

Devon Hotel ★★★
Exeter-by-Pass, Matford, Exeter,
EX2 8XU
T: (01392) 259268
F: (01392) 413142
E: info@devonhotel.co.uk
I: www.devonhotel.co.uk

Ebford House Hotel ★★★
Exmouth Road, Ebford, Exeter,
Devon EX3 0QH
T: (01392) 877658
F: (01392) 874424
E: ebford@eclipse.co.uk
I: www.eclipse.co.uk/ebford

Fairwinds Hotel ★★
Kennford, Exeter, Devon
EX6 7UD
T: (01392) 832911

The Great Western Hotel ★★
Station Approach, St David's,
Exeter, EX4 4NU
T: (01392) 274039
F: (01392) 425529

The Lord Haldon Hotel ★★★
Dunchideock, Exeter, Devon
EX6 7YF
T: (01392) 832483
F: (01392) 833765

The Red House Hotel ★★
2 Whipton Village Road, Exeter,
EX4 8AR
T: (01392) 256104
F: (01392) 666145
E: redhouse.hotel@eclipse.co.uk
I: www.scoot.co.
uk/redhouse_hotel

St Andrews Hotel ★★
28 Alphington Road, Exeter,
EX2 8HN
T: (01392) 276784
F: (01392) 250249

St Olaves Court Hotel ★★★
Mary Arches Street, Exeter,
EX4 3AZ
T: (01392) 217736
F: (01392) 413054
E: info@olaves.co.uk
I: www.olaves.co.uk

Thistle Exeter ★★★★
Queen Street, Exeter, EX4 3SP
T: (01392) 254982
F: (01392) 420928
E: exeter@thistle.co.uk

EXFORD
Somerset

Exmoor White Horse Hotel
★★
Exford, Minehead, Somerset
TA24 7PY
T: (01643) 831229
F: (01643) 831246
E: exmoorwhitehorse.demon.co.
uk
I: www.exmoor-hospitality-inns.
co.uk

EXMOUTH
Devon

Ashton Court Hotel ★★
Louisa Terrace, Exmouth, Devon
EX8 2AQ
T: (01395) 263002
F: (01395) 263747
E: ashton.court@exmouth.co.uk
I: www.exmouth.co.uk

The Barn Hotel ★★
Foxholes Hill, off Marine Drive,
Exmouth, Devon EX8 2DF
T: (01395) 224411
F: (01395) 225445

Cavendish Hotel ★★
11-12 Morton Crescent, The
Esplanade, Exmouth, Devon
EX8 1BE
T: (01395) 272528
F: (01395) 269361

Devoncourt Hotel ★★★
Douglas Avenue, Exmouth,
Devon EX8 2EX
T: (01395) 272277
F: (01395) 269315

The Kerans Hotel ★
Esplanade, Exmouth, Devon
EX8 1DS
T: (01395) 275275
E: kerans@eclipse.co.uk
I: www.exmouth-guide.co.
uk/kerans.htm

Manor Hotel ★★
The Beacon, Exmouth, Devon
EX8 2AG
T: (01395) 272549 & 274477
F: (01395) 225519

The Royal Beacon Hotel ★★★
The Beacon, Exmouth, Devon
EX8 2AF
T: (01395) 264886
F: (01395) 268890
E: reception@royalbeaconhotel.
co.uk
I: www.royalbeaconhotel.co.uk

EYPE
Dorset

Eype's Mouth Country Hotel
★★
Eype, Bridport, Dorset DT6 6AL
T: (01308) 423300
F: (01308) 420033
E: eypehotel@aol.com

FALMOUTH
Cornwall

Broadmead Hotel ★★
Kimberley Park Road, Falmouth,
Cornwall TR11 2DD
T: (01326) 315704 & 318036
F: (01326) 311048

Budock Vean The Hotel on the
River ★★★★
Mawnan Smith, Falmouth,
Cornwall TR11 5LG
T: (01326) 250288 & 252100
F: (01326) 250892
I: www.budockvean.co.uk

Crill Manor Hotel ★★
Roscarrack Road, Budock Water,
Falmouth, Cornwall TR11 5BL
T: (01326) 211880
F: (01326) 211229

Green Lawns Hotel
★★★ SILVER AWARD
Western Terrace, Falmouth,
Cornwall TR11 4QJ
T: (01326) 312734 & 312007
F: (01326) 211427
E: info@green-lawns-hotel.co.
uk
I: www.green-lawns-hotel.co.uk

Gyllyngdune Manor Hotel
★★★
Melvill Road, Falmouth,
Cornwall TR11 4AR
T: (01326) 312978
F: (01326) 211881

Park Grove Hotel ★★
Kimberley Park Road, Falmouth,
Cornwall TR11 2DD
T: (01326) 313276
F: (01326) 211926
E: reception@parkgrovehotel.
com
I: www.connexions.co.
uk/parkgrovehotel/

Penmere Manor ★★★
Mongleath Road, Falmouth,
Cornwall TR11 4PN
T: (01326) 211411
F: (01326) 317588
E: andrew@penmere.co.uk
I: www.penmere.co.uk

Penmorvah Manor Hotel
★★★
Budock Water, Falmouth,
Cornwall TR11 5ED
T: (01326) 250277
F: (01326) 250509
E: enquiries@penmorvah.
force9.co.uk
I: www.westcountry-hotels.co.
uk/penmorvah

Royal Duchy Hotel ★★★★
Cliff Road, Falmouth, Cornwall
TR11 4NX
T: (01326) 313042
F: (01326) 319420
E: infoeroyalduchy.co.uk
I: www.brend-hotels.co.uk

St Michael's Hotel ★★
Seafront, Gyllyngvase Beach,
Falmouth, Cornwall TR11 4NB
T: (01326) 312707
F: (01326) 211772

FOWEY
Cornwall

Cormorant Hotel ★★
Golant, Fowey, Cornwall
PL23 1LL
T: (01726) 833426
F: (01726) 833426
E: cormorant@eclipse.co.uk
I: www.cornwall-online.co.
uk/cormorant

Marina Hotel
★★ SILVER AWARD
Esplanade, Fowey, Cornwall
PL23 1HY
T: (01726) 833315
F: (01726) 832779
E: marina.hotel@dial.pipex.com
I: www.cornwall-online.co.
uk/marina_hotel/

Establishments printed in blue have a detailed entry in this guide

GALMPTON
Devon

The Maypool Park Hotel
★★ SILVER AWARD
Maypool, Galmpton, Brixham,
Devon TQ5 0ET
T: (01803) 842442
F: (01803) 845782
E: peacock@maypoolpark.co.uk
I: www.maypoolpark.co.uk

GITTISHAM
Devon

**Combe House Hotel at
Gittisham** ★★★
Gittisham, Honiton, Devon
EX14 3AD
T: (01404) 540400
F: (01404) 46004
E: stay@thishotel.com
I: www.thishotel.com

HEDDONS MOUTH
Devon

Heddons Gate Hotel
★★ SILVER AWARD
Heddons Mouth, Parracombe,
Barnstaple, Devon EX31 4PZ
T: (01598) 763313
F: (01598) 763363
E: info@hgate.co.uk
I: www.hgate.co.uk

HELSTON
Cornwall

Gwealdues Hotel ★★
Falmouth Road, Helston,
Cornwall TR13 8JX
T: (01326) 572808
F: (01326) 561388
E: gwealdues@hotel44.
freeserve.co.uk

Nansloe Manor
★★ SILVER AWARD
Meneage Road, Helston,
Cornwall TR13 0SB
T: (01326) 574691
F: (01326) 564680
E: info@nansloe-manor.co.uk
I: www.nansloe-manor.co.uk

HINDON
Wiltshire

Grosvenor Arms ★★
High Street, Hindon, Salisbury
SP3 6DJ
T: (01747) 820696
F: (01747) 820869

HOLFORD
Somerset

Combe House Hotel
★★ SILVER AWARD
Holford, Bridgwater, Somerset
TA5 1RZ
T: (01278) 741382
F: (01278) 741322
E: John@combehouse.co.uk

HOLSWORTHY
Devon

**Court Barn Country House
Hotel** ★★
Clawton, Holsworthy, Devon
EX22 6PS
T: (01409) 271219
F: (01409) 271309
I: www.hotels-devon.com

HONITON
Devon

The Belfry Country Hotel ★★
Yarcombe, Honiton, Devon
EX14 9BD
T: (01404) 861234
F: (01404) 861579

**Home Farm Hotel and
Restaurant** ★★ SILVER AWARD
Wilmington, Honiton, Devon
EX14 9JR
T: (01404) 831278 & 831246
F: (01404) 831411

Honiton Motel ★★
Turks Head Corner, Exeter Road,
Honiton, Devon EX14 1BL
T: (01404) 43440 & 45400
F: (01404) 47767

HOPE COVE
Devon

Cottage Hotel ★★
Hope Cove, Kingsbridge, Devon
TQ7 3HJ
T: (01548) 561555
F: (01548) 561455
E: info@cottage-hotel.co.uk
I: www.hopecove.com

Lantern Lodge Hotel
★★ SILVER AWARD
Hope Cove, Kingsbridge, Devon
TQ7 3HE
T: (01548) 561280
F: (01548) 561736
I: www.lantern-lodge.co.uk

HORRABRIDGE
Devon

Overcombe Hotel ★★
Horrabridge, Yelverton, Devon
PL20 7RA
T: (01822) 853501 & 853602
F: (01822) 853501

ILCHESTER
Somerset

The Ilchester Arms ★★
The Square, Ilchester, Yeovil,
Somerset BA22 8LN
T: (01935) 840220
F: (01935) 841353

ILFRACOMBE
Devon

Beechwood Hotel ★★
Torrs Park, Ilfracombe, Devon
EX34 8AZ
T: (01271) 863800
F: (01271) 863800
E: info@beechwoodhotel.co.uk
I: www.beechwoodhotel.co.uk

Cairn House Hotel ★
43 St Brannocks Road,
Ilfracombe, Devon EX34 8EH
T: (01271) 863911
F: 07070 800630

The Darnley Hotel ★★
3 Belmont Road, Ilfracombe,
Devon EX34 8DR
T: (01271) 863955
F: (01271) 864076
E: darnley.hotel@btinternet.
com

Elmfield Hotel ★★
Torrs Park, Ilfracombe, Devon
EX34 8AZ
T: (01271) 863377
F: (01271) 866828

Granville Hotel ★
Granville Road, Ilfracombe,
Devon EX34 8AT
T: (01271) 862002 & 862015
F: (01271) 862803
E: bookings@devoniahotels.co.
uk
I: www.devoniahotels.co.uk

The Ilfracombe Carlton Hotel
★★
Runnacleave Road, Ilfracombe,
Devon EX34 8AR
T: (01271) 862446 & 863711
F: (01271) 865379
E: downrew@globalnet.co.uk
I: www.downrew.co.uk

Montebello Hotel ★
Fore Street, Ilfracombe, Devon
EX34 9DL
T: (01271) 862040
F: (01271) 862040

Palm Court Hotel ★★
Wilder Road, Ilfracombe, Devon
EX34 8AR
T: (01271) 866644
F: (01271) 863581

**Score Valley Country House
Hotel** ★★ SILVER AWARD
Score Valley, Ilfracombe, Devon
EX34 8NA
T: (01271) 862195
F: (01271) 864805
E: info@scorevalley.co.uk
I: www.scorevalley.co.uk

The Torrs Hotel ★
Torrs Park, Ilfracombe, Devon
EX34 8AY
T: (01271) 862334
F: (01271) 862334

Tracy House Hotel ★★
Belmont Road, Ilfracombe,
Devon EX34 8DR
T: (01271) 863933

Trimstone Manor ★★
Trimstone, Ilfracombe, Devon
EX34 8NR
T: (01271) 862841
F: (01271) 863808

Westwell Hall Hotel ★
Torrs Park, Ilfracombe, Devon
EX34 8AZ
T: (01271) 862792
F: (01271) 862792

Wildersmouth Hotel ★
Sommers Crescent, Ilfracombe,
Devon EX34 9DP
T: (01271) 862002 & 862015
F: (01271) 862803
E: booking@devoniahotel.co.uk
I: www.devoniahotels.co.uk

ILLOGAN
Cornwall

Aviary Court Hotel
★★ SILVER AWARD
Marys Well, Illogan, Redruth,
Cornwall TR16 4QZ
T: (01209) 842256
F: (01209) 843744
E: aviarycourt@connexions.uk

ILSINGTON
Devon

Ilsington Hotel
Ilsington, Newton Abbot, Devon
TQ13 9RR
T: (01364) 661452
F: (01364) 661307
E: hotel@ilsington.co.uk
I: www.ilsington.co.uk

INSTOW
Devon

The Commodore Hotel ★★★
Marine Parade, Instow, Devon
EX39 4JN
T: (01271) 860347
F: (01271) 861233

ISLES OF SCILLY

Atlantic Hotel ★★
Hugh Town, St Mary's, Isles of
Scilly TR21 0PL
T: (01720) 422417
F: (01720) 423009
E: atlantichotel@btinternet.com

Bell Rock Hotel ★★
Church Street, St Mary's, Isles of
Scilly TR21 0JS
T: (01720) 422575
F: (01720) 423093
E: bellrock.hotel@btclick.com

Hotel Godolphin ★★
St Mary's, Isles of Scilly
TR21 0JR
T: (01720) 422316
F: (01720) 422252
E: enquiries@hotelgodolphine.
co.uk
I: www.hotelgodophin.co.uk

Harbourside Hotel ★★
The Quay, St Mary's, Isles of
Scilly TR21 0HU
T: (01720) 422352
F: (01720) 422590
E: tony@harbourside1.
freeserve.co.uk
I: www.isles-of-scilly.co.uk

Hell Bay Hotel
★★★ SILVER AWARD
Bryher, Isles of Scilly TR23 0PR
T: (01720) 422947
F: (01720) 423004

Star Castle Hotel
★★★ SILVER AWARD
The Garrison, St Mary's, Isles of
Scilly TR21 0JA
T: (01720) 422317 & 423342
F: (01720) 422343

Tregarthen's Hotel ★★
St Mary's, Isles of Scilly
TR21 0PP
T: (01720) 422540
F: (01720) 422089
I: www.tregarthens/hotel.co.uk

IVYBRIDGE
Devon

Ermewood House Hotel
★★ SILVER AWARD
Totnes Road, Ermington,
Ivybridge, Devon PL21 9NS
T: (01548) 830741
F: (01548) 830741
E: info@ermewood-house.co.uk
I: www.ermewood-house.co.uk

KEYNSHAM
Bath & North East Somerset

Grange Hotel ★★
42 Bath Road, Keynsham, Bristol
BS31 1SN
T: (0117) 986 9181
F: (0117) 986 6373

Long Reach House Hotel ★★
321 Bath Road, Keynsham,
Bristol BS31 1TJ
T: (01225) 400500 & 400600
F: (01225) 400700
E: lrhouse@aol.com
I: www.bath.co.uk

KINGSBRIDGE
Devon

Sun Bay Hotel
Rating Applied For
Hope Cove, Nr Salcombe,
Kingsbridge, Devon TQ7 3HH
T: (01548) 561371
F: (01548) 561371
E: sunbayhotel@aol.co.uk

KINGSTEIGNTON
Devon

Passage House Hotel ★★★
Hackney Lane, Kingsteignton,
Newton Abbot, Devon TQ12 3QH
T: (01626) 355515
F: (01626) 363336
E: mail@passagehousehotel.co.uk
I: www.passagehousehotel.co.uk

LANDS END
Cornwall

The Land's End Hotel ★★★
Lands End, Cornwall TR19 7AA
T: (01736) 871844
F: (01736) 871599
E: info@landsend-landmark.co.uk
I: www.landsend-landmark.co.uk

LIFTON
Devon

Arundell Arms Hotel
★★★ SILVER AWARD
Lifton, Devon PL16 0AA
T: (01566) 784666
F: (01566) 784494
E: arundellarms@btinternet.com

Lifton Hall ★★
Lifton, Devon PL16 0DR
T: (01566) 784263 & 784863
F: (01566) 784770

LONG SUTTON
Somerset

Devonshire Arms ★★★
Long Sutton, Langport, Somerset
TA10 9LP
T: (01458) 241271 &
07785 348800
F: (01458) 241037

LONGBRIDGE DEVERILL
Wiltshire

The George Inn
Rating Applied For
Longbridge Deverill, Warminster,
Wiltshire BA12 7DG
T: (01985) 840396

LOOE
Cornwall

Allhays Country House Hotel
★★
Talland Bay, Looe, Cornwall
PL13 2JB
T: (01503) 272434
F: (01503) 272929
E: allhayscountryhouse@
BTinternet.com

Fieldhead Hotel
★★ SILVER AWARD
Portuan Road, Hannafore, West
Looe, Looe, Cornwall PL13 2DR
T: (01503) 262689
F: (01503) 264114
E: field.head@virgin.net
I: www.chycor.co.uk/fieldhead

**Rivercroft Hotel and
Apartments** ★★
Station Road, East Looe, Looe,
Cornwall PL13 1HL
T: (01503) 262251
F: (01503) 265494
E: rivercrofthotel@virgin.net
I: www.rivercrofthotel.co.uk

Trelaske Hotel and Restaurant
★★★
Polperro Road, Looe, Cornwall
PL13 2JS
T: (01503) 262159
F: (01503) 265360
E: trelakehotel@netscapeonline.co.uk

LOSTWITHIEL
Cornwall

**Lostwithiel Hotel Golf &
Country Club** ★★★
Lower Polscoe, Lostwithiel,
Cornwall PL22 0HQ
T: (01208) 873550
F: (01208) 873479
E: reception@golf-hotel.co.uk
I: www.golf-hotel.co.uk

LOXTON
North Somerset

The Webbington Hotel ★★★
Loxton, Axbridge, Somerset
BS26 2XA
T: (01934) 750100
F: (01934) 750020
E: webbington@
meridianleisure.com
I: meridianleisure.com

LYDFORD
Devon

Lydford House Hotel ★★
Lydford, Okehampton, Devon
EX20 4AU
T: (01822) 820347 & 820321
F: (01822) 820442
E: relax@lydfordhouse.co.uk
I: ww.lydfordhouse.co.uk

LYME REGIS
Dorset

Alexandra Hotel ★★★
Pound Street, Lyme Regis,
Dorset DT7 3HZ
T: (01297) 442010
F: (01297) 443229
E: enquiries@hotelalexandra.co.uk
I: www.hotelalexandra.co.uk

Bay Hotel ★★
Marine Parade, Lyme Regis,
Dorset DT7 3JQ
T: (01297) 442059

Hotel Buena Vista ★★
Pound Street, Lyme Regis,
Dorset DT7 3HZ
T: (01297) 442494

Devon Hotel
Rating Applied For
Lyme Road, Uplyme, Lyme Regis,
Dorset DT7 3TQ
T: (01297) 443231
F: (01297) 445836

Dorset Hotel ★★
Silver Street, Lyme Regis, Dorset
DT7 3HX
T: (01297) 442482
F: (01297) 443970
E: dorsethotel@lymeregis.com
I: www.lymeregis.com/dorset-hotel

The Dower House Hotel
★★★ SILVER AWARD
Rousdon, Lyme Regis, Dorset
DT7 3RB
T: (01297) 21047
F: (01297) 24748

Mariners Hotel ★★
Silver Street, Lyme Regis, Dorset
DT7 3HS
T: (01297) 442753
F: (01297) 442431

Orchard Country Hotel ★★
Rousdon, Lyme Regis, Dorset
DT7 3XW
T: (01297) 442972
F: (01297) 443670
E: the.orchard@btinternet.com

Swallows Eaves Hotel
★★ SILVER AWARD
Colyford, Colyton, Devon
EX24 6QJ
T: (01297) 553184
F: (01297) 553574

LYNMOUTH
Devon

Bath Hotel ★★
Lynmouth, Devon EX35 6EL
T: (01598) 752238
F: (01598) 752544
E: bathhotel@torslynmouth.co.uk
I: www.torslynmouth.co.uk

Shelley's Hotel
★★ SILVER AWARD
Watersmeet Road, Lynmouth,
Devon EX35 6EP
T: (01598) 753219

The Tors Hotel ★★★
Lynmouth, Devon EX35 6NA
T: (01598) 753236
F: (01598) 752544
E: torshotel@tonslynmouth.co.uk
I: www.torslynmouth.co.uk

LYNTON
Devon

Chough's Nest Hotel ★
North Walk, Lynton, Devon
EX35 6HJ
T: (01598) 753315

Highcliffe House ★
Sinai Hill, Lynton, Devon
EX35 6AR
T: (01598) 752235
F: (01598) 752235
E: highcliffe.hotel@excite.co.uk
I: www.smoothhound.co.uk/hotels/highcli.html

Lynton Cottage Hotel ★★★
North Walk, Lynton, Devon
EX35 6ED
T: (01598) 752342
F: (01598) 752774
E: enquiries@lynton-cottage.co.uk
I: www.lynton-cottage.co.uk

North Cliff Hotel ★
North Walk, Lynton, Devon
EX35 6HJ
T: (01598) 752357

Sandrock Hotel ★★
Longmead, Lynton, Devon
EX35 6DH
T: (01598) 753307
F: (01598) 752665

Seawood Hotel
★ SILVER AWARD
North Walk Drive, Lynton, Devon
EX35 6HJ
T: (01598) 752272
F: (01598) 752272

Valley of Rocks
Rating Applied For
Lee Road, Lynton, Devon
EX35 6HS
T: (01598) 752349
F: (01598) 752349

MAENPORTH
Cornwall

Trelawne Hotel
★★★ SILVER AWARD
Maenporth Road, Maenporth,
Falmouth, Cornwall TR11 5HS
T: (01326) 250226
F: (01326) 250909

MALMESBURY
Wiltshire

Knoll House Hotel ★★★
Swindon Road, Malmesbury,
Wiltshire SN16 9LU
T: (01666) 823114
F: (01666) 823897
E: knollhotel@malmesbury64.freeserve.co.uk
I: www.knoll-house.com

Mayfield House Hotel ★★
Crudwell, Malmesbury, Wiltshire
SN16 9EW
T: (01666) 577409 & 577198
F: (01666) 577977
E: mayfield@callnetuk.com

MANACCAN
Cornwall

Tregildry Hotel
★★ SILVER AWARD
Gillan, Manaccan, Helston,
Cornwall TR12 6HG
T: (01326) 231378
F: (01326) 231561
E: trgildry@globalnet.co.uk
I: www.tregildryhotel.co.uk

MARLBOROUGH
Wiltshire

The Castle and Ball ★★★
High Street, Marlborough,
Wiltshire SN8 1LZ
T: (01672) 515201
F: (01672) 515895

Establishments printed in blue have a detailed entry in this guide

MARTINHOE
Devon

Old Rectory Hotel ★★
Martinhoe, Barnstaple, Devon
EX31 4QT
T: (01598) 763368
F: (01598) 763567
E: reception@oldrectoryhotel.
co.uk
I: www.oldrectoryhotel.co.uk

MAWGAN PORTH
Cornwall

Tredragon Hotel ★★
Mawgan Porth, Newquay,
Cornwall TR8 4DQ
T: (01637) 860213
F: (01637) 860269
E: tredragon@btinternet.com
I: www.cornwallonline.com

MELKSHAM
Wiltshire

Shaw Country Hotel ★★
Bath Road, Shaw, Melksham,
Wiltshire SN12 8EF
T: (01225) 702836 & 790321
F: (01225) 790275
E: shawcountryhotel@
ukbusiness.com
I: www.ukbusiness.
com/shawcountryhotel

MEVAGISSEY
Cornwall

**The Sharks Fin Hotel and
Waterside Restaurant★★**
The Quay, Mevagissey, St
Austell, Cornwall PL26 6QU
T: (01726) 843241
F: (01726) 842552
E: sharksfin@hotel.sagehost.co.
uk
I: www.hotel.sagehost.co.uk

Tremarne Hotel ★★
Mevagissey, St Austell, Cornwall
PL26 6UY
T: (01726) 842213
F: (01726) 843420
E: tremarne@talk21.com
I: www.tremarne-hotel.co.uk

Trevalsa Court Hotel ★★
Polstreath Hill, Mevagissey, St
Austell, Cornwall PL26 6TH
T: (01726) 842468
F: (01726) 844482
E: trevalsacourthotel@yahoo.
co.uk
I: www.smoothound.co.
uk/hotels/trevalsa.html

MIDSOMER NORTON
Bath & North East Somerset

**Centurion Hotel
★★★ SILVER AWARD**
Charlton Lane, Midsomer
Norton, Bath BA3 4BD
T: (01761) 417711
F: (01761) 418357
E: centurion@centurionhotel.
demo.co.uk
◎

The Old Priory ★★
Church Square, Midsomer
Norton, Bath BA3 2HX
T: (01761) 416784
F: (01761) 417851
E: reservations@theoldpriory.
com

MINEHEAD
Somerset

Beaconwood Hotel ★★
Church Road, North Hill,
Minehead, Somerset TA24 5SB
T: (01643) 702032
F: (01643) 702032
E: beaconwood@madasafish.
com
I: www.beaconwoodhotel.co.uk

**Channel House Hotel
★★ GOLD AWARD**
Church Path, Off Northfield
Road, Minehead, Somerset
TA24 5QG
T: (01643) 703229
F: (01643) 708925
E: channel.house@virgin.net
I: www.channelhouse.co.uk

**Wyndcott Hotel
★★ SILVER AWARD**
Martlet Road, Minehead,
Somerset TA24 5QE
T: (01643) 704522
F: (01643) 707577
E: minheadhotel@msn.com
I: www.wyndcott.co.uk
◎

MONKTON
Devon

Monkton Court Inn ★★
Monkton, Honiton, Devon
EX14 9QH
T: (01404) 42309
F: (01404) 46861
E: tony@thosking.freeserve.co.
uk
I: www.travelcheck.co.
uk/hotel/1004.html

MONTACUTE
Somerset

Kings Arms ★★
Montacute, Somerset TA15 6UU
T: (01935) 822513
F: (01935) 826549

MORETONHAMPSTEAD
Devon

**Manor House Hotel and Golf
Course★★★★ SILVER AWARD**
Moretonhampstead, Newton
Abbot, Devon TQ13 8RE
T: (01647) 440355
F: (01647) 440961
I: www.principalhotels.co.uk

MORTEHOE
Devon

Lundy House Hotel ★
Chapel Hill, Mortehoe,
Woolacombe, Devon EX34 7DZ
T: (01271) 870372
F: (01271) 871001
E: llbido.london@virgin.net
I: www.lundyhouse.freeserve.co.
uk
◎

Rockham Bay Hotel ★★
North Morte Road, Mortehoe,
Woolacombe, Devon EX34 7EG
T: (01271) 870993
F: (01271) 870107

MULLION
Cornwall

**Polurrian Hotel, Apartments
and Leisure Club★★★**
The Lizard Peninsula, Mullion,
Helston, Cornwall TR12 7EN
T: (01326) 240421 & 240929
F: (01326) 240083
E: polurotel@aol.com
I: www.scoot.co.
uk/polurrian_hotel/
◎

NETHER STOWEY
Somerset

**Castle of Comfort Country
House
Rating Applied For**
Dodington, Nether Stowey,
Bridgwater, Somerset TA5 1LE
T: (01278) 741264 &
07050 642002
F: (01278) 741144
E: castle.comfort@virgin.net
I: www.castle-of-comfort.co.uk
◎

NEWQUAY
Cornwall

**Arundell Hotel
Rating Applied For**
86/90 Mount Wise, Newquay,
Cornwall TR7 2BS
T: (01637) 872481
F: (01637) 850001

Hotel Bristol ★★★
Narrowcliff, Newquay, Cornwall
TR7 2PQ
T: (01637) 875181
F: (01637) 879347
E: info@hotelbristol.co.uk
I: www.hotelbristol.co.uk

Carnmarth Hotel ★★
22 Headland Road, Fistral Beach,
Newquay, Cornwall TR7 1HN
T: (01637) 872519
F: (01637) 878770
E: carnmarth@connexions.co.uk
◎

Cedars Hotel ★★
Mountwise, Newquay, Cornwall
TR7 2BA
T: (01637) 874225
F: (01637) 850421

Edgcumbe Hotel ★★★
Narrowcliff, Newquay, Cornwall
TR7 2RR
T: (01637) 872061
F: (01637) 852524
E: edgcumbe@silverquick.com

The Esplanade Hotel ★★★
9 Esplanade Road, Pentire,
Newquay, Cornwall TR7 1PS
T: (01637) 873333
F: (01637) 851413
E: info@newquay-hotels.co.uk
I: www.newquay-hotels.co.uk

Great Western Hotel ★★
Cliff Road, Newquay, Cornwall
TR7 2PT
T: (01637) 872010
F: (01637) 874435

Philema Hotel ★★
1 Esplanade Road, Pentire,
Newquay, Cornwall TR7 1PY
T: (01637) 872571
F: (01637) 873188
E: info@philema.demon.co.uk
I: www.smoothhound.co.
uk/hotels/philema.html

Trebarwith Hotel ★★★
Newquay, Cornwall TR7 1BZ
T: (01637) 872288
F: (01637) 875431
E: enquiry@trebarwith-
hotel.co.uk
I: www.trebarwith-hotel.co.uk

Tregurrian Hotel ★
Watergate Bay, Newquay,
Cornwall TR8 4AB
T: (01637) 860280
F: (01637) 860540
E: tregurrian.hotel@virginnet.
co.uk
I: www.holidaysincornwall.net

**Tremont Hotel
Rating Applied For**
Pentire Avenue, Newquay,
Cornwall TR7 1PB
T: (01637) 872984
F: (01637) 851984

Hotel Victoria ★★★
East Street, Newquay, Cornwall
TR7 1DB
T: (01637) 872255
F: (01637) 859295
E: res@hotelvictoria.prestel.co.
uk
I: www.web-direct.co.uk/victoria

**Whipsiderry Hotel
★★ SILVER AWARD**
Trevelgue Road, Porth,
Newquay, Cornwall TR7 3LY
T: (01637) 874777
F: (01637) 874777
E: whipsiderry@cornwall.net
I: www.cornwall.net/whipsiderry

NEWTON ABBOT
Devon

Hazelwood Hotel ★
33a Torquay Road, Newton
Abbot, Devon TQ12 2LW
T: (01626) 366130
F: (01626) 365021

NORTH HUISH
Devon

**Brookdale House
★★★ SILVER AWARD**
North Huish, South Brent,
Devon TQ10 9NR
T: (01548) 821661
F: (01548) 821606
E: brookdalehouse@yahoo.com
I: www.brookdale-house.com
◎

OKEHAMPTON
Devon

Oxenham Arms ★★
South Zeal, Okehampton, Devon
EX20 2JT
T: (01837) 840244
F: (01837) 840791
E: jhenry1928@aol.com

White Hart Hotel ★★
Fore Street, Okehampton, Devon
EX20 1HD
T: (01837) 52730 & 54514
F: (01837) 53979
E: graham@whitehart hotel.
telme.com

OTTERY ST MARY
Devon

Salston Manor Hotel ★★★
Fluxton Road, Ottery St Mary,
Exeter, Devon EX11 1RQ
T: (01404) 815581
F: (01404) 815581
E: smh@cosmic.org.uk
I: www.salstonhotel.co.uk

The Tumbling Weir Hotel ★★
Ottery St Mary, Devon EX11 1AQ
T: (01404) 812752
F: (01404) 812752
E: bpyoung@compuserve.com
I: www.
106120,2702@compuserve.com

PADSTOW
Cornwall

Green Waves Hotel ★★
West View, Trevone Bay,
Padstow, Cornwall PL28 8RD
T: (01841) 520114
F: (01841) 520568

The Old Ship Hotel ★★
Mill Square, Padstow, Cornwall
PL28 8AE
T: (01841) 532357
F: (01841) 533211

PAIGNTON
Devon

Esplanade Hotel
Rating Applied For
Sands Road, Paignton, Devon
TQ4 6EG
T: (01803) 556333
F: (01803) 666786

Goodrington Lodge Hotel ★★
23 Alta Vista Road, Paignton,
Devon TQ4 6DA
T: (01803) 558382
F: (01803) 550066

**Harwin Hotel and Apartments
★★**
Alta Vista Road, Goodrington
Sands, Paignton, Devon TQ4 6DA
T: (01803) 558771
F: (01803) 558771
E: enquires@hotel-harwin.co.uk
I: www.hotel-harwin.co.uk

Preston Sands Hotel ★★
10/12 Marine Parade, Sea Front,
Paignton, Devon TQ3 2NU
T: (01803) 558718
F: (01803) 522875

Queens Hotel ★★
Queens Road, Paignton, Devon
TQ4 6AT
T: (01803) 551048
F: (01803) 551048

Redcliffe Hotel ★★★
Marine Drive, Paignton, Devon
TQ3 2NL
T: (01803) 526397
F: (01803) 528030
E: Redclfe@aol.com
I: www.redcliffehotel.co.uk
ⓐ

Torbay Holiday Motel ★★
Totnes Road, Paignton, Devon
TQ4 7PP
T: (01803) 558226
F: (01803) 663375
E: enquiries@thm.co.uk
I: www.thm.co.uk

PELYNT
Cornwall

Jubilee Inn ★★
Pelynt, Looe, Cornwall PL13 2JZ
T: (01503) 220312
F: (01503) 220920
E: rickard@jubileeinn.freeserve.
co.uk

PENZANCE
Cornwall

Beachfield Hotel
★★★ SILVER AWARD
The Promenade, Penzance,
Cornwall TR18 4NW
T: (01736) 362067 & 366882
F: (01736) 331100
E: beachfield@eclipse.co.uk
I: www.cornwall_online.co.
uk/beachfield

Estoril Hotel ★
46 Morrab Road, Penzance,
Cornwall TR18 4EX
T: (01736) 362468 & 367471
F: (01736) 367471
E: estorilhotel@aol.com
I: www.chycor.co.
uk/tourism/hotels/penzance-
hotel-assoc

**Mount Haven Hotel and
Restaurant★★**
Turnpike Road, Marazion,
Penzance, Cornwall TR17 0DQ
T: (01736) 710249
F: (01736) 711658
E: mounthaven@compuserve.
com
I: www.mounthaven.co.uk

The Queens Hotel ★★★
The Promenade, Penzance,
Cornwall TR18 4HG
T: (01736) 362371
F: (01736) 350033
E: enquiries@queens-hotel.com
I: www.queens-hotel.com
ⓐ

The Sea and Horses Hotel ★
6 Alexandra Terrace, Sea Front,
Penzance, Cornwall TR18 4NX
T: (01736) 361961
F: (01736) 330499
ⓐ

PERRANPORTH
Cornwall

Beach Dunes Hotel ★★
Ramoth Way, Perranporth,
Cornwall TR6 0BY
T: (01872) 572263
F: (01872) 573824
E: beachdunes@thenet.co.uk
I: www.s-h-systems.co.
uk/hotels/beach_d.html

The Seiners Arms ★★
The Beach, Perranporth,
Cornwall TR6 0DP
T: (01872) 573118
F: (01872) 573024
E: seiners@connexions.co.uk
I: www.connexions.co.
uk/seiners/index.html

PLYMOUTH
Devon

**The Copthorne Plymouth
★★★★**
Armada Way, Plymouth, Devon
PL1 1AR
T: (01752) 224161
F: (01752) 670688
E: sales.plymouth@mill-cop.
com
I: www.mill-cop.com
ⓖ

Duke of Cornwall Hotel ★★★
Millbay Road, Plymouth, Devon
PL1 3LG
T: (01752) 266256
F: (01752) 275854
E: duke@heritagehotels.co.uk
I: www.heritagehotels.co.uk

The Grand Hotel ★★★
Elliot Street, The Hoe, Plymouth,
Devon PL1 2PT
T: (01752) 661195
F: (01752) 600653
E: info@plymouthgrand.com
I: www.plymouthgrand.com

Grosvenor Park Hotel ★
114-116 North Road East,
Plymouth, PL4 6AH
T: (01752) 229312
F: (01752) 252777
I: www.smoothhound.co.
uk/hotels/grosvpk.html

Invicta Hotel ★★
11/12 Osborne Place, Lockyer
Street, The Hoe, Plymouth,
PL1 2PU
T: (01752) 664997
F: (01752) 664994
I: www.invictahotel.co.uk

**Kitley House Hotel and
Restaurant ★★★**
Kitley Estate, Yealmpton,
Plymouth PL8 2NW
T: (01752) 881555
F: (01752) 881667
E: sales@kitleyhousehotel.com
I: www.kitleyhousehotel.com
ⓐ

New Continental Hotel ★★★
Millbay Road, Plymouth, Devon
PL1 3LD
T: (01752) 220782
F: (01752) 227013
E: newconti@aol.com
I: www.newcontinental.co.uk

Novotel Plymouth ★★★
Marsh Mills, Plymouth, PL6 8NH
T: (01752) 221422
F: (01752) 223922
ⓕ

Strathmore Hotel ★★★
Elliot Street, The Hoe, Plymouth,
PL1 2PR
T: (01752) 662101
F: (01752) 223690

Victoria Court Hotel ★
62/64 North Road East,
Plymouth, PL4 6AL
T: (01752) 668133
F: (01752) 668133
E: victoria.court@btinternet.
com

POLPERRO
Cornwall

The Claremont Hotel ★
The Coombes, Polperro, Looe,
Cornwall PL13 2RG
T: (01503) 272241
F: (01503) 272152
E: wmsmith1@aol.com
ⓐ

POLZEATH
Cornwall

Seascape Hotel ★★
Polzeath, Cornwall PL27 6SX
T: (01208) 863638 &
07968 010644
F: (01208) 862940
E: information@seascapehotel.
co.uk
I: www.seascapehotel.co.uk

PORLOCK
Somerset

Anchor and Ship Hotel ★★★
Porlock Harbour, Porlock,
Minehead, Somerset TA24 8PB
T: (01643) 862753
F: (01643) 862843
E: anchorhotel@clara.net

Porlock Vale House
★★ SILVER AWARD
Porlock Weir, Minehead,
Somerset TA24 8NY
T: (01643) 862338
F: (01643) 863338
E: info@porlockvale.co.uk
I: www.porlockvale.co.uk

PORT GAVERNE
Cornwall

Port Gaverne Hotel ★★
Port Gaverne, Port Isaac,
Cornwall PL29 3SQ
T: (01208) 880244 &
0500 657867
F: (01208) 880151
E: pghotel@telinco.co.uk

PORTH
Cornwall

Porth Cliff Hotel
Rating Applied For
Watergate Road, Porth,
Newquay, Cornwall TR7 3LX
T: (01637) 872503
F: (01637) 872503
E: porthcliff@hotel163.
freeserve.co.uk
I: www.porthcliffhotel.co.uk

PORTLAND
Dorset

Portland Heights Hotel ★★★
Yeates Corner, Portland,
Weymouth, Dorset DT5 2EN
T: (01305) 821361
F: (01305) 860081
E: reception@phh.wdi.co.uk
I: www.resort-guide.co.uk/phh/
ⓐ

PORTLOE
Cornwall

**Lugger Hotel and Restaurant
★★★**
Portloe, Truro, Cornwall TR2 5RD
T: (01872) 501322
F: (01872) 501691

REDRUTH
Cornwall

Crossroads Hotel ★★
Scorrier, Redruth, Cornwall
TR16 5BP
T: (01209) 820551
F: (01209) 820392
E: crossroads.hotel@talk21.com

ROCK
Cornwall

The Mariners Hotel ★★
The Slipway, Rock, Wadebridge,
Cornwall PL27 6LD
T: (01208) 862312
F: (01208) 863827
E: amiller767@aol.com
I: www.chycor.co.uk/mariners/

RUAN HIGH LANES
Cornwall

The Hundred House Hotel
★★ SILVER AWARD
Ruan High Lanes, Truro,
Cornwall TR2 5JR
T: (01872) 501336
F: (01872) 501151

Establishments printed in blue have a detailed entry in this guide

ST AGNES
Cornwall

Rose-in-Vale Country House Hotel★★★
Mithian, St Agnes, Cornwall
TR5 0QD
T: (01872) 552202
F: (01872) 552700
E: reception@
rose-in-vale-hotel.co.uk
I: www.rose-in-vale-hotel.co.uk

Sunholme Hotel ★★
Goonvrea Road, St Agnes,
Cornwall TR5 0NW
T: (01872) 552318

ST AUSTELL
Cornwall

Cliff Head Hotel Limited
★★★ SILVER AWARD
Sea Road, Carlyon Bay, St
Austell, Cornwall PL24 3RB
T: (01726) 812345
F: (01726) 815511
E: cliffheadhotel@btconnect.
com
I: www.cornishriviera.co.
uk/cliffhead

ST IVES
Cornwall

Chy-an-Dour Hotel ★★
Trelyon Avenue, St Ives,
Cornwall TR26 2AD
T: (01736) 796436
F: (01736) 795772
E: chyndour@aol.com
I: www.connexions.co.
uk/chyanhotel

Garrack Hotel and Restaurant
★★★
Higher Ayr, Burthallan Lane, St
Ives, Cornwall TR26 3AA
T: (01736) 796199
F: (01736) 798955
E: garrack@accuk.co.uk
I: www.garrack.com

Porthminster Hotel ★★★
The Terrace, St Ives, Cornwall
TR26 2BN
T: (01736) 795221
F: (01736) 797043
E: reception@
posthminster-hotel.co.uk
I: www.porthminster-hotel.co.uk

St Ives Bay Hotel
Rating Applied For
The Terrace, St Ives, Cornwall
TR26
T: (01736) 795106
F: (01736) 793216

Tregenna Castle ★★★
Treloyan Avenue, St Ives,
Cornwall TR26 2DE
T: (01736) 795254
F: (01736) 796066
I: tregenna-castle.demon.co.uk

ST KEYNE
Cornwall

The Old Rectory Country House Hotel
St Keyne, Liskeard, Cornwall
PL14 4RL
T: (01579) 342617
F: (01579) 342293
I: www.theoldrectorystkeyne.
com

ST WENN
Cornwall

Wenn Manor Hotel
Rating Applied For
St Wenn, Bodmin, Cornwall
PL30 5PS
T: (01726) 890240
F: (01726) 890680

SALCOMBE
Devon

Bolt Head Hotel
★★★ SILVER AWARD
Sharpitor, Salcombe, Devon
TQ8 8LL
T: (01548) 843751
F: (01548) 843061
E: info@bolthead-salcombe.co.
uk
I: www.bolthead-salcombe.co.uk

Heron House Hotel
★★★ SILVER AWARD
Thurlestone Sands, Salcombe,
Devon TQ7 3JY
T: (01548) 560438 & 561600
F: (01548) 560180
I: www.heron-house.co.uk

South Sands Hotel
★★★ SILVER AWARD
South Sands, Salcombe, Devon
TQ8 8LL
T: (01548) 843741
F: (01548) 842112
E: enquire@southsands.com
I: www.southsands.com

Sunny Cliff Hotel ★
Cliff Road, Salcombe, Devon
TQ8 8JX
T: (01548) 842207
F: (01548) 843388

Thurlestone Hotel
★★★★ GOLD AWARD
Thurlestone, Kingsbridge, Devon
TQ7 3NN
T: (01548) 560382
F: (01548) 561069
E: enquiries@thurlestone.co.uk
I: www.thurlestone.co.uk

Tides Reach Hotel
★★★ SILVER AWARD
South Sands, Salcombe, Devon
TQ8 8LJ
T: (01548) 843466
F: (01548) 843954
E: enquire@tidesreach.com
I: www.tidesreach.com

SALISBURY
Wiltshire

The Inn at High Post ★★
High Post, Salisbury, Wiltshire
SP4 6AT
T: (01722) 782592
F: (01722) 782630

Rose and Crown Hotel ★★★
Harnham Road, Salisbury,
SP2 8JQ
T: (01722) 399955
F: (01722) 339816
E: reservations@corushotels.
com
I: www.corushotels.com

SAUNTON
Devon

Saunton Sands Hotel ★★★★
Saunton, Braunton, Devon
EX33 1LQ
T: (01271) 890212
F: (01271) 890145
E: info@sauntonsands.co.uk
I: www.sauntonsands.co.uk

SENNEN
Cornwall

The Old Success Inn ★★
Sennen Cove, Penzance,
Cornwall TR19 7DG
T: (01736) 871232
F: (01736) 871457

SHALDON
Devon

Ness House Hotel ★★
Marine Parade, Shaldon,
Teignmouth, Devon TQ14 0HP
T: (01626) 873480
F: (01626) 873486
E: nesshtl@dialntart.net

SHEPTON MALLET
Somerset

The Shrubbery Hotel ★★
Commercial Road, Shepton
Mallet, Somerset BA4 5BU
T: (01749) 346671
F: (01749) 346581

SHERBORNE
Dorset

Antelope Hotel ★★★
Greenhill, Sherborne, Dorset
DT9 4EP
T: (01935) 812077
F: (01935) 816473

Eastbury Hotel ★★★
Long Street, Sherborne, Dorset
DT9 3BY
T: (01935) 813131
F: (01935) 817296

SIDMOUTH
Devon

Bedford Hotel ★★★
The Esplanade, Sidmouth, Devon
EX10 8NR
T: (01395) 513047
F: (01395) 578563

The Belmont Hotel
★★★★ SILVER AWARD
The Esplanade, Sidmouth, Devon
EX10 8RX
T: (01395) 512555
F: (01395) 579101
E: info@belmont-hotel.co.uk
I: www.belmont-hotel.co.uk

Devoran Hotel
★★ SILVER AWARD
The Esplanade, Sidmouth, Devon
EX10 8AU
T: (01395) 513151 &
0800 317171
F: (01395) 579929
E: devoran@cosmic.org.uk
I: www.devoran.com

Fortfield Hotel ★★★
Sidmouth, Devon EX10 8NU
T: (01395) 512403
F: (01395) 512403

Kingswood Hotel
★★ SILVER AWARD
Esplanade, Sidmouth, Devon
EX10 8AX
T: (01395) 516367
F: (01395) 513185
E: kingswood.hotel@virgin.net
I: www.kingswood-hotel.co.uk

Hotel Riviera
★★★★ GOLD AWARD
The Esplanade, Sidmouth, Devon
EX10 8AY
T: (01395) 515201
F: (01395) 577775
E: enquiries@hotelriviera.co.uk
I: www.hotelriviera.co.uk

Royal Glen Hotel ★★★
Glen Road, Sidmouth, Devon
EX10 8RW
T: (01395) 513221 & 513456
F: (01395) 514922
E: sidmouthroyalglen.hotel@
virgin.net

Royal York and Faulkner Hotel
★★ SILVER AWARD
Esplanade, Sidmouth, Devon
EX10 8AZ
T: 0800 220714 &
(01395) 513043
F: (01395) 577472
E: yorkhotel@eclipse.co.uk
I: www.royal-york-hotel.co.uk

Salcombe Hill House Hotel
★★★
Beatlands Road, Sidmouth,
Devon EX10 8JQ
T: (01395) 514697
F: (01395) 578310
E: salcombehillhousehotel@
eclipse.co.uk

The Victoria Hotel
★★★★ SILVER AWARD
The Esplanade, Sidmouth, Devon
EX10 8RY
T: (01395) 512651
F: (01395) 579154
E: 42551 exonia g ref brend 2

Woodlands Hotel ★★
Cotmaton Cross, Station Road,
Sidmouth, Devon EX10 8HG
T: (01395) 513120 & 513166
F: (01395) 513348
E: info@woodlands-hotel.com
I: www.woodlands-hotel.com

SOURTON
Devon

Collaven Manor Hotel ★★★
Sourton, Okehampton, Devon
EX20 4HH
T: (01837) 861522
F: (01837) 861614
I: www.trevean.com/collaven

STANTON ST QUINTIN
Wiltshire

**Stanton Manor Hotel &
Burghleys Restaurant★★★**
Stanton St Quintin,
Chippenham, Wiltshire
SN14 6DQ
T: (01666) 837552
F: (01666) 837022
E: reception@stantonmanor.co.
uk
I: www.stantonmanor.co.uk

STREET
Somerset

Wessex Hotel ★★★
High Street, Street, Somerset
BA16 0EF
T: (01458) 443383
F: (01458) 446589
E: wessex@hotel-street.
freeserve.co.uk
I: www.travel-uk.
net/wessexhotel

SWINDON
Wiltshire

Blunsdon House Hotel and Leisure Club★★★★
Blunsdon, Swindon SN26 7AS
T: (01793) 721701
F: (01793) 721056
E: info@blunsdonhouse.co.uk
I: www.blunsdonhouse.co.uk

Goddard Arms Hotel
Rating Applied For
High Street, Old Town, Swindon,
Wiltshire SN1 3EG
T: (01793) 692313
F: (01793) 512984

Swindon Marriott ★★★★
Pipers Way, Swindon, Wiltshire
SN3 1SH
T: (01793) 512121
F: (01793) 513114
I: marriott.com/marriott/swidt

Thistle Swindon
Rating Applied For
Fleming Way, Swindon, SN1 1TN
T: (01793) 528282
F: (01793) 541283

Villiers Inn
Rating Applied For
Moormead Road, Wroughton,
Swindon, Wiltshire SN4 9BY
T: (01793) 814744
F: (01793) 814119
E: info@villiersinn.co.uk
I: www.villiersinn.co.uk

TAUNTON
Somerset

**Express by Holiday Inn
Taunton**
Travel Accommodation
Blackbrook Business Park,
Blackbrook Park Avenue,
Taunton, Somerset TA1 2RW
T: (01823) 624000
F: (01823) 624024
I: www.hiexpress.com/taunton

Roadchef Lodge
Travel Accommodation
Taunton Deane Motorway
Service Area, M5 Southbound,
Trull, Taunton, Somerset
TA1 4BA
T: (01823) 332228 &
0800 834719
F: (01823) 338131

Rumwell Manor Hotel
★★★ SILVER AWARD
Rumwell, Taunton, Somerset
TA4 1EL
T: (01823) 461902
F: (01823) 254861
E: rumhotel@aol.com

TEFFONT EVIAS
Wiltshire

**Howards House Hotel
★★ SILVER AWARD**
Teffont Evias, Salisbury SP3 5RJ
T: (01722) 716392 & 716821
F: (01722) 716820
E: paul.firmin@virgin.net
I: www.howardshousehotel.co.
uk

TEIGNMOUTH
Devon

London Hotel ★★★
Bank Street, Teignmouth, Devon
TQ14 8AW
T: (01626) 776336
F: (01626) 778457

TINTAGEL
Cornwall

Atlantic View Hotel ★★
Treknow, Tintagel, Cornwall
PL34 0EJ
T: (01840) 770221
F: (01840) 770995
E: atlantic-view@eclipse.co.uk
I: www.holidayscornwall.com

Bossiney House Hotel ★★
Bossiney Road, Tintagel,
Cornwall PL34 0AX
T: (01840) 770240 &
07770 951411
F: (01840) 770501
E: bossineyhh@eclipse.co.uk
I: www.cornwall-online.co.
uk/bossiney

Willapark Manor Hotel ★★
Bossiney, Tintagel, Cornwall
PL34 0BA
T: (01840) 770782

**The Wootons Country Hotel
★★**
Fore Street, Tintagel, Cornwall
PL34 0DD
T: (01840) 770170
F: (01840) 770170

TIVERTON
Devon

The Tiverton Hotel ★★★
Blundells Road, Tiverton, Devon
EX16 4DB
T: (01884) 256120
F: (01884) 258101
E: reservations.tivertonhotel@
virgin.net
I: www.devonhotels.com

TORCROSS
Devon

Greyhomes Hotel ★
Torcross, Kingsbridge, Devon
TQ7 2TH
T: (01548) 580220
F: (01548) 580832
E: howard@greyhomeshotel.co.
uk
I: www.greyhomeshotel.co.uk

TORMARTON
South Gloucestershire

Compass Inn ★★
Tormarton, Badminton GL9 1JB
T: (01454) 218242
F: (01454) 218741
I: www.compass-inn.co.uk

TORPOINT
Cornwall

Whitsand Bay Hotel ★★
Portwrinkle, Torpoint, Cornwall
PL11 3BU
T: (01503) 230276
F: (01503) 230329

TORQUAY
Devon

Abbey Court Hotel ★★
Falkland Road, Torquay, Devon
TQ2 5JR
T: (01803) 297316
F: (01803) 297316

Anstey's Cove Hotel ★★
327 Babbacombe Road, Torquay,
Devon TQ1 3TB
T: 0800 0284953 &
(01803) 200900
F: (01803) 211150
E: info@ansteyscove.co.uk
I: www.ansteyscove.co.uk

Ansteys Lea Hotel ★★
Babbacombe Road, Wellswood,
Torquay, Devon TQ1 2QJ
T: (01803) 294843
F: (01803) 214333
E: stay@ansteys-lea.com
I: www.ansteys-lea.com

Apsley Hotel ★★
Torwood Gardens Road,
Torquay, Devon TQ1 1EG
T: (01803) 292058 & 293939
F: (01803) 215105

Ashley Court Hotel ★★
107 Abbey Road, Torquay, Devon
TQ2 5NP
T: (01803) 292417 & 296078
F: (01803) 215035
E: reception@ashleycourt.
demon.co.uk
I: www.ashleycourt.demon.co.uk

Hotel Balmoral ★★
Meadfoot Sea Road, Torquay,
Devon TQ1 2LQ
T: (01803) 299224
F: (01803) 293381

**Barn Hayes Country Hotel
★★ SILVER AWARD**
Brim Hill, Maidencombe,
Torquay, Devon TQ1 4TR
T: (01803) 327980
F: (01803) 327980
E: info@
barnhayescountryhotel.co.uk
I: www.
barnhayescountryhotel.co.uk

Belgrave Hotel ★★★
Belgrave Road, Torquay, Devon
TQ2 5HE
T: (01803) 296666
F: (01803) 211308

The Berbury Hotel ★★
64 Bampfylde Road, Torquay,
Devon TQ2 5AY
T: (01803) 297494
F: (01803) 215902
E: bsellick@berbury.co.uk
I: www.berbury.co.uk

Bishops Court ★★★
Lower Warberry Road, Torquay,
Devon TQ1 1QS
T: (01803) 294649
F: (01803) 291175

Burlington Hotel ★★
462-466 Babbacombe Road,
Torquay, Devon TQ1 1HN
T: (01803) 210950
F: (01803) 200189
E: burlington.hotel@virgin.net
I: www.torquayhotels.co.uk

Bute Court Hotel ★★
Belgrave Road, Torquay, Devon
TQ2 5HQ
T: (01803) 213055
F: (01803) 213429
I: www.bute-court-hotel.co.uk

Carlton Hotel ★★
Falkland Road, Torquay, Devon
TQ2 5JJ
T: (01803) 400300
F: (01803) 400130
E: carltonetlh.co.uk
I: www.tlh.co.uk

County Hotel ★★
52/54 Belgrave Road, Torquay,
Devon TQ2 5HS
T: (01803) 294452
F: (01803) 294452

**The Court Hotel
★★ SILVER AWARD**
Lower Warberry Road, Torquay,
Devon TQ1 1QS
T: (01803) 212011
F: (01803) 292648
E: teresa@court-hotel
I: court-hotel.co.uk

Derwent Hotel ★★
Belgrave Road, Torquay, Devon
TQ2 5HT
T: (01803) 400100
F: (01803) 400110
E: derwent@tlh.co.uk
I: tlh.co.uk

Exmouth View Hotel ★
St Albans Road, Babbacombe,
Torquay, Devon TQ1 3LG
T: (01803) 327307
F: (01803) 326697
E: relax@exmouth-view.co.uk
I: www.exmouth-view.co.uk

Frognel Hall ★★
Higher Woodfield Road,
Torquay, Devon TQ1 2LD
T: (01803) 298339
F: (01803) 215115
E: frognel@btinternet.com
I: www.frognelhall.co.uk

Hotel Gleneagles ★★★
Asheldon Road, Wellswood,
Torquay, Devon TQ1 2QS
T: (01803) 293637 & 215621
F: (01803) 295106
E: HotelGleneagles@lineone.net
I: www.hotel-gleneagles.com

Gresham Court Hotel ★★
Babbacombe Road, Torquay,
TQ1 1HG
T: (01803) 293007 & 293658
F: (01803) 215951
E: gresham@thorpelodge.
freeserve.co.uk
I: www.gresham-court-hotel.co.
uk

Establishments printed in blue have a detailed entry in this guide

Livermead Cliff Hotel ★★★
Sea Front, Torquay, TQ2 6RQ
T: (01803) 299666
F: (01803) 294496
E: enquiries@livermeadcliff.co.uk
I: www.livermeadcliff.co.uk

Livermead House Hotel ★★★
Sea Front, Torquay, Devon
TQ2 6QJ
T: (01803) 294361
F: (01803) 200758
E: rewhotels@aol.com
I: www.hotellink.co.uk/livermead.html

Manor House Hotel ★★
Seaway Lane, Torquay, Devon
TQ2 6PS
T: (01803) 605164
F: (01803) 606841
E: mark@manor-house-hotel.co.uk
I: www.manor-house-hotel.co.uk

Norcliffe Hotel ★★
Sea Front, Babbacombe Downs,
Torquay, Devon TQ1 3LF
T: (01803) 328456
F: (01803) 328023

Osborne Hotel
★★★ SILVER AWARD
Hesketh Crescent, Meadfoot
Beach, Torquay, Devon TQ1 2LL
T: (01803) 213311
F: (01803) 296788

The Overmead Hotel ★★
Daddyhole Road, Torquay,
Devon TQ1 2EF
T: (01803) 295666
F: (01803) 299899
I: www.torbayhotels.com

Palace Hotel ★★★★
Babbacombe Road, Torquay,
Devon TQ1 3TG
T: (01803) 200200
F: (01803) 299899
E: mail1@palacetorquay.co.uk
I: www.palacetorquay.co.uk

Princes Hotel ★
Park Hill Road, Torquay, Devon
TQ1 2DU
T: (01803) 291803
F: (01803) 292113
E: derek@rpinceshotel.fsnet.co.uk

Rawlyn House Hotel ★★
Rawlyn Road, Chelston, Torquay
TQ2 6PL
T: (01803) 605208
F: (01803) 607040

Red House Hotel ★★
Rousdown Road, Chelston,
Torquay TQ2 6PB
T: (01803) 607811
F: (01803) 200592
E: stay@redhouse-hotel.co.uk
I: www.redhouse-hotel.co.uk

Hotel Regina ★★
Victoria Parade, Torquay,
TQ1 2BE
T: (01803) 292904
F: (01803) 290270

Richmond ★★★
27 Croft Road, Torquay,
TQ2 5UD
T: (01803) 298457
F: (01803) 215866
I: www.torquayhotels.co.uk

Roseland Hotel ★★
Warren Road, Torquay, TQ2 5TT
T: (01803) 213829
F: (01803) 291266
I: www.torquayhotels.co.uk

Rothesay Hotel ★
Scarborough Road, Torquay,
TQ2 5UH
T: (01803) 293161
F: (01803) 293421

Seascape Hotel ★★
8-10 Tor Church Road, Torquay,
Devon TQ2 5UT
T: (01803) 292617
F: (01803) 299260
E: enquiries@torquayseascape.co.uk
I: www.torquayseascape.co.uk

Shedden Hall Hotel ★★
Shedden Hill, Torquay, TQ2 5TX
T: (01803) 292964
F: (01803) 295306
E: sheddenhtl@aol.com
I: www.sheddenhallhotel.co.uk

Sydore Hotel ★★
Meadfoot Road, Torquay,
TQ1 2JP
T: (01803) 294758
F: (01803) 294489
E: john@sydore.co.uk
I: www.sydore.co.uk

Toorak Hotel ★★★
Chestnut Avenue, Torquay,
Devon TQ2 5JS
T: (01803) 400400
F: (01803) 400140
E: toorak@tlh.co.uk
I: www.tlh.co.uk

Tor Park Hotel
Rating Applied For
24 Vansittart Road, Torquay,
TQ2 5BW
T: (01803) 295151
F: (01803) 200584
I: www.shearings-holidays.co.uk

Torcroft Hotel ★★
Croft Road, Torquay, TQ2 5UE
T: (01803) 298292
F: (01803) 291799

Victoria Hotel ★★
Belgrave Road, Torquay, Devon
TQ2 5HL
T: (01803) 400200
F: (01803) 400120
E: victoria@tlh.co.uk
I: www.tlh.co.uk

Westwood Hotel ★
111 Abbey Road, Torquay,
TQ2 5NP
T: (01803) 293818
F: (01803) 293818
E: reception@westwoodhotel.co.uk
I: www.westwoodhotel.co.uk

Old Church House Inn ★★★
Torbryan, Newton Abbot, Devon
TQ12 5UR
T: (01803) 812372 & 812180
F: (01803) 812180

Royal Seven Stars Hotel ★★
The Plains, Totnes, Devon
TQ9 5DD
T: (01803) 862125 & 863241
F: (01803) 867925
I: www.smoothhound.co.uk/hotels/royal7.html

Waterbeach Hotel ★★
Treyarnon Bay, Padstow,
Cornwall PL28 8JW
T: (01841) 520292
F: (01841) 521102
E: waterbeach@aol.com
I: members.aol.com/waterbeach/

Hilbury Court Hotel ★★
Hilperton Road, Trowbridge,
Wiltshire BA14 7JW
T: (01225) 752949
F: (01225) 777990

Alverton Manor ★★★
Tregolls Road, Truro, Cornwall
TR1 1ZQ
T: (01872) 276633
F: (01872) 222989
E: alverton@connexions.co.uk

Carlton Hotel ★★
Falmouth Road, Truro, Cornwall
TR1 2HL
T: (01872) 272450
F: (01872) 223938

The Royal Hotel
★★★ SILVER AWARD
Lemon Street, Truro, Cornwall
TR1 2QB
T: (01872) 270345
F: (01872) 242453

Prince Hall Hotel
★★ SILVER AWARD
Two Bridges, Yelverton, Devon
PL20 6SA
T: (01822) 890403
F: (01822) 890676
E: bookings@princehall.co.uk
I: www.princehall.co.uk

The Molesworth Arms Hotel ★★
Molesworth Street, Wadebridge,
Cornwall PL27 7DP
T: (01208) 812055
F: (01208) 814254
E: sarah@molesworth.ision.co.uk
I: www.molesworth.ndirect.co.uk

Trehellas House
★★ SILVER AWARD
Washaway, Bodmin, Cornwall
PL30 3AD
T: (01208) 72700 & 74499
F: (01208) 73336
I: www.crescom.co.uk/trehellas

Old Bell Hotel
Rating Applied For
42 Market Place, Warminster,
Wiltshire BA12 9AN
T: (01985) 216611
F: (01985) 217111

Downfield House Hotel
★★ SILVER AWARD
16 St Decuman's Road, Watchet,
Somerset TA23 0HR
T: (01984) 631267
F: (01984) 634369

Watergate Bay Hotel ★★★
Watergate Bay, Cornwall
TR8 4AA
T: (01637) 860543
F: (01637) 860333
E: hotel@watergate.co.uk
I: www.watergate.co.uk

Ancient Gate House Hotel ★
20 Sadler Street, Wells, Somerset
BA5 2RR
T: (01749) 672029
F: (01749) 670319

Charlton House
★★★ GOLD AWARD
Charlton Road, Shepton Mallet,
Somerset BA4 4PR
T: (01749) 342008
F: (01749) 346362
E: reservations-charltonhouse@btinternet.com

The Market Place Hotel and Restaurant
Wells, Somerset BA5 2RW
T: (01749) 672616
F: (01749) 679670
E: marketplace@bhere.co.uk
I: www.bhere.co.uk

Swan Hotel
★★★ SILVER AWARD
Sadler Street, Wells, Somerset
BA5 2RX
T: (01749) 678877
F: (01749) 677647
E: swan@bhere.co.uk
I: www.bhere.co.uk

The White Hart Hotel ★★
Sadler Street, Wells, Somerset
BA5 2RR
T: (01749) 672056
F: (01749) 672056
E: whitehart@wells.demon.co.uk
I: www.wells.demon.co.uk

Establishments printed in blue have a detailed entry in this guide

WEST BEXINGTON
Dorset

The Manor Hotel ★★
West Bexington, Dorchester,
Dorset DT2 9DF
T: (01308) 897616 & 897785
F: (01308) 897035
E: themanorhotel@btconnect.
com
I: www.dorset-info.co.
uk/manor_hotel_bexington.htm

WEST LOOE
Cornwall
Hannafore Point ★★★
Marine Drive, West Looe, Looe,
Cornwall PL13 2DG
T: (01503) 263273
F: (01503) 263272
E: hannafore@aol.com

WESTBURY
Wiltshire
The Cedar Hotel ★★
Warminster Road, Westbury,
Wiltshire BA13 3PR
T: (01373) 822753
F: (01373) 858423

WESTON-SUPER-MARE
North Somerset
Arosfa Hotel ★★
Lower Church Road, Weston-
super-Mare, BS23 2AG
T: (01934) 419523
F: (01934) 636084
E: info@arosfahotel.co.uk
I: www.arosfahotel.co.uk

Beachlands Hotel ★★★
17 Uphill Road North, Weston-
super-Mare, BS23 4NG
T: (01934) 621401
F: (01934) 621966
E: beachlands@wsmare96.
freeserve.co.uk
I: www.travel-uk.net/beachlands

Daunceys Hotels ★★
9-14 Claremont Crescent,
Weston-super-Mare, BS23 2EE
T: (01934) 621144 & 621212
F: (01934) 620281
E: daunceyshotel.fsnet.co.uk

The New Ocean Hotel ★★
1 Manilla Crescent, Madeira
Cove, Weston-super-Mare,
Somerset BS23 2BS
T: (01934) 621839
F: (01934) 626474

**The Old Colonial Hotel
Restaurant and Bar★★★**
30 Knightstone Road, Weston-
super-Mare, BS23 2AW
T: (01934) 620739
F: (01934) 642725

**Queenswood Hotel
★★ SILVER AWARD**
Victoria Park, Weston-super-
Mare, Somerset BS23 2HZ
T: (01934) 416141
F: (01934) 621759
E: queenswood.hotel@
btinternet.com
I: www.s-h-systems.co.
uk/hotels/queesw.html

Royal Pier Hotel ★★
Birnbeck Road, Weston-super-
Mare, BS23 2EJ
T: (01934) 626644
F: (01934) 624169
⊛

WEYMOUTH
Dorset
The Glenburn Hotel ★★
42 Preston Road, Weymouth,
Dorset DT3 6PZ
T: (01305) 832353
F: (01305) 835610

Hotel Rembrandt ★★★
12-18 Dorchester Road,
Weymouth, Dorset DT4 7JU
T: (01305) 764000
F: (01305) 764022
E: reception@hotelrembrandt.
co.uk
I: www.hotelrembrandt.co.uk

Hotel Rex ★★★
29 The Esplanade, Weymouth,
Dorset DT4 8DN
T: (01305) 760400
F: (01305) 760500
E: rex@kingshotels.f9.co.uk

**Royal Hotel
Rating Applied For**
90-91 The Esplanade,
Weymouth, Dorset DT4 4AX
T: (01305) 782777
F: (01305) 761088

WHEDDON CROSS
Somerset
**Raleigh Manor Country House
Hotel★★**
Wheddon Cross, Minehead,
Somerset TA24 7BB
T: (01643) 841484
E: raleighmanor@easynet.co.uk
I: www.raleighmanorhotel.co.uk

WICK
Bath & North East Somerset
**Tracy Park Golf & Country Club
★★★**
Bath Road, Wick, Bristol
BS30 5RN
T: (0117) 9372251
F: (0117) 9374288
E: hotel@tracypark.com
I: www.tracypark.com

WINCANTON
Somerset
Holbrook House Hotel ★★★
Wincanton, Somerset BA9 8BS
T: (01963) 32377
F: (01963) 32681
E: holbrookhotel@compuserve.
com
I: www.holbrookhotelinfo.co.uk

WINSFORD
Somerset
**Royal Oak Inn
★★★ SILVER AWARD**
Exmoor National Park, Winsford,
Minehead, Somerset TA24 7JE
T: (01643) 851455
F: (01643) 851040
E: enquiries@
royaloak-somerset.co.uk
I: www.royaloak-somerset.co.uk

WOODBURY
Devon
**Woodbury Park Hotel, Golf &
Country Club★★★★**
Woodbury Castle, Woodbury,
Exeter EX5 1JJ
T: (01395) 233382
F: (01395) 233384

WOOLACOMBE
Devon
**Crossways Hotel
★ SILVER AWARD**
The Esplanade, Woolacombe,
Devon EX34 7DJ
T: (01271) 870395
F: (01271) 870395
I: www.smoothhound.co.
uk/hotels/crossway.html

Little Beach Hotel ★★
The Esplanade, Woolacombe,
Devon EX34 7DJ
T: (01271) 870398
⊛

Narracott Grand Hotel ★★
Beach Road, Woolacombe,
Devon EX34 7BS
T: (01271) 870418
F: (01271) 870600
E: narracott.co.uk
I: www.narracott.co.uk

**Pebbles Hotel and Restaurant
★**
Combesgate Beach, Mortehoe,
Woolacombe, Devon EX34 7EA
T: (01271) 870426
E: enquiries@pebbleshotel.com
I: www.pebbleshotel.com

**Watersmeet Hotel
★★★ SILVER AWARD**
Mortehoe, Woolacombe, Devon
EX34 7EB
T: (01271) 870333
F: (01271) 870890
E: watersmeethotel@
compuserve.com
I: www:watersmeethotel.co.uk

Woolacombe Bay Hotel ★★★
South Street, Woolacombe,
Devon EX34 7BN
T: (01271) 870388
F: (01271) 870613
E: woolacombe.bayhotel@
btinternet.com
I: www.woolacombe-bay-hotel

YEOVIL
Somerset
Preston Hotel and Motel ★
64 Preston Road, Yeovil,
Somerset BA20 2DL
T: (01935) 474400
F: (01935) 410142
E: prestonhotel.freeserve.co.uk

**Yeovil Court Hotel
★★★ SILVER AWARD**
West Coker Road, Yeovil,
Somerset BA22 2HE
T: (01935) 863746
F: (01935) 863990
E: fred@yeovil-courthotel.co.uk

SOUTH OF ENGLAND

ABINGDON
Oxfordshire
**Abingdon Four Pillars Hotel
★★★**
Marcham Road, Abingdon,
Oxfordshire OX14 1TZ
T: (01235) 553456
F: (01235) 554117

ALDERSHOT
Hampshire
**Potters International Hotel
★★★**
1 Fleet Road, Aldershot,
Hampshire GU11 2ET
T: (01252) 344000
F: (01252) 311611

ALRESFORD
Hampshire
The Swan Hotel ★★
11 West Street, Alresford,
Hampshire SO24 9AD
T: (01962) 732302 & 734427
F: (01962) 735274
E: swanhotel@btinternet.com

ALTON
Hampshire
**Alton Grange Hotel &
Restaurant ★★★**
London Road, Alton, Hampshire
GU34 4EG
T: (01420) 86565
F: (01420) 541346
E: Info@AltonGrange.co.uk
I: www.AltonGrange.co.uk

ANDOVER
Hampshire
The Bourne Valley Inn
St Mary Bourne, Andover,
Hampshire SP11 6BT
T: (01264) 738361
F: (01264) 738126
E: bourneinn@aol.com
I: www.townpages.com

The Danebury Hotel ★★
High Street, Andover, Hampshire
SP10 1NX
T: (01264) 323332
F: (01264) 334021

ASCOT
Berkshire
The Highclere Hotel ★★
Kings Road, Sunninghill, Ascot,
Berkshire SL5 9AD
T: (01344) 625220
F: (01344) 872528

AYLESBURY
Buckinghamshire
Posthouse Aylesbury ★★★
Aston Clinton Road, Aylesbury,
Buckinghamshire HP22 5AA
T: 0870 400 9002
F: (01296) 734191

Establishments printed in blue have a detailed entry in this guide

West Lodge Hotel ★★
45 London Road, Aston Clinton,
Aylesbury, Buckinghamshire
HP22 5HL
T: (01296) 630331 & 630362
F: (01296) 630151
E: jib.@westlodge.co.uk
I: www.westlodge.co.uk

BASINGSTOKE
Hampshire

**Audleys Wood (A Thistle
Country House Hotel)** ★★★★
Alton Road, Basingstoke,
Hampshire RG25 2JT
T: (01256) 817555
F: (01256) 817500
E: audleys.wood@thistle.co.uk
I: www.hotelbook.
com/live/welcome/13059

Basingstoke Country Hotel
★★★★ SILVER AWARD
Scures Hill, Nately Scures,
Basingstoke, Hampshire
RG27 9JS
T: (01256) 764161
F: (01256) 768341
E: maxine.butler@awhotels.com

Hampshire Centrecourt
★★★ SILVER AWARD
Centre Drive, Chineham,
Basingstoke, Hampshire
RG24 8FY
T: (01256) 816664
F: (01256) 816727
E: hampshirec@marstonhotels.
co.uk
I: www.marstonhotels.co.uk

Red Lion Hotel ★★★
24 London Street, Basingstoke,
Hampshire RG21 7NY
T: (01256) 328525
F: (01256) 844056
E: redlion@msihotels.co.uk
I: www.msihotels.co.uk

BEACONSFIELD
Buckinghamshire

**Chequers Inn Hotel &
Restaurant** ★★
Kiln Lane, Wooburn Common,
High Wycombe,
Buckinghamshire HP10 0JQ
T: (01628) 529575
F: (01628) 850124
E: info@chequers-inn.com
I: www.chequers-inn.com

BEMBRIDGE
Isle of Wight

Bembridge Coast Hotel ★★★
Fishermans Walk, Bembridge,
Isle of Wight PO35 5TH
T: (01983) 873931
F: (01983) 874693

Windmill Hotels Ltd
Rating Applied For
1 Steyne Road, Bembridge, Isle
of Wight PO35 5UH
T: (01983) 872875
F: (01983) 874760
E: enquiries@windmillhotel.com
I: www.windmillhotel.com

BLANDFORD FORUM
Dorset

Anvil Hotel & Restaurant ★★
Salisbury Road, Pimperne,
Blandford Forum, Dorset
DT11 8UQ
T: (01258) 453431 & 480182
F: (01258) 480182

Crown Hotel
★★★ SILVER AWARD
8 West Street, Blandford Forum,
Dorset DT11 7AJ
T: (01258) 456626
F: (01258) 451084

BONCHURCH
Isle of Wight

Leconfield Hotel
★★ SILVER AWARD
85 Leeson Road, Upper
Bonchurch, Bonchurch, Ventnor,
Isle of Wight PO38 1PU
T: (01983) 852196
F: (01983) 856525
E: admin@leconfieldhotel.co.uk
I: www.leconfieldhotel.co.uk

BOURNEMOUTH
Dorset

Babbacombe Court Hotel ★★
28 West Hill Road, West Cliff,
Bournemouth, Dorset BH2 5PG
T: (01202) 552823 & 551746
F: (01202) 789030

Bay View Court Hotel ★★★
35 East Overcliff Drive,
Bournemouth, Dorset BH1 3AH
T: (01202) 294449
F: (01202) 292883
E: enquiry@bayviewcourt.co.uk
I: www.bayviewcourt.co.uk

Belvedere Hotel ★★★
Bath Road, Bournemouth,
Dorset BH1 2EU
T: (01202) 297556 & 293336
F: (01202) 294699
E: Belvedere_Hotel@msn.com
I: www.belvedere-hotel.co.uk

Bonnington Hotel ★★
44 Tregonwell Road,
Bournemouth, Dorset BH2 5NT
T: (01202) 553456
F: (01202) 317797
E: bonnington.bournemouth@
btinternet.com
I: www.bonnington.co.uk

Burley Court Hotel ★★★
Bath Road, Bournemouth,
Dorset BH1 2NP
T: (01202) 552824 & 556704
F: (01202) 298514

Cecil Court Hotel ★★
4 Durley Road, West Cliff,
Bournemouth, Dorset BH2 5JL
T: (01202) 553160

Chesterwood Hotel ★★★
East Overcliff Drive,
Bournemouth, Dorset BH1 3AR
T: (01202) 558057
F: (01202) 556285
E: chesterwood@aol.com

Chine Hotel ★★★
Boscombe Spa Road,
Bournemouth, Dorset BH5 1AX
T: (01202) 396234
F: (01202) 391737
E: reservations@chinehotel.co.
uk
I: www.chinehotel.co.uk

Chinehurst Hotel ★★
18-20 Studland Road, Alum
Chine, Bournemouth, Dorset
BH4 8JA
T: (01202) 764583
F: (01202) 762854

Cliffeside Hotel ★★★
East Overcliff Drive,
Bournemouth, Dorset BH1 3AQ
T: (01202) 555724
F: (01202) 314534

The Connaught Hotel
★★★ SILVER AWARD
West Hill Road, West Cliff,
Bournemouth, Dorset BH2 5PH
T: (01202) 298020
F: (01202) 298028
E: sales@theconnaught.co.uk
I: www.theconnaught.co.uk

The Cottage Private Hotel ★★
12 Southern Road, Southbourne,
Bournemouth, Dorset BH6 3SR
T: (01202) 422764
F: (01202) 381442
E: ron+val@rjvhalliwell.force9.
co.uk
I: www.SmoothHound.co.
uk/hotels/cottage3.html

Cottonwood Hotel ★★
Grove Road, East Cliff,
Bournemouth, Dorset BH1 3AP
T: (01202) 553183
F: (01202) 299225

The County Hotel ★★
Westover Road, Bournemouth,
Dorset BH1 2BT
T: (01202) 552385
F: (01202) 297255

Cumberland Hotel ★★★
East Overcliff Drive,
Bournemouth, Dorset BH1 3AF
T: (01202) 290722
F: (01202) 311394
I: www.arthuryoung.co.uk

Durley Hall Hotel ★★★
7 Durley Chine Road,
Bournemouth, Dorset BH2 5JS
T: (01202) 751000
F: (01202) 757585
E: sales@durleyhall.co.uk
I: www.durleyhall.co.uk

Durlston Court Hotel ★★★
47 Gervis Road, East Cliff,
Bournemouth, Dorset BH1 3DD
T: (01202) 316316
F: (01202) 316999
E: dch@seaviews.co.uk
I: www.seaviews.co.uk

Elstead Hotel
★★★ SILVER AWARD
Knyveton Road, Bournemouth,
Dorset BH1 3QP
T: (01202) 293071
F: (01202) 293827
E: info@the-elstead.co.uk
I: www.the-elstead.co.uk

Fircroft Hotel ★★
Owls Road, Bournemouth,
Dorset BH5 1AE
T: (01202) 309771
F: (01202) 395644
I: www.fircrofthotel.co.uk

The Five Ways Hotel ★★
23 Argyll Road, Sea Road,
Boscombe, Bournemouth,
Dorset BH5 1EB
T: (01202) 301509 & 304971
F: (01202) 391107

Grosvenor Hotel ★★★
Bath Road, Bournemouth,
Dorset BH1 2EX
T: (01202) 558858
F: (01202) 298332
E: grosvenor@post.
bournemouth.net.co.uk.

The Hermitage Hotel
★★★ SILVER AWARD
Exeter Road, Bournemouth,
Dorset BH2 5AH
T: (01202) 557363
F: (01202) 559173
E: info@hermitage-hotel.co.uk
I: www.hermitage-hotel.co.uk

Hilton Bournemouth ★★★★
Westover Road, Bournemouth,
Dorset BH1 2BZ
T: (01202) 557681
F: (01202) 554918
E: general.manager@
bournemouth.stakis.co.uk
I: www.stakis.co.uk

Hinton Firs ★★★
Manor Road, East Cliff,
Bournemouth, Dorset BH1 3HB
T: (01202) 555409
F: (01202) 299607
E: hintonfirs@bournemouth.co.
uk
I: www.pageant.co.uk

Kensington Hotel ★★
18 Durley Chine Road, West
Cliff, Bournemouth, Dorset
BH2 5LE
T: (01202) 557434
F: (01202) 290562
E: kensington.hotel@talk21.com
I: www.plu44.com/o/kensington/

Kiwi Hotel ★★
West Hill Road, Bournemouth,
Dorset BH2 5EG
T: (01202) 555889
F: (01202) 789567

Lynden Court Hotel ★★
8 Durley Road, West Cliff,
Bournemouth, Dorset BH2 5JL
T: (01202) 553894
F: (01202) 317711

Majestic Hotel
Rating Applied For
34 Derby Road, East Cliff,
Bournemouth, Dorset BH1 3QE
T: (01202) 294771
F: (01202) 310962

Manor House Hotel ★★
34 Manor Road, East Cliff,
Bournemouth, Dorset BH1 3EZ
T: (01202) 396669
F: (01202) 396669

Mansfield Hotel ★★
West Cliff Gardens,
Bournemouth, Dorset BH2 5HL
T: (01202) 552659
E: bournemouthhotel.net
I: www.bournemouthhotel.net

Marsham Court Hotel ★★★
Russell-Cotes Road, East Cliff,
Bournemouth, Dorset BH1 3AB
T: (01202) 552111
F: (01202) 294744
E: reservations@marshamcourt.
co.uk
I: www.marshamcourt.co.uk

Establishments printed in blue have a detailed entry in this guide

Mayfair Hotel ★★★
27 Bath Road, Bournemouth,
Dorset BH1 2NW
T: (01202) 551983
F: (01202) 298459
E: info@themayfair.com
I: www.themayfair.com

New Durley Dean Hotel ★★★
West Cliff Road, Bournemouth,
Dorset BH2 5HE
T: (01202) 557711
F: (01202) 292815

The New Westcliff Hotel ★★
27 Chine Crescent, West Cliff,
Bournemouth, Dorset BH2 5LB
T: (01202) 551062
F: (01202) 315377

Norfolk Royale Hotel ★★★★
Richmond Hill, Bournemouth,
Dorset BH2 6EN
T: (01202) 551521
F: (01202) 299729
E: norfolkroyale@
englishrosehotels.co.uk
I: www.englishrosehotels.co.uk
🏃

Overcliff Hotel ★★
58 Grand Avenue, Southbourne,
Bournemouth, Dorset BH6 3PA
T: (01202) 428300
F: (01202) 430718

Palm Court Hotel ★★
38 Christchurch Road,
Bournemouth, Dorset BH1 3PD
T: (01202) 558088 & 268898
F: (01202) 789318

Pavilion Hotel ★★★
22 Bath Road, Bournemouth,
Dorset BH1 2NS
T: (01202) 291266
F: (01202) 559264

Quality Hotel ★★★
8 Poole Road, Bournemouth,
Dorset BH2 5QU
T: (01202) 763006
F: (01202) 766168
E: admin@gb641.u-net.com
I: www.qualityinn.
com/hotel/gb641

Queen's Hotel ★★★
Meyrick Road, East Cliff,
Bournemouth, Dorset BH1 3DL
T: (01202) 554415
F: (01202) 294810
E: hotels@arthuryoung.co.uk
I: www.arthuryoung.co.uk

Hotel Riviera ★★
5 West Cliff Gardens,
Bournemouth, Dorset BH2 5HL
T: (01202) 552845
F: (01202) 317717
E: info@hotel-riviera.co.uk
I: www.hotel-riviera.co.uk

Riviera Hotel ★★
12-16 Burnaby Road, Alum
Chine, Bournemouth, Dorset
BH4 8JF
T: (01202) 763653
F: (01202) 768422
I: www.smouthhound.co.
uk/calotels.html

Roysdean Manor ★★
5 Derby Road, Bournemouth,
Dorset BH1 3PT
T: (01202) 554933
F: (01202) 780916
E: sales@roysdeanmanor.co.uk
I: www.roysdeanmanor.co.uk

Russell Court Hotel ★★
Bath Road, Bournemouth,
Dorset BH1 2EP
T: (01202) 295819
F: (01202) 293457
E: russelcrt@aol.com

Sandy Beach Hotel ★★
43 Southwood Avenue,
Southbourne, Bournemouth,
Dorset BH6 3QB
T: (01202) 424385
F: (01202) 424385
E: sandybeach@bournemouth.
co.uk
🌐

Shelley Villa Private Hotel ★
22 Wilfred Road, Boscombe,
Bournemouth, Dorset BH5 1ND
T: (01202) 302400
F: (01202) 397514
E: holiday@shelley-villa.co.uk
I: www.shelley-vila.co.uk
🏃

**The Strouden Park Hotel
Rating Applied For**
519 Castle Lane West,
Bournemouth, Dorset BH8 9TN
T: (01202) 514315
F: (01202) 510132

Sun Court Hotel ★★
West Hill Road, West Cliff,
Bournemouth, Dorset BH2 5PH
T: (01202) 551343
F: (01202) 316747

Suncliff Hotel ★★★
East Overcliff Drive,
Bournemouth, Dorset BH1 3AG
T: (01202) 291711
F: (01202) 293788
I: www.smouthhound.co.
uk/calotels.html

Sydney House Hotel ★★
6 West Cliff Road, West Cliff,
Bournemouth, Dorset BH2 5EY
T: (01202) 555536
F: (01202) 555536
E: sww@fsmail.net

Tralee Hotel ★★★
West Hill Road, West Cliff,
Bournemouth, Dorset BH2 5EQ
T: (01202) 556246
F: (01202) 295229
E: hotel@tralee.co.uk
🌐

Trouville Hotel ★★★
Priory Road, West Cliff,
Bournemouth, Dorset BH2 5DH
T: (01202) 552262
F: (01202) 293324
E: hotels@arthuryoung.co.uk
I: www.arthuryoung.co.uk

Ullswater Hotel ★★
Westcliff Gardens,
Bournemouth, Dorset BH2 5HW
T: (01202) 555181
F: (01202) 317896
E: enq@ullswater.uk.com
I: www.ullswater.uk.com

**West Cliff Towers Hotel
★★ SILVER AWARD**
12 Priory Road, Bournemouth,
Dorset BH2 5DG
T: (01202) 553319
F: (01202) 553313

Westleigh Hotel ★★
26 West Hill Road, West Cliff,
Bournemouth, Dorset BH2 5PG
T: (01202) 296989
F: (01202) 296989

Winterbourne Hotel ★★★
Priory Road, Bournemouth,
Dorset BH2 5DJ
T: (01202) 296366
F: (01202) 780073
E: reservations@winterbourne.
co.uk
I: www.winterbourne.co.uk
🌐

Woodcroft Tower Hotel ★★
Gervis Road, East Cliff,
Bournemouth, Dorset BH1 3DE
T: (01202) 558202
F: (01202) 551807
E: enquiries@woodcrofthotel.
co.uk
I: www.woodcrofthotel.co.uk

BRACKNELL
Berkshire

**Coppid Beech Hotel
★★★★ SILVER AWARD**
John Nike Way, Bracknell,
Berkshire RG12 8TF
T: (01344) 303333
F: (01344) 302045
E: reservations@
coppid-beech-hotel.co.uk
I: www.coppidbeech.com
🌐 ♿

Dial House Hotel ★★
62 Dukes Ride, Crowthorne,
Berkshire RG45 6DL
T: (01344) 776941
F: (01344) 777191

BRAMSHAW
Hampshire

Bramble Hill Hotel ★★
Bramshaw, Lyndhurst,
Hampshire SO43 7JG
T: (023) 8081 3165
F: (023) 8081 2126

BROCKENHURST
Hampshire

**Cloud Hotel
★★ SILVER AWARD**
Meerut Road, Brockenhurst,
Hampshire SO42 7TD
T: (01590) 622165
F: (01590) 622818
E: enquiries@cloudhotel.co.uk
I: www.cloudhotel.co.uk
🌐

The Watersplash Hotel ★★
The Rise, Brockenhurst,
Hampshire SO42 7ZP
T: (01590) 622344
F: (01590) 624047
🏃

**Whitley Ridge Country House
Hotel ★★★ SILVER AWARD**
Beaulieu Road, Brockenhurst,
Hampshire SO42 7QL
T: (01590) 622354
F: (01590) 622856
E: whitleyridge@brockenhurst.
co.uk
I: www.newforest-hotels.co.uk
🌐

BUCKINGHAM
Buckinghamshire

**Buckingham Four Pillars Hotel
★★★**
A421 Ring Road South,
Buckingham, Buckinghamshire
MK18 1RY
T: (01280) 822622
F: (01280) 823074
E: buckingham@four-pillars.co.
uk
I: www.four-pillars.co.uk

Villiers Hotel
★★★ SILVER AWARD
3 Castle Street, Buckingham,
Buckinghamshire MK18 1BS
T: (01280) 822444
F: (01280) 822113
E: villiers@villiers-hotels.
demon.co.uk

BURFORD
Oxfordshire

The Bay Tree ★★★
Sheep Street, Burford,
Oxfordshire OX18 4LW
T: (01993) 822791
F: (01993) 823008
E: bookings@
cotswold-inns-hotels.co.uk
I: www.cotswold-inns-hotels.co.
uk

**Cotswold Gateway Hotel
★★★**
Cheltenham Road, Burford,
Oxford, Oxfordshire OX18 4HX
T: (01993) 822695 & 823345
F: (01993) 823600
E: cotswold.gateway@dial.
pipex.com
I: www.cotswold-gateway.co.uk

Golden Pheasant Hotel ★★
High Street, Burford, Oxford,
Oxfordshire OX18 4QA
T: (01993) 823223
F: (01993) 822621

BURLEY
Hampshire

The Burley Inn ★★
The Cross, Burley, Ringwood,
Hampshire BH24 4AB
T: (01425) 403448
F: (01425) 402058

Moorhill House Hotel ★★★
Burley, Ringwood, Hampshire
BH24 4AG
T: (01425) 403285
F: (01425) 403715
E: information@carehotels.co.
uk
I: www.carehotels.co.uk
🌐

CALBOURNE
Isle of Wight

**Swainston Manor Hotel &
Restaurant★★★★**
Calbourne, Newport, Isle of
Wight PO30 4HX
T: (01983) 521121
F: (01983) 521406
E: hotel@swainstonmanor.
freeserve.com.uk

CHALE
Isle of Wight

**Clarendon Hotel & Wight
Mouse Inn★★**
Nr Blackgang, Chale, Isle of
Wight PO38 2HA
T: (01983) 730431
F: (01983) 730431
E: wightmouse@aol.com
I: www.tradinns.co.uk/clarendon

CHESTERTON
Oxfordshire

**Bignell Park Hotel
★★ SILVER AWARD**
Chesterton, Bicester, Oxfordshire
OX6 8UE
T: (01869) 241444 & 241192
F: (01869) 241444

Establishments printed in blue have a detailed entry in this guide

CHIPPING NORTON
Oxfordshire

The Crown & Cushion Hotel, Conference & Leisure Centre ★★★
23 High Street, Chipping Norton, Oxfordshire OX7 5AD
T: (01608) 642533
F: (01608) 642926

CHRISTCHURCH
Dorset

Tyrrells Ford Hotel ★★★
Avon, Christchurch, Dorset BH23 7BH
T: (01425) 672646
F: (01425) 672262

CORFE CASTLE
Dorset

Mortons House Hotel ★★★ SILVER AWARD
East Street, Corfe Castle, Wareham, Dorset BH20 5EE
T: (01929) 480988
F: (01929) 480820
E: stay@mortonshouse.co.uk
I: www.mortonshouse.co.uk

COWES
Isle of Wight

New Holmwood Hotel ★★★
Queens Road, Egypt Point, Cowes, Isle of Wight PO31 8BW
T: (01983) 292508
F: (01983) 295020
E: nholnwoodh@aol.com
I: www.newholmwoodhotel.co.uk

Rawlings Hotel ★★
30 Sun Hill, Cowes, Isle of Wight PO31 7HY
T: (01983) 297507
F: (01983) 281701

DEDDINGTON
Oxfordshire

Holcombe Hotel & Restaurant ★★★ SILVER AWARD
High Street, Deddington, Banbury, Oxfordshire OX15 0SL
T: (01869) 338274
F: (01869) 337167
E: reception@holcombehotel.freeserve.co.uk
I: www.bestwestern.co.uk

DROXFORD
Hampshire

Upland Park Hotel ★★
Garrison Hill (A32), Droxford, Southampton, Hampshire SO32 3QL
T: (01489) 878507
F: (01489) 877853
E: clarelay@globalnet.co.uk

EMSWORTH
Hampshire

The Brookfield Hotel ★★★
Havant Road, Emsworth, Hampshire PO10 7LF
T: (01243) 373363
F: (01243) 376342
E: hermit@mcmail.com

FAREHAM
Hampshire

The Red Lion Hotel ★★
East Street, Fareham, Hampshire PO16 0BP
T: (01329) 822640
F: (01329) 823579

The Roundabout Hotel ★★
Wallington Shore Road, Fareham, Hampshire PO16 8SB
T: (01329) 822542
F: (01329) 234533
E: rhhotel@aol.com

FARINGDON
Oxfordshire

Faringdon Hotel ★★
Market Place, Faringdon, Oxfordshire SN7 7HL
T: (01367) 240536
F: (01367) 243250

Portwell House Hotel ★
Market Place, Faringdon, Oxfordshire SN7 7HU
T: (01367) 240197 & 242413
F: (01367) 244330
E: portwellh@aol.com

FARNBOROUGH
Hampshire

The Falcon Hotel ★★★
68 Farnborough Road, Farnborough, Hampshire GU14 6TH
T: (01252) 545378
F: (01252) 522539

FENNY STRATFORD
Buckinghamshire

Campanile Milton Keynes Hotel
Rating Applied For
Travel Accommodation
40 Penn Road, Fenny Stratford, Milton Keynes, Buckinghamshire MK2 2AU
T: (01908) 649819
F: (01908) 649818

FORDINGBRIDGE
Hampshire

Ashburn Hotel & Restaurant ★★ SILVER AWARD
Fordingbridge, Hampshire SP6 1JP
T: (01425) 652060
F: (01425) 652150
E: ashburn@minstral.co.uk

FRESHWATER
Isle of Wight

Farringford Hotel ★★
Bedbury Lane, Freshwater, Isle of Wight PO40 9PE
T: (01983) 752500 & 752700
F: (01983) 756515
E: enquiries@farringford.co.uk
I: www.farringford.co.uk

FRESHWATER BAY
Isle of Wight

Albion Hotel ★★★
Freshwater Bay, Isle of Wight PO40 9RA
T: (01983) 753631
F: (01983) 755295

GILLINGHAM
Dorset

Stock Hill Country House Hotel ★★★ GOLD AWARD
Stock Hill, Gillingham, Dorset SP8 5NR
T: (01747) 823626
F: (01747) 825628
E: Reception@Stockhill.net
I: www.stockhill.net

GOSPORT
Berkshire

Belle Vue Hotel ★★★
39 Marine Parade East, Lee on the Solent, Hampshire PO13 9BW
T: (023) 9255 0258
F: (023) 9255 2624
E: information@bellevue-hotel.co.uk
I: www.bellevue-hotel.co.uk

The Manor Hotel ★★
Brewers Lane, Gosport, Hampshire PO13 0JY
T: (01329) 232946
F: (01329) 220392
E: tony_lid@msn.com
I: www.smoothhound.co.uk/hotels/manorhtml

GREAT MILTON
Oxfordshire

Le Manoir aux Quat' Saisons ★★★★ GOLD AWARD
Church Road, Great Milton, Oxford, Oxfordshire OX44 7PD
T: (01844) 278881
F: (01844) 278847
E: lemanoir@blanc.co.uk
I: www.manoir.com

HAVANT
Hampshire

Bear Hotel ★★
East Street, Havant, Hampshire PO9 1AA
T: (023) 9248 6501
F: (023) 9247 0551

HAYLING ISLAND
Hampshire

Newtown House Hotel ★★★
Manor Road, Hayling Island, Hampshire PO11 0QR
T: (023) 9246 6131
F: (023) 9246 1366

HECKFIELD
Hampshire

The New Inn ★★ SILVER AWARD
Heckfield, Hook, Hampshire RG27 0LE
T: (0118) 932 6374
F: (0118) 932 6550

HEDGE END
Hampshire

Botleigh Grange Hotel
Rating Applied For
Grange Road, Hedge End, Southampton, Hampshire SO30 2GA
T: (01489) 787700
F: (01489) 788535
E: enquiries@botleighgrangehotel.co.uk
I: www.botleighgrangehotel.co.uk

HOOK
Hampshire

Raven Hotel ★★★
Station Road, Hook, Hampshire RG27 9HS
T: (01256) 762541
F: (01256) 768677

HUNGERFORD
Berkshire

The Bear at Hungerford ★★★
Charnham Street, Hungerford, Berkshire RG17 0EL
T: (01488) 682512
F: (01488) 684357
I: www.jarvis.co.uk

Littlecote House Hotel ★★★ SILVER AWARD
Hungerford, Berkshire RG17 0SS
T: (01488) 682509
F: (01488) 682341

HYTHE
Hampshire

Fountain Court Hotel ★
Frost Lane, Hythe, Southampton, Hampshire SO45 3NE
T: (023) 8084 6310
F: (023) 8084 7295

KINGSTON BAGPUIZE
Oxfordshire

Fallowfields Country House Hotel ★★★
Faringdon Road, Kingston Bagpuize with Southmoor, Oxford, Oxfordshire OX13 5BH
T: (01865) 820416
F: (01865) 821275
E: stay@fallowfields.com
I: www.fallowfields.com

KNOWL HILL
Berkshire

Bird In Hand ★★★
Bath Road, Knowl Hill, Reading, Berkshire RG10 9UP
T: (01628) 822781 & 826622
F: (01628) 826748
E: birdinhand.co.uk
I: www.birdinhand.co.uk

LIPHOOK
Hampshire

Old Thorns Hotel, Golf & Country Club★★★
Griggs Green, Liphook, Hampshire GU30 7PE
T: (01428) 724555
F: (01428) 725036
E: reservations@oldthornsfreeserve.co.uk
I: www.oldthorns.co.uk

LYMINGTON
Hampshire

Passford House Hotel ★★★ SILVER AWARD
Mount Pleasant Lane, Lymington, Hampshire SO41 8LS
T: (01590) 682398
F: (01590) 683494

South Lawn Hotel ★★★ SILVER AWARD
Lymington Road, Milford-on-Sea, Lymington, Hampshire SO41 0RF
T: (01590) 643911
F: (01590) 644820
E: enquiries@southlawn.co.uk
I: www.southlawn.co.uk

Stanwell House Hotel ★★★
Jane McIntyre Hotels Ltd, 15
High Street, Lymington,
Hampshire SO41 9AA
T: (01590) 677123
F: (01590) 677756
I: www.scoot.
uk/stanwell_house_hotel/.

LYNDHURST
Hampshire

Knightwood Lodge ★
Southampton Road, Lyndhurst,
Hampshire SO43 7BU
T: (023) 8028 2502
F: (023) 8028 3730

The Stag Hotel ★★
69 High Street, Lyndhurst,
Hampshire SO43 7BE
T: (023) 8028 2999
F: (023) 8028 2999

Woodlands Lodge Hotel ★★★
Bartley Road, Woodlands,
Southampton, Hampshire
SO40 7GN
T: (023) 8029 2257
F: (023) 8029 3090
E: woodlands@nortels.ltd.uk
I: www.nortels.ltd.uk

MAIDENHEAD
Berkshire

Elva Lodge Hotel ★
Castle Hill, Maidenhead,
Berkshire SL6 4AD
T: (01628) 622948 & 634883
F: (01628) 778954
E: reservations@elvalodgehotel.
demon.co.uk
I: www.elvalodgehotel.demon.
co.uk

Monkey Island Hotel
★★★★ SILVER AWARD
Metropolitan International Ltd,
Bray-on-Thames, Bray,
Maidenhead, Berkshire SL6 2EE
T: (01628) 623400
F: (01628) 784732
E: monkeyisland@btconnect.
com
I: www.monkeyisland.co.uk

MARLOW
Buckinghamshire

Danesfield House
★★★★ SILVER AWARD
Henley Road, Marlow-on-
Thames, Marlow,
Buckinghamshire SL7 2EY
T: (01628) 891010
F: (01628) 890408
E: sales@danesfieldhouse.co.uk
I: www.danesfieldhouse.co.uk

MILFORD-ON-SEA
Hampshire

Westover Hall Hotel
★★★ GOLD AWARD
Park Lane, Milford-on-Sea,
Lymington, Hampshire SO41 0PT
T: (01590) 643044
F: (01590) 644490
E: westoverhallhotel@barclays.
net
I: www.westoverhallhotel.com

MILTON COMMON
Oxfordshire

The Oxford Belfry ★★★
Milton Common, Thame,
Oxfordshire OX9 2JW
T: (01844) 279381
F: (01844) 279624
E: oxfordbelfry@marstonhotels.
co.uk
I: www.marstonhotels.co.uk

MILTON KEYNES
Buckinghamshire

Calverton Lodge Hotel ★★
38 Horsefair Green, Stony
Stratford, Milton Keynes,
Buckinghamshire MK11 1JP
T: (01908) 261241
F: (01908) 265924
E: calvert@powernet.co.uk
I: www.calvertonlodge.co.uk.

The Different Drummer Hotel
★★
94 High Street, Stony Stratford,
Milton Keynes, Buckinghamshire
MK11 1AH
T: (01908) 564733
F: (01908) 260646

Parkside Hotel ★★★
Newport Road, Woughton on
the Green, Milton Keynes,
Buckinghamshire MK6 3LR
T: (01908) 661919
F: (01908) 676186

Quality Hotel ★★★
Monks Way, Two Mile Ash,
Milton Keynes, Buckinghamshire
MK8 8LY
T: (01908) 561666
F: (01908) 568303
E: admin@gb616.u-net.com
I: choicehotelseurope.com

Swan Revived Hotel ★★
High Street, Newport Pagnell,
Milton Keynes, Buckinghamshire
MK16 8AR
T: (01908) 610565
F: (01908) 210995
E: swanrevived@btinternet.com
I: www.swanrevived.co.uk

MINSTER LOVELL
Oxfordshire

The Mill & Old Swan
★★★ SILVER AWARD
Minster Lovell, Oxford,
Oxfordshire OX8 5RN
T: (01993) 774441
F: (01993) 702002
E: themill@initialstyle.co.uk
I: www.initialstyle.co.uk

NEW MILTON
Hampshire

**Chewton Glen Hotel, Health &
Country Club**
★★★★★ GOLD AWARD
Christchurch Road, New Milton,
Hampshire BH25 6QS
T: (01425) 275341
F: (01425) 272310
E: reservations@chewtonglen.
com
I: www.chewtonglen.com

NEWBURY
Berkshire

**Donnington Valley Hotel &
Golf Course**
★★★★ SILVER AWARD
Old Oxford Road, Donnington,
Newbury, Berkshire RG14 3AG
T: (01635) 551199
F: (01635) 551123
E: general@donningtonvalley.
co.uk
I: www.donningtonvalley.co.uk

The Queen's Hotel
Rating Applied For
Market Place, Newbury,
Berkshire RG14 5BD
T: (01635) 47447 & 231053
F: (01635) 569626

Regency Park Hotel
★★★★ SILVER AWARD
Bowling Green Road, Thatcham,
Berkshire RG18 3RP
T: (01635) 871555
F: (01635) 871571
E: regencypark@bestwestern.co.
uk
I: www.regencyparkhotel.co.uk

The Vineyard at Stockcross
★★★★★ GOLD AWARD
Stockcross, Newbury, Berkshire
RG20 8JU
T: (01635) 528770
F: (01635) 528398
E: general@the-vineyard.co.uk
I: www.the-vineyard.co.uk

NITON UNDERCLIFF
Isle of Wight

The Windcliffe Manor Hotel
★★★
Sandrock Road, Niton Undercliff,
Ventnor, Isle of Wight PO38 2NG
T: (01983) 730215
F: (01983) 730215
E: enquires@windcliffe.co.uk
I: www.windcliffe.co.uk

ODIHAM
Hampshire

George Hotel ★★
High Street, Odiham, Hook,
Hampshire RG29 1LP
T: (01256) 702081
F: (01256) 704213

OXFORD
Oxfordshire

The Balkan Lodge Hotel ★★
315 Iffley Road, Oxford,
Oxfordshire OX4 4AG
T: (01865) 244524
F: (01865) 251090
I: www.oxfordcity.
co.uk/hotels/balkan

Cotswold Lodge Hotel ★★★★
66A Banbury Road, Oxford,
Oxfordshire OX2 6JP
T: (01865) 512121
F: (01865) 512490

Mount Pleasant ★★
76 London Road, Headington,
Oxford, Oxfordshire OX3 9AJ
T: (01865) 762749
F: (01865) 762749

Old Bank Hotel
★★★★ GOLD AWARD
92-94 High Street, Oxford,
Oxfordshire OX1 4BN
T: (01865) 799599
F: (01865) 799598
E: info@oldbank-hotel.co.uk

The Old Parsonage Hotel
★★★ SILVER AWARD
1 Banbury Road, Oxford,
Oxfordshire OX2 6NN
T: (01865) 310210
F: (01865) 311262
E: info@oldparsonage-hotel.co.
uk
I: www.
oxford-hotels-restaurants.co.uk

Otmoor Lodge Hotel ★★
Horton Hill, Horton cum Studley,
Oxford, Oxfordshire OX33 1AY
T: (01865) 351235
F: (01865) 351721
E: otmoorlodge@btinternet.
com
I: www.otmoorlodge.co.uk

Studley Priory Hotel
★★★ SILVER AWARD
Horton cum Studley, Oxford,
Oxfordshire OX33 1AZ
T: (01865) 351203 & 351254
F: (01865) 351613
E: res@studley-priory.co.uk
I: www.studley-priory.co.uk

Victoria Hotel ★★
180 Abingdon Road, Oxford,
Oxfordshire OX1 4RA
T: (01865) 724536
F: (01865) 794909
I: www.oxfordcity.co.
uk/hotels/victoria

PANGBOURNE
Berkshire

**The Copper Inn Hotel &
Restaurant**
★★★ SILVER AWARD
Church Road, Pangbourne,
Reading, Berkshire RG8 7AR
T: (0118) 984 2244
F: (0118) 984 5542
E: reservations@copper-inn.co.
uk
I: www.copper-inn.co.uk

PETERSFIELD
Hampshire

Langrish House Hotel ★★
Langrish, Petersfield, Hampshire
GU32 1RN
T: (01730) 266941
F: (01730) 260543

POOLE
Dorset

Harbour Heights Hotel ★★★
73 Haven Road, Sandbanks,
Poole, Dorset BH13 7LW
T: (01202) 707272
F: (01202) 708594

Quarterdeck Hotel ★★
2 Sandbanks Road, Poole, Dorset
BH14 8AQ
T: (01202) 740066 & 748448
F: (01202) 736780

Thistle Poole
Rating Applied For
The Quay, Poole, Dorset
BH15 1HD
T: (01202) 666800
F: (01202) 684470
E: poole@thistle.co.uk
I: www.thistlehotels.com

Establishments printed in blue have a detailed entry in this guide

POOLE-SANDBANKS
Dorset

Haven Hotel ★★★★
Banks Road, Sandbanks, Poole,
Dorset BH13 7QL
T: (01202) 707333
F: (01202) 708796
E: reservations@havenhotel.co.
uk
I: www.havenhotel.co.uk

Sandbanks Hotel ★★★
15 Banks Road, Sandbanks,
Poole, Dorset BH13 7PS
T: (01202) 707377
F: (01202) 708885
E: reservations@
sandbankshotel.co.uk
I: www.sandbankshotels.co.uk

PORTSMOUTH & SOUTHSEA
Hampshire

Beaufort Hotel ★★
71 Festing Road, Southsea,
Portsmouth, Hampshire
PO4 0NQ
T: (023) 9282 3707
F: (023) 9287 0270
E: res/enq@beauforthotel.co.uk

Glendower Hotel ★★
22-23 South Parade, Southsea,
Hampshire PO5 2JF
T: (023) 9282 7169
F: (023) 9283 8738
E: sylvia@yeganehs.freeserve.
co.uk

**Ocean Hotel & Apartments
★★**
8-10 St Helens Parade,
Southsea, Hampshire PO4 0RW
T: (023) 92734233 & 92734342
F: (023) 92297046
E: feris@oceanhotel.freeserve.
co.uk
I: www.oceanhotel.freeserve.co.
uk

The Queen's Hotel ★★★
Clarence Parade, Southsea,
Hampshire PO5 3LJ
T: (023) 9282 2466
F: (023) 9282 1901
E: reservationsatqueenshotel-
southsea.co.uk/cjgil93131@aol.
com
I: www.queenshotel-southsea.
co.uk

Salisbury Hotel ★
57-59 Festing Road, Southsea,
Hampshire PO4 0NQ
T: (023) 92823606 & 07775
660034
F: (023) 92820955
E: feris@oceanhotel.freeserve.
co.uk
I: www.oceanhotel.freeserve.co.
uk

The Sandringham Hotel ★★
7 Osborne Road, Southsea,
Hampshire PO5 3LR
T: (023) 9282 6969 & 9282 2914
F: (023) 9282 2330

Solent Hotel ★★
14-17 South Parade, Southsea,
Hampshire PO5 2JB
T: (023) 9287 5566
F: (023) 9287 2023

**Westfield Hall Hotel
★★ SILVER AWARD**
65 Festing Road, Southsea,
Hampshire PO4 0NQ
T: (023) 9282 6971
F: (023) 9287 0200
E: jdanie@westfield-hall-hotel.
co.uk
I: www.users.globalnet.co.
uk/§jdanie

READING
Berkshire

Abbey House Hotel ★★
118 Connaught Road, Reading,
Berkshire RG30 2UF
T: (0118) 959 0549
F: (0118) 956 9299
E: abbey.house@btinternet.com

Comfort Inn Reading ★★
119 Kendrick Road, Reading,
Berkshire RG1 5EB
T: (0118) 931 1311
F: (0118) 931 4136
I: www.hotelchoice.
com/travelweb

**The Great House at Sonning
★★★**
Thames Street, Sonning-on-
Thames, Reading, Berkshire
RG4 6UT
T: (0118) 969 2277
F: (0118) 944 1296
E: greathouse@btconnect.com

Rainbow Corner Hotel ★★
132-138 Caversham Road,
Reading, Berkshire RG1 8AY
T: (0118) 958 8140
F: (0118) 958 6500
E: enquiries@rainbowhotel.co.uk
I: www.rainbowhotel.co.uk

Upcross Hotel ★★★
68 Berkeley Avenue, Reading,
Berkshire RG1 6HY
T: (0118) 959 0796
F: (0118) 957 6517
E: reservations@upcrosshotel.
co.uk

RINGWOOD
Hampshire

**Moortown Lodge Hotel &
Restaurant★★**
244 Christchurch Road,
Ringwood, Hampshire BH24 3AS
T: (01425) 471404
F: (01425) 476052
E: hotel@burrows-jones.
freeserve.co.uk
I: www.newforest-hotel.co.uk

The Struan Country Inn ★★
Horton Road, Ashley Heath,
Ringwood, Hampshire BH24 2EG
T: (01425) 473553
F: (01425) 480529

ROTHERWICK
Hampshire

**Tylney Hall Hotel
★★★★ GOLD AWARD**
Rotherwick, Hook, Hampshire
RG27 9AZ
T: (01256) 764881
F: (01256) 768141
E: sales@tylneyhall.com
I: www.tylneyhall.com

RYDE
Isle of Wight

**Biskra Beach Hotel &
Restaurant ★★**
17 St Thomas Street, Ryde, Isle
of Wight PO33 2DL
T: (01983) 567913 & 615272
F: (01983) 616976
E: info@biskra-hotel.co
I: www.biskra-hotel.com

**Royal Esplanade Hotel
Rating Applied For**
16 The Esplanade, Ryde, Isle of
Wight PO33 2ED
T: (01983) 562549
F: (01983) 563918

Seahaven Hotel ★★
36 St Thomas Street, Ryde, Isle
of Wight PO33 2DL
T: (01983) 563069
F: (01983) 563570
E: seahaven@netguides.co.uk

ST LAWRENCE
Isle of Wight

Rocklands Hotel ★★
Undercliff Drive, St Lawrence,
Ventnor, Isle of Wight PO38 1XH
T: (01983) 852964
E: rocklandhotel@compuserve
I: www.rocklandshotel.co.uk

ST LEONARDS
Dorset

The St Leonards Hotel ★★★
185 Ringwood Road, St
Leonards, Ringwood, Hampshire
BH24 2NP
T: (01425) 471220
F: (01425) 480274

SANDOWN
Isle of Wight

Burlington Hotel ★★
5-9 Avenue Road, Sandown, Isle
of Wight PO36 8BN
T: (01983) 403702
F: (01983) 402307

Chad Hill Hotel ★★
7 Hill Street, Sandown, Isle of
Wight PO36 9DD
T: (01983) 403231
F: (01983) 403231
E: chadhillhotel@supanet.com

Friends Hotel ★★
8 Hill Street, Sandown, Isle of
Wight PO36 9DD
T: (01983) 403429
F: (01983) 403429

Grange Hall Hotel ★★
Grange Road, Sandown, Isle of
Wight PO36 8NE
T: (01983) 403531

Melville Hall Hotel ★★★
Melville Street, Sandown, Isle of
Wight PO36 9DH
T: (01983) 406526
F: (01983) 407093
E: enquiries@melvillehall.co.uk
I: www.melvillehall.co.uk

Montrene Hotel ★★
Avenue Road, Sandown, Isle of
Wight PO36 8BN
T: (01983) 403722
F: (01983) 405553
E: info@montrene.co.uk

The Ocean Hotel ★★
The Esplanade, Sandown, Isle of
Wight PO36 8AB
T: (01983) 402351 & 402352
F: (01983) 406699
E: ocean hotel@aol.com
I: www.ocean-hotel.co.uk

The Parkbury Hotel ★★★
29/31 The Broadway, Sandown,
Isle of Wight PO36 9BB
T: (01983) 402508
F: (01983) 404471
E: sean@parkbury.freeserve.co.
uk
I: www.smoothhound.co.
uk/hotels/parkbury.html

Regina Hotel ★★
Esplanade, Sandown, Isle of
Wight PO36 8AE
T: (01983) 403219

Riviera Hotel ★★
2 Royal Street, Sandown, Isle of
Wight PO36 8LP
T: (01983) 402518
F: (01983) 402518
E: riviera@hotel4326.freeserve.
co.uk

**The Royal Cliff Hotel
Rating Applied For**
Beachfield Road, Sandown, Isle
of Wight PO36 8NA
T: (01983) 402138
F: (01983) 402138

Royal Pier Hotel ★★
Esplanade, Sandown, Isle of
Wight PO36 8JP
T: (01983) 403187 & 405567
F: (01983) 408155

Sandringham Hotel ★★
Esplanade, Sandown, Isle of
Wight PO36 8AH
T: (01983) 406655
F: (01983) 404395
I: www.sandringhamhotel.co.uk

Sands Hotel ★★
Culver Parade, Sandown, Isle of
Wight PO36 8AT
T: (01983) 402305
F: (01983) 402305

Trouville Hotel ★★
Sandown Esplanade, Sandown,
Isle of Wight PO36 8LB
T: (01983) 402141
F: (01983) 403143

SAUNDERTON
Buckinghamshire

The Rose & Crown Inn ★★
Wycombe Road, Saunderton,
Princes Risborough,
Buckinghamshire HP27 9NP
T: (01844) 345299
F: (01844) 343140
E: rose.crown@btinternet.
comm
I: www.rose.crown.btinternet.co.
uk

SEAVIEW
Isle of Wight

**SpringVale Hotel and
Restaurant ★★**
Springvale, Seaview, Isle of
Wight PO34 5AN
T: (01983) 612533
F: (01983) 812905

Establishments printed in blue have a detailed entry in this guide

SHAFTESBURY
Dorset

The Royal Chase Hotel ★★★
Salisbury Road, Shaftesbury,
Dorset SP7 8DB
T: (01747) 853355
F: (01747) 851969
E: royalchasehotel@btinternet.
com

Sunridge Hotel ★★
Bleke Street, Shaftesbury, Dorset
SP7 8AW
T: (01747) 853130
F: (01747) 852139
E: sunridgehotel@talk21.com

SHANKLIN
Isle of Wight

Appley Private Hotel ★★
13 Queens Road, Shanklin, Isle
of Wight PO37 6AW
T: (01983) 862666
F: (01983) 863895
E: appley.htl@lineone.net
I: www.appleyhotel.co.uk

Aqua Hotel ★★ SILVER AWARD
17 The Esplanade, Shanklin, Isle
of Wight PO37 6BN
T: (01983) 863024
F: (01983) 864841
E: info@aquahotel.co.uk
I: www.aquahotel.co.uk

The Auckland Hotel ★★
10 Queens Road, Shanklin, Isle
of Wight PO37 6AN
T: (01983) 862960
F: (01983) 862175

Birkdale Hotel
Rating Applied For
Grange Road, Shanklin, Isle of
Wight PO37 6NN
T: (01983) 862949
F: (01983) 862949

Bourne Hall Country Hotel
★★★ SILVER AWARD
Luccombe Road, Shanklin, Isle of
Wight PO37 6RR
T: (01983) 862820
F: (01983) 865138
E: bhch@dialstart.net

Braemar Hotel ★★
1 Grange Road, Shanklin, Isle of
Wight PO37 6NN
T: (01983) 863172
F: (01983) 863172

Brunswick Hotel ★★★
Queens Road, Shanklin, Isle of
Wight PO37 6AN
T: (01983) 863245
F: (01983) 868398

Channel View Hotel ★★
Hope Road, Shanklin, Isle of
Wight PO37 6EH
T: (01983) 862309
F: (01983) 868400
E: enquiries@channelview.
demon.co.uk
I: www.netguides.co.
uk/wight/channel.html

Chine Court Hotel ★★
Popham Road, Shanklin, Isle of
Wight PO37 6RG
T: (01983) 862732
F: (01983) 862732

Cliff Hall Hotel ★★
Crescent Road, Shanklin, Isle of
Wight PO37 6DH
T: (01983) 862828

Clifton Hotel ★
Keats Green, 1 Queens Road,
Shanklin, Isle of Wight
PO37 6AN
T: (01983) 863015
F: (01983) 865911

Craven Court Hotel ★★
5 Highfield Road, Shanklin, Isle
of Wight PO37 6PP
T: (01983) 862009

Curraghmore Hotel ★★
22 Hope Road, Shanklin, Isle of
Wight PO37 6EA
T: (01983) 862605
F: (01983) 867431

Eastmount Hotel ★★
Eastmount Road, Shanklin, Isle
of Wight PO37 6DN
T: (01983) 862531

Fernbank Hotel ★★
Highfield Road, Shanklin, Isle of
Wight PO37 6PP
T: (01983) 862790
F: (01983) 864412

Hambledon Hotel ★★
11 Queens Road, Shanklin, Isle
of Wight PO37 6AW
T: (01983) 862403
F: (01983) 867894
E: hambledon@netguides.co.uk
I: www.netguides.co.
uk/wight/standard/hambledon.
html

Harrow Lodge Hotel ★★
Eastcliff Promenade, Shanklin,
Isle of Wight PO37 6BD
T: (01983) 862800
F: (01983) 868889

**Hartland Hotel & Victorian
Restaurant★★★**
Victoria Avenue, Shanklin, Isle of
Wight PO37 6LT
T: (01983) 863123
F: (01983) 865800

Heatherleigh Hotel ★★
17 Queens Road, Shanklin, Isle
of Wight PO37 6AW
T: (01983) 862503
F: (01983) 862503

Keats Green Hotel ★★★
3 Queens Road, Shanklin, Isle of
Wight PO37 6AN
T: (01983) 862742
F: (01983) 868572

Luccombe Hall Hotel ★★★
Luccombe Road, Shanklin, Isle of
Wight PO37 6RL
T: (01983) 862719 & 864590
F: (01983) 863082
E: reservations@luccombehallo.
co.uk
I: www.luccombehall.co.uk

Malton House Hotel ★★
8 Park Road, Shanklin, Isle of
Wight PO37 6AY
T: (01983) 865007
F: (01983) 865576
E: christos@excite.co.uk

Marlborough Hotel ★★
16 Queens Road, Shanklin, Isle
of Wight PO37 6AN
T: (01983) 862588
F: (01983) 862588

Montrose Hotel
Rating Applied For
Wilton Park Road, Shanklin, Isle
of Wight PO37 7BU
T: (01983) 862160
F: (01983) 862319

Orchardcroft Hotel ★★
Victoria Avenue, Shanklin, Isle of
Wight PO37 6LT
T: (01983) 862133
F: (01983) 862133
E: nicklaffan@hotmail.com

Overstrand Hotel ★★
5 Howard Road, Shanklin, Isle of
Wight PO37 6HD
T: (01983) 862100
F: (01983) 862100

Parkway Hotel ★★
6 Park Road, Shanklin, Isle of
Wight PO37 6AZ
T: (01983) 862740
F: (01983) 862740
E: parkwayhotel@msn.com

Roseberry Hotel ★★
3 Alexandra Road, Shanklin, Isle
of Wight PO37 6AF
T: (01983) 862805
F: (01983) 862805

Rylstone Manor Hotel
★★★ SILVER AWARD
Rylstone Gardens, Popham
Road, Shanklin, Isle of Wight
PO37 6RG
T: (01983) 862806
E: rylstone@dialstart.net
I: www.rylstone-manor.co.uk

St George's House Hotel ★★
St George's Road, Shanklin, Isle
of Wight PO37 6BA
T: (01983) 863691
F: (01983) 863691
E: jawithers@aol.com

Seaways Hotel ★★
34 Prospect Road, Shanklin, Isle
of Wight PO37 6AE
T: (01983) 862447

The Shanklin Hotel ★★
Clarendon Road, Shanklin, Isle of
Wight PO37 6DP
T: (01983) 862286
F: (01983) 865533

**Shanklin Manor House Hotel
★★★**
Manor Road, Old Village,
Shanklin, Isle of Wight
PO37 6QX
T: (01983) 862777
F: (01983) 863464

Sherwood Court Hotel ★★
Atherley Road, Shanklin, Isle of
Wight PO37 7AU
T: (01983) 862518
F: (01983) 867646

Snowdon Hotel ★★
19 Queens Road, Shanklin, Isle
of Wight PO37 6AW
T: (01983) 862853

Somerton Lodge Hotel ★★
43 Victoria Avenue, Shanklin,
Isle of Wight PO37 6LT
T: (01983) 862710 & 862718
F: (01983) 862710
E: somerton@talk21.com

Victoria Lodge Hotel ★★
Alexandra Road, Shanklin, Isle of
Wight PO37 6AF
T: (01983) 862361
F: (01983) 862361

West Coombe Hotel ★★
5 Westhill Road, Shanklin, Isle of
Wight PO37 6PT
T: (01983) 866323
F: (01983) 862124
E: bookings@iowhotel.co.uk
I: www.iowhotel.co.uk

SOUTHAMPTON
Hampshire

**Botley Park Hotel, Golf &
Country Club**
★★★★ SILVER AWARD
Winchester Road, Boorley Green,
Botley, Southampton,
Hampshire SO32 2UA
T: (01489) 780888
F: (01489) 789242
E: info@botleypark.
macdonald-hotels.co.uk
I: www.macdonaldhotels.co.uk

Nirvana Hotel ★
386 Winchester Road, Bassett,
Southampton, Hampshire
SO16 7DH
T: (023) 8079 0087 & 8079 0993
F: (023) 8079 0575

Novotel Southampton ★★★
1 West Quay Road,
Southampton, Hampshire
SO15 1RA
T: (023) 8033 0550
F: (023) 8022 2158
E: h1073@accom-hotels.com
I: www.accom-hotels.com

SPARSHOLT
Hampshire

The Wessex Centre
★★ SILVER AWARD
Sparsholt College, Sparsholt,
Winchester, Hampshire
SO21 2NF
T: (01962) 797259
F: (01962) 776636
E: info@thewessexcentre.co.uk
I: www.thewessexcentre.co.uk

STEEPLE ASTON
Oxfordshire

The Holt Hotel
Oxford Road, Steeple Aston,
Oxford, Oxfordshire OX6 3QQ
T: (01869) 340259
F: (01869) 340865
E: info@holthotel-oxford.co.uk
I: www.holthotel.co.uk

STOCKBRIDGE
Hampshire

Grosvenor Hotel ★★★
High Street, Stockbridge,
Hampshire SO20 6EU
T: (01264) 810606
F: (01264) 810747

STOKE POGES
Buckinghamshire

Stoke Park Club
★★★ GOLD AWARD
Park Road, Stoke Poges, Slough,
Buckinghamshire SL2 4PG
T: (01753) 717171
F: (01753) 717181
E: info@stokepark.clubcom
I: www.stokepark.clubcom

Establishments printed in blue have a detailed entry in this guide

STOKENCHURCH
Buckinghamshire
The King's Arms Hotel
★★★ SILVER AWARD
Oxford Road, Stokenchurch,
High Wycombe,
Buckinghamshire HP14 3TA
T: (01494) 609090
F: (01494) 484582
E: kares@dhillonhotels.co.uk
I: www.dhillonhotels.co.uk

STONOR
Oxfordshire
The Stonor Arms Hotel
★★★ SILVER AWARD
Stonor, Henley-on-Thames,
Oxfordshire RG9 6HE
T: (01491) 638866
F: (01491) 638863
E: stonorarms.hotel@virgin.net
I: www.stonor.arms.co.uk

STRATFIELD TURGIS
Hampshire
The Wellington Arms ★★★
Stratfield Turgis, Hook,
Hampshire RG27 0AS
T: (01256) 882214
F: (01256) 882934

STREATLEY
Berkshire
The Bull
Rating Applied For
Reading Road, Streatley,
Reading, Berkshire RG8 9JT
T: (01491) 872392
F: (01491) 875231

The Swan Diplomat Hotel
★★★★ SILVER AWARD
Streatley on Thames, Streatley,
Reading, Berkshire RG8 9HR
T: (01491) 878800
F: (01491) 872554
E: sales@swan-diplomat.co.uk
I: www.diplomat-hotel.se.

STUDLAND
Dorset
The Manor House Hotel ★★
Beach Road, Studland, Swanage,
Dorset BH19 3AU
T: (01929) 450288
F: (01929) 450288

SWANAGE
Dorset
Burlington House Hotel ★
Highcliffe Road, Swanage,
Dorset BH19 1LW
T: (01929) 422422
E: burlingtonhousehotel@
btinternet.com

The Castleton Hotel
Rating Applied For
1 Highcliffe Road, Swanage,
Dorset BH19 1LW
T: (01929) 423972
F: (01929) 422901

The Grand Hotel ★★★
Burlington Road, Swanage,
Dorset BH19 1LU
T: (01929) 423353
F: (01929) 427068
E: grandhotel@
bournemouth-net.co.uk
I: www.resort-guide.co.uk/grand

Havenhurst Hotel ★★
3 Cranborne Road, Swanage,
Dorset BH19 1EA
T: (01929) 424224
F: (01929) 422173

The Pines Hotel ★★★
Burlington Road, Swanage,
Dorset BH19 1LT
T: (01929) 425211
F: (01929) 422075
E: reservations@pineshotel.co.
uk
I: www.pineshotel.co.uk

Purbeck House Hotel ★★★
91 High Street, Swanage, Dorset
BH19 2LZ
T: (01929) 422872
F: (01929) 421194
E: purbeckhouse@easynet.co.
uk.
I: www.purbeckhousehotel.co.uk

SWAY
Hampshire
**String of Horses & Carriages
Restaurant**★★★
Mead End Road, Sway,
Lymington, Hampshire
SO41 6EH
T: (01590) 682631
F: (01590) 682911
E: relax@stringofhorses.co.uk
I: www.stringofhorses.co.uk

White Rose Hotel ★★
Village Centre, Sway, Lymington,
Hampshire SO41 6BA
T: (01590) 682754
F: (01590) 682955

THAME
Oxfordshire
Peacock Hotel & Restaurant
★★
Henton, Oxford, Oxfordshire
OX9 4AH
T: (01844) 353519
F: (01844) 353891

The Spread Eagle Hotel ★★★
Cornmarket, Thame, Oxfordshire
OX9 2BW
T: (01844) 213661
F: (01844) 261380

THATCHAM
Berkshire
The Swan
Rating Applied For
Station Road, Thatcham,
Newbury, Berkshire RG13 4QL
T: (01635) 862084
F: (01635) 871851

TOTLAND BAY
Isle of Wight
Country Garden Hotel ★★★
Church Hill, Totland Bay, Isle of
Wight PO39 1QE
T: (01983) 754521
F: (01983) 754521
E: pat.burton@oneline.net

The Nodes Country Hotel
Rating Applied For
Alum Bay Old Road, Totland Bay,
Isle of Wight PO39 0HZ
T: (01983) 752859
F: (023) 9220 1226

VENTNOR
Isle of Wight
Bonchurch Manor ★★★
Bonchurch Shute, Bonchurch,
Ventnor, Isle of Wight PO38 1NU
T: (01983) 852868
F: (01983) 852443
E: bonchurchmanorhotel.co.uk

Burlington Hotel
★★★ SILVER AWARD
Bellevue Road, Ventnor, Isle of
Wight PO38 1DB
T: (01983) 852113
F: (01983) 853862

Eversley Hotel ★★★
Park Avenue, Ventnor, Isle of
Wight PO38 1LB
T: (01983) 852244
F: (01983) 853948
E: eversleyhotel@fsbdial.co.uk
I: www.eversleyhotel.com

Hillside Hotel ★★
Mitchell Avenue, Ventnor, Isle of
Wight PO38 1DR
T: (01983) 852271
F: (01983) 852271
E: netguides@hillside.co.uk

Old Park Hotel ★★
St Lawrence, Ventnor, Isle of
Wight PO38 1XS
T: (01983) 852583
F: (01983) 854920
I: www.parkhotel.co.uk

St Maur Hotel ★★
Castle Road, Ventnor, Isle of
Wight PO38 1LG
T: (01983) 852570
F: (01983) 852306

The Ventnor Towers Hotel
★★★
Madeira Road, Ventnor, Isle of
Wight PO38 1QT
T: (01983) 852277
F: (01983) 855536
E: ventnor@inc.co.uk
I: www.wightonline.co.
uk/ventnortowers

WANTAGE
Oxfordshire
The Bear Hotel ★★★
Market Place, Wantage,
Oxfordshire OX12 8AB
T: (01235) 766366
F: (01235) 768826
E: thebearhotel@hotmail.com
I: www.SmoothHound.co.
uk/hotels/bear/html

WAREHAM
Dorset
Kemps Country House Hotel
★★
East Stoke, Wareham, Dorset
BH20 6AL
T: (01929) 462563
F: (01929) 405287

The Priory Hotel
★★★ GOLD AWARD
Church Green, Wareham, Dorset
BH20 4ND
T: (01929) 551666
F: (01929) 554519
E: reception@theprioryhotel.co.
uk
I: www.theprioryhotel.co.uk

**Springfield Country Hotel &
Leisure Club**★★★
Grange Road, Wareham, Dorset
BH20 5AL
T: (01929) 552177
F: (01929) 551862

Worgret Manor Hotel ★★
Worgret Road, Wareham, Dorset
BH20 6AB
T: (01929) 552957
F: (01929) 554804
E: worgretmanorhotel@
freeserve.co.uk
I: www.smoothhound.co.
uk/hotels/worgret.html

WENDOVER
Buckinghamshire
The Red Lion Hotel ★★
9 High Street, Wendover,
Aylesbury, Buckinghamshire
HP22 6DU
T: (01296) 622266
F: (01296) 625077
E: redlion@regentinns.plc.uk

WEST LULWORTH
Dorset
Cromwell House Hotel ★★
Lulworth Cove, West Lulworth,
Wareham, Dorset BH20 5RJ
T: (01929) 400253 & 400332
F: (01929) 400566
E: catriona@lulworthcove.co.uk
I: www.lulworthcove.co.uk

Shirley Hotel
West Lulworth, Wareham,
Dorset BH20 5RL
T: (01929) 400358
F: (01929) 400167
E: durdle@aol.com

WIMBORNE MINSTER
Dorset
Beechleas Hotel & Restaurant
★★ SILVER AWARD
17 Poole Road, Wimborne
Minster, Dorset BH21 1QA
T: (01202) 841684
F: (01202) 849344

WINCHESTER
Hampshire
Harestock Lodge Hotel ★★★
Harestock Road, Winchester,
Hampshire SO22 6NX
T: (01962) 881870 & 880038
F: (01962) 886959
I: www.hants.gov.
uk/tourist/hotels/harestocklodge

Royal Hotel ★★★
St Peter Street, Winchester,
Hampshire SO23 8BS
T: (01962) 840840
F: (01962) 841582
E: info@the-royal.com
I: www.the-royal.com

The Wessex
★★★★ SILVER AWARD
Paternoster Row, Winchester,
Hampshire SO23 9LQ
T: 0870 400 8126
F: (01962) 841503

WINDSOR
Berkshire
Aurora Garden Hotel ★★
Bolton Avenue, Windsor,
Berkshire SL4 3JF
T: (01753) 868686
F: (01753) 831394
E: aurora@auroragarden.co.uk
I: www.auroragarden.co.uk

Fairlight Lodge Royal Windsor Hotel★★
41 Frances Road, Windsor,
Berkshire SL4 3AQ
T: (01753) 861207
F: (01753) 865963
E: fairlightlodge@hotmail.com
I: www.fairlightlodge.webjump.com

Grovefield Hotel ★★★
Taplow Common Road,
Burnham, Buckinghamshire
SL1 8LP
T: (01628) 603131
F: (01628) 668078

Sir Christopher Wren's House, Hotel & Business Centre
★★★ GOLD AWARD
Thames Street, Windsor,
Berkshire SL4 1PX
T: (01753) 861354
F: (01753) 860172
E: hotels@wrensgroup.com
I: www.wrensgroup.com

Stirrups Country House Hotel
★★★ SILVER AWARD
Maidens Green, Bracknell,
Berkshire RG42 6LD
T: (01344) 882284
F: (01344) 882300
E: reception@stirrupshotel.co.uk
I: www.stirrupshotel.co.uk

WINKTON
Dorset

Fisherman's Haunt Hotel ★★
Salisbury Road, Winkton,
Christchurch, Dorset BH23 7AS
T: (01202) 477283 & 484071
F: (01202) 478883

WITNEY
Oxfordshire

The Marlborough Hotel ★★
28 Market Square, Witney,
Oxfordshire OX8 7BB
T: (01993) 776353
F: (01993) 702152

Witney Four Pillars Hotel
★★★
Ducklington Lane, Witney,
Oxfordshire OX8 7TJ
T: (01993) 779777
F: (01993) 703467
E: @fourpillars.co.uk
I: www.four_pillars.co.uk.

WOKINGHAM

Cantley House Hotel ★★★
Milton Road, Wokingham,
Berkshire RG40 5QG
T: (0118) 978 9912
F: (0118) 977 4294
E: reception@cantleyhotel.co.uk

WOODLANDS
Hampshire

Busketts Lawn Hotel ★★
174 Woodlands Road,
Woodlands, Southampton,
Hampshire SO40 7GL
T: (023) 8029 2272 & 8029 2077
F: (023) 8029 2487

WOODSTOCK
Oxfordshire

The Bear ★★★
Park Street, Woodstock, Oxford,
Oxfordshire OX20 1SZ
T: 0870 400 8202
F: (01993) 813380
E: heritagehotels_woodstock.
bear@fortehotels.com
I: www.heritage-hotels.com

The Kings Arms Hotel ★★
19 Market Street, Woodstock,
Oxford, Oxfordshire OX20 1SU
T: (01993) 813636
F: (01993) 813737
E: user@kings-woodstock.fsnet.
co.uk

YARMOUTH
Isle of Wight

The Bugle Hotel ★★
The Square, Yarmouth, Isle of
Wight PO41 0NS
T: (01983) 760272
F: (01983) 760883

ALFRISTON
East Sussex

The Star Inn ★★★
Alfriston, Polegate, East Sussex
BN26 5TA
T: 0870 400 8102
F: (01323) 870922

ARUNDEL
West Sussex

Burpham Country House Hotel
★★★ SILVER AWARD
Burpham, Arundel, West Sussex
BN18 9RJ
T: (01903) 882160
F: (01903) 884627

Swan Hotel ★★★
27-29 High Street, Arundel,
West Sussex BN18 9AG
T: (01903) 882314
F: (01903) 883759
E: info@swan-hotel.co.uk
I: www.swan-hotel.co.uk

ASHFORD
Kent

Eastwell Manor Hotel
★★★★ GOLD AWARD
Eastwell Park, Boughton Lees,
Ashford, Kent TN25 4HR
T: (01233) 219955
F: (01233) 635530
E: eastwell@btinternet.com

Holiday Inn Garden Court Ashford/Kent★★★
A20 Maidstone Road, Hothfield,
Ashford, Kent TN26 1AR
T: (01233) 713333 & 713950
F: (01233) 712082

ASHINGTON
West Sussex

The Mill House Hotel
★★★ SILVER AWARD
Mill Lane, Ashington,
Pulborough, West Sussex
RH20 3BX
T: (01903) 892426
F: (01903) 892855
E: millinfo@aol.com

BATTLE
East Sussex

Netherfield Place
★★★ SILVER AWARD
Battle, East Sussex TN33 9PP
T: (01424) 774455
F: (01424) 774024
E: reservations@
netherfieldplace.demon.co.uk.
I: www.netherfieldplace.demon.
co.uk.

BEXHILL
East Sussex

Jarvis Cooden Beach Hotel
★★★
Cooden Beach, Bexhill, East
Sussex TN39 4TT
T: (01424) 842281
F: (01424) 846142
I: www.jarvis.co.uk

The Northern Hotel ★★
72-82 Sea Road, Bexhill, East
Sussex TN40 1JL
T: (01424) 212836
F: (01424) 213036
E: reception@northernhotel.co.
uk
I: www.northernhotel.co.uk

BOGNOR REGIS
West Sussex

Aldwick Hotel ★★
Aldwick Road, Aldwick, Bognor
Regis, West Sussex PO21 2QU
T: (01243) 821945
F: (01243) 821316

Beachcroft Hotel ★★
Clyde Road, Felpham, Bognor
Regis, West Sussex PO22 7AH
T: (01243) 827142
F: (01243) 827142
E: reservations@
beachcroft-hotel.co.uk
I: www.beachcroft-hotel.co.uk

Camelot Hotel & Restaurant
★★
3 Flansham Lane, Felpham,
Bognor Regis, West Sussex
PO22 6AA
T: (01243) 585875
F: (01243) 587500

The Royal Hotel ★★
The Esplanade, Bognor Regis,
West Sussex PO21 1SZ
T: (01243) 864665
F: (01243) 863175

The Royal Norfolk ★★
The Esplanade, Bognor Regis,
West Sussex PO21 2LH
T: (01243) 826222
F: (01243) 826325

BRIGHTON & HOVE
East Sussex

The Belgrave Hotel ★★★★
64 Kings Road, Brighton, East
Sussex BN1 1NA
T: (01273) 323221
F: (01273) 321485
I: www.infinitihotels.com

Brighton Thistle
Rating Applied For
Kings Road, Brighton, East
Sussex BN1 2GS
T: (01273) 206700
F: (01273) 820692
I: www.thistlehotels.co.uk

Excelsior Hotel (Hove) Ltd ★
205-209 Kingsway, Hove,
Brighton, East Sussex BN3 4FD
T: (01273) 773991
F: (01273) 746363
E: excelsior@mistral.co.uk

The Granville Hotel ★★★
124 Kings Road, Brighton, East
Sussex BN1 2FA
T: (01273) 326302
F: (01273) 728294
E: granville@brighton.co.uk
I: granvillehotel.co.uk

Hilton Brighton West Pier
★★★★
137 Kings Road, Brighton, East
Sussex BN1 2JF
T: (01273) 329744
F: (01273) 775877
E: paul.nason@bedfordbright.
stakis.co.uk.
I: www.stakis.co.uk

Imperial Hotel ★★★
First Avenue, Hove, Brighton,
East Sussex BN3 2GU
T: (01273) 777320
F: (01273) 777310
E: imperialhotel@pavilion.co.uk

Jarvis Norfolk Hotel ★★★
149 Kings Road, Brighton, East
Sussex BN1 2PP
T: (01273) 738201
F: (01273) 821752
I: www.jarvis.co.uk

Jarvis Preston Park Hotel
★★★
216 Preston Road, Brighton,
East Sussex BN1 6UU
T: (01273) 507853
F: (01273) 540039
E: www.jarvis.uk.com

Langfords Hotel ★★★
Third Avenue, Hove, Brighton,
East Sussex BN3 2PX
T: (01273) 738222
F: (01273) 779426
E: langfords@pavilion.co.uk

Old Ship Hotel ★★★
King's Road, Brighton, East
Sussex BN1 1NR
T: (01273) 329001
F: (01273) 820718
E: oldship@paramount-hotels.
co.uk
I: www.paramount-hotels.co.uk

Premier Lodge
Travel Accommodation
144 North Street, Brighton, East
Sussex BN1 1DN
T: (01273) 746833
F: (01273) 323878
I: www.premierlodge.co.uk

Princes Marine Hotel ★★★
153 Kingsway, Hove, East Sussex
BN3 4GR
T: (01273) 207660
F: (01273) 325913
E: princesmarine@bestwestern.
co.uk

Quality Hotel ★★★
West Street, Brighton, East
Sussex BN1 2RQ
T: (01273) 220033
F: (01273) 778000
E: admin@gb057.u-net.com

Sackville Hotel ★
189 Kingsway, Hove, East Sussex
BN3 4GU
T: (01273) 736292
F: (01273) 731598

St Catherines Lodge Hotel ★★
Kingsway, Hove, East Sussex
BN3 2RZ
T: (01273) 778181
F: (01273) 774949

Stakis Brighton Metropole
★★★★ GOLD AWARD
Kings Road, Brighton, East
Sussex BN1 2FU
T: (01273) 775432
F: (01273) 207764
E: reservations@brightonmet.
stakis.co.uk

BROADSTAIRS
Kent
Admiral Dundonald Hotel
Rating Applied For
43 Belvedere Road, Broadstairs,
Kent CT10 1PF
T: (01843) 862236

CAMBERLEY
Surrey
Burwood House Hotel ★★
15 London Road, Camberley,
Surrey GU15 3UQ
T: (01276) 685686
F: (01276) 62220

CANTERBURY
Kent
Canterbury Hotel and
Restaurant ★★
71 New Dover Road, Canterbury,
Kent CT1 3DZ
T: (01227) 450551
F: (01227) 780145
E: canterbury.hotel@btinternet.
com

County Hotel ★★★
High Street, Canterbury, Kent
CT1 2RX
T: (01227) 766266
F: (01227) 451512
E: info@county.
macdonald-hotels.co.uk
I: www.macdonaldhotels.co.
uk/county-hotel

The Dickens Inn at House of
Agnes Hotel★★
71 St Dunstan's Street,
Canterbury, Kent CT2 8BN
T: (01227) 472185
F: (01227) 471616
E: enq@dickens-inn.co.uk
I: www.dickens-inn.co.uk

Ebury Hotel
★★ SILVER AWARD
65-67 New Dover Road,
Canterbury, Kent CT1 3DX
T: (01227) 768433
F: (01227) 459187
E: info@ebury-hotel.co.uk
I: www.ebury-hotel.co.uk

The Garden Hotel & Restaurant
★★★
167-169 The Street, Boughton
Under Blean, Canterbury, Kent
ME13 9BH
T: (01227) 751411
F: (01227) 751801
E: garden-hotel@lineone.net
I: www.garden-hotel.co.uk

The Old Coach House ★★
Dover Road (A2), Barham,
Canterbury, Kent CT4 6SA
T: (01227) 831218
F: (01227) 831932

Pointers Hotel ★★
1 London Road, Canterbury,
Kent CT2 8LR
T: (01227) 456846
F: (01227) 452786
E: pointers.hotel@.dial.pipex.
com
I: www.pointers.hotel.dial.pipex.
com

Slatters Hotel ★★★
St Margarets Street, Canterbury,
Kent CT1 2TR
T: (01227) 463271
F: (01227) 764117
E: slatters@netcomuk.co.uk
I: members.xoom.
com/sign_hotels/slatters.htm

Woodpeckers Country Hotel
★★
Womenswold, Canterbury, Kent
CT4 6HB
T: (01227) 831319
F: (01227) 831403

CHICHESTER
West Sussex
Crouchers Bottom Country
Hotel★★★
Birdham Road, Apuldram,
Chichester, West Sussex
PO20 7EH
T: (01243) 784995
F: (01243) 539797
E: crouchers_bottom@
btconnect.com
I: www.crouchersbottom.com

The Inglenook ★★★
255 Pagham Road, Nyetimber,
Pagham, Bognor Regis, West
Sussex PO21 3QB
T: (01243) 262495 & 265411
F: (01243) 262668
E: inglenooke@btinternet.com
I: www.btinternet.
com/$inglenook/

Jarvis Chichester Hotel ★★★
Westhampnett, Chichester, West
Sussex PO19 4UL
T: (01243) 786351
F: (01243) 782371
I: www.jarvis.co.uk

Marriott Goodwood Park Hotel
& Country Club
★★★★ SILVER AWARD
Goodwood, Chichester, West
Sussex PO18 0QB
T: (01243) 775537
F: (01243) 520120
I: www.marriotthotels.com

Millstream Hotel & Restaurant
★★★ SILVER AWARD
Bosham Lane, Bosham,
Chichester, West Sussex
PO18 8HL
T: (01243) 573234
F: (01243) 573459

Ship Hotel ★★★
North Street, Chichester, West
Sussex PO19 1NH
T: (01243) 778000
F: (01243) 788000
I: www.shiphotel.com

Woodstock House Hotel
★★ SILVER AWARD
Charlton, Chichester, West
Sussex PO18 0HU
T: (01243) 811666
F: (01243) 811666

CLIFTONVILLE
Kent
Grand Hotel ★★
Eastern Esplanade, Cliftonville,
Margate, Kent CT9 2LE
T: (01843) 221444
F: (01843) 227073
I: www.grandhotelgroup.co.uk

Walpole Bay Hotel ★★
Fifth Avenue, Cliftonville,
Margate, Kent CT9 2JJ
T: (01843) 221703
F: (01843) 297399

COPTHORNE
Surrey
The Copthorne London
Gatwick
★★★★ SILVER AWARD
Copthorne Way, Copthorne,
Gatwick, West Sussex RH10 3PG
T: (01342) 348800
F: (01342) 348833
E: coplgw@mill-cop.com
I: www.stay.with-us.com

CRAWLEY
West Sussex
The George
Rating Applied For
High Street, Crawley, West
Sussex RH10 1BS
T: (01293) 524215
F: (01293) 548565

Jarvis International Gatwick
★★★
Tinsley Lane South, Three
Bridges, Crawley, West Sussex
RH10 2XH
T: (01293) 561186
F: (01293) 561169

CUCKFIELD
West Sussex
Hilton Park Hotel ★★★
Cuckfield, Haywards Heath,
West Sussex RH17 5EG
T: (01444) 454555
F: (01444) 457222
E: hiltonpark@janus-systems.
com
I: wwwjanus-systems.
com/hiltonpark.htm

DARTFORD
Kent
Thistle Brands Hatch Hotel
Rating Applied For
Brands Hatch, Dartford, Kent
DA3 8PE
T: (01474) 854900
F: (01474) 853220
E: brands.hatch@thistle.co.uk
I: www.thistlehotels.com

DEAL
Kent
Dunkerleys Restaurant and
Hotel★★★ SILVER AWARD
19 Beach Street, Deal, Kent
CT14 7AH
T: (01304) 375016
F: (01304) 380187
E: dunkerleysofdeal@btinternet.
com
I: www.dunkerleys.co.uk

Royal Hotel
★★ SILVER AWARD
Beach Street, Deal, Kent
CT14 6JD
T: (01304) 375555
F: (01304) 375555

DORKING
Surrey
Gatton Manor Hotel, Golf &
Country Club★★★
Standon Lane, Ockley, Dorking,
Surrey RH5 5PQ
T: (01306) 627555
F: (01306) 627713
E: gattonmanor@enterprise.net
I: www.smoothhound.co.
uk/hotels/gatton.html

DOVER
Kent
The Churchill ★★★
Dover Waterfront, Dover, Kent
CT17 9BP
T: (01304) 203633
F: (01304) 216320
E: enquiries@churchill-hotel.
com
I: www.churchill-hotel.com

St Margaret's Holiday Park
Hotel
Rating Applied For
Reach Road, St-Margarets-at-
Cliffe, Dover, Kent CT15 6AE
T: (01304) 853262
F: (01304) 853434

Walletts Court Hotel &
Restaurant
★★★ SILVER AWARD
West-Cliffe, St-Margarets-at-
Cliffe, Dover, Kent CT15 6EW
T: (01304) 852424
F: (01304) 853430
E: wc@wallettscourt.com
I: www.wallettscourt.com

EASTBOURNE
East Sussex
Carlton Court Hotel ★★
10 Wilmington Square,
Eastbourne, East Sussex
BN21 4EA
T: (01323) 430668
F: (01323) 732787
E: carlton@carltoncourthotel.
co.uk
I: www.carltoncourthotel.co.uk

Chatsworth Hotel ★★★
Grand Parade, Eastbourne, East
Sussex BN21 3YR
T: (01323) 411016
F: (01323) 643270
E: peter@chatsworth-hotel.
demon.co.uk
I: www.virtualhotels.
com/chatsworth-hotel
⊛

Congress Hotel ★★
31-41 Carlisle Road, Eastbourne,
East Sussex BN21 4JS
T: (01323) 732118 & 644605
F: (01323) 720016
🏃

Cumberland Hotel ★★★
Grand Parade, Eastbourne, East
Sussex BN21 3YT
T: (01323) 730342
F: (01323) 646314

The Grand Hotel
★★★★★ GOLD AWARD
King Edwards Parade,
Eastbourne, East Sussex
BN21 4EQ
T: (01323) 412345
F: (01323) 412233
E: sales@grandeastbourne.co.uk
I: www.grandeastbourne.co.uk
⊛ 🎛 🏃

Hydro Hotel
★★★ SILVER AWARD
Mount Road, Eastbourne, East
Sussex BN20 7HZ
T: (01323) 720643
F: (01323) 641167
⊛

The Jevington Hotel ★★
7-11 Jevington Gardens,
Eastbourne, East Sussex
BN21 4HR
T: (01323) 732093
F: (01323) 431569

Langham Hotel ★★
Royal Parade, Eastbourne, East
Sussex BN22 7AH
T: (01323) 731451
F: (01323) 646623
E: langhamhotel@mistral.co.uk
I: www3.mistral.co.
uk/langhamhotel
⊛ 🎛

Lansdowne Hotel
★★★ SILVER AWARD
King Edward's Parade,
Eastbourne, East Sussex
BN21 4EE
T: (01323) 725174
F: (01323) 739721
E: the.lansdowne@btinternet.
com
I: www.btinternet.com/-the.
lansdowne/
⊛

Lathom Hotel ★★
4-6 Howard Square, Eastbourne,
East Sussex BN21 4BG
T: (01323) 641986
F: (01323) 416405

The Lynwood Hotel ★★
31-33 Jevington Gardens,
Eastbourne, East Sussex
BN21 4HP
T: (01323) 638716
F: (01323) 412846

**Majestic Hotel
Rating Applied For**
26-34 Royal Parade, Eastbourne,
East Sussex BN22 7AN
T: (01323) 730311

New Wilmington Hotel ★★
25 Compton Street, Eastbourne,
East Sussex BN21 4DU
T: (01323) 721219
F: (01323) 721219
E: reservations@
new-wilmington.sagehost.co.uk
I: www.smoothhound.co.
uk/hotels/wilmington.html

Princes Hotel ★★★
Lascelles Terrace, Eastbourne,
East Sussex BN21 4BL
T: (01323) 722056
F: (01323) 727469
E: princeshotel@easicom.com
I: www.smoothhound.co.uk

The Wish Tower Hotel ★★★
King Edward's Parade,
Eastbourne, East Sussex
BN21 4EB
T: (01323) 722676
F: (01323) 721474

York House Hotel ★★
14-22 Royal Parade, Eastbourne,
East Sussex BN22 7AP
T: (01323) 412918
F: (01323) 646238
E: info@yorkhousehotel.co.uk
I: www.yorkhousehotel.co.uk
⊛

EGHAM
Surrey

Great Fosters ★★★★
Stroude Road, Egham, Surrey
TW20 9UR
T: (01784) 433822
F: (01784) 472455
E: GreatFosters@compuserve.
com
I: www.greatfosters.co.uk

Runnymede Hotel and Spa
★★★★ SILVER AWARD
Windsor Road, Egham, Surrey
TW20 0AG
T: (01784) 436171
F: (01784) 436340
E: Info@runnymedehotel.com
I: www.runnymedehotel.com

ENGLEFIELD GREEN
Surrey

Savill Court Hotel ★★★
Wick Lane, Englefield Green,
Egham, Surrey TW20 0XN
T: (01784) 472000
F: (01784) 472200
E: reservations@
savillcourt-macdonaldhotels.co.
uk
I: www.hotelselection.co.uk

ESHER
Surrey

Haven Hotel ★★
Portsmouth Road, Esher, Surrey
KT10 9AR
T: (020) 8398 0023 & 8398 7793
F: (020) 8398 9463

FARNHAM
Surrey

**The Bishop's Table Hotel &
Restaurant**
★★★ SILVER AWARD
27 West Street, Farnham, Surrey
GU9 7DR
T: (01252) 710222
F: (01252) 733494
E: bishops.table@btinternet.
com

FAWKHAM
Kent

**Brands Hatch Place Hotel
★★★**
Fawkham Valley Road,
Fawkham, Sevenoaks, Kent
DA3 8NQ
T: (01474) 872239
F: (01474) 879652

FOLKESTONE
Kent

The Burlington Hotel ★★★
Earls Avenue, Folkestone, Kent
CT20 2HR
T: (01303) 255301
F: (01303) 251301
E: sales@theburlingtonhotel.
com
I: www.theburlingtonhotel.com

Clifton Hotel ★★★
The Leas, Clifton Gardens,
Folkestone, Kent CT20 2EB
T: (01303) 851231
F: (01303) 851231
E: reservation@cliftonhotel.com
I: www.the cliftonhotel.com

The Garden House Hotel ★★
142 Sandgate Road, Folkestone,
Kent CT20 2TE
T: (01303) 242526
F: (01303) 257020
⊛

Wards Restaurant Hotel ★★
39 Earls Avenue, Folkestone,
Kent CT20 2HB
T: (01303) 245166
F: (01303) 254480
E: Reservations@wardshotel.co.
uk
I: www.wardshotel.co.uk
⊛

FOREST ROW
East Sussex

**Ashdown Forest Golf Hotel
★★**
Chapel Lane, Forest Row, East
Sussex RH18 5BB
T: (01342) 824866
F: (01342) 824869
E: enquiries@ashgolf.co.uk
I: www.ashgolf.co.uk

FRIMLEY GREEN
Surrey

**Lakeside International Hotel
★★★**
Wharf Road, Frimley Green,
Camberley, Surrey GU16 6JR
T: (01252) 838000
F: (01252) 837857

GRAVESEND
Kent

**The Inn on the Lake Hotel
★★★**
A2, Shorne, Gravesend, Kent
DA12 3HB
T: (01474) 823333
F: (01474) 823175

HADLOW
Kent

Leavers Manor Hotel ★★
Goose Green, Hadlow,
Tonbridge, Kent TN11 0JH
T: (01732) 851442
F: (01732) 851875
E: info@leaversmanor.freeserve.
co.uk
I: www.leaversmanor.co.uk

HAILSHAM
East Sussex

**Olde Forge Hotel and
Restaurant★★** SILVER AWARD
Magham Down, Hailsham, East
Sussex BN27 1PN
T: (01323) 842893
F: (01323) 842893
E: theoldeforgehoteland
restaurant@tesco.net

HASLEMERE
Surrey

**Lythe Hill Hotel
★★★★** SILVER AWARD
Petworth Road, Haslemere,
Surrey GU27 3BQ
T: (01428) 651251
F: (01428) 644131
E: lythe@lythehill.co.uk
I: www.lythehill.co.uk

HASTINGS
East Sussex

**Beauport Park Hotel
★★★** SILVER AWARD
Battle Road, Hastings, East
Sussex TN38 8EA
T: (01424) 851222
F: (01424) 852465
E: Reservations@
beauportparkhotel.demon.co.uk
I: www.beauportparkhotel.
demon.co.uk

The Chatsworth Hotel ★★
Carlisle Parade, Hastings, East
Sussex TN34 1JG
T: (01424) 720188
F: (01424) 445865

Cinque Ports Hotel ★★★
Summerfields, Bohemia Road,
Hastings, East Sussex TN34 1ET
T: (01424) 439222
F: (01424) 437277
E: cphotel@dircon.co.uk
I: www.cinqueports.co.uk

High Beech Hotel ★★★
Battle Road, St Leonards-on-
Sea, Hastings, East Sussex
TN37 7BS
T: (01424) 851383
F: (01424) 854265

Lansdowne Hotel ★★
1 Robertson Terrace, Hastings,
East Sussex TN34 1JE
T: (01424) 441615
F: (01424) 447046
E: lansdowne.hotel@btinternet.
com
I: www.infotel.co.
uk/hotels/46686.htm

Royal Victoria Hotel ★★★
Marina, St Leonards-on-Sea,
Hastings, East Sussex TN38 0BD
T: (01424) 445544
F: (01424) 721995
E: receptioneroyal-vic-hotel.
demon.co.uk
I: www.uk-travelguide.co.
uk/royal-vic.hotel

Establishments printed in blue have a detailed entry in this guide

Yelton Hotel ★★
1-7 White Rock, Hastings, East
Sussex TN34 1JU
T: (01424) 422240
F: (01424) 432350

Hotel '66
Rating Applied For
9 White Rock Road, Hastings,
East Sussex TN34 1LE
T: (01424) 460510
F: (01424) 447334

HAYWARDS HEATH
West Sussex

**The Birch Hotel (Heathland
Hotels) Ltd** ★★★
Lewes Road (A272), Haywards
Heath, West Sussex RH17 7SF
T: (01444) 451565
F: (01444) 440109
E: info@birch-hotel.com
I: www.birch-hotel.com

HINDHEAD
Surrey

Devil's Punchbowl ★★★
London Road, Hindhead, Surrey
GU26 6AG
T: (01428) 606565
F: (01428) 605713
I: www.lionheartinns.demon.co.
uk

HOLLINGBOURNE
Kent

**Jarvis Great Danes Hotel &
Country Club** ★★★
Ashford Road, Hollingbourne,
Maidstone, Kent ME17 1RE
T: (01622) 631163
F: (01622) 735290

HORLEY
Surrey

Posthouse Gatwick ★★★
Povey Cross Road, Horley, Surrey
RH6 0BA
T: 0870 400 9030
F: (01293) 771054

Stanhill Court Hotel
★★★ SILVER AWARD
Stanhill, Charlwood, Horley,
Surrey RH6 0EP
T: (01293) 862166
F: (01293) 862773
E: enquiries@stanhillcourthotel.
co.uk
I: www.stanhillcourthotel.co.uk

HORSHAM
West Sussex

Wimblehurst Hotel ★★
Wimblehurst Road, Horsham,
West Sussex RH12 2ED
T: (01403) 251122
F: (01403) 251155
E: wimble@globalnet.co.uk

HYTHE
Kent

The Hythe Imperial
★★★★ SILVER AWARD
Princes Parade, Hythe, Kent
CT21 6AE
T: (01303) 267441
F: (01303) 264610
E: hytheimperial@
marstonhotels.co.uk
I: www.marstonhotels.co.uk

Stade Court Hotel ★★★
West Parade, Hythe, Kent
CT21 6DT
T: (01303) 268263
F: (01303) 261803
E: stadecourt@marstonhotels.
co.uk
I: www.marstonhotels.co.uk

LEATHERHEAD
Surrey

Bookham Grange Hotel ★★
Little Bookham Common,
Bookham, Leatherhead, Surrey
KT23 3HS
T: (01372) 452742
F: (01372) 450080

LEWES
East Sussex

Shelleys Hotel
★★★ SILVER AWARD
High Street, Lewes, East Sussex
BN7 1XS
T: (01273) 472361
F: (01273) 483152

LITTLEBOURNE
Kent

Bow Window Inn & Restaurant
★★
50 High Street, Littlebourne,
Canterbury, Kent CT3 1ST
T: (01227) 721264
F: (01227) 721250

LOWER BEEDING
West Sussex

Brookfield Farm Hotel ★★
Winterpit Lane, Lower Beeding,
Horsham, West Sussex RH13 6LY
T: (01403) 891191 & 891192
F: (01403) 891499

MAIDSTONE
Kent

Grangemoor Hotel ★★
St Michael's Road, Maidstone,
Kent ME16 8BS
T: (01622) 677623
F: (01622) 678246
E: reservations@grangemoor.
co.uk

MARGATE
Kent

Clintons ★★
9 Dalby Square, Cliftonville,
Margate, Kent CT9 2ER
T: (01843) 290598 & 299550

Glenwood Hotel ★★
19-25 Edgar Road, Cliftonville,
Margate, Kent CT9 2EG
T: (01843) 292137 & 228124
F: (01843) 294398

Lonsdale Court Hotel ★★
51-61 Norfolk Road, Cliftonville,
Margate, Kent CT9 2HX
T: (01843) 221053
F: (01843) 299993
E: enquiries@lonsdale.court.
demon.co.uk
I: www.lonsdale-court.demon.
co.uk

Palm Court Hotel ★★★
Eastern Esplanade, Cliftonville,
Margate, Kent CT9
T: (01843) 229980
F: (01843) 299993

MINSTER-IN-SHEPPEY
Kent

**The Abbey Hotel & Conference
Centre** ★★★
The Broadway, Minster-in-
Sheppey, Sheerness, Kent
ME12 2DA
T: (01795) 872873
F: (01795) 874728
E: abbey.hotel@virgin.net
I: www.abbey.hotel@virgin.net

NEW ROMNEY
Kent

Broadacre Hotel ★★
North Street, New Romney, Kent
TN28 8DR
T: (01797) 362381
F: (01797) 362381
E: broadacrehotel@
newromney1.fsnet.co.uk
I: www.uk-travelguide.co.
uk/kent/newromney/
broadacrehotel.html

PEASLAKE
Surrey

The Hurtwood Inn Hotel
★★★ SILVER AWARD
Peaslake, Guildford, Surrey
GU5 9RR
T: (01306) 730851
F: (01306) 731390
E: sales@hurtwoodinnhotel.
com

PULBOROUGH
West Sussex

Chequers Hotel
★★ SILVER AWARD
Old Rectory Lane, Pulborough,
West Sussex RH20 1AD
T: (01798) 872486
F: (01798) 872715
E: admin@minotel.com
I: www.chequershotel.com

QUEENBOROUGH
Kent

**The Trafalgar Hotel &
Restaurant**
Rating Applied For
10-13 Rushenden Road,
Queenborough, Kent ME11 5HB
T: (01795) 662342 & 663365
F: (01795) 580885
E: trafalgarhotel@bardays.net

RAMSGATE
Kent

Jarvis Marina Hotel ★★★
Harbour Parade, Ramsgate, Kent
CT11 8LZ
T: (01843) 588276
F: (01843) 586866
I: www.jarvis.co.uk

San Clu Hotel ★★★
Victoria Parade, East Cliff,
Ramsgate, Kent CT11 8DT
T: (01843) 592345
F: (01843) 580157
E: sancluhotel@lineone.net
I: www.san-clu-hotel.co.uk

REDHILL
Surrey

Nutfield Priory
★★★★ GOLD AWARD
Nutfield, Redhill, Surrey RH1 4EL
T: (01737) 824400
F: (01737) 823321
E: nutpriory@aol.com
I: www.nutfield-priory.com

ROCHESTER

Bridgewood Manor Hotel
★★★★
Bridgewood Roundabout,
Walderslade Woods, Chatham,
Kent ME5 9AX
T: (01634) 201333
F: (01634) 201330
E: bridgewoodmanor@
marstonhotels.co.uk
I: www.marstonhotels.co.uk

King Charles Hotel ★★
Brompton Road, Gillingham,
Kent ME7 5QT
T: (01634) 830303
F: (01634) 829430
E: enquiries@kingcharleshotel.
co.uk
I: www.kingcharleshotel.co.uk

Medway Manor Hotel Ltd ★
14-16 New Road, Rochester,
Kent ME1 1BG
T: (01634) 847985
F: (01634) 832430
E: http://members.
aol/com/medmanhotl/hotel.htm

ROYAL TUNBRIDGE WELLS
Kent

Jarvis International Hotel
★★★
8 Tonbridge Road, Pembury,
Royal Tunbridge Wells, Kent
TN2 4QL
T: (01892) 823567
F: (01892) 823931

Royal Wells Inn ★★★
Mount Ephraim, Royal
Tunbridge Wells, Kent TN4 8BE
T: (01892) 511188
F: (01892) 511908
E: info@royalwells
I: www.roualwells.co.uk

The Spa Hotel ★★★
Mount Ephraim, Royal
Tunbridge Wells, Kent TN4 8XJ
T: (01892) 520331
F: (01892) 510575
E: info@spahotel.co.uk
I: www.spahotel.co.uk/

Swan Hotel ★★★
The Pantiles, Royal Tunbridge
Wells, Kent TN2 5TD
T: (01892) 543319
F: (01892) 541465
E: hotelswan@cs.com
I: www.theswanhotel.com

RYE
East Sussex

**Flackley Ash Hotel &
Restaurant** ★★★
London Road, Peasmarsh, Rye,
East Sussex TN31 6YH
T: (01797) 230651
F: (01797) 230510
E: flackleyash@marstonhotels.
co.uk
I: www.marstonhotels.co.uk

The George ★★★
High Street, Rye, East Sussex
TN31 7JP
T: (01797) 222114
F: (01797) 224065

The River Haven Hotel ★★
Quayside, Winchelsea Road, Rye,
East Sussex TN31 7EL
T: (01797) 227982
F: (01797) 227983

Rye Lodge Hotel
★★★ SILVER AWARD
Hilders Cliff, Rye, East Sussex
TN31 7LD
T: (01797) 223838 & 226688
F: (01797) 223585
E: info@ryelodge.co.uk
I: www.ryelodge.co.uk

ST MICHAELS
Kent

London Beach Golf Hotel
★★★★
Ashford Road, St Michaels,
Tenterden, Kent TN30 6SP
T: (01580) 766279
F: (01580) 766681
E: pierre@edmondsgolf.
freeserve.co.uk
I: www.edmondsgolf.freeserve.
co.uk

SALTDEAN
East Sussex

Grand Ocean Hotel
Rating Applied For
Longridge Avenue, Saltdean,
Brighton, East Sussex BN2 8RP
T: (01273) 302291 &
0870 7780333
F: (01273) 304255
I: www.grandhotelgroup.co.uk

SANDWICH
Kent

Bell Hotel ★★★
The Quay, Sandwich, Kent
CT13 9EF
T: (01304) 613388
F: (01304) 615308
E: hotel@princes-leisure.co.uk
I: www.princes-leisure.co.uk

**The Blazing Donkey Country
Hotel & Restaurant★★★**
Hay Hill, Ham, Sandwich, Kent
CT14 0ED
T: (01304) 617362
F: (01304) 615264
E: reservations@blazingdonkey.
co.uk
I: www.blazingdonkey.co.uk.

SEALE
Surrey

Jarvis Hog's Back Hotel ★★★
Hog's Back, Seale, Farnham,
Surrey GU10 1EX
T: (01252) 782345
F: (01252) 783113

SHEPPERTON
Surrey

The Ship Hotel ★★
Russell Road, Shepperton,
Middlesex TW17 9HX
T: (01932) 227320
F: (01932) 226668

STEYNING
West Sussex

**The Old Tollgate Restaurant &
Hotel ★★★ SILVER AWARD**
The Street, Bramber, Steyning,
West Sussex BN44 3WE
T: (01903) 879494
F: (01903) 813399
E: otr@fastnet.co.uk
I: home.fastnet.co.uk/otr

TENTERDEN
Kent

**Little Silver Country Hotel
★★★ SILVER AWARD**
Ashford Road, St Michaels,
Tenterden, Kent TN30 6SP
T: (01233) 850321
F: (01233) 850647
E: enquiries@little-silver.co.uk
I: www.little-silver.co.uk

TICEHURST
East Sussex

**Dale Hill Hotel & Golf Club
★★★★ GOLD AWARD**
Ticehurst, Wadhurst, East Sussex
TN5 7DQ
T: (01580) 200112
F: (01580) 201249
E: info@dalehill.co.uk
I: www.dalehill.co.uk

TONBRIDGE
Kent

The Rose & Crown ★★★
125 High Street, Tonbridge, Kent
TN9 1DD
T: (01732) 357966
F: (01732) 357194

WEST CHILTINGTON
West Sussex

Roundabout Hotel ★★★
Monkmead Lane, West
Chiltington, Pulborough, West
Sussex RH20 2PF
T: (01798) 813838
F: (01798) 812962
E: roundabouthotelltd@
btinternet.com
I: www.bestwestern.co.uk

WOKING
Surrey

Northfleet Hotel ★★
Claremont Avenue, Woking,
Surrey GU22 7SG
T: (01483) 722971
F: (01483) 756376
E: gill@northfleethotel.demon.
co.uk
I: www.northfleet.com.uk

WORTHING
West Sussex

Cavendish Hotel ★★
115-116 Marine Parade,
Worthing, West Sussex
BN11 3QG
T: (01903) 236767
F: (01903) 823840
E: thecavendish@mistral.co.uk
I: www3.mistral.co.
uk/thecavendish/

WYCH CROSS
East Sussex

**Ashdown Park Hotel
★★★★ GOLD AWARD**
Wych Cross, Forest Row,
Gatwick, West Sussex RH18 5JR
T: (01342) 824988
F: (01342) 826206
E: sales@ashdownpark.com
I: www.ashdownpark.com

Establishments printed in blue have a detailed entry in this guide

USE YOUR *i*'s

There are more than 550 Tourist Information Centres throughout England offering friendly help with accommodation and holiday ideas as well as suggestions of places to visit and things to do.

You'll find TIC addresses in the local Phone Book.

www.travelengland.org.uk

Log on to travelengland.org.uk and discover something different around every corner. Meander through pages for ideas of places to visit and things to do. Spend time in each region and discover the diversity – from busy vibrant cities to rural village greens; rugged peaks to gentle rolling hills; dramatic coastline to idyllic sandy beaches. England might be a small country but it is brimming with choice and opportunity. Visit www.travelengland.org.uk and see for yourself.

England

Ratings you can trust

English Tourism Council

★ ★ ★

HOTEL

When you're looking for a place to stay, you need a rating system you can trust. The **English Tourism Council's** ratings are your clear guide to what to expect, in an easy-to-understand form. Properties are visited annually by our trained, impartial assessors, so you can have confidence that your accommodation has been thoroughly checked and rated for quality before you make a booking.

Based on the internationally recognised rating of One to Five Stars, the system puts great emphasis on quality and is based on research which shows exactly what consumers are looking for when choosing an hotel.

Ratings are awarded from One to Five Stars - the more Stars, the higher the quality and the greater the range of facilities and level of services provided.

Look out, too, for the English Tourism Council's Gold and Silver Awards, which are awarded to properties achieving the highest levels of quality within their Star rating. While the overall rating is based on a combination of facilities and quality, the Gold and Silver Awards are based solely on quality.

The ratings are your sign of quality assurance, giving you the confidence to book the accommodation that meets your expectations.

Information

The
Quality Assurance Scheme

English Tourism Council

★ ★ ★
HOTEL

When you're looking for a place to stay, you need a rating system you can trust. The English Tourism Council's ratings are your clear guide to what to expect, in an easy-to-understand form. Properties are visited annually by our trained, impartial assessors, so you can have confidence that your accommodation has been thoroughly checked and rated for quality before you make a booking.

Based on the internationally recognised rating of One to Five Stars, the system puts great emphasis on quality and is based on research which shows exactly what consumers are looking for when choosing a hotel.

Ratings are awarded from One to Five Stars - the more Stars, the higher the quality and the greater the range of facilities and level of services provided.

Look out, too, for the English Tourism Council's Gold and Silver Awards, which are awarded to properties achieving the highest levels of quality within their Star rating. While the overall rating is based on a combination of facilities and quality, the Gold and Silver Awards are based solely on quality.

Star ratings are your sign of quality assurance, giving you the confidence to book the accommodation that meets your expectations.

What to expect at each rating level

In a One Star Hotel you will find an acceptable level of quality, services and a range of facilities. Moving up the One to Five Star rating scale, you will find progressively higher quality standards providing ever better guest care as well as a wider range of facilities and a higher level of services.

● **At a ONE STAR hotel you will find:**
Practical accommodation with a limited range of facilities and services, but a high standard of cleanliness throughout. Friendly and courteous staff to give you the help and information you need to enjoy your stay. Restaurant/eating area open to you and your guests for breakfast and dinner. Alcoholic drinks will be served in a bar or lounge. 75% of bedrooms will have en-suite or private facilities.

● **At a TWO STAR hotel you will find**
(in addition to what is provided at ONE STAR):
Good overnight accommodation with more comfortable bedrooms, better equipped - all with en-suite or private facilities and colour TV. A relatively straightforward range of services and a personal style of service. Food and drink is of a slightly higher standard. A restaurant/dining room for breakfast and dinner. A lift normally available.

● **At a THREE STAR hotel you will find**
(in addition to what is provided at ONE and TWO STAR):
Possibly larger establishments, but all offering significantly greater quality and higher standard of facilities and services, and usually more spacious public areas and bedrooms. A more formal style of service with a receptionist on duty and staff responding well to your needs and requests. Room service of continental breakfast. Laundry service available. Greater attention to quality of food.

● **At a FOUR STAR hotel you will find**
(in addition to what is provided at ONE, TWO and THREE STAR):
Accommodation offering superior comfort and quality; all bedrooms with en-suite bath, fitted overhead shower and WC. Strong emphasis on food and drink. Staff will have very good technical and social skills, anticipating and responding to your needs and requests. Room service of all meals and 24 hour drinks, refreshments and snacks.

● **At a FIVE STAR hotel you will find**
(in addition to what is provided at ONE, TWO, THREE and FOUR STAR):
A spacious, luxurious establishment offering you the highest international quality of accommodation, facilities, services and cuisine. It will have striking accommodation throughout, with a range of extra facilities. You will feel very well cared for by professional, attentive staff providing flawless guest services. A hotel setting the highest standards for the industry, with an air of luxury, exceptional comfort and a very sophisticated ambience.

General
Advice & Information

MAKING A BOOKING

When enquiring about accommodation, make sure you check prices and other important details. You will also need to state your requirements, clearly and precisely - for example:

- **Arrival and departure dates**, with acceptable alternatives if appropriate.
- **The type of accommodation you need;** for example, room with twin beds, private bathroom.
- **The terms you want;** for example, room only, bed and breakfast, half board, full board.
- **If you have children with you;** their ages, whether you want them to share your room or be next door, any other special requirements, such as a cot.
- **Particular requirements you may have,** such as a special diet.

Booking by letter

Misunderstandings can easily happen over the telephone, so we strongly advise you to confirm your booking in writing if there is time.

Please note that the English Tourism Council does not make reservations - you should write direct to the accommodation.

DEPOSITS

If you make your reservation weeks or months in advance, you will probably be asked for a deposit. The amount will vary according to the time of year, the number of people in your party and how long you plan to stay. The deposit will then be deducted from the final bill when you leave.

PAYMENT ON ARRIVAL

Some establishments, especially large hotels in big towns, ask you to pay for your room on arrival if you have not booked it in advance. This is especially likely to happen if you arrive late and have little or no luggage.

If you are asked to pay on arrival, it is a good idea to see your room first, to make sure it meets your requirements.

CANCELLATIONS

Legal contract

When you accept accommodation that is offered to you, by telephone or in writing, you enter a legally binding contract with the proprietor.

This means that if you cancel your booking, fail to take up the accommodation or leave early, the proprietor may be entitled to compensation if he cannot re-let for all or a good part of the booked period. You will probably forfeit any deposit you have paid, and may well be asked for an additional payment.

The proprietor cannot make a claim until after the booked period, however, and during that time every effort should be made by the proprietor to re-let the accommodation.

If there is a dispute it is sensible for both sides to seek legal advice on the matter.

If you do have to change your travel plans, it is in your own interests to let the proprietors know in writing as soon as possible, to give them a chance to re-let your accommodation.

And remember, if you book by telephone and are asked for your credit card number, you should check whether the proprietor intends charging your credit card account should you later cancel your reservation. A proprietor should not be able to charge your credit card account with a cancellation unless he or she has made this clear at the time of your booking and you have agreed. However, to avoid later disputes, we suggest you check with the proprietor whether he or she intends to charge your credit card account if you cancel.

INSURANCE

A travel or holiday insurance policy will safeguard you if you have to cancel or change your holiday plans. You can arrange a policy quite cheaply through your insurance company or travel agent. Some hotels also offer their own insurance schemes.

ARRIVING LATE

If you know you will be arriving late in the evening, it is a good idea to say so when you book. If you are delayed on your way, a telephone call to say that you will be late will help prevent any problems when you arrive.

SERVICE CHARGES AND TIPPING

These days many places levy service charges automatically. If they do, they must clearly say so in their offer of accommodation, at the time of booking. Then the service charge becomes part of the legal contract when you accept the offer of accommodation.

If a service charge is levied automatically, there is no need to tip the staff, unless they provide some exceptional service. The usual tip for meals is ten per cent of the total bill.

TELEPHONE CHARGES

Hotels can set their own charges for telephone calls made through their switchboard or from direct-dial telephones in bedrooms. These charges are often much higher than telephone companies' standard charges (to defray the cost of providing the service).

Comparing costs

It is a condition of the quality assurance scheme, that a hotel's unit charges are on display, by the telephones or with the room information. But in practice it is not always easy to compare these charges with standard telephone rates. Before using a hotel telephone for long-distance calls, you may decide to ask how the charges compare.

SECURITY OF VALUABLES

You can deposit your valuables with the proprietor or manager during your stay, and we recommend you do this as a sensible precaution. Make sure you obtain a receipt for them.

Some places do not accept articles for safe custody, and in that case it is wisest to keep your valuables with you.

Disclaimer

Some proprietors put up a notice which disclaims liability for property brought on to their premises by a guest. In fact, they can only restrict their liability to a minimum laid down by law (The Hotel Proprietors Act 1956).

Under that Act, a proprietor is liable for the value of the loss or damage to any property (except a motor car or its contents) of a guest who has engaged overnight accommodation, but if the proprietor has the notice on display as prescribed under that Act, liability is limited to £50 for one article and a total of £100 for any one guest. The notice must be prominently displayed in the reception area or main entrance. These limits do not apply to valuables you have deposited with the proprietor for safe-keeping, or to property lost through the default, neglect of wilful act of the proprietor or his staff.

BRINGING PETS TO ENGLAND

The quarantine laws have recently changed in England and a pilot Pet Travel Scheme (PETS) is currently in operation. Under this new scheme pet dogs are able to come into Britain from over 35 countries via certain sea, air and rail routes into England.

Dogs that have been resident in these countries for more than 6 months may enter the UK under the Pilot Scheme providing they are accompanied by the appropriate documentation.

For dogs to be able to enter the UK without quarantine under the PETS Pilot Scheme they will have to meet certain conditions and travel with the following documents: the Official PETS Certificate, a certificate of treatment against tapeworm and ticks and a declaration of residence.

For details of participating countries, routes, operators and further information about the PETS Pilot Scheme please contact the Ministry of Agriculture, Fisheries and Food, 1a Page Street, London SW1P 4PQ

Tel: +44 (0) 870 241 1710 Fax: +44 (0) 20 7904 6834 Email: pets@ahvg.maff.gsi.gov.uk, or visit their web site at www.maff.gov.uk/animalh/quarantine

CODE OF CONDUCT

All the places featured in this guide have agreed to observe the following Codes of Conduct:

1   To ensure high standards of courtesy and cleanliness, catering and service appropriate to the type of establishment.

2   To describe fairly to all visitors and prospective visitors the amenities, facilities and services provided by the establishment, whether by advertisement, brochure, word of mouth or any other means. To allow visitors to see accommodation, if requested, before booking.

3   To make clear to visitors exactly what is included in all prices quoted for accommodation, meals and refreshments, including service charges, taxes and other surcharges. Details of charges, if any, for heating or additional service of facilities should also be made clear.

4   To adhere to, and not to exceed, prices current at time of occupation for accommodation or other services.

5   To advise visitors at the time of booking, and subsequently of any change, if the accommodation offered is in an unconnected annexe, or similar, or by boarding out; and to indicate the location of such accommodation and any difference in comfort or amenities from accommodation in the main establishment.

6   To give each visitor, on request, details of payments due and a receipt if required.

7   To deal promptly and courteously with all enquiries, requests, reservations, correspondence and complaints from visitors.

8   To allow an English Tourism Council representative reasonable access to the establishment, on request, to confirm that the Code of Conduct is being observed.

COMMENTS AND COMPLAINTS

Hotels and the law

Places that offer accommodation have legal and statutory responsibilities to their customers, such as providing information about prices, providing adequate fire precautions and safeguarding valuables. Like other businesses, they must also abide by the Trades Description Acts 1968 and 1972 when they describe their accommodation and facilities.

All the places featured in this guide have declared that they do fulfil all applicable statutory obligations.

Information

The proprietors themselves supply the descriptions of their establishments and other information for the entries, and they pay to be included in the regional sections of the guide. All the acommodation featured in this guide has also been assessed or has applied for assessment under the quality assurance scheme.

The English Tourism Council cannot guarantee accuracy of information in this guide, and accepts no responsibility for any error or misrepresentation. All liability for loss, disappointment, negligence or other damage caused by reliance on the information contained in this guide, or in the event of bankruptcy or liquidation or cessation of trade of any company, individual or firm mentioned, is hereby excluded.

We strongly recommend that you carefully check prices and other details when you book your accommodation.

Problems

Of course, we hope you will not have cause for complaint, but problems do occur from time to time.

If you are dissatisfied with anything, make your complaint to the management immediately. Then the management can take action at once to investigate the matter and put things right. The longer you leave a complaint, the harder it is to deal with it effectively.

In certain circumstances, the English Tourism Council may look into complaints. However, the Council has no statutory control over establishments or their methods of operating. The Council cannot become involved in legal or contractual matters.

If you do have problems that have not been resolved by the proprietor and which you would like to bring to our attention, please write to: Quality Standards Department, English Tourism Council, Thames Tower, Black's Road, Hammersmith, London W6 9EL.

About the
Guide Entries

LOCATIONS

Places to stay are listed under the town, city or village where they are located. If a place is out in the countryside, you will find it listed under the nearest village or town.

Town names are listed alphabetically within each regional section of the guide, along with the name of the county or unitary authority they are in (see note on page 14), and their map reference.

Map references

These refer to the colour location maps at the front of the guide. The first figure shown is the map number, the following letter and figure indicate the grid reference on the map.

Some entries were included just before the guide went to press, so they do not appear on the maps.

Addresses

County names, which appear in the town headings, are not repeated in the entries. When you are writing, you should of course make sure you use the full address and postcode.

Telephone numbers

Telephone numbers are listed below the accommodation address for each entry. Area codes are shown in brackets.

PRICES

The prices shown in Where to Stay 2001 are only a general guide; they were supplied to us by proprietors in summer 2000. Remember, changes may occur after the guide goes to press, so we strongly advise you to check prices when you book your accommodation.

Prices are shown in pounds sterling and include VAT where applicable. Some places also include a service charge in their standard tariff so check this when you book.

Standardised method

There are many different ways of quoting prices for accommodation. We use a standardised method in the guide to allow you to compare prices. For example when we show:

Bed and breakfast, the prices shown are for overnight accommodation with breakfast, for single and double rooms.

The double-room price is for two people. If a double room is occupied by one person there is sometimes a reduction in price.

Halfboard, the prices shown are for room, breakfast and evening meal, per person per day.

Some places provide only a continental breakfast in the set price, and you may have to pay extra if you want a full English breakfast.

Checking prices

According to the law, hotels with at least four bedrooms or eight beds must display their overnight accommodation charges in the reception area or entrance. In your own interests, do make sure you check prices and what they include.

Children's rates

You will find that many places charge a reduced rate for children especially if they share a room with their parents.

Some places charge the full rate, however, when a child occupies a room which might otherwise have been let to an adult.

The upper age limit for reductions for children varies from one hotel to another, so check this when you book.

Seasonal packages

Prices often vary through the year, and may be significantly lower outside peak holiday weeks. Many places offer special package rates - fully inclusive weekend breaks, for example - in the autumn, winter and spring.

You can get details of bargain packages from the establishment themselves, the Regional Tourist Boards or your local Tourist Information Centre (TIC).

Your local travel agent may also have information, and can help you make bookings.

BATHROOMS

Each accommodation entry shows you the number of en-suite and private bathrooms available, the number of private showers and the number of public bathrooms.

'En-suite bathroom' means the bath or shower and WC are contained behind the main door of the bedroom. 'Private bathroom' means a bath or shower and WC solely for the occupants of one bedroom, on the same floor, reasonably close and with a key provided. 'Private shower' means a shower en-suite with the bedroom but no WC.

Public bathrooms normally have a bath, sometimes with a shower attachment. If the availability of a bath is important to you, remember to check when you book.

MEALS

If an establishment serves evening meals, you will find the starting time and the last order times shown in the listing; some smaller places may ask you at breakfast or at midday whether you want an evening meal.

The prices shown in each entry are for bed and breakfast or half board, but many places also offer lunch, as you will see indicated in the entry.

OPENING PERIOD

All places are open for the months indicated in their entry.

SYMBOLS

The at-a-glance symbols included at the end of each entry show many of the services and facilities available at each place. You will find the key to these symbols on the back cover flap. Open out the flap and you can check the meanings of the symbols as you go.

SMOKING

Many places provide non-smoking areas - from no-smoking bedrooms and lounges to no-smoking sections of the restaurant. Some places prefer not to accommodate smokers, and in such cases the descriptions in each entry makes this clear.

PETS

Many places accept guests with dogs, but we do advise that you check this when you book, and ask if there are any extra charges or rules about exactly where your pet is allowed. The acceptance of dogs is not always extended to cats and it is strongly advised that cat owners contact the establishment well in advance. Some establishments do not accept pets at all. These places are indicated with the symbol 🐾.

The quarantine laws have recently changed in England and pet dogs are able to come into Britain from selected European countries. For details of the Pet Travel Scheme (PETS) please turn to page 366.

CREDIT AND CHARGE CARDS

The credit and charge cards accepted by a place are listed in the entry following the letters CC.

If you do plan to pay by card, check that the establishment will take your card before you book.

Some proprietors will charge you a higher rate if you pay by credit card rather than cash or cheque. The difference is to cover the percentage paid by the proprietor to the credit card company.

If you are planning to pay by credit card, you may want to ask whether it would, in fact, be cheaper to pay by cheque or cash. When you book by telephone, you may be asked for your credit card number as 'confirmation'. But remember, the proprietor may then charge your credit card account if you cancel your booking. See under Cancellations on page 365.

CONFERENCES AND GROUPS

Places which cater for conferences and meetings are marked with the symbol ♟ (the number that follows the symbol shows the capacity). Rates are often negotiable, depending on the time of year, numbers of people involved and any special requirements you may have.

Awaiting confirmation of rating

At the time of going to press some establishments featured in this guide had not yet been assessed for their rating for the year 2001 and so their new rating could not be included.

For your information, the most up-to-date information regarding these establishments' ratings is in the listings pages at the back of this guide.

Central Reservations
Offices

Some of the accommodation establishments in the regional sections of this guide are members of hotel groups or consortia which maintain a central reservations office. These are identified with the symbol ⓒⓡ, and the name of the group or consortium, which will appear in the coloured band on the right of the entry. Bookings or enquiries can be made directly with the establishment or to the central reservations office.

Ashley Courtenay Ltd
16 Little London,
Chichester,
West Sussex PO19 1PA
Reservations: (01243) 780129
Tel: (01243) 775521
Fax: (01243) 531331
E-mail: enquiries@stay-at.com
Internet: www.stay-at.com

Best Western
Best Western Hotels,
Amy Johnson Way,
Clifton Moor,
York YO30 4GP
Reservations: 08457 747474
Fax: (01904) 695401

Care Hotels plc
The Lodge,
Pikes Hill,
Lyndhurst,
Hampshire SO43 7AS
Tel: 0800 444441
Fax: (023) 802 83719

Choice Hotels Europe
Central Reservations,
112-114 Station Road,
Edgware,
Middlesex HA8 7BJ
Freephone: 0800 444 444
Internet: www.choicehotels.com

The Circle
Independent Hospitality Marketing,
20 Church Road,
Horspath,
Oxford OX33 1RU
Tel: (01865) 875888
Fax: (01865) 875777
E-mail: circlehotels@dial.pipex.com
Internet: www.circlehotels.co.uk

Corus and Regal hotels
5th Floor, Elgar House,
Shrub Hill Road,
Worcester WR4 9EE
Tel: 0845 300 2000
Fax: (01905) 730 311

Cotswolds Inns and Hotels Ltd
PO Box 26,
Broadway,
Worcestershire W12 7RQ
Tel: 0800 9751629

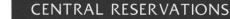

Grand Heritage Hotels

First Floor,
Warwick House,
181-183 Warwick Road,
London W14 8PU
Tel: (020) 7244 6699
0800 0560457 (toll free)
Fax: (020) 7244 7799
E-mail: enquiries@grandheritage.com
Internet: www.grandheritage.com

GuestAccom Good Room Guide

'Maytrees' Downend,
Chieveley,
West Berkshire RG20 8TF
Tel: (01635) 247444
Fax: (01635) 248287
E-mail: office@questaccom.co.uk
Internet: www.questaccom.co.uk

The Independents

The Independents Hotel Association,
Beambridge,
Sampford Arundel,
Wellington,
Somerset TA21 0HB
Information line: (01823) 672100
Bookings: 0800 885544
Fax: (01823) 673100
E-mail: info@theindependents.co.uk
Internet: www.theindependents.co.uk

Jarvis Hotels

Jarvis Central Reservations,
Castle House,
Desborough Road,
High Wycombe,
Buckinghamshire HP11 2PR
Tel: 0845 7 30 30 40
(calls charged at local rate)
Fax: (01494) 686737

Minotel Great Britain Ltd

37 Springfield Road,
Blackpool FY1 1PZ
Tel: (01253) 292000
Fax: (01253) 291191
E-mail: info@minotel.co.uk

Principal Hotels Group

Central Reservations Office,
15A Prospect Place,
Harrogate HG1 1LA
Freephone: 0800 454454
Fax: (01423) 503555

Small Luxury Hotels of the World

James House,
Bridge Street,
Leatherhead,
Surrey KT22 7EP
Reservations Toll Free Number: 00800 525 4 8000
Internet: www.slh.com

Thistle Hotels

Central Reservations,
2 The Calls,
Leeds LS2 7JU
Tel: 0800 18 17 16
Fax: (0113) 246 1357
Internet: www.thistlehotels.com

Utell

14th Floor,
Quadrant House,
The Quadrant, Sutton,
Surrey SM2 5AR
Tel: 08705 300200

Distance Chart

The distances between towns on the chart below are given to the nearest mile, and are measured along routes based on the quickest travelling time, making maximum use of motorways or dual-carriageway roads. The chart is based upon information supplied by the Automobile Association.

To calculate the distance in kilometres multiply the mileage by 1.6

For example: *Brighton to Dover 82 miles x 1.6 =131.2 kilometres*

	Aberdeen	Aberystwyth	Barnstaple	Birmingham	Brighton	Bristol	Cambridge	Cardiff	Carlisle	Carmarthen	Colchester	Dorchester	Dover	Edinburgh	Exeter	Fort William	Glasgow	Gloucester	Guildford	Holyhead	Hull	Inverness	Kendal	Leeds	Lincoln	Liverpool	Maidstone	Manchester	Middlesbrough	Newcastle	Norwich	Nottingham	Oxford	Penzance	Perth	Plymouth	Sheffield	Southampton	Stranraer	Taunton	York
Aberystwyth	468																																								
Barnstaple	603	214																																							
Birmingham	431	124	180																																						
Brighton	605	288	208	171																																					
Bristol	513	128	99	90	169																																				
Cambridge	462	215	267	97	120	170																																			
Cardiff	531	110	127	109	201	44	203																																		
Carlisle	231	236	372	199	375	282	257	300																																	
Carmarthen	513	48	190	171	264	106	266	67	282																																
Colchester	516	289	292	171	112	195	48	227	310	290																															
Dorchester	595	206	94	172	119	62	179	119	363	182	206																														
Dover	587	325	273	207	82	206	124	238	400	301	116	200																													
Edinburgh	125	335	470	298	473	380	333	398	98	381	385	462	458																												
Exeter	585	196	53	162	175	82	249	109	353	172	274	55	245	453																											
Fort William	156	446	581	409	584	491	466	509	209	491	518	573	590	133	563																										
Glasgow	147	333	468	296	472	379	353	397	96	379	405	461	478	49	451	102																									
Gloucester	479	111	125	56	155	35	150	61	247	124	171	117	192	347	107	456	343																								
Guildford	563	224	175	128	44	106	91	138	332	201	103	97	97	432	147	541	428	99																							
Holyhead	459	101	339	167	343	250	259	201	227	149	333	332	369	327	322	436	323	215	300																						
Hull	375	228	321	140	258	231	138	249	170	312	191	313	262	247	303	379	266	196	239	219																					
Inverness	106	494	630	457	633	540	514	558	257	540	566	622	639	158	612	66	174	505	591	485	428																				
Kendal	279	190	325	153	329	236	245	254	47	236	319	318	355	147	308	256	143	201	286	181	164	305																			
Leeds	331	174	302	121	263	212	146	230	126	220	200	294	271	202	284	335	222	177	220	165	60	383	71																		
Lincoln	387	199	276	89	216	186	95	204	182	267	147	245	220	258	258	391	278	151	173	204	46	439	176	72																	
Liverpool	357	110	274	102	277	184	193	202	126	163	268	266	304	225	256	335	222	150	235	101	128	383	79	74	140																
Maidstone	548	286	234	168	50	167	85	199	361	262	77	161	41	419	206	570	458	153	58	329	223	619	315	233	181	263															
Manchester	356	134	261	89	264	171	160	189	123	180	212	253	291	223	243	332	219	137	222	125	97	381	77	44	85	35	251														
Middlesbrough	276	245	357	177	318	268	198	286	95	291	251	350	322	147	340	280	191	233	276	236	89	308	84	63	123	145	283	115													
Newcastle	234	276	388	208	349	299	229	317	60	322	282	381	353	106	371	239	154	264	307	267	142	266	102	94	154	176	314	146	38												
Norwich	488	277	329	159	171	233	63	264	282	327	61	241	175	359	311	491	379	212	162	320	150	540	276	173	104	241	135	186	223	254											
Nottingham	393	162	234	54	195	144	86	163	188	226	139	226	218	265	216	397	284	110	153	178	92	446	164	74	38	112	179	71	129	160	119										
Oxford	503	159	170	68	109	73	81	105	271	168	124	115	146	371	152	480	367	48	67	239	189	529	225	171	130	173	106	161	226	257	144	103									
Penzance	697	308	108	274	287	194	361	221	465	284	386	167	357	565	111	674	562	219	259	433	414	723	419	396	369	367	317	355	451	482	423	328	264								
Perth	87	382	518	345	521	428	402	446	145	428	454	510	527	42	500	102	62	393	478	373	315	114	193	268	327	271	487	266	192	151	428	334	418	611							
Plymouth	628	239	67	205	218	125	292	152	396	215	316	98	288	496	45	605	492	150	190	364	345	654	350	326	300	298	248	286	382	413	354	259	195	77	542						
Sheffield	365	167	272	76	233	182	122	201	159	264	176	264	247	236	254	368	255	148	191	158	66	417	125	36	47	79	207	39	100	131	147	44	141	366	281	297					
Southampton	570	225	142	135	66	106	131	138	339	201	159	53	152	439	109	548	435	100	49	307	257	596	292	238	197	241	112	228	293	324	193	171	67	221	484	152	208				
Stranraer	232	342	478	305	481	388	363	406	106	388	415	470	487	133	460	188	86	354	439	333	276	258	153	228	288	231	448	226	201	163	388	294	378	572	146	503	265	446			
Taunton	554	165	50	132	160	51	218	79	323	142	243	45	224	423	32	532	419	77	126	291	272	581	276	253	227	225	184	212	308	339	280	186	121	144	469	75	223	94	429		
York	322	202	315	134	276	225	155	243	117	248	209	307	280	193	297	326	213	191	233	193	38	374	91	24	80	103	240	72	50	89	180	86	184	409	238	340	58	251	223	266	
London	544	238	216	120	59	120	60	152	313	215	61	128	79	413	198	522	409	102	30	281	186	571	266	198	143	215	39	202	253	284	115	131	56	310	458	241	168	80	419	167	211

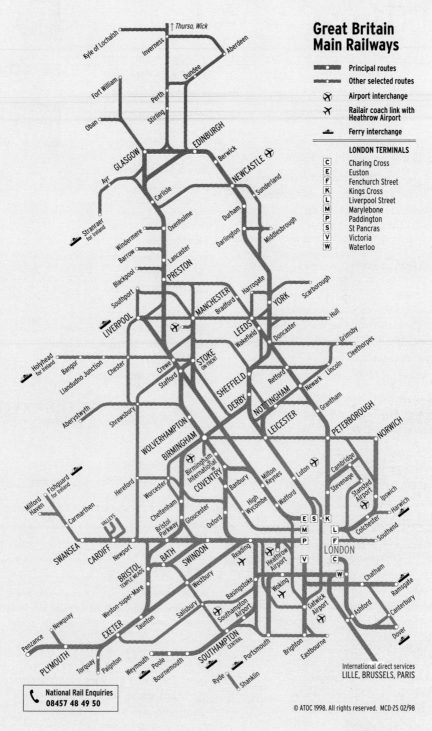

Great Britain Main Railways

Legend:
- ▬▬▬ Principal routes
- ▬▬▬ Other selected routes
- ✈ Airport interchange
- ✈ Railair coach link with Heathrow Airport
- ⛴ Ferry interchange

LONDON TERMINALS

C	Charing Cross
E	Euston
F	Fenchurch Street
K	Kings Cross
L	Liverpool Street
M	Marylebone
P	Paddington
S	St Pancras
V	Victoria
W	Waterloo

International direct services
LILLE, BRUSSELS, PARIS

☎ National Rail Enquiries
08457 48 49 50

© ATOC 1998. All rights reserved. MCD-2S 02/98

01/MRE/1134

A selection of events for
2001

This is a selection of the many cultural, sporting and other events that will be taking place throughout England during 2001. Please note, as changes often occur after press date, it is advisable to confirm the date and location before travelling.

* Provisional at time of going to press.

January 2001

4-28 January
Holiday on Ice 2001: Xotica - A Journey to the Heart
Brighton Centre, Kings Road, Brighton, East Sussex
Contact: (0870) 900 9100

5-14 January
47th London International Boat Show
Earls Court Exhibition Centre, Warwick Road,
London SW5
Contact: (01784) 473377

6 January
Old Custom: Haxey Hood Game
The Village, Haxey, Doncaster, South Yorkshire
Contact: (01427) 752845

20-21 January
Motorbike 2001
Springfields Exhibition Centre, Camelgate,
Spalding, Lincolnshire
Contact: (01775) 724843

February 2001

1-3 February
Wakefield Rhubarb Trail and Festival of Rhubarb
Various venues, Wakefield, West Yorkshire
Contact: (01924) 305841

3-4 February
The 22nd Bristol Classic Car Show
The Royal Bath and West Showground,
Shepton Mallet, Somerset
Contact: (0117) 907 1000

15-17 February
Garrick Drama Festival
Civic Hall, Castle Dyke, Lichfield, Staffordshire
Contact: (01543) 308797

17-18 February*
Motorsport Day
Brooklands Museum, Brooklands Road,
Weybridge, Surrey
Contact: (01932) 857381

17-25 February
National Boat, Caravan and Leisure Show
National Exhibition Centre, Birmingham,
West Midlands
Contact: (024) 7622 1443

March 2001

1 March
Lancashire Food Festival
Accrington Town Hall, Accrington, Lancashire
Contact: (01254) 872595

8-11 March
Crufts 2001
National Exhibition Centre, Birmingham,
West Midlands

13-15 March
Cheltenham Gold Cup National Hunt Racing Festival
Cheltenham Racecourse, Cheltenham, Gloucestershire
Contact: (01242) 513014

25-28 March
Diesel Gala - GWR (Gloucestershire/Warwickshire)
The Railway Station, Toddington, Cheltenham,
Gloucestershire
Contact: (01242) 621405

April 2001

1 April-23 December*
Cornwall 2001 Festival of Steam and Invention
Various venues, Wakefield, West Yorkshire,
Contact: (01924) 305841

5-7 April
Grand National Festival
Aintree Racecourse, Ormskirk Road, Aintree,
Liverpool, Merseyside
Contact: (0151) 523 2600

8 April
World Dock Pudding Championship
Mytholmroyd Community Centre, Elphaborough,
Mytholmroyd, Hebden Bridge, West Yorkshire
Contact: (01422) 883023

13-20 April
Harrogate International Youth Music Festival
Various venues, Harrogate, North Yorkshire
Contact: (01306) 744360

15-16 April
Easter Egg Hunt
Crealy Park, Clyst St Mary, Exeter, Devon
Contact: (01395) 233200

28-29 April*
South West Custom and Classic Bike Show
The Royal Bath and West Showground,
Shepton Mallet, Somerset
Contact: (01749) 822222

May 2001

4-7 May
Hastings Traditional Jack in the Green Morris
Dance Festival
Various venues, Hastings, East Sussex
Contact: (01424) 716576

4-7 May*
Lincoln Folk Festival
The Lawn, Union Road, Lincoln, Lincolnshire
Contact: (01522) 523000

6-7 May
Bexhill 100 Festival of Motoring
Seafront, De La Warr Parade, Bexhill, East Sussex
Contact: (01424) 730564

9-13 May*
Royal Windsor Horse Show
Windsor Home Park, Datchet Road, Windsor, Berkshire
Contact: (01753) 860633

18 May-3 June
Bath International Music Festival
Various venues, Bath
Contact: (01225) 463362

26-28 May
Window on the World International Music Festival
North Shields Fishquay and Town, Tyne & Wear
Contact: (0191) 200 8909

28 May
Luton International Carnival
Town Centre and nearby, Luton, Bedfordshire
Contact: (01582) 877282

28 May
Northumberland County Show
Tynedale Park, Corbridge, Northumberland
Contact: (01697) 747848

June 2001

1 June
Robert Dover's Cotswold Olimpick Games
Dovers Hill, Weston Subedge, Chipping Campden,
Gloucestershire
Contact: (01384) 274041

*1-30 June***

Royal Cornwall Show

Royal Cornwall Showground, Wadebridge, Cornwall

Contact: (01208) 812183

7-9 June

South of England Agricultural Show

South of England Showground, Ardingly,

Haywards Heath, West Sussex

Contact: (01444) 892700

*8-10 June***

Wimborne Folk Festival 2001

Town Centre, Wimborne Minster, Dorset

Contact: (01202) 743465

*9 June***

Trooping the Colour – The Queen's Birthday Parade

Horse Guards Parade, London, SW1

Contact: (020) 7414 2479

10 June

Manchester to Blackpool Veteran Vintage and Classic Car Run

Granada Studios, Manchester, Greater Manchester

Contact: (01925) 791922

*12-14 June***

Three Counties Show

Three Counties Showground, The Showground,

Malvern, Worcestershire

Contact: (01684) 584900

*13-19 June***

Grosvenor House Art and Antiques Fair

Le Meridien Grosvenor House, Park Lane, London, W1A

Contact: (020) 7399 8100

22 June-1 July

Newcastle Hoppings

Town Moor, Newcastle upon Tyne, Tyne & Wear

Contact: (07831) 458774

24-30 June

Alnwick Medieval Fair

Market Square, Alnwick, Northumberland

Contact: (01665) 602552

*25 June-8 July***

Wimbledon Lawn Tennis Championships

All England Lawn Tennis and Croquet Club,

Church Road, London, SW19

Contact: (020) 8946 2244

*29 June-1 July***

Milton Keynes International Festival

Milton Keynes Theatre & Gallery,

Central Milton Keynes, Buckinghamshire

Contact: (01908) 610564

30 June

Toe Wrestling

Wetton, Staffordshire

Contact: (01782) 283377

July 2001

*1-31 July***

The Balloon and Flower Festival

Southampton Common, Southampton, Hampshire

Contact: (023) 8083 2525

4-8 July

Henley Royal Regatta

Henley-on-Thames, Oxfordshire

Contact: (01491) 572153

7-8 July

Sunderland International Kite Festival

Northern Area Playing Fields, District 12, Washington,

Tyne & Wear

Contact: (0191) 514 1235

*7 July-11 August***

Cookson Country Festival

Various venues, South Shields, Tyne & Wear

Contact: (0191) 427 1717

10-12 July

Great Yorkshire Show

Great Yorkshire Showground, Harrogate,

North Yorkshire

Contact: (01423) 541000

14 July

Tendring Hundred Show

Lawford House Park, Lawford, Manningtree, Essex

Contact: (01206) 571517

14-15 July

Tewkesbury Medieval Festival

The Gastons, Gloucester Road, Tewkesbury,

Gloucestershire

Contact: (01684) 297607

19-22 July
Golf: The Open Championship 2001
Royal Lytham St Annes Golf Club, Lytham St Annes,
Lancashire
Contact: (01253) 725610

20 July-15 September
Henry Wood Promenade Concerts
Royal Albert Hall, London, SW7
Contact: (020) 7765 5575

25 July
Sandringham Flower Show
Sandringham Park, Sandringham, Norfolk
Contact: (01485) 540860

27 July-5 August*
Stockton International Riverside Festival
Various venues, Stockton-on-Tees, Cleveland
Contact: (0191) 276 9911

28 July-4 August
Cowes Week
Cowes, Isle of Wight
Contact: (01703) 620006

August 2001

3-4 August
Living History Weekend
Northernhay Gardens, Exeter, Devon
Contact: (01392) 265118

4-11 August
Alnwick International Music and Dance Festival
Market Place, Alnwick, Northumberland
Contact: (01665) 606033

10-12 August
**Saltburn International Festival of Folk Music,
Dance and Song**
Various venues, Saltburn-by-the-Sea, Cleveland
Contact: (01947) 840928

11-18 August
Billingham International Folklore Festival
Town Centre, Queensway, Billingham, Cleveland
Contact: (01642) 553220

12-18 August*
Falmouth Regatta Week
Helford River, Carrick Roads and Falmouth Bay,
Cornwall
Contact: (01326) 211555

25-26 August
Saddleworth Rushcart Festival
Various venues, Uppermill, Saddleworth,
Greater Manchester
Contact: (01457) 834871

25-27 August
Herstmonceux Castle Medieval Festival
Herstmonceux, Hailsham, East Sussex
Contact: (0891) 172902

25-27 August*
The Chelmsford Spectacular
Hylands Park, Writtle, Chelmsford, Essex
Contact: (01245) 606985

26-27 August*
Notting Hill Carnival
Streets around Ladbroke Grove, London, W11
Contact: (020) 8964 0544

31 August-2 September
The Long Weekend - Clevedon's Annual Jazz Festival
Prince's Hall, Clevedon, North Somerset
Contact: (01275) 343210

September 2001

1-2 September
Berwick Military Tattoo
Berwick Barracks, Berwick-upon-Tweed,
Northumberland
Contact: (01289) 307426

EVENTS

*1-30 September**
New Brighton Classic Car Show
Fort Perch Rock Car Park, off Kings Parade,
New Brighton, Wirral, Merseyside
Contact: (0151) 647 6780

*1-30 September**
Ocean Race – Round the World Yacht Race
Mayflower Park, Town Quay, Southampton, Hampshire
Contact: (023) 8083 2453

*14-23 September**
Southampton International Boat Show
Western Esplanade, Southampton, Hampshire
Contact: (01784) 473377

*26-30 September**
Horse of the Year Show
Wembley Arena, Middlesex
Contact: (020) 8900 9282

October 2001

*1-31 October**
Great North Run, The World's Biggest Half Marathon
Various venues throughout Tyne & Wear,
Newcastle upon Tyne, Tyne & Wear
Contact: (0191) 402 0016

13-27 October
Canterbury Festival
Various venues, Canterbury, Kent
Contact: (01227) 452853

*21 October**
Trafalgar Day Parade – The Sea Cadet Corps
Trafalgar Square, London, WC2
Contact: (020) 7928 8978

November 2001

*4 November**
London to Brighton Veteran Car Run
Hyde Park, London, W2
Contact: (01753) 681736

4 November
Old Custom: Rolling of the Tar Barrels
Town Centre, Ottery St Mary, Devon
Contact: (01404) 813964

*10 November**
Lord Mayor's Show
City of London, London
Contact: (020) 7606 3030

*11 November**
Remembrance Day Service and Parade
Cenotaph, Whitehall, London, SW1
Contact: (020) 7273 3498

16-25 November
International Guitar Festival of Great Britain
Various venues, Wirral, Merseyside
Contact: (0151) 666 5060

17 November-23 December
Thursford Christmas Spectacular
Thursford Green, Fakenham, Norfolk
Contact: (01328) 878477

21 November-2 December
Huddersfield Contemporary Music Festival
Various venues, Huddersfield
Contact: (01484) 425082

December 2001

6-13 December
Victorian Christmas in Maldon
High Street, Maldon, Essex

24 December
Old Custom: Tolling the Devil's Knell
All Saints Parish Church, Rishworth Road,
Dewsbury, West Yorkshire
Contact: (01484) 223200

31 December
The Snow Ball – New Years Eve Party
Sheffield Ski Village, Parkwood Springs,
Sheffield, South Yorkshire
Contact: (0114) 276 9459

TOWN INDEX

The following cities, towns and villages all have accommodation listed in this guide. If the place where you wish to stay is not shown, the location maps (starting on page 16) will help you to find somewhere suitable in the same area.

381

CHECK THE MAPS

The colour maps at the front of this guide show all the cities, towns and villages for which you will find accommodation entries. Refer to the town index to find the page on which it is listed.

FINDING ACCOMMODATION
IS AS EASY AS *1 2 3*

Where to Stay makes it quick and easy to find a place to stay.
There are several ways to use this guide.

1 Town Index

The town index, starting on page 381, lists all the places with
accommodation featured in the regional sections. The index
gives a page number where you can find full accommodation
and contact details.

2 Colour Maps

All the place names in black on the colour maps at the front
have an entry in the regional sections. Refer to the town index
for the page number where you will find one or more
establishments offering accommodation in your chosen
town or village.

3 Accommodation listing

Contact details for all English Tourism Council assessed
accommodation throughout England, together with their
national Star rating is given in the listing section of this guide.
Establishments with a full entry in the regional sections are
shown in blue. Look in the town index for the page number on
which their full entry appears.